FOR THE SAKE OF SILENCE

FOR THE SAKE OF
SILENCE

MICHAEL CAWOOD GREEN

QUARTET

for Cas

First published in 2010 by
Quartet Books Limited
A member of the Namara Group
27 Goodge Street, London W1T 2LD
First published in 2008 by Umuzi,
An imprint of Random House Struik, South Africa

A catalogue record for this book
is available from the British Library

ISBN 978 0 7043 7198 9

Cover design based on author's photograph of St Michael's mission,
southern KwaZulu-Natal (formally East Griqualand).
The map on page 256 is reproduced by kind permission
of the Superior of Mariannhill monastery.

Printed and bound by
T J International, Padstow, Cornwall

Death and life are in the power of the tongue.

– Book of Proverbs

Translator's Note

I, FR ADALBERT KREUTZNAER, am the compiler, editor and one of the contributors to *Die Mariannhiller Mission 1882–1922: Bilder aus dem afrikanischen Missionsleben*. What I put before you now, an account by Fr Joseph Cupertino, is not listed as a source in that work. Nor am I sure that it should have been, even if circumstances allowed. Certainly, all that may be checked as fact is correct in Fr Joseph's account, but there is much in it that is beyond my power to confirm or deny.

Fr Joseph's work may not appear in mine, but I was amused to discover that I appear in his story – as a character, I suppose one would say. I say "story", but who knows what Fr Joseph's account really is. It does read in part like a story – which is what he himself calls it, as you will see, for extremely troubling reasons. But much of it is what we more properly think of as a history, although he does not. Given that it is true to the facts as they are known, I call it what he says is the proper term for God's work in the world, a chronicle. I should add that he gave his manuscript no name, only a quotation from the Book of Proverbs which was scored deeply into the last page he wrote.

Here then, without IMPRIMI POTEST or IMPRIMATUR, is another perspective on the way in which Mariannhill moved from being a Trappist monastery to the modern mission it is now. I must remind you that our "images out of African mission life" has the approval of the Superior Regionalis of Mariannhill and the episcopal licence of our Bishop whereas Fr Joseph's story – without the crucial corroboration that some of its more striking claims call for – must remain just that, a story. Still, it is our hope that his tale will increase interest, both within and outside the Church, in the process of enquiry into the public veneration of the figure at its centre, Abbot Francis Pfanner, which we plan to put before the Congregation of Sacred Rites.

Fr Joseph's account surfaced only when a well-meaning Sister on Emmaus, the remote mission station where he spent the last years of his life, thought of letting me know of the papers that had been piling up for years in a cupboard in the office of the Superior of the station. So lost was she in her prayer and work that she gave no thought to the possible significance of these papers beyond their effect on the condition of the one obsessed with writing them. In the course of her nursing duties she added the last of the pages to this pile just as my own work was rolling off our press in Reimlingen.

The last few pages, she tells me, were written by Fr Joseph hours before his soul left his broken body.

FR ADALBERT KREUTZNAER, CMM
Feast of Christ the King, 1923
Würzburg

Emmaus, 11th June 1909

I HAVE LEARNED at last to measure grace by silence. But only by doing the unspeakable.

~

I was not there when Franz succumbed to his final agony. While his suffering was at its greatest, I was struggling to find my way back to Emmaus. The injured child I had been called away to baptise died before I reached it. Night had fallen on the hills of Skimpers Nek and I had been riding hopelessly for hours before stumbling upon the path. It was Sr Angela who, at twenty-five minutes to two o'clock, heard the last word Franz spoke – "Light". As she knelt next to him, he slipped away. She told me that he turned his dying eyes to the door again and again, watching for me. By the time I arrived in the blue murk of four o'clock, all that was left for me to do was to close those eyes fixed upon the door and give the first blessing over the body.

Later, in a dawn shrouded with mist, I said the Mass for the Dead. Then I stood back as Sr Angela, still shaking with grief, went to the kitchen and came back with our largest knife in her hands. I said nothing as she stood with her arms raised, the blade gleaming in the light of the candles we had arranged around his body in the dark room. And I said nothing when the knife (a knife that, it struck me in that instant, in all its long service had never known flesh or bone or blood) suddenly flashed down and was buried in his chest. The sound of cutting and carving was strange in the quiet of the morning, and I withdrew into that stillness as the weeping Sister squelched about and finally lifted out the heart. This she brought bleeding to me. I took it in my hands, uncoffined, and walked out into a morning that was spreading like a bruise over Emmaus.

Alone I started up the steep steps the old man had himself cut into the hill immediately behind the station, his place of exile. With just a field hoe and a crowbar he had built in only six weeks the Way of the Cross up this hill he called Calvary. I held his heart out before me each step of the way and, as he had done every morning until his strength failed him, I

9

stopped at each of the fourteen Stations on the zigzagging path, but only to catch my breath. On the summit is a great cross of iron. At the foot of this cross I dug a hole and in it I placed his heart. I packed it in with sand and stone and stood up, wiping my hands on the worn white wool of my habit. Beneath me the featureless expanse once known as Nomansland stretched away for miles in every direction.

No, I was not there when Franz died, his tongue paralysed and still at last. But his blood is on my hands and, being mortal, the sins I have committed for the sake of silence bind me to – what? Confession, I almost said, but the heart of he who is, even now, the one to whom I am bound to confess is hidden on that bare hill, and his body buried amidst the community from which we were expelled. If he, in death, has been welcomed back to the house that rejected him in life, no such charity has been extended to me. Nor could it be. For just as there is now no proper authority to absolve me of my sins, so too there is no community left to accept me back into its embrace if ever I could make proper reparation for those sins.

It may be true that anything I have to confess is best left to silence, but what then of silence itself, at least the silence I sought to safeguard? If this has to be put before you in so many, many words, well, that is because I, more than most, have had to come to terms with the secrets that lie on the other side of silence. All I can offer you is the certainty that each word I write is a penance for the things I did in silence, for the sake of silence. And I shall consider myself absolved only when I am free to slip back into the silence for which I did such dreadful things.

~

When I speak of silence, I am being quite, quite literal; I was once, after all, a monk of the Order of the Cistercians of the Strict Observance or, as they are more popularly known, the Trappists. *The ninth degree of humility*, says St Benedict in his Rule for Monasteries, *is that a monk restrain his tongue and keep silence.* This is so overt a feature of his Rule that Trappists are continually caught in the paradox of having to explain it. Their silence is something of a scandal to those outside the Order, but Trappists are – or should be – too much a part of the mystery of silence to formulate an apologetic for it; quite simply, it is an essential part of our withdrawal from the world. The central mystery of a Trappist's vocation is his entry into the silence of God within the hidden life of the monastery.

Ah, the monastery! That retreat of piety and learning, that hidden community of the humble and holy, that still centre of solitude, that house of assiduous prayer and joyful penitence. Why, when the world thinks of a monastery, does it think of murder? What is it about a cloister that brings killing to mind?

Well, I must admit to you now that I shall have to give in to such gothic imaginings. I will give you evil under the habit, a death's head in a cowl, sinister intent in the hiss of sandals slipping along empty corridors of echoing stone. And I must, indeed, give you murders – thirteen at a stroke, I shall have to report. And the old man himself, perhaps – but every accident of our history must be counted out, each detail clicking by as if a bead on a rosary. One decade for each mystery, I dare to say, though all the mysteries here are sorrowful ones, where the sacred and profane mix so intimately in my intentions.

Forgive me. I am rushing ahead to my intentions, no less, when I have not even told you who I am. And was it not our very own St Bernard who condemned the rationalist Abélard for his sceptical teaching that an act is to be judged by the intention of the doer in doing it?

But there I go again, off in every direction but that of the plain facts in plain speech. Off after an arcane elaboration that is nothing more than a vain attempt to use my little and rusty scholastic skill to take the sting out of the truth. *In much speaking*, says the Rule, *you will not escape sin*. And did not the founder of the Trappists, in the holy zeal with which he returned us to St Benedict's ancient Rule, forbid intellectual work? *It is written*, after all, as the Rule reminds us, *that a wise man is known by the fewness of his words*.

So, to the plain truth of it. My name is Eduard Biegner. I was born in Moravia on the 27th September 1845 and, to all intents and purposes, died at Emmaus in East Griqualand on the 24th May 1909 – well beloved in life, I am sure it will be said, and much mourned in death.

Given even these simple facts, you may well be more confused than helped by my efforts towards plain speech. I am called to explain many things, which in itself undoes a proper sense of contrition. "If I justify myself, mine own mouth will condemn me," says Job. But there is nothing else for it. At times I shall have to correct the records as they stand, change the light in which they are seen, add here, take there – in the end, desert eternity for history, God for the historian.

~

What have the historians had to say about Fr Joseph so far? The records throw up only a random name in the odd list, a half-hidden, reluctant face in a formal photograph, a figure noted as present in the crowd at some ceremony or other. For the most part he quickly fades into the background after these moments of exposure, intriguing only for hovering a little mysteriously at the margins of some curious incidents.

And how will the small glimpses of him in the records end? "Fr Joseph fell from a horse" it will in all likelihood be noted (any one of his brethren will tell you what a terrible rider he was); "he did not recover from the accident, and died on –" When? Not the date I have given you above – although that is by far the more important date in the story that the historians are after, a story that really came to an end then, and has left Fr Joseph – Eduard Biegner as he once was – to linger on, hidden and forgotten, a part of no story in particular, for however many years he has left in him to tell you of the matters closest to his heart.

Yes, the purgatory I endure is a distinctly earthly one, and the dust to which I have gone is all too real, as you would know if you ever had to last out a winter in the cold, high, dry hills of this Nomansland in which I must end my days.

Do not be alarmed. Even the many years pent up behind my present impulse to tell everything could not keep me boiling off at this rate. I have been gabbling like a novice on porter duty at one of our monasteries, delirious to indulge his dispensation to speak to anyone who might appear at the gates. I am tumbling over details, wandering between complexities, tugging you this way and that, with no regard for your patience. You may have noticed, too, the occasional lapse in tone, little befitting our serious theme or my station. *The eleventh degree of humility*, says the Rule, *is that when a monk speaks he does so gently and without laughter, humbly and seriously, in few and sensible words, and that he be not noisy in his speech.*

But it is clear to me that, if I am to have any hope of putting these things before you properly, I must learn the full scale of expression again. For the things I have to tell you do not all fit so easily into the life I profess, and we must pace ourselves for intricacies of plot and incident far beyond the simple certainties of that world. Solitude, silence and sanctity there will be. But I have been forced by the task I have taken upon myself to give you murders, and murders you shall have. Possession and exorcism too, well documented. Wars, love stories, foreign places, and much, much more, all a necessary part of this – what? Again, I hesitate to give what I have to tell you a name.

If not a confession, could this be that other practice so central to a Trappist house, a proclamation? In encouraging us to accuse our brethren, the founder of the Order to which I once belonged was, after all, following Holy Father Bernard himself, who says, "Let Divine zeal, love of justice and hatred of iniquity flare up in us, Brothers. Let no one smooth over any vices, let no one cover up any sins."

Who then do I proclaim? Who else but that dying man I have brought to you in his final agony. Yes, it is that old man whom I must name in the long Chapter of Faults to which my memory is now reduced. And the wonder of it is that I will do this for the most part in his own words.

Well, who else would he choose but his most trusted friend and companion to take down, in the last dark years of our many years together, the story of his life? I was there, after all, for much of that life, and so when his physical afflictions made his own scribbling (Franz always had terrible handwriting) more and more difficult, it was me he used, sitting at his desk inscribing as neatly as I could whilst he strode around his room for hours, spit and gesticulations filling the air as he dictated at a furious pace.

Locked fast into my vow of obedience, I became the conduit for the torrent of words he poured out through my hand. Everything went into it – people, places, dates, eternity even, and God himself – everything, so long as it was all dissolved into words. And even when he became too weak to stride about, his voice did not give out. No, then I would have to sit next to his deathbed, taking down word for word his apparently interminable last words, as if he would talk death itself into submission. Until I found, almost too late, the courage to match sin with sin, to master words with words, to become if you will, as far as Franz's story is concerned, the last word.

~

I know, of course, that any proclamation against Franz will occasion some surprise. If I remain silent, it will not be long, I suspect, before novenas will be made to him. He will no doubt soon have his life, virtue and ministry before the Congregation for the Causes of Saints, even though he lived and died as a member of an Order that shuns all recognition in the world – an Order that has not produced a single genius of learning or of art, let alone a saint recognised by the Church as such. It is the overwhelming aim

13

of the members of our Order, after all, to be forgotten by men so that they can be remembered more securely by God.

Can anything like this be said of the boy once known as Wendel – or, more formally, Wendelin – Pfanner, who, upon receiving his Trappist habit, was called Franciscus and was to be known throughout his life as plain Franz? "We do not augment or diminish the fault we proclaim by interpreting the intention of the Brother," our Regulations state, "whether to his disadvantage or to his advantage. We simply expose the fault as it appears." But will Franz's fault appear so simply, here where we have to do with sins that are themselves a claim to beatification?

For if there were to be a novena for Abbot Franz, the first day would have to praise his apostolic zeal. "He laboured unceasingly to carry the glad tidings of God's kingdom to the ends of the world. Inflame our hearts also with apostolic zeal for the spreading of your kingdom on earth" is, perhaps, the way it would be put, with a suitable number of Our Fathers appended.

And what fault, well may you ask, could lie in that? Well, bear with me, if you will, and you shall find how the Devil may hide in the heart of salvation, how the saving of souls may in itself be a sin that cries to heaven.

~

What a road lies before us before I can hope that you will understand this. Or, at least, understand it in the way that a poor old man clattering about the iron-hard ground of the cold and desolate countryside that stretches out endlessly on all sides of him understands it. An old man perched between the wheels of his crudely made "chariot" (determined, you see, to keep at bay for as long as possible the death I have predicted), prevented only by his gentleness from cursing the horses given to him – old Boerperds as curmudgeonly as he himself might have been had he not petrified into the kindness for which he was known and would be remembered. The leather of his reins tough from the freezing air cuts into his hands as he rides about, hands still soft from never having learned the labour that should have been one half of his life. His arms are sore from the effort of trying to keep the bucking and shying beasts straight before his odd little cart as he visits the sick – no, not just the sick, but the terminally ill, the dying, those it has become his special gift to comfort as he sees them on their way. All, that is, except his oldest friend and companion, the one he leaves to find his own way in the darkness closing in on them both.

Yes, I see myself all too clearly, rheumy eyes and all. But will I be able to show you *him*; he who, despite my carping, is still – apart from one other – the only one I have truly loved in my long and lonely time on this earth? To do this I will have to describe conditions perhaps quite foreign to you, delve into motives for actions all but incomprehensible, and give some background to circumstances otherwise impenetrably strange. In short, I shall have to tell you a story.

A story, but not the kind of story the Church will tell. For the faithful there is, after all, no story as such to be told. Not, that is, if one thinks of a story as a way of explaining things in terms of one event leading to another, this resulting in that, the logic of cause and effect. If stories are only the record of Providence in action, then what becomes of causality? The cause of any event is simply God's will that it should happen. And explanation? Explanation is only an excuse for forgetting God. The true explanation of any event lies in understanding its place in the plot of Providence.

For the same reason there is in the eyes of the Church no history as such. Forgive me, our busy historian, but the Church has no need of historians, only accurate chroniclers, accountants of time (it can be no accident that a Franciscan friar invented double-entry bookkeeping) who set down a strict register of occurrences, no more, no less. There is no reason for them to consider motives, explain connections, guess at reasons. The true historian of the Church searches only for God, tracking the echo of His footsteps as they fade into the clangour of passing events, seeking only His trace as it cools and evaporates into the night air you call history. He seeks to reconstruct nothing less than God's will by following painstakingly the clues it leaves in the passage of time.

I, however, am left with only that sinful thing, a story – sinful in itself, for in it there is no hope of absolution. Some understanding, perhaps, in which strange things may become a degree or two more intelligible, and thus, hopefully, slightly less reprehensible, but no contrition or satisfaction or reparation. Certainly no grace, the grace that lies in a silence it has taken me the whole of this story to learn.

MARIAWALD

I WAS NOT THERE at the end, as I have said, and neither was I there at the beginning. Brother Zacharias was on porter duty at the remote monastery of Mariawald that September day in 1863, hardly expecting to indulge his dispensation to speak to anyone who might appear at the doors of the monastery. Few ever had reason to penetrate the dense forests that kept Mariawald, perched high amongst the hills of the desolate Eifel region of the Prussian Rhineland, almost entirely secluded. Cologne, the nearest major city, seemed unthinkably far away, and even little Heimbach, the nearest village, was a good distance down the hills amidst which the monastery was lost.

There was not even a sign in the village to indicate the direction to be taken to the monastery. As only one road led out of the tumble of buildings, travellers were forced to follow this. About half a mile out of the town they came across a humble wooden plaque that announced MARIAWALD ÜBER MARIANNEHÖHE. This pointed to a narrow opening in the trees that gave access to an obscure path climbing sharply through the forbidding woods. No other marker pointed the way to Mariawald, but the determined traveller would suddenly find himself disgorged from the forest with the walls of the monastery glistening white before him against the surrounding Marianne Hills. It was in this way that Franz emerged unexpectedly out of the depths of the autumnal trees, striding as energetically as his then shaky health would allow.

Brother Zacharias was especially nervous as he fumbled with the door, for the Prior of Mariawald was away and he had no one to direct him in his response to this stranger. A stranger who, from his priestly garb, clearly had a special claim on the monastery. *Let all guests who arrive be received like Christ*, says the Rule, *and to all let due honour be shown, especially to the domestics of the faith and to pilgrims.*

Franz stopped to take in a clear view of the Trappist house he had chosen for himself on deciding to enter the Order, and I imagine that a grim look of satisfaction passed over his face as he took in its state of disrepair. After a few moments of efficient surveying, he approached the doors and introduced himself as the person who had inquired by letter about becoming a novice.

To Brother Zacharias Franz must have seemed rather mature in years for a novice (he was thirty-eight years old at the time). Although entering an Order late in life was by no means uncommon, conditions at the recently revived Mariawald were notoriously hard, even for fit young men – of whom there were far too few. The community was made up of just seven Fathers and seven Brothers and most of them were elderly, Brother Zacharias being a youthful exception. Indeed, no other Choir novice was to enter the community during the time of Franz's noviciate.

The reasons for this were precisely what attracted Franz to Mariawald in the first place. Founded by the Cistercians of the line of Morimund, the monastery's existence had always been tenuous. Plundered by Protestants along with the rest of the Cologne region, it was later threatened by the Plague and then destroyed during the Thirty Years War. After almost two hundred years, restoration was begun early in the eighteenth century but cut short when the dissolution imposed by the revolutionary French came into effect. Mariawald's silver, altar, pulpit, organ, even its Gothic stained glass, were auctioned off, and its lands and buildings put up for sale. There was little interest in such a remote property; the tanner who bought it in 1802 for three hundred francs considered the deal a bad one. He sold it after two years and a long period of desultory changing of hands followed, during which Mariawald's lands returned to wilderness and its buildings fell into ruin.

The revival of the monastery in which Franz had decided he should play a part was begun when the Abbot of the Trappist abbey of Ölenberg in Alsace purchased the property in 1860 with the intention of founding a branch house in Germany. "I chose the mission," Franz dictated to me a lifetime later from his sickbed, not noticing my discomfort with this word, "over the motherhouse because I thought there would be a shining new zeal there. As for the privations, well, these simply meant that there would be more for the soul to gain."

On this reckoning the spiritual advantages at Mariawald were great. Its rebuilding had begun two years earlier and only a few rooms had been made habitable by the time Franz announced himself at its gates. Even Mariawald's centrepiece, its once beautiful Gothic chapel dedicated to St

Michael, was still open to the elements that contributed to its desolation, standing as it did without windows, doors, roof or bell tower.

Brother Zacharias could think of nothing better to do than show Franz – or Fr Wendelin Pfanner as he was then – to the guest quarters, such as they were. Certainly, without the Prior's authority there was no more he could do, but while the aspirant Trappist was still a guest Brother Zacharias could not resist exploiting the technicality that allowed him to engage in a little conversation. *An exception shall be made*, states the Rule, *if the need of speaking to guests should arise.*

His polite inquiries regarding Franz's journey elicited a response that overpowered this relaxation of the Rule. Not even the extremely rough and makeshift road that brought him to Heimbach, began Franz, could shake out of him the awe he felt before the Dom in Aachen, the last town of any significance one passes through before arriving at Mariawald. He was still full of wonder at having stood at the chancel beneath which the very bones of Charlemagne lay, and feeling himself glow in the rich light that entered through the stained glass ringing the cathedral's fifteenth-century choir. This was a building worthy of the time when the town was the capital of the Frankish empire, and the Carolingian family had encouraged and enforced the observance of the Benedictine Rule to which he, humble Wendelin Pfanner, was now about to submit himself! He recounted enthusiastically the emotions that overcame him as he gazed up at the Dom's glorious spire stabbing at the sky as the pealing of its bells rang out heavenwards and then fell like spiritual rain down, round, over him.

Caught up in the grandeur of this experience, Franz was unaware of the porter's retreat further into himself. In all probability he did not know that Brother Zacharias, good Cistercian of the Strict Observance that he was, could not approve of these over-elaborate features of the cathedral. Mariawald's reconstructed church would be – as befitted a Cistercian house – plain and unadorned, without silver or jewelled crosses and ornaments, without even a bell tower, the present ruin of which was to be removed and not rebuilt. Carried away by his enthusiasm, Franz switched to the praises of the cathedral at Cologne which surpassed everything, he said, even though it was not yet finished …

His listener's gaze, fixed as it was on the flagstone at his feet, led Franz to realise that something was amiss. This, he decided, was the result of his very different German, coming as he did from the Vorarlberg, which was isolated from the rest of the Empire. "We are very independent," he explained to Brother Zacharias, "even in the way we speak. Other Austrians say we are strange and give us funny names. They call us 'Gsi-bergers' – you get the joke? You hear I use the verb form 'gsi' a lot? So they say we put a 'gsi' before the verb just as we come before the mountain. You get it? *Gsi*-verb, *Vor*-berg? Well, it's not that funny anyway – an insult really, as they also say we are odd mountain types, hidden away in our valleys and cut off by snow, so much so that we reproduce through incest and so on, the usual nonsense."

With the oddness of what he had just said ringing in his ears, Franz flailed on, concerned that the porter might choose this moment to end the interview. "All the time I sat in the cathedral while waiting for the train to Aachen," he told Brother Zacharias, trying to redeem himself, "I was not in the mood for looking at the stained glass windows or the beautiful architecture of this building which made such an impression on me. Why should I, I said to myself. All is vanity. As a Trappist it will not help me any more and when I arrive at the monastery I will not be permitted to speak about these things any more anyway …"

The significance of these words sank in as Franz uttered them and his voice finally trailed off. Brother Zacharias used the opportunity to bow himself out. With a few words of rather lame welcome he returned, somewhat shaken, to his solitary duty as porter.

~

The guestroom to which Franz was taken had, true to the Rule, received priority in the reconstruction of Mariawald. St Benedict instructs the Cellarer *to take the greatest care of guests* (along with the sick, children and the poor), and thus their quarters are intended to be less austere than the rest of the monastery. The room, on this chilly autumn day, was relatively warm, and so, with typical passionate thoroughness, Franz opened the windows and door, took off his travelling cloak and sat exposed to the damp chill of evening as it drew in. He immediately caught a devastating cold.

His aching lungs and shortness of breath reminded Franz of his reasons for seeking out the seclusion of this monastery. It was, given his ambitions earlier in life, an odd place to be. He had trained originally for the secular priesthood, and in the third year of his studies at the seminary in Brixen (then its proper Austrian self and not yet overrun by the Italians) he felt, as he related, "an uncontrollable urge to go to the foreign missions". Whenever Franz recited the *Miserere*, which the students had to do every day, one verse stood out for him: "I will teach the unjust Thy ways, and the wicked shall be converted to Thee." The yearning and desire to work in the missions tormented him and gave him no rest until, at last, he submitted his case to the Bishop for a decision. One of the reasons the request was refused was that he was not physically strong enough to stand the vigorous life of a missionary, something that Franz recalled with amusement much later in his long life.

In direct contrast to his desire to carry the Word to the far corners of the earth, Franz was, upon graduating from the seminary, appointed as priest to a small parish not far from his home town. The Bishop's assessment of his health was confirmed when, despite this sheltered assignment, his lungs collapsed after only a few years and he was sent to a sanatorium to recover from tuberculosis. His lungs seemed destined to remain weak for the rest of his life, and he also began to develop an inguinal hernia. His next appointment – to the restful duties of confessor to a convent in Agram in Croatia – drove home his sense that there was very little he could do, and little time in which to do it. He felt no desire to return to parish work; the longer he remained amongst the Sisters, the more he liked the solitude of the cloister. Such thoughts led him to decide that he should retire to the seclusion of a monastery and prepare himself spiritually for his end.

And what ironies of Providence, fate, history, call it what you will (for I am not sure), made the rigours and strictures of the life of the Order he chose the perfect cure for his ailments? As far as Franz was concerned, it was Providence in its most traditional guise that intervened directly in the decisions he was making.

"While I was battling over what should become of me," he dictated, "two Trappist Brothers from Belgium came to beg. They told me many interesting things about their way of life. It went through my soul like a bolt of lightning. I heard a voice in me say, That is for you."

Whose voice, I thought as I wrote this down. I who will have to share with you a terrifying array of voices from worlds beyond.

After the noon meal Franz took the Trappists to his room and, pretending an interest as a confessor who should be able to answer the inquiries of any potential postulants, he questioned them about their Order down to the smallest detail. He was fascinated by what he heard, although this fascination was governed more by thoughts of death than life. "With my frail body, I thought I didn't have long to live," Franz intoned into the cold night air of our final retreat all those years later. "This was, I decided, the best preparation for death."

For death, perhaps, it may have been, but not for the life that followed, a life that swept me up in its destructive wake.

~

Franz could not be admitted into the community while the Prior of Mariawald was away (he was attending the General Chapter of the Order in France) and so he lived for several weeks in the guest quarters. He insisted on being put to use in the monastery's rebuilding programme during this period and the silent monks flitting about allowed him some limited duties – mainly cleaning up after their more vigorous endeavours or a bit of gardening. The monk assigned as Master of Novices had not had occasion to gain much experience in this role, but he did visit Franz in the guest quarters now and then for conversations intended to probe the sincerity of his intentions. He also set out the exercises and observances of a house of the Congregation of the Cistercian Monks of Notre-Dame de la Trappe.

"Our strict withdrawal from the world into the seclusion of our monasteries," he told Franz, "makes us mysterious to many and our silence has encouraged the spread of all sorts of rumours. We do not greet each other with the *memento mori*, nor are we made to dig a part of our grave each day. In meeting we salute each other by a simple inclination of the head, and a grave is dug only after a Brother is ready to be placed in it."

Franz smiled and began to explain that the Trappist Brothers who visited him in Croatia had given him some idea of the nature of Trappist life. He was cut short quietly but firmly by the Novice Master, who rebuked him in the words of the Rule: *Speaking and teaching belong to the master; the disciple's part is to be silent and to listen.* Franz was taken aback at this rebuke, but far more so by the Master's next words – "Friend, what have you come for?" What, he thought, have the words that Jesus spoke to Judas immediately after his kiss of betrayal to do with me?

"St Bernard used to address this question to all his novices," said the Master, answering Franz's unspoken question. "St Benedict asked it particularly of priests so that they would know that they too have to observe the whole discipline of the Rule and that nothing would be relaxed in their favour. I ask you again, Friend, what have you come for?"

24

With this question hanging in the air, the Master of Novices pulled his cowl over his head and withdrew from the guest room into the quiet of the general life of the monastery. Franz stared out through the rudimentary door frame that marked him off from the community and felt an isolation stronger than anything else he had experienced before. Stronger even than when he took up his first church appointment, as parish priest to the village of Haselstauden.

~

Haselstauden! – that town almost as silly and stupid as its name. Franz still burned with the shame he felt when his father, who had proudly accompanied his son on the four-hour journey from their home town, Langen, to his first parish, found that there was not a soul there to welcome the new priest or help him unload the wagon that his family had done up as a *brautfuder*, or wedding load. No mayor, no old chaplain, not even a curious parishioner. And this for a young priest fresh from the glories of his First Mass celebrations at home, where a parade of welcoming friends and relatives met him at the Austrian border as he returned from Brixen.

The parade had grown into a veritable triumphal procession as Franz approached the family farm. There he was overwhelmed by the green ceremonial arches, the garlands his stepmother was still finishing as he dismounted amongst relatives eager for the first priestly blessing, the celebratory mortar shots still ringing in his ears as he stood in the deathly stillness of the empty streets of Haselstauden.

He and his father had to carry the load of beautiful furniture, linen and clothes into the run-down priest's house themselves. "Strange people living here," his father had muttered while they laboured. As the joy of his first Mass cooled before the reality of Haselstauden, Franz could see again the indifference that his father felt for anything other than farming. And, standing there in that street, he felt again the sickening lurch of years before when the cart he was driving overturned and spilled its load of sand onto one of the roads that were the pride of his father's farm. And again he heard his father yell, "You are no good at it, Wendel! Johannes will have to take over the farm – you go and study!"

Johannes was Franz's twin brother, and he was the one who would go on in his father's footsteps, farming their land. Franz, as one of his hagiographers has written, was instead to spend his life "farming souls". But he never forgot the feel of the wheel in the rut, the tug of the earth as it pulled him over, and the bitter taste of failure as he stood next to the cart lying on its side, one wheel spinning meaninglessly in the air, the load of sand strewn across the neatness of his father's road. Even then he could not abide failure, albeit at something in which he had no real wish to succeed. It is no wonder that in his many years of farming souls he was to establish one actual farm after another, and build, build, build, never with more satisfaction than when pushing new roads through virgin landscapes.

Now I am not one to explain or excuse our lives in terms of the tangled complexities of birth and growing up. In Christ we are transfigured by faith, that is to say, raised above our historical condition. This is what our change of name upon being received into a monastery is meant to signify. For Franz – Franciscus – young Wendelin, or Wendel as he was nicknamed, was someone from some other life, to be thought of in the third person. Still, one could not ignore the hurt in his voice when he described how his entry into the life of learning he desired came about through a command: "You will go," his father had said, giving him no choice. "Your godfather can give you your first Latin lessons and, come September, you will be sent to the high school at Feldkirch."

His father had stalked off then, as he did now in Haselstauden. An even greater stillness fell in his wake. Standing alone in the fading rumble of his father's wagon, the young priest's pride in being selected from amongst the newly ordained as the one least likely to be intimidated by this, the most difficult of pastoral posts, wilted.

It almost goes without saying that Wendel was to turn that absence of supportive comment into boisterous success. "In the following years the parish blossomed within a new spiritual revival brought about by the loving husbandry of Fr Pfanner," writes one of his admirers. As the Master of Novices at Mariawald had begun to suspect, Franz knew all about the sense of self-importance that goes with being a successful and popular priest.

His achievements were marred only by the collapse of his lungs. The sanatorium to which he was sent was in Switzerland and when his health allowed him to return it was to an overwhelming welcome from a loving and grateful crowd of overjoyed parishioners. Their affection was displayed in sums of money given for the restoration of the church, which he spent on embroidered altar linen and vestments and stained glass windows in the sanctuary. In a haze of well-being and pride, Franz made the kind of commitment to the town that only thoughts of a not too distant death allowed him. He used some of the money showered upon him to buy burial plots in the church cemetery for himself and his sister Crescentia, who had joined him in Haselstauden as his housekeeper.

But Franz was never entirely convinced by his own attempts at establishing himself in the village. Fr Pfanner's parishioners did not know the strange emptiness that haunted their by now beloved priest. At the height of his success at Haselstauden he secretly volunteered to serve as military chaplain to Austrian troops in the war with Napoleon iii. The war ended before he could receive a directive from his Bishop in this regard, but within the year another came, appointing him chaplain to the Austrian Sisters of Charity in Croatia. Franz was not certain if this was in consideration of his convalescent state or a rebuke of his restlessness, but in any event it was from the stunningly monotonous duties of ministering to a group of nuns in Agram that he had fled to lose himself in the enclosed world of Mariawald.

~

Mariawald was a world a thousand years removed from the one Franz had inhabited as a secular priest. Those who chose to live there wore medieval clothes, ate a medieval diet, and followed a set of observances drawn up in the Middle Ages.

At first Franz never knew when the Master of Novices would choose to visit him in the guest quarters. He realised that in some way as yet still strange to him these visits were generated out of the rhythms governing the activities around him. Living as he still was in secular time, he was never quite prepared for the sallow face at his door, the downcast eyes, the soft speech that he sometimes struggled to catch.

"The Rule is for us the guide of our life and our basic spirituality," the Master told Franz in the pre-dawn light of their next meeting in words that seemed to be imprinted on Franz's memory. "We will hear it over and over and over in our monastic life. We hope that every time we hear it, we are able to accept it as our guide and our way of living. To hear it once is never enough. To have studied it in the past is never enough. We must hear it and revere it. We must hear it and strive each time to put it into practice in our daily lives. It is not a Rule that we just study or just read. It must become our life."

He then began to give Franz a history of the Rule. History – of necessity a labyrinth of words – was to be entered into only to follow the thread of faith through the labyrinth to silence. Language was God-given that God might be talked about, since faith came by hearing and our tongues are the keys that open heaven to others. But when the Lord comes as a bridegroom nothing remains to be said except that He is coming and that we must go out to meet Him.

After this the Master of Novices fell silent and remained so for so long that Franz began to wonder if the history he had been promised was to be held at bay by the silence that was its goal. But, eventually, the Master of Novices began to speak, his eyes closed and his voice coming from far away: "The words He utters are words full of silence, they are a bait to draw us into silence ..."

His eyes suddenly opened wide and he settled into the story of our Order that I, in turn, have had to repeat to more novices now than I can ever remember.

~

According to scholars, St Benedict of Nursia produced a Rule for his monks in the sixth century. Living in what he perceived to be an age of monastic decadence, he sought to embody sound practice in a Rule for Monasteries, preserved in writing against the vicissitudes of his age and ages to come. Over a period of four hundred years or more, Benedict's Rule slowly gained an increasing hold. Where Christians were once encouraged to venerate holy men like St Guthlac, locked in combat with demons and enduring duckings, beatings, draggings through bog and fen, the ideal of a quiet community living in harmony under the Rule's gentle discipline and sweet order now came to be held as the highest form of religious life. It was expected to last eternally as the only secure road to heaven.

Out of this very success came failure. Adopted and promoted by the secular powers, Benedictine monasteries became dependent upon the splendour and ceremony they believed befitted their status. Their rich possessions, enormous properties and architectural grandeur became increasingly difficult to sustain as the Order expanded. The simple yet careful balance of prayer and manual work formulated by St Benedict in his Rule was lost in mere custom and routine and the details of liturgical worship.

But even as the great Benedictine institutions began to flounder, signs of a resurgence of the spirit of the Rule began to appear. People gathered together to live lives of self-sacrifice and denial, devoted to solitary prayer and labour, although they came together in community to worship. Remote sites were usually chosen for worship, and one group of hermits migrated to an inaccessible swamp surrounded by thickets and thorns, inhabited only by wild beasts. There they founded a house that they called Cîteaux and, in gratitude to God for the mortification of the swamp He had made their home, they called themselves Cistercians. They were also called White Monks because of the white habit they adopted to differentiate themselves from the Benedictines in their traditional black habits. They set themselves apart as a community committed to return to the strict interpretation of the monastic rules set forth by St Benedict.

Bernard of Clairvaux, a man of fiery and dynamic spirituality, joined the new Order at Cîteaux, becoming its most brilliant propagandist. He was the most influential spiritual leader of his time, and was largely responsible for the rapid expansion of the Cistercians. Soon there were more than three hundred Cistercian monasteries. By the end of the Middle Ages the Order had spread through almost the whole of Europe and to the Levant. But, as the Order spread and prospered the Cistercians too began to fall away from their ascetic ideals, which could not be reconciled with their spectacular growth. When they, like the Benedictines, became too great for their own good, they fell into decline. The first thing that went was the fire of contemplation.

Nevertheless, the Rule of St Benedict proved stronger than the foundations growing out of it. New reformed groups of Cistercians that sought a return to the spirit of the Rule began to emerge, the best known of them the Order that Franz now wished to join. Its founder, Armand-Jean le Bouthillier de Rancé, was a nobleman and commendatory Abbot of the Cistercian abbey of Notre Dame de la Trappe. In 1662 he deepened the Cistercian austerities at La Trappe and instituted strict reforms, which he set down in the Constitutions of de Rancé.

The abbey of La Trappe flourished even after the death of its venerated reformer, but its reforms did not spread easily beyond its walls. In the course of nearly a century it founded only three other houses, and it was from the time of these earliest foundations that those who embraced the way of life at La Trappe became known as Trappists. Subsequently, however, many other Trappist houses were established, including the motherhouse at Ölenberg from which we have sprung.

As far as the Master of Novices at Mariawald was concerned, the history of the Trappist Order effectively ended here. It was enough that the members of his house were heirs to an ancient tradition that had been delivered safely by Providence into the present. The history of the present was too messy a text in which to read the purity of the Rule. Like the bad monks described at the beginning of the Rule, it was best left out. *Of the miserable conduct of all such*, says St Benedict, *it is better to be silent than to speak.*

And so the Master of Novices simply passed over the differences that continued to arise amongst those who sought to adhere to the Rule of St Benedict. When Franz entered Mariawald, there were two separate Trappist congregations. These stemmed from a disagreement that developed between two of the principal houses, primarily to do with the hour for dinner and the length of time that was to be devoted to manual labour. I, mere scribe that I am, append this note on the present because, as I have learned to my deepest cost, the air of timelessness that we Religious may exude is never enough to extinguish the tensions of the times. Disagreements over not much more than when to eat and how long to work would be enough to bring down my house, and it was through them that history would, quietly at first and unnoticed until it was too late, seep into our story.

~

I may seem to be keeping Franz in the guest quarters for far longer than the few weeks he was there, but we must return to him as he watches from his guestroom the life of the community of Mariawald revolving around the ancient axes of monastic life – *ora et labora*, prayer and work.

Franz did more than watch. Whilst still an outsider he tried as far as possible to regulate his daily life to that around him. The monks rose at two and gathered in Choir in the ruins of the chapel to recite the Matins and Lauds of Our Lady's Office. This was the beginning of the daily round of Divine service prescribed by the Rule, which took up seven hours of each day. Half an hour of private meditation followed, and, at three o'clock in the morning, they joined together again for the Night Office. This would take an hour, after which they again occupied themselves with private meditation or, if there was sufficient light, read until Prime at five-thirty. Chapter followed Prime and, thereafter, the monks who did not wish to fast until dinner, as many did, were given fifteen minutes for Mist, a very light breakfast.

After Prime and Chapter, the pattern of the day followed a different course depending on the season. Franz had arrived towards the end of summer and so he joined the monks as they worked at manual labour of some kind from a quarter to seven until they broke for Terce, High Mass, and Sext at nine-thirty. In winter this Office was held at a quarter to eight, with the monks reading or praying until this time. Work would begin in the murky winter dawn at nine, although even then it was only just possible to see enough to do what one had to do.

The Rule obliged the monks to live by the labour of their hands and be entirely self-supporting. Five hours of their day in summer and four in winter were given to work. (The hour freed from work in winter was devoted to further private prayer; no time was ever granted for recreation.) They worked seriously at whatever task was given to them, be it the rebuilding of the monastery, cultivating the stony soil of the surrounding hills, or engaging in the chores necessary for their day-to-day subsistence.

Franz worked with the others until eleven, when they broke for dinner in the dining hall. He ate alone and allowed himself the hour-long siesta after dinner which was compulsory for the monks in summer. Later he found he preferred the winter routine, when a short period of reading and prayer replaced the siesta. The monks woke to None, Examen of Conscience, and Angelus at one, and then read or prayed until two. Franz joined the others again when they engaged in two and a half hours of work, stopping at four-thirty for reading and prayer. Vespers was at five-fifteen, followed by fifteen minutes of meditation. Supper was served at six and Lecture (usually a pious reading), Compline, Salve, and Angelus began at seven. In summer the monks retired to bed at eight.

In winter the timetable for the afternoon was moved forward by a little less than an hour, and the monks retired at seven o'clock. This compensated for the loss of the siesta and kept constant the seven hours of sleep allowed in the course of one day. Franz was soon to learn how momentous even these minor seasonal adjustments were in the rigorously fixed routine of Trappist life.

It was neither work nor prayer that was to strike Franz as a particular hardship at first – it was the food, which was strictly vegetarian and particularly tasteless. Even the meals he was given whilst in the guest quarters were almost inedible. "We follow a strict vegetarian diet," the Master of Novices told him, "not for our health as some modern people these days think, but so as to avoid promoting carnal thoughts. Our food consists of bread, vegetables and fruits. Milk and cheese may also be given, except in Advent, Lent, and all Fridays out of Paschal time. Flesh of any kind – meat, fish and eggs – is forbidden at all times, except to the sick. Besides following the ordinary times of fasting set out by the Church, we also observe further extensive fasting as laid down by our Rule."

A hurdle even more difficult for Franz, as you may guess, was the most prominent feature of Trappist life: its silence. The monks were not allowed to speak amongst themselves within the monastery. Even standing together uselessly was punished as a breach of silence. The only break in this observance was when the one in charge of a particular project was allowed to give the necessary directions. Monks could also speak to their immediate Superiors in a case of extreme necessity, but never during the night, which is known as the "Solemn" or "Great" Silence. Otherwise, they communicated with the traditional Cistercian method of signs.

Nothing at first made Franz feel more of a foreigner in this world, even when the Prior returned and admitted him into the community, than his inability to speak its language.

~

According to the Prior at his first meeting with Franz, the Trappists' reputation for excessive austerity had been overemphasised. The Trappist Order, he said, was, simply, a contemplative Order that strove to meditate upon the Divine with the help of exactly defined means of contemplation, as laid down by the Rule of St Benedict. A chapter of the Rule was read daily in Chapter in the Chapter Room, so named for this reason.

Second only to the Rule of St Benedict was the *Ecclesiastica Officia* or "Liturgical Duties" of the Cistercian Order, also known as the Usages or – as was preferred – the Regulations. They set out in the finest detail the form of work for God for every day of the year, every hour of the day, and every moment of each hour. Every prayer, recitation, response, reading, action, preparation – everything, including silence itself – was prescribed for every possible occurrence in the life of a monk. Placing a copy of the Regulations on the table between them, the Prior told Franz, "Our whole lives are carefully regulated by these one thousand eight hundred and two paragraphs. This is to keep away all unnecessary cares and disturbing influences, so that neither anxiety nor insecurity can arise in our striving to be in a state of constant union with God."

It was the Master of Novices who would take Franz through the Regulations. In the way they were set out, the Prior told him, he would find that they showed no interest in explaining why things were as they were. Most paragraphs simply began with the word *sciendum* – "an item to be known" and the words "because" or "therefore" were rarely to be found. Nor was there a neat system to the Liturgy, which had simply to be memorised item by item.

Any adjustments to the Regulations that might be necessary were already, the Prior informed Franz, covered in the Regulations; one of the most frequent words therein was *nisi*, meaning "unless" – indicative of the endless effort to foresee every exception to every prescription. Such exhaustiveness was a vital part of the attempt to leave a monk free of all other thought or decision-making other than his life in God, regardless of any change in circumstances. The Regulations, he concluded, were the very shape of their association in prayer as a community, which took its dignity and efficacy from the belief that through them came association with the Mystical Body of Christ.

The Prior was surprisingly young, Franz thought – in his early thirties, he guessed – given the predominance of older monks in the community. It was difficult for Franz to gauge much more about him as his welcome was as distant as it was formal. For some minutes after his speech, minutes in which Franz stood awkward and unsure as to whether to make some kind of response, the Prior remained silent. Then, quite suddenly, he turned to look directly at Franz.

"There is no need, I take it," he said, "to remind you that, as a contemplative Order, we Trappists are not unconcerned with the spreading of God's word, and that it is the contemplative life itself that is our way of participating in the mission of Christ and his Church. Keep in mind, then, as is stated in Constitution Number Thirty One" – he tapped the closed copy of the *Constitutions and Statutes of the Monks of the Cistercian Order of the Strict Observance* carefully laid in the centre of his desk – "that we cannot, therefore, be called upon to render assistance in the various pastoral ministries or in any external activity, no matter how urgent the needs of the active apostolate."

Franz felt a momentary start of guilt at this although his features remained impassive.

"Always remember," said the Prior, quoting the *Constitutions* again, "that fidelity to the monastic way of life has its own hidden mode of apostolic fruitfulness, and that it is through this that monks perform a service for God's people and the whole human race." With this the Prior brought the interview to an abrupt end. Franz, he said, had been able to observe their practices for some weeks and participate to some degree and the Master of Novices was prepared, tentatively, to receive him into the community at Mariawald. He could collect his things from the guesthouse and enter the enclosure.

And thus it was, on the 9th October 1863, the Feast of the Holy Patriarch Abraham, that Wendelin Pfanner was invested and accepted formally into the Trappist Order, receiving the name Franciscus by which he was supposed to be known thereafter. From the first, however, there was something about the new monk that led to his being referred to always and only as Franz. Some have since chosen to call the date of Franz's investiture "strangely prophetic", for did not God say to Abraham, "Go forth out of thy country and from thy kindred, and out of thy father's house and come into a new land which I shall show thee."

But this prophecy could come about only at the expense of the Order Franz joined that day as stability of place is the object of a special vow for Trappists. Enclosure within the monastery is perpetual, and in joining the Order Franz took it upon himself to be confined to this house and its immediate environs for life.

2

When Franz entered the enclosure, he was given his oblate's habit. He fumbled for some minutes with the complications of the underwear, a pair of white canvas drawers of fifteenth-century design. But he could not deny enjoying on this cool day being enfolded in the white robe and scapular, with a white cloth band around his waist and a white cloak over his shoulders, all made of pure, rough wool.

As he dressed, the Master of Novices – whom he was now to call Father Master – introduced Franz to the way in which his life without words was to be conducted. "The Religious shall have no communication with each other," he said, quoting from the Regulations, "either by word of mouth or writing. When they have anything useful to communicate, they do so by signs. Noises with the mouth, although inarticulate, and useless signs are expressly forbidden. The Choir Religious speak ordinarily to two persons only, the first Superior and the Prior. The novices can speak to the first Superior and to their Father Master."

Franz was permitted to ask the Father Master any questions he wished whilst he was being instructed into his new way of life but was cautioned that he should do so with restraint. It was imperative that he leave speech behind as soon as he could and learn the signs quickly. In this he would be assisted by the Father Master but his primary source would be the Regulations.

The Father Master first took Franz to the chapel-in-progress and indicated the section he could use as a novice. An austere space that would forever remain as bare of decoration as it was then, the broken beauty of St Michael's chapel depended upon the play of light that warmed its stone. Franz could not wait to become part of the labour that would again allow the prayers of the faithful to be drawn up into the dark embrace of its intersecting arches.

The chapel formed the northern wall of the enclosure. Franz and the Father Master left via the stairs in the south transept that linked the chapel to the dormitories – for ease of access during the Night Office, explained the Father Master – and stepped into the covered walk that surrounded the central quadrangle. This was the cloister, so much the heart of any monastery as to stand for the whole. The Father Master pointed to the stone basins against the outer chapel wall and indicated that they were intended for washing one's feet before entering the chapel. He and Franz then walked along the eastern side of the cloister, passing the armarium – Franz was allowed a brief look into this tiny library behind which lay the sacristy – and the Chapter Room. They left the cloister by means of another flight of stairs between the Chapter Room and the *sprechzimmer* (where monks were allowed to address their Superior) that led to the dormitories.

"All our duties and exercises always take place in common, never in private rooms," said the Father Master in a speech Franz would come to know by heart after delivering it himself so often in the years to come. "We sleep in this common dormitory, the beds being divided from each other only by these curtains. Your name and number will be written above your bed. The bed, as you see, consists of a mattress and pillow stuffed with straw.

You will be given covering just sufficient for the needs of the season," he told Franz before continuing with his list of directives.

"No one is allowed to enter the dormitory without necessity, much less take rest there without permission.

"We are obliged to sleep in our regular clothing, removing only our shoes and, if permission is given because of the heat, our cowls.

"Nothing within the enclosure may be referred to as belonging to you. When you refer to this bed, you will refer to it as 'our' bed, and even to your shoes as 'our' shoes."

Next Franz was taken to the washroom, where the Brother appointed by the Prior as barber stood waiting to take care of his beard and tonsure. Franz was expected to lather himself, but the barber would always do the actual shaving. The Regulations specify the exact way in which each monk's beard is to be kept: "The beard is shaved every week. The Superior may, however, in certain cases permit the Religious to shave more often." The crown – as the tonsure, once the mark of the slave in the secular world, is called – is renewed once a month, leaving a ring of hair, about three-quarters of an inch in width all the way around the head.

Once the shaving was done, Franz followed the Father Master back up the stairs into the cloister. As they walked along the southern side of the quadrangle to the dining area, the Father Master instructed him in how to comport himself: "The Religious ought always to observe the greatest modesty, walking without haste and without turning the head … "

Quoting the Regulations, he continued, "Except in the church, we always keep the hands in the sleeves of the cowl. If we are in scapular – which you will only receive on taking First or Simple Vows – we keep the hands hidden under the scapular, above the girdle, or in the sleeves of the robe. If one of the hands is occupied, we keep the other under the scapular, above the girdle."

The southern side of the enclosure was made up of the calefactory (or Warming Room), the monks' refectory, and the kitchen. The Brothers' refectory was the first of the rooms making up the western end of the enclosure and was separated from the kitchen by a passage that entered the cloister at this point to allow access to the chapel. Across the quadrangle Franz could see the workshop and the large storeroom (presided over by the most strict of Cellarers) that completed the western boundary of the enclosure.

The Father Master showed Franz into the monks' refectory just before the monks were due to file in. A large room, well lit by windows facing north and still bright from being newly whitewashed, it was entirely bare except for a big wooden crucifix on the east wall, some candleholders, and narrow wooden tables set against the walls. The Prior's table stood beneath the crucifix. There were three small, hard stools at each table, and three identical place settings: a white linen napkin formed into a perfect oblong around a place mat resting on top of an earthenware bowl, with knife, fork and spoon, all made of wood, tucked inside along the edge closest to the eater. A thin plaque with the name of the Religious was laid on top of this, and a metal plate rested at a set angle against the right-hand side of the box formed by the napkin.

Between each setting a pine board was placed upon the table on which stood an earthenware jug of water flanked by the low metal dishes that the monks on either side used for drinking water.

Franz described for me each of these details, by now the very fabric of our world, with all the intensity with which they must first have struck him. His eyes were closed and, although sitting as quietly as possible, I felt like an intruder on his earliest memories of Trappist life.

The monks had entered, he said, and he joined them as they ate – soup, bread, vegetables, an apple – in silence. When they drank they did so, as specified by the Regulations, "with both hands holding the cup". After the meal he followed them as they cleared up according to the Regulations: each washed his knife, fork and spoon in the leftover drinking water in his dish, dried these items on his napkin, emptied his mug into the soup bowl and dried it on his napkin, then left everything in its original place on the table.

It still being technically summer, a siesta was allowed after dinner. Franz lay on his new bed, rough and hard, listening as each of the monks fell asleep. He must have fallen asleep himself in the last few minutes before the community was awoken. He was confused by his strange surroundings, and he felt an immediate need for the lavatory. The Father Master was not to hand, so in the midst of the silent business of the other monks getting ready to go to work, Franz had to fumble through his copy of the Regulations to find the necessary sign. This proclaimed its ancient origins in signalling "house of shame".

Franz felt he had fallen asleep in the nineteenth century and awoken in the eleventh. He was soon to learn the real beauty of the medieval structuring of the hours and days, and he took much comfort in the venerable rituals and practices in which he was expected to lose himself. The ancient rituals that now governed his worship took on a life of their own, and the liturgies a poetry that, for a while, lent a lyricism to even his, the most prosaic of souls.

Every moment of every day was now accounted for, the absence of choice consoling after the enormous choice Franz made in leaving the nunnery he had administered and after the uncertain years of his studies, followed as they were by having to lead a difficult and fractious community as a secular priest. Caught up now in the huge, unending, unchanging work of the Liturgy and its stately procession through the graceful medieval ordering of his days, Franz felt the hundred cares, the necessary ones and the unnecessary ones, that had filled his life begin to slip away. He found peace in never having to worry about anything except what was given to him to do each day, and comfort in the simplicity the new austerity of his life afforded him.

~

In giving up speech, Franz learned that the language of signs had a surprising complexity and subtlety. Using primarily the right hand and forefinger, Trappist monks have over four hundred signs. These signify everyday objects – words for work, food, clothing – and liturgical articles and practices: Breviary, vessel, Office, and so on.

Theological signs often have a simple poetry about them: "God" is signified by a triangle with the thumbs and raised forefingers, to which a hand extended like a wing is added to signify "Holy Ghost". The sign for "Devil" introduces a note of medieval melodrama into the vocabulary: again one describes a wing, but this time by placing the end of the thumb on the corner of the mouth, spreading out the hand and moving it whilst striking the head in several places with the tip of the finger.

In general there is a gracious courtesy to the language of signs. To thank someone, one throws a kiss; to ask pardon, one strikes one's breast; for a casual greeting, a bow. The signs related to structuring the day are the most direct: for "morning" one touches the under eyelid, and for "night" the thumb and forefinger are put over the eyes. "Fast" is signified by pressing the lips together with thumb and forefinger. Many words are made up of combinations of other signs – "candle", for example, is signified by the combination of the sign for "bee" (shorthand for "beeswax") and "light" – and herein lies the potential, despite the stricture against useless signs, for generating new signs.

A cat had forced the monastery to adopt it by simply sitting on a broken piece of wall through wind, rain and shine until it was fed (it evinced an unexpected fondness for vegetables, especially squash of any kind). This informal pet was referred to by making the sign for "animal" – curving the finger and moving it at the end of the nose – and adding "pulled at the moustache".

The latter sign came from the gentle humour that had crept into the language of the community. In the chapter of the Rule that answers the question "What Are the Instruments of Good Works?" St Benedict specifies: *Not to speak useless words or words that move to laughter* and *Not to love much or boisterous laughter*. The usual subjects nevertheless became the butt of jokes, such jokes at least as could be expressed in a community that had dispensed almost entirely with speech. Humour at the expense of a person's nationality, for example, survived the translation into signs perfectly well: an Englishman was represented by a snobbish raising of the nose with the forefinger and a Frenchman by the twirling of imaginary moustachios.

This last example brings us back to the cat, the sign for which was developed by a German Brother who first fed the animal, and was something of a dig at the more "frenchified" monks who had come from the Alsace region to found this Trappist branch house in the Prussian Rhineland.

~

A joke was to be the occasion of Franz's first real experience of the strong penitential streak in de Rancé's reforms.

Cistercians, more than most monastic orders, believe that in offering up the rigours of their lives as a sacrifice, they provide some atonement for the evil of the world. (Indeed, it is still my fervent prayer, exiled as I am from the Order, that the suffering I endure in writing this may in some small way diminish the agonies I describe.) All our austerities are directed to this end, and de Rancé increased them in proportion to his strong sense of the wickedness of the world. "The cloister is a prison in which everybody is held as guilty before God whether he has lost his innocence or not," he wrote in *De la Sainteté et des Devoirs*. And again: "Monastic congregations are bodies of men reckoned as criminals, men considered, by reason of their very state, as public penitents and who no longer have any claim on the goodness of God until they have made satisfaction to His justice by chastisements worthy of their sins."

A regular feature at Mariawald, as of most other monasteries and certainly all other Trappist houses, was the Chapter of Faults. The Regulations allow this to be held on a daily basis, although its frequency depends on the wishes of the Superior. In the Chapter of Faults, the Superior invites monks to come forward and accuse themselves of exterior faults against the Rule, the customs of the house, and the special rulings he, as Superior, has made. Monks may also accuse themselves of secret thoughts and bad dispositions.

The Rule of St Benedict calls for *a due proportion between the seriousness of the fault and the measure of discipline*. A "less serious" fault may incur the penance of exclusion from the common table at meal times, or being deprived of specific duties in the oratory. A monk might have to prostrate himself on the presbytery steps at each Office, or he might have to accuse himself aloud during meal times, or read from some relevant pious work, or say a prayer with his arms extended in the shape of the cross. He might have to kiss the feet of the whole community, standing and bowing to each of his brothers between each kiss.

More serious faults can result in a monk having to remove part or all of his regular habit, or having to use publicly in Chapter his "discipline" – the small whip that he keeps in his cell to scourge his shoulders regularly in private. Others, too, can administer the "taking of the discipline", whipping the culprit before his brothers. Monks are also charged, as I have had occasion to note, with proclaiming the faults of others, "in the spirit of charity and with zeal for the glory of God". Indeed, de Rancé called this practice "the mainstay and nerve of the whole regular discipline of a house".

De Rancé departed diametrically from the Rule of St Benedict in withdrawing the right of the proclaimed to explain themselves, either to the community at large or, in particular, to their accusers. Any attempt by word or sign to indicate that one has not committed the fault for which one is proclaimed (even if one is innocent of it) he named "an unforgivable fault", and called for the assembled brethren to express their "great horror" of it by immediately prostrating en masse. The proclaimed monk is also "totally forbidden" the expression of any indignation to the one who proclaims him, or from criticising the sentence imposed by the Superior. He may not speak of his proclamation or make signs about it outside of Chapter – "Whoever presumes to do otherwise," states the Regulations, "is to be beaten in Chapter for six successive days."

It was, by what accident of history or irony I do not know, a proclamation that led to Franz's first experience of the way in which a serious fault was handled, although the proclaimed Brother in question saved himself from the penance owing to the most serious of faults by not attempting to defend himself in the least. At one of the first Chapter of Faults Franz attended a monk came forward, bowed low, and said, "I proclaim Brother Isembard." The Prior then indicated that the monk should go on and state the fault he had noticed. "Brother Isembard told a joke," said the monk. Franz could feel an intake of breath by all around him at this double sin.

It was fairly common for monks to accuse themselves of breaking St Benedict's ninth and tenth degrees of humility, which concern talking too much or laughing too much. But to break the silence with the intention of provoking laughter is to compound the sin in question, and is expressly forbidden by the Rule: "As for coarse jests and idle words or words that move to laughter," the chapter "On the Spirit of Silence" reads, "these we condemn everywhere with a perpetual ban, and for such conversation we do not permit a disciple to open his mouth." Making anything at all laughable is to impose a ludicrous style on the seriousness of reality, and as such is part of the weakness, corruption and foolishness of the world.

The Prior immediately instructed Brother Isembard to prostrate himself at the door of the refectory, so that everyone had to step over him when entering for meals; he was also to take his meals on a small stool in the middle of the room instead of at the table. Brother Isembard was ordered to do this for a week, but if the Prior had known the nature of the joke in question, Franz – who had overheard it in the washroom, although he was still too nervous and new to proclaim it – was quite sure the penance would have been far more serious. For not only did the telling of the joke and its provocation to laughter constitute a twin breach of the observance of silence; the observance of silence was itself the subject of the joke.

Many, many years later, when Franz's frustrations with the Trappists were at their height, I would hear him share this joke with some of the visitors he received in his exile. By then it had lost the shock he first felt on hearing it, measuring as it did just how far monks are capable of falling from the image of high seriousness attached to their vocation. Franz had by then, too, a good stock of other examples of such a falling away, many of them not in the least bit funny. He would re-tell this joke with a certain grim edge, perhaps playing up the reception it received in the washroom of Mariawald more than was necessary as he added to it a hint of his own struggles with authority and silence.

Brother Francis, he would begin, stopping almost immediately to add that the Franciscans with their reputation for goodwill and humour were the standard target of jokes told in other Orders, which explained the first suppressed giggles these words raised in Brother Isembard's small and secret audience. Brother Francis, he would go on, entered a Trappist monastery and the Superior said, "Brother, we observe silence in this monastery; you are welcome here as long as you like, but you may not speak until I direct you to do so."

Brother Francis lived in the monastery for a full year before the Superior said to him, "Brother Francis, you have been here a year now, you may speak two words." Brother Francis said, "Hard bed." "I'm sorry to hear that," the Superior said. "We will get you a better bed." (The thought of such a response from a Trappist Superior set off a second set of giggles, more difficult to suppress.)

The next year, the Superior called in Brother Francis. "You may say another two words, Brother Francis." "Bad food," said Brother Francis, and the Superior assured him that the food would be better in the future (you can imagine the sniggers at this!).

On his third anniversary at the monastery, the Superior again called Brother Francis in. "Two words you may say today," said the Superior. "I resign," said Brother Francis. The small group nearly exploded in its attempts to suppress its hilarity as Brother Isembard closed in with the punch line: "It is probably best," he said in the voice of their own Superior. "All you have done since you got here is complain."

~

Now I hope I do not show disrespect for my Order in sharing this lapse with you. It is not only thoughts of melodramatic perversion that monks inspire amongst the worldly but also levity based upon the imagined "restrictions" of their lives. There is nothing profound in this; our vows of abstinence go against what is perceived as natural and are, therefore, either the subject of awe or a joke. Celibacy is invariably the chief butt (nothing is more funny in the sense of ridiculous than sex, which is one reason I am glad to be free of it), but for those wits who are aware of the rule of silence, it too provides a rich source of laughter.

Jokes about silence have the greater ability to cut to the quick of our observances. I remember as a young boy being told of a clown who went to a venerable sage to ask him if there was a secret to being funny. The sage remained quiet for a long, long time and then said, "Yes, there is. Silence." There have been days when, just for a moment, the silence of the monastery has struck me as the punch line at the end of creation.

That I have been forced to hear versions of the joke told by Brother Isembard at Mariawald on a number of occasions over the years corroborates one of the chief dangers of jokes noted by the Church Fathers – although their meaning is spurious, they can survive with a tenacity stronger than truth. And that tenacity results from jokes being either impervious to explanation or dying before it. No form of speech is more resistant to rational analysis than the incongruity that causes laughter. Whilst the juxtaposition of the Superior's response to the limited number of words spoken by Brother Francis in Brother Isembard's joke is clearly ludicrous, I have never been sure whether it is speech or silence that is ultimately the object of the joke. But I am sure that if I were to make up my mind on this score the joke would lose its interest for me. For if we really understood what was funny about any joke it would cease to be funny. Even Aristotle was finally able to define the laughable only in circular fashion: that which makes us laugh.

Jokes bear a startling similarity in this regard to the mystery of our vocation as monks. I said earlier that the monk, cut off by choice from the world, cannot explain himself to the world. Hidden in the silence of God, it is foolishness for him to attempt a clear, definite, easily understandable explanation of this state. If he thought he could, then he would also think that he has understood the mystery of his vocation. If he really did understand his vocation, then there would be no more mystery. And if there were no more mystery, then could there really be any longer a vocation? Any more, at least, than there would be a joke after one had explained what was humorous in it to someone who did not understand?

Those moderns then who cannot comprehend St Benedict's grudging attitude towards laughter (the tenth degree of humility is *Be not ready and quick to laugh, for it is written "The fool lifts up his voice in laughter"*) miss the thin line between vocation and joke that he clearly understood so well. The mystery in which each finds its meaning is something they have frighteningly in common; indeed, the desire to lose oneself in the infinite silence of God is never far from the desire to howl with laughter into the depths of oblivion. There would be no point to faith, whose task it is to differentiate the two, if this were not so.

And so you see I shall never try to explain the mystery of my vocation to you, or the real motivation behind the ends to which it drove me. I can tell you the story of their unfolding, but words are only the threshold of the mystery. The silence of God's love, selecting a soul for this strange hidden life in Himself, is too vast an ocean to be lapped up by the human tongue.

~

Our monasteries may well be among the most austere in the Church, but oh, the sweet and regular rhythm of that life, its ebb and flow so ingrained as to be of nature itself, a perfect conduit to the ultimate silence beyond, where the Lord comes to meet us.

It was not, for Franz, to last. His growing awareness that he could not live entirely at this elevated level did not begin with any resentment of the hardships of his new life, or a desire to be free from its restrictions, or dissatisfaction with his fellow monks. It arose, rather, from the rediscovery of his old self which, in a terrible irony, the Trappist way of life revived. It began, quite literally (for was there ever a more literal person than Franz?), with his appetite.

The heart of monastic life is a turning away from self-will and an obsession with one's appetites towards a desire only to know and do the will of God. To Franz's amazement, the rigours of monastic life gave him instead, in his own words, a big, even a terrible appetite. He noticed that at table he outdid his neighbours by far, and that he no longer needed the cat skin which he had been wearing over his stomach for perhaps ten years to ward off attacks of colic and cramp.

Franz attributed this to the vegetarian diet followed by the Trappists, but also to their regime of manual labour. In a life dedicated to work and prayer, he quite quickly found the former by far the more attractive. As his appetite and health returned, the many, many hours of formal prayer began to chafe. The long, slow hours in Choir became a torment, and his worst trial the liturgical life: the Divine Office, the singing and chanting, even the psalms (which he had chosen to make the special study of his noviciate) because in the Cistercian Breviary, unlike the Roman, they were all included every week.

In his newfound sense of his physicality Franz deeply resented being forced, within a few months of entering the monastery, to spend nearly a month in the infirmary. This was because he, like many of the other monks, had developed a swelling of the knees similar to water on the knee from the amount of time he was required to spend on his knees in prayer. And this just as he was beginning to discover again, for the first time since leaving his father's farm, the delight of a really active existence. The intense labour in which he was engaged for five hours each day became his true passion in monastic life. But it also gave him back what he felt he had lost in his years of study – real hunger. Soon his improved appetite turned ravenous. "As long as I was working I didn't feel it," he dictated for my scribbling hand. "But while singing None and Vespers for an hour and a half before dinner, as was prescribed during Lent, I felt like eating the very walls of the chapel."

It was his hunger for work, however, that really signalled the beginning of Franz's difficulties at Mariawald.

~

On the first day after his investiture the Sub-Prior ordered Franz to collect fallen walnuts with the other monks. Franz wanted to climb into the trees to knock more down, but upon rather clumsily signing this to the Sub-Prior he was told that only the Brothers, whose duties were meant to be of a more manual kind, could do this. The Fathers, weighed down by their Holy Orders as much as their age, were considered too weak and likely to fall. Many objections could have been made against that, thought Franz, but the observance of silence did not allow him to express his opinion. Later on, as a Superior himself, he took grim satisfaction in ensuring that the Fathers did as much physical labour as their greater commitment to prayer allowed.

Next Franz was taken along to the only road serving the monastery, the rough track that led to Heimbach. The monks were in the process of repairing this, and large amounts of dirt and gravel had to be moved in wheelbarrows. The monk in charge asked Franz if he would be able to assist, and now it was Franz's turn to suppress his laughter. Two monks already

45

busy with the task were presented to him as an example of how he should tackle it and Franz watched in amazement as they wobbled about with a half-full wheelbarrow that they dumped along with its load over the slope they were trying to fill. They then laboriously dragged the wheelbarrow up and began the whole process again.

Franz felt the father he had not even visited between leaving Agram and entering the monastery looking on in apoplectic anger. Under his stern gaze, he grabbed a wheelbarrow, loaded it to the full, rolled it expertly to the slope, and tipped the sand out over the brink to exactly where it was needed before returning for another load without the wheelbarrow ever leaving his hands. Alone he was able to do four loads to every one delivered by the pair of monks who had been set as his example. When it came to shovelling, he braced the tool against his knee and thigh and – under his father's watchful eye – took a wide shovelful each time whilst the other monks puttered around with the end of the handle and point of the blade.

It was soon noticed that Franz showed more strength and dexterity than anyone else in the monastery, even the younger and apparently stronger Brothers, and so, to his delight, he was always given the hardest work to do. The lighter tasks, such as sweeping and cleaning, were given to the older and weaker monks and Franz gloried in only once being required to do the dishes in the kitchen. He celebrated his ever improving health by doing road repairs, clearing underbrush, digging irrigation trenches, and chopping wood, his favourite work.

As winter closed in on Mariawald, it began to snow heavily and there was virtually no work apart from chopping firewood. Various kinds had to be prepared: three-foot pieces for the baker, shorter ones for the kitchen stove, and smaller ones for the heating stoves. "The first time I took a block of wood in one hand to chop it with the other," Franz dictated with glee, "the work supervisor came running and cried, 'No, no! For heaven's sake! That way you will cut off your other hand or arm! Hold the axe with both hands!' I said to the good monk, 'If obedience demands it I shall do it, but if it is up to me I shall chop it the way I have been doing since I was eight years old.' Then with one blow I split the log I was holding with my left hand. After that, he let me do what I wanted, although he often closed his eyes or looked away when the axe came down right close to my thumb!"

It is not surprising that Franz felt that the few avenues there were for speech at Mariawald – primarily occasions when a Superior wished to instruct him at his work – were more of an irritation than anything else. Nothing was more pleasant, he found, than not having to talk or be talked to under these circumstances. Even being addressed in sign language disturbed him, so he made a private resolution not to use his eyes for anything that was not essential. To this he added a vow to do penance every time he allowed himself so much as an unnecessary glance.

He would thus go to work in the fields and come back without ever having looked at the sky, he would rise for the Night Office without glancing at the stars, he ignored the sunrise when it loomed after Terce and, most importantly, he avoided the signs that the other Choir Religious made on their way to and from saying the daily Office in the remains of the chapel. He was gratified to notice that they soon stopped using signs in his presence because they knew he would ignore them. He also gained a reputation for knowing hardly anything about signing as he deliberately neglected to learn the language of silence. "The less a novice knows about this sign language," Franz would proclaim throughout his life, "the quieter he remains."

So, in ignorance even of the name of the confrere seated next to him at table (when ordered to call on him in Chapter he had to say "the Brother who sits next to me"), Franz threw himself into the physical side of Trappist life with passion. He was never happier than when working at some solitary task in a remote corner of the monastery's lands. The secluded heights of the Marianne Hills soothed him, the more so when they rang with the rhythmic echoes of some form of repetitive labour in which he could lose himself. The very name of the hills was a comfort, for was not Maria Anna the name of his mother? And if she had died when he was but three years old, was his family not blessed when his father remarried and the name of his new wife was again Maria Anna? A special bond had quickly grown between Franz and his stepmother, a bond forged in her appreciation of his courageous spirit and, especially, his hardworking disposition.

The enthusiasm with which he took on work again at Mariawald meant that Franz fell asleep easily and slept deeply, another fact that, along with his improved appetite, he took as a sign of how well life in the monastery suited him. The deeper he got into his noviciate, the easier everything – Choir excluded – seemed to him, until he began to worry that he was not living a penitential life at all. "I was eating with a princely appetite," he recalled, "sleeping like a log, without cares and pains, and getting stronger and healthier by the day. What was left as a penance?"

In order to have at least something to bear (obviously he could not openly proclaim Choir as his penance), Franz "made the intention", connected with a severe penance if he failed, not to go to the stove to warm himself that winter of his noviciate. Trappist monasteries are not heated, but they do have one room – the calefactory – which is warmed by a communal stove where the monks are allowed, at strictly regulated times, to take a little of the edge off winter. Instead of availing himself of this, Franz chose to chop yet more wood in order to keep himself warm.

The unrelenting sound of Franz's axe ringing through the enclosure provoked some irritation amongst certain members of the community. Already the monk serving in the refectory had begun the little game of putting more and more bread, even more than the one-pound piece prescribed by St Benedict, at Franz's place to see if he could finally get him to leave some. The others watched to see who would win, and when, as always, Franz finished whatever was put before him, even the more venerable Brothers allowed themselves a little humour in saying that the new novice was a man who cut his way through everything, not only at wood-chopping but also at table.

These relatively benign responses to Franz's determination to excel began to take on a harder edge. One older Father, well known for assuming so many private devotions that he was never able to complete the physical labour he was given, took particular exception to the energy Franz expended on work. He was in charge of a party repairing the monastery roof one day and Franz was one of those carrying roof tiles up in baskets. The old Father remained on the ground filling the baskets and made a point of giving Franz double the load of any of the others.

Franz submitted silently, straining into each load without objecting. But at the end of the day he knocked on the Prior's door and, invoking the injunction in the Rule that no one should be given too heavy a burden, asked if it was his Superior's will that he should carry as much as the Father in charge had given him. In Chapter the next day the Prior announced that "no one owed obedience to this impudent Father". Franz took this as a victory of work done in obedience over private prayer.

Trappist monasteries of old followed the principle of not teaching novices how to work. Work was a form of prayer as far as they were concerned, and each monk was to work the way he wanted and in the way he knew how. Franz's presence at Mariawald changed this. It began when he was sent out as part of a work party to clear a small piece of woodland so that an adjacent field could be enlarged. In charge was a genial old Swiss cantor. He stared at the wood and then, in Franz's words, "he asked me very frankly in the openness of his Swiss nature, 'Ha, what should I do here? I don't know where to begin.' Being the work supervisor he could speak and was supposed to tell us what to do, but he turned to me and said, 'You, Father Francis, must tell us how this is done.' And so I showed them how to cut down the beech and oak trees, demonstrating how to strike heavy blows and make the tree fall in the right direction."

From then on Franz was required regularly to take the lead in work parties by teaching or silent example, and so it was no surprise when, within weeks of making his profession, he was made Sub-Prior. At that time Simple Vows were taken after a year and, even in so holy an atmosphere, there was some resentment at this hasty promotion.

Now in a position of authority, Franz took his dispensation to speak as seriously as he did the general charge given to him for all outdoor work. Going into the fields on his first morning as a Superior, he gave his party of monks a talk on how he hoped that from now on the work would proceed at a faster and more efficient pace. Before any job was embarked upon he demonstrated exactly how it was to be done, and he had difficulty hiding his frustration at the clumsiness of the monks, especially the older ones who had never had any real experience of work and had been allowed to muddle on in their own way for years.

The old cantor was an exception – "all eye- and ear-watching in order to learn different works", as Franz put it. Round red face wet with sweat, he looked up eagerly to Franz and explained that he had wanted to learn to work properly for a long time but there was never anyone to show him how. He wanted to perfect the work that was his prayer as much as the prayer that was his work when he led the singing in chapel with great precision and dedication. His bulk prevented him from being adept at most forms of labour, but when Franz showed him how to bundle sheaves and make the ties for them, he was overjoyed at finding some form of work he could do well. Even when the prescribed time for work ended, he was to be found huffing and puffing over his sheaves until the very last moment allowed him. An exception, however, the old cantor was to remain.

~

A few months after Franz was made Sub-Prior the Father Visitator made his annual appearance. It is required by the Rule that every monastery be inspected once a year by the highest Superior, the Vicar General, or by an Abbot appointed by the General Chapter. At this visitation every professed Choir Religious is called to speak to the Visitator and disclose any break from the Rule or the Regulations in the running of the monastery. In this case the Visitator was the Abbot of Mariawald's motherhouse, Abbot Ephrem of Ölenberg.

As the most recently professed monk, Franz was called in last. The Abbot-Visitator was pacing up and down the room when Franz entered, his hands between his belt and his good-sized belly. After pacing silently for some time he gave Franz the Benedicite, that is, permission to speak, and then said, "Father Francis, you are an Austrian are you not?"

"Venerable Father," Franz answered, "once I was an Austrian, but now I am neither an Austrian or a Prussian – I am a Trappist." (Franz was always one for a ringing phrase.)

"That is as may be," said the Visitator, "but you still have not laid aside the corporal's rod!"

Franz knew exactly what he meant, and could well imagine what had been said by those called to the Visitator before him. He remained silent, nevertheless, and the Visitator went on: "You are always hurrying the monks to work and forcing a faster tempo when they are busy with their assigned duties." To this Franz replied that he had the Prior's approval.

"So, the Father Prior!" snapped the Visitator, at which point Franz knew he could not expect to look for support, such as it was, in that direction for much longer. "Father Prior or not," went on the Visitator, "this haste is against all religious custom. You may not introduce anything new to the monastery. Is that clear?"

There was a long pause, and then the Visitator inquired if Franz had anything else to say about Mariawald. Franz remained silent, and the Visitator asked, "What have you to say about the Brothers?"

"I find them very industrious and pious," Franz answered.

With these words, the session ended.

~

The next year, 1865, went by in much the same way, with Franz chafing at the indolence all about him. The Prior added Master of Novices to Franz's duties, but since no novices entered Mariawald that year or, as I have said, at any other time while Franz was there, this patent attempt to find a channel for his extra energy led nowhere. A better opportunity presented itself when the Prior left for the General Chapter again in the next year, and Franz, as Sub-Prior, was entrusted with the running of the house.

This happened at a time when there were a number of feast days – Corpus Christi, May devotions, Sacred Heart devotions, the Visitation Feast of the Blessed Mother, the devotions for the Saints John the Baptist, Aloysius, Peter and Paul, and so on. Franz had not been told whether he should preach on these occasions or not, but as it was the custom at Mariawald that a sermon be delivered on all the higher feasts, Franz decided to do so. With a wealth of material still available to him from his secular priest days (after a little alteration to take into account the circumstances of the monastery), Franz decided to preach on lower feast days and ordinary Sundays as well. The community of Mariawald, even those who took exception to Franz's blunt speaking in Chapter, enjoyed the sermons. Franz was nothing if not good with words.

The Prior returned to hear constant acclaim at the enthusiasm with which Franz had preached and held Chapter. When the Prior called Franz in to see him, Franz could sense him retreating further into his characteristic distance. He was somewhat surprised then when the Prior asked him to preach at the approaching feast of the Nativity of our Lady. He was less surprised when he discovered the afternoon before the feast that his volume of the sermons of St Bernard had disappeared from his box in the scriptorium. Clearly he was meant to prove that his talent for preaching did not lie in reproducing the words of the saint, and Franz rose to the occasion with particular aplomb.

His theme was "A Worm called Pride" and it was one to which he was to revert on many occasions:

"Oh," he would declare, "that one's own dear self finds its way into the strictest monastery! It is a tapeworm that grows until its head is taken out of the body, ripped out of the body and crushed! If this is not done, the living worm begins to rumble deep within the flesh, to rumble and to slither, to work its way up even into the throat, making us desperately nauseous but still unable to vomit it up. So we choke on ourselves, with the worm filling us from the gut to the mouth, and stirring all the more each time we come near the thing that threatens our pride. And this is why, when we try to stay silent in the presence of the thing that threatens our pride, our mouths are forced open, and the head of the worm appears in all its ugliness from between our teeth, the tongue to all that is wicked within us …

"The worm is clever too. It can sleep within, lulled when we reap the rewards for appearing pious, zealous, industrious, and God-fearing, when we are crowned with a halo while sitting on top of the shining and polished tower of our own dear self as it glitters in the sun of public recognition, our thirst for power temporally slaked, our ambition satisfied for a short while. But if, like St Elizabeth, we would come down from the castle of our conceitedness and have a shovel or pitchfork put in our hands, and be made to spread manure or level molehills under the direction of a supervisor most learned in theology and the arts and philosophy but entirely ignorant of the basics of field work, then we would know whether the worm of pride is dead or only sleeping, its own tail in its mouth until it is ready to gnaw away again at stomach and throat …"

This sermon was Franz's last at Mariawald. The next day he was deposed as Sub-Prior and Novice Master.

"Now again I was a 'commoner', one of the ranks," Franz told me, the hurt still showing after all the years between the event and the telling, "and my mouth was closed again. I kept very quiet and calm, and I could do this in the proper sense now, for I did not have to talk to anyone any more – *et silui a bonis*, I kept silent even about the good."

But the real target of his sermon had been the Prior of Mariawald. Franz was certain that the Prior, who was a titular Prior only and not a Prior for life, was threatened by his abilities as a preacher and a worker. He found evidence for this in his being assigned to housework once he was removed from office. He was ordered to sweep the floors, but when in all obedience he attempted to do this, he found there were no brooms. When he reported this to the Prior, the icy response he received was "What is that to do with me?" Franz's temper flared and he found himself shouting at his lawful Superior. The Prior snarled, "I'll throw you out," and Franz yelled back, "I do not need you to throw me out. I shall be leaving on my own!"

The first degree of humility, the Rule says, *is obedience without delay*, and Franz realised even as he spoke that he had gone too far. The two men stared at each other for a moment and then the Prior drew himself up and stepped back. Franz turned and hurried out.

~

Nothing more was said, and Franz was reassigned to his favourite occupation, chopping wood. The other monks knew just enough about what had happened (the raised voices had rung through the enclosure) to avoid aligning themselves with him, although the old cantor signalled signs of comfort and one or two of the younger men seemed to look at him with increased interest. Working silently and alone in the falling snow of his next winter at Mariawald, Franz again retreated into himself and found a strange peace, even a certain joy, in being the *abjection plebis*, the outcast of the community.

This status was reinforced by circumstances outside the enclosure of the monastery, even though Franz, along with all those properly oriented towards their vocation, was almost oblivious of them. For the year was 1866, and the rivalry that constantly threatened the alliance between Prussia and Austria finally gave way to open aggression. A few of the Brothers disappeared quietly from the monastery, called up to Prussian military service, and Franz was vaguely aware of others making the signs for swords and shooting. There was an almost imperceptible hardening of attitudes against the few Austrians at Mariawald, the assumption being that they held themselves superior on the grounds of Austria being an Empire while Prussia was but a kingdom.

In any event, even as the Prussian army with its murderous breech-loading needle guns swept over the Austrians in the Seven Weeks War, Franz determinedly kept his eyes on the ground (he had reinvoked his private vow regarding the avoidance of "unnecessary glances") and his mouth and ears from speech.

~

When spring broke Abbot Ephrem again appeared in his role as Visitator, riding up with his party between the dripping trees. He was stern-faced as he marched into the monastery and even Franz could not help noticing that the interrogation he was carrying out this time was a particularly strict one. Fathers and Brothers were hurried in and out of his quarters. Franz was again amongst the last to be called in, and he could see that the questions on this occasion would have little to do with whether a particular Sub-Prior was over-enthusiastic about the pace of work in the monastery.

The Visitator asked Franz to be seated in a comfortable chair and, leaning forward, asked him earnestly what he thought about the house and its Prior. His answer to the Visitator's question was frank and hard:

"Venerable Father, I think things are going badly here." You and I may have expected Franz to go on and recount the petty unpleasantnesses that had passed between himself and the Prior, but Franz came out with far more damaging revelations that did not seem to surprise Abbot Ephrem.

"Why do you say this?" he asked with the air of someone gathering further confirmation of suspicions already held.

"Venerable Father," answered Franz, "you have here a Prior who wants to betray our house."

"On what do you base this?"

"When the Prior did not yet know me well," Franz replied, "and when he was still well-inclined towards me, he asked me whether I wouldn't go along with him in a plan he was preparing. This was to separate from the motherhouse, sell the monastery, and move to America, taking the younger Brothers with him."

"And what did you answer?" the Visitator asked.

"I said, 'For that I wouldn't, perhaps, be useful.'"

The Visitator became pensive and sat lost in thought for some time. Then he signalled that the interview was over and Franz walked out into the cold spring air and went about his usual duties. By nightfall it was clear that everything was no longer normal at Mariawald. Franz was aware there was much running about and a general air of commotion, although, as a "commoner" again in the hierarchy of the monastery, he was not told what this was about.

In the morning the announcement was made that the Prior had left. Not only had he left Mariawald, but he had also asked for dispensation from his vows and returned to the world. The other monks were flabbergasted and milled about in a confused state; Franz stood silent and still amongst them, sure of his having put the finishing touch to the religious life of the Superior he had always felt was beneath him.

This turned out to be a hollow victory, however. Franz stayed on at Mariawald for some months more, but the heart had gone out of his vow of stability. Resentment at his presence was high amongst his confrères, and the new Prior was not the sort of man able to clear the air. He was not so much humble as completely ineffectual. What little he knew of the circumstances at Mariawald before his arrival did not help the decisions he took, which consisted mainly of devolving decision-making to others – or one other, I should say.

With a vague sense that Franz had been important in the incident that had led to his becoming Superior, the new Prior made Franz Sub-Prior and Master of Novices again, as well as appointing him as his secretary. This did not help Franz's standing in the community of Mariawald at all, but the new Prior was too caught up in his own rather strange world to notice. He was quite happy simply to leave the monks to their own devices, allowing tensions at Mariawald to fester. His very ineffectualness created new tensions; more by default than anything else it created a reign of mildness and indulgence to which some of the monks took avidly. Others looked to their Sub-Prior, some in a new light, for leadership that would keep their house to the strict and ancient discipline of their Order.

Franz's awkward position was finally and completely undermined when Abbot Ephrem returned as Visitator a mere six months after his last visitation. No one was surprised at his concern about conditions at Mariawald, and Franz was more than ready to launch into a litany of complaints. When it came to his turn to be interviewed though, the Visitator waved him aside and told him to be silent. Clearly the favour in which he had previously stood was now withdrawn and Franz felt deeply rejected. Then, as he stepped out of the Visitator's quarters, the Prior approached him and informed him that he had been removed from all administrative work. It was back to the common life and silence for Franz.

Franz could have no idea then how his losing favour with Abbot Ephrem would come back to haunt him in later years. As it was, he had barely taken in what this meant at the time when Brother Zacharias approached him in a flurry of signs.

~

Over the three years or so that Franz had been at Mariawald, Brother Zacharias had remained at the periphery of the turbulence set up by Franz, avoiding any alliance that would unsettle his own place within the Order. Now Brother Zacharias found himself being pushed inexorably towards making a commitment to one or another of the conflicting factions. To him Franz represented the clearest example of a true Trappist vocation, and so, when Franz's situation was made virtually untenable by the turn of events, he stepped forward with his plan.

Apparently the Visitator had let Brother Zacharias know that he feared the schism at Mariawald would come to the ears of Rome and, almost in passing, had said that the only way of settling the division between the zealous and the less fervent monks was for them to be in different monasteries. Exactly, signed Brother Zacharias excitedly, so why don't we apply to found a new monastery elsewhere?

Clearly Brother Zacharias took this idea to others as well, for the next day Franz returned from his solitary work in the fields to be informed rather peremptorily that it had been decided that he and Brother Zacharias were to leave Mariawald and lay the foundations of a new monastery in Austria. Within days preparations were made for their leaving, the bulk of which concerned nominating those of the community who were to join the two of them once a suitable site had been found. The division should have been fairly simple, but several of the monks felt that neither option really suited them. Dissatisfied with the Prior they may have been, but was Franz the person with whom to throw in one's lot – especially when that lot entailed wandering out into a world by now very foreign to men who took their vow of stability of place seriously?

3

On the 23rd July 1867, the day of their departure, Fr Franz and Brother Zacharias exchanged the kiss of peace with each member of the community of Mariawald in a somewhat forced ceremony and then stepped through the doors that the one had opened for the other in what felt, for Franz at least, like another lifetime. They had nothing about them other than a missal, a few days' travelling money, and the letters of obedience it was required for travelling monks to display when asked to confirm that they had been given permission to move around. The doors, now much more impressive and imposing than on the day of Franz's arrival, closed behind them with a thud and the two stepped out on to the road Franz had done so much to build. Then they began their descent through the Marianne Hills, the one feature of Mariawald Franz had truly come to love.

They reached Heimbach within the hour, strode on boldly towards Wollersheim, and from there were to be seen energetically making their way through Zülpich, Euskirchen and Rheinbach to Mehlem. From Mehlem they followed the Rhine upstream and Brother Zacharias, in a moment of almost complete disorientation, suddenly realised that he was now well and truly a part of the world with which Franz had overwhelmed him when he swept through the doors of Mariawald wrapped in the smell of distance.

~

In the days when Christianity was still establishing itself in Europe the worst crimes were punished by exile. A landless man with no kin was regarded as an outcast. The Christian pilgrim placed himself voluntarily in this position, deliberately making himself a stranger wherever he went in search of his place of devotion. Franz and Brother Zacharias had something of this ancient sense of homelessness as they wandered off towards Austria, but they were all the more strangers for not even having a specific destination. The sacred site they sought was purely in their imagination, a place to be created, not found.

Within days of leaving Mariawald, the meagre travelling funds given to Franz and Brother Zacharias were exhausted. Although Trappists, like most monks, are used to collecting funds for their holy endeavours, their present circumstances made Franz feel that any appeal for alms would smack too much of outright begging. Franz was soon forced to retreat, reluctantly, to his old home with the Sisters of Mercy at Agram in Croatia.

He and Brother Zacharias had not been in Agram long when two letters arrived for each of them. First, they each received a letter from Mariawald extending their original three-month period of absence; these they had expected as their original letters of obedience were about to expire. Brother Zacharias's second letter, however, ordered him to return, not even to Mariawald (this was expressly forbidden) but to the motherhouse of Ölenberg. This letter was from the Abbot of Ölenberg, Abbot Ephrem, written in his capacity as the newly elected Vicar General of the Trappist Order. So was Franz's second letter.

For decades Franz shared the contents of his letter from the Abbot with no one (although he carefully preserved both his and Brother Zacharias's letters of obedience, which are still available for scrutiny in the archives of his final foundation). Only the most urgent of circumstances led him to reveal what Abbot Ephrem had written to him – and then this was to me, a sure indication of how desperate he was.

In his letter, Franz told me in the flat blankness of an African night many, many years later, the Abbot gave him this "fatherly" advice: "Go back into the world to your diocese. You can still do much good!"

He was devastated, and saw nothing fatherly in the advice given by the man he had known only as the Visitator to Mariawald. For the second time he was being asked to renounce the Order to which he had sworn stability. He read the letter over and over. The Abbot did not actually command him to leave the Order, but how could a Superior even "advise" him to break his vows, to ask for dispensation from Rome, without giving any reason? And how could he, in this same letter, tell him that he may not return either to Mariawald or Ölenberg? This was, in effect, the same as expelling him from both monasteries and the Order itself.

Franz was up the whole night, working through the blunt dismissal with all his creative skills. "Now I was faced with a canonical question," he said to me, reliving the moment in full. "Which of the two letters had the more force? The one came from the lesser Superior, the Prior, but was official, the other from the greater, the Abbot, but not in official form. The Abbot was also Vicar General of the Trappists, so there was no higher authority within the Order. But his letter was only a private one, and what is more, it contradicted itself," Franz said as if the triumph of his logic was still fresh. "On the one hand it emphatically threw me out, but on the other it only advised me to leave. If the Abbot could throw me out, then he could also order me to leave! But he did not accuse me of any crime for which he would have been able to throw me out. He simply gave as a reason, 'in the world you will still be able to do much good'. But according to Canon Law this is not a sufficient reason to expel someone from the Order."

There was only one thing that Franz was sure of, and that was that he would never leave the Order. As far as he was concerned, he told me, as he was yet again on the verge of being expelled from that same Order, the Abbot could only ask him to give up the attempt to found a new monastery for the Trappists or order him back to his old monastery, Mariawald, where he had taken his vow of stability.

Even as Franz and Brother Zacharias were coming to terms with these letters, two monks from Mariawald arrived at the convent in Agram. They had demanded of the Prior that they be allowed to follow Franz and their soft and dithering Superior had let them go with very ambiguous letters of obedience. This forced the issue even more for Franz, making it plain that his situation had to be resolved so that he could take up the leadership that clearly was being thrust upon him. He decided that he and Brother Zacharias should go directly to Rome and put their case to the Procurator

General of the Trappists. Brother Jacobus and Brother Benedict, the two new arrivals from Mariawald, would have to accompany them because he could not, as he put it, "let them stay alone in the world".

In Rome began a long, slow, and frustrating period of waiting for Franz before his case was heard. It was during this time that the four monks were commissioned to restore the derelict monastery of Tre Fontane, built on the site where tradition holds it that St Paul was beheaded. The monastery, the full name of which is "Three Fountains of St Paul", had indeed been built between three springs, an obvious choice for Cistercians. However, even their attraction to swamps and skill at making them liveable had been defeated by Tre Fontane. The surrounding marsh was a perfect breeding ground for mosquitoes, and the malaria they spread was still at the time a disease for which there was no known treatment.

It took a real act of discipline for Franz and his fellow monks just to stay at the ruined monastery overnight. Sweating in their habits they lay in the dark, hearing the dreadful malarial fever rage about them in the buzz of its tiny insect carriers. Within weeks Brother Benedict, a cheerful and simple soul who, not being the best of workers, found his usefulness in serving as cook to the group, contracted the disease. Over four painful days Brother Jacobus nursed him, knowing all too well that this was to no avail.

Still, Franz laboured on at Tre Fontane. He was busy planting one of the eucalyptus trees that he had decided would be the most efficient deterrent to the mosquitoes when an ancient white-haired beggar called to him through the grate of the heavy iron door in the wall of the garden. The beggar asked for food and, as was the Trappist custom, Franz gave the old man some bread. This he stuffed into his nearly toothless mouth and chewed energetically. Then, instead of leaving, he stood at the door, staring about with crumbs and spittle on his face, making odd small noises and meaningless jerky gestures. Franz tried to ignore him and continue working, but suddenly the beggar called out to him, "Why are you labouring here so vainly? Go rather to Turkey; there you will find much more to do than in Rome." Or was it, "Why this drudgery here? Go to Turkey, there is more work there for you than in Rome"?

In any event, this is another of those quotations so often repeated in accounts of Franz's life that it is enshrined now in his story in one form or another. Whatever version you hear depends on the time he told it, the translations it has been through, or the source that has cast it forever in a particular way in the printed word. But, I hear you say, there is hardly any difference between the versions I offer you here. I who have remained silent for so long will answer that I have learned what worlds of difference may lurk in the tiniest variations of any tale. A comma here, a connective there, this synonym over that, and a whole other story looms up at you through the surface of your grammar, finding its new logic in the web of your syntax even as you keep your eye upon the grander scale of plot, character, theme. In language, the devil truly lies in the detail.

Devil or angel, when Franz spun around in annoyance to send the old man on his way, he had vanished, disappeared into the air. And so Franz found himself the subject of what seemed to him, increasingly over the years, a mystical experience. Events to come would turn the beggar into a prophet, or so Franz would say when pondering upon this experience, as he sometimes did.

In any event, it cannot be denied that it was the very day after the old beggar's strange pronouncement that Franz was called before Cardinal von Reisach of the Papal Curia, who told him that he had been acquitted by the highest authority in Rome, the Congregation for Religious. "They say you were too hasty at Mariawald," the Cardinal told Franz, "that was all they could find to bring against you and it is not enough. You have won your case against your Superior and may continue with the task given to you of founding an independent monastery."

The shortest of leave-takings was all that was required of Franz and his brethren before they left Rome and Italy far behind them.

~

Franz now remembered that a Slavonian priest whose parish he passed through on his way to Rome had mentioned that it was possible to acquire land in Bosnia. He headed back to this priest's parish in Altgradisca, where the priest was not only able to confirm this information but was willing to accompany him across the dangerous Verbasthal to a place that he thought might suit Franz's needs. He arranged transportation for them on a wagon loaded with hay that was going to Banjaluka, a town in Bosnia about a ten-hour journey from the Austro-Slavonian border. "The way led I knew not where," Franz intoned in one of his more lyrical moments. "I just drove into the unknown. The nearer we came to the mountains, the more romantic it became, and the more I liked it."

But there was more to the setting of Banjaluka than this, as Franz's hagiographers have been quick to note. For what saint worthy of his status has not followed the direction of angels? And what else could that grotesque old beggar have been but an angel, spitting and drooling out his apparently idiotic advice to Franz in the gardens of Tre Fontane? What else, indeed, when one remembers that at the time Bosnia was still, as it had been for the past four hundred years, a province of the Ottoman Empire.

Now let us be clear about this: one hagiographer may announce that "Father Francis was now on his own land – in the middle of the Turkish Empire!" and then ask with a triumphant rhetorical flourish, "What had that old man said at Tre Fontane?" But this is to push prophetic annunciation too far, for it is an exceedingly long stretch of the imagination to place Banjaluka anywhere near the "middle" of Turkey. It was in reality a frontier town in the furthest flung province of Turkey's empire, on its most western border, rubbing right up against Austrian-controlled Croatia. Banjaluka already boasted an Austrian Consul – a broad-shouldered, loud-voiced captain who seemed especially designed by nature to bully the Turks. Franz received a friendly welcome from this man, and an offer of as much assistance as he would need in muscling in on Turkish territory.

And assistance he would need. The Turkish authorities did all they could to discourage the establishment of a Christian institution in Bosnia, beginning with the land Franz wished to purchase. This was an hour's journey from Banjaluka on the slopes of a mountain that towered over the Verbas River, and Franz was forced to let a Greek merchant buy it and then sell it to him at a vastly inflated rate.

When the deal was settled, he was finally able to move his monks to the site of their new foundation. By now four more members of the Mariawald community had joined the group, and the whole party was certainly needed to get the wagon there. It took an entire week to cut a passage along the unbeaten track, and when they finally arrived at the property, the monks were dumbstruck. They found Franz standing in the midst of a dense plum-tree wood, itself surrounded by a thick oak forest. A few scattered huts leaned at a variety of angles around a small clearing, the most substantial of these located in the middle of a cemetery. This then was to be the new home they had travelled so far to find; they were to start their lives anew not only in the middle of nowhere, but in the middle of the dead!

"Most Christian burial grounds in Bosnia are hidden deep in the woods as a result of the Turks being seized, suddenly and unpredictably, with a desire to persecute the Christians every now and then," Franz explained eagerly as he darted around his new property. "During these periods Holy Mass would be held in the cemeteries, which could well be called the Bosnian Catacombs! We are starting our new lives much as Christian life itself was started," he told his small community.

Franz's enthusiasm was infectious. In a hut five feet wide and three feet long and surrounded by graves he celebrated his first Holy Mass in a foundation of his own.

~

That night the tiny new community made its bed upon fern leaves, with mantles as covers and bundles as pillows. The next day they began clearing the largest hut, which the previous owner had used as a stable for calves and pigs and, as a collection of broken vats bore mute evidence, a plum-brandy still. I shall resist the temptation of making the obvious comparison that some of these details bring to mind, but I am sure that in due course it will occur to some hagiographer somewhere to mention that this stall truly was the cradle of the beautiful monastery that hangs today like a star above forest and river high in the Bosnian mountains.

In those first months, that stall served Father Franz and his brethren as refectory, dormitory, infirmary, lavatory, office, Chapter Room, study hall, choir, sacristy, and, on rainy days, workroom. It was a single room constructed out of oak planks so crooked that sparrows and small wild animals had free entry. About seven-foot high with a pyramid-like shingle roof, it had no windows – not that these were necessary, as more light and air came through the crevices than was required. There was still a plank across the door that the farmer used to keep his pigs from running away.

Apart from two large maize barrels, there was no furniture in the room. The new community hung their coats and *cucullas* around the walls and stored their shoes in a nook under the roof shingles. Their more precious items – books, breviaries, paper, ink, chalice, missal, cruets, candles, and Mass vestments – were placed in the maize barrels, on top of what maize remained. This worked well at first, but as the maize was used it grew increasingly hard to reach these valuables. The community's decorum was seriously threatened one morning when one of the shorter Brothers, stretching down as far as he could for the articles needed for saying Mass, fell headfirst into one of the barrels.

In the woods there was a small spring that provided the only drink the community had, and the table boasted only beans and maize bread, maize bread and beans. There was neither vegetables nor milk and not even potatoes, nor would there be for two years. The first season's planting was ruined by drought and the second was taken up with tilling rather than planting.

Franz began building as soon as he could. At this stage the community did not include a carpenter or a mason, so in the first months strangers came amongst the monks to construct the first monastery building. Franz paid for their hire from the largest donation made to the new foundation, two thousand gulden given by a Cistercian monastery in Saxony called Mariastern. In gratitude for this, and the guidance he was given in finding the stable in which his new foundation would be born (there, you see I could not resist this after all!), he too took "Mary, the Star" as the name of his monastery.

The new building added primitive fabrication to Trappist severity. Forty-two feet long and sixteen broad, this simple structure of unburned brick was divided into four compartments, one of which served as a chapel, another as chapter, the third as a refectory and the fourth as a cell for the Prior, which doubled as a workroom. It was ready for occupation within three months and Franz chose the 8th September 1869 – the Feast of the Nativity of the Blessed Virgin Mary – as the day of its inauguration. On the same occasion, the first two postulants recruited to his project received the habit. He did not, in accepting them into their noviciate, need to say much as far as inciting them to the practice of poverty was concerned. "We have, you see," Franz would repeat in the first months at Mariastern, "the true poverty of Bethlehem."

~

It was on this humble stage that I was to make my entry into the story. "On the evening before the Feast," it is recorded, "at the moment when the monks were entering the house for the first time, a new postulant arrived from Vienna, Herr Biegner, who later became and is now Father Joseph Cupertino, who from that day forward never more forsook Father Franz."

Or so I put it in one of the few mentions I was to make of myself in the first version of "The Life of Abbot Francis" I was to write. This is useful enough in its way, but there was so much then that I could not afford to tell, things being as they were, which now slowly, carefully, I will bring before you in the safety of the shadow of my own death, that refuge from earthly prosecution and your guarantee that I tell the full truth at last.

4

Back then – back in Vienna, I mean – I was young and full of life, although I felt far from either when word came to me through the Congregation of Mary of a new foundation being started in Bosnia by two monks who had addressed our Congregation some two years before.

I had not paid much attention to Franz and Brother Zacharias when they wandered through the city in which I was quietly making my way. I remembered that they seemed rather thrown upon the world, lonely and unsure of where they were going. Everything that I felt about myself at that time – melodramatically, I am sure, and for very different reasons. If they had had no clear hold on my attention at the time it was because this was completely taken up by my being in love. Or, more correctly, very recently out of love, as far as she was concerned – yes, there is a woman somewhere behind this story of stern celibate men striding the earth.

I had been doing quite well in Vienna; very well to be sure, for a young man born in a small rural town in southern Moravia. Not that my background was anything to be ashamed of, you understand: my family was, of course, German, both my father and mother being descendants of the waves of immigrants washing into the Czech lands in the full tide of the Counter-Reformation. This meant that we were not quite as well established as those Germans who came to Bohemia and Slovakia to work the seams of silver and gold discovered in the thirteenth century. Still, my father, like his father and grandfather before him, was a Master Baker, so he was well established within the strict hierarchy of the crafts.

As a Master Baker, my father had the right not just to make bread and cakes but also to own the shop in which he sold them. He strengthened this advantage by marrying the daughter of a miller, and the combination of bakery, shop and convenient access to flour allowed us to continue living comfortably even as the first factories, all belching smoke and clanging metal, began to materialise on the edges of the town. Exciting as these developments were for a small boy peering through fences to catch glimpses of flaring furnaces, I could not help feeling superior to the new children of steel and steam as I joined them, fresh from my soft and powdery old world of warmth and comforting smells, on our way to school on a wintry morning.

My childhood days were conventionally happy, filled as they were for the most part by a boy's usual designs upon all the small creatures he encounters – trying to herd ducks into the millrace to see if they would get caught in the wheel was a particular favourite – and such preoccupations were only partially interrupted by classes in the town's elementary school. Here, when not the object of the teacher's attention, I would lie with my cheek against the cool wood of my desk and listen for the random thud of apples falling from the trees that grew in every corner of our town, spilling out of the orchards on the slopes of the hills and sprouting like welcome weeds in every nook and cranny. Some speak of the smell of apples reminding them of home when they are away, others of the blossoms turning the valley in which our town made itself cosy into a nest of pink and white, but for me it is always the steady if irregular thuds of late September that are the most evocative memory of the fullness of youth, abundance dropping beyond our ability to use it.

From that classroom window too I would gaze out at the three buildings that dominated the horizon of my childhood, ranged as they were along the skyline created by the hills that form the immediate backdrop to Letovice. First, the parish church of St Procopius – or St Prokop as the Czechs called him, reminding us of the distinction erased by the Latinate version of his name between this Bohemian saint and the German Saint Procopius, Fool for Christ.

Next was the Monastery of the Merciful Brothers, a comparatively recent addition begun in 1751 and more or less completed in time for Joseph II's dissolution of the monasteries in 1782. Its chapel, dedicated to St Wenceslas, was a baroque confection of plaster, paint and gilt that was to me in my youth and ignorance achingly beautiful. The sharp lead spire of St Procopius looked pointed and plain next to the serene and billowing half-balloon of St Wenceslas's spire, which seemed to float above the town and somehow caught for me the gentle beauty of the community behind the monastery's walls. I am sure it was from this building that the mystery of retirement, with kindness and healing welling from its secret centre, first won my heart.

But this was not the highest of the triumvirate of buildings that watched over Letovice, calling out to my youthful imagination. Third and last, squat and solid, its honey-coloured walls glowing and its huge red-tiled roof flashing in the sun, the Kalnok chateau loomed from the peak of the hills behind the town. The privilege the Kalnoks represented, which still evoked at the time of my youth that strange blend of resentment and pride typical of the residue of a feudal past, mingled with my fascination with the Merciful Brothers. It was the Kalnok's dead, joined with their own in the crypt, above whom the monks worshipped in their chapel, and it was only a few minutes' walk from the glories of that chapel to the massive gates that allowed one tantalising glimpses into the gracious life of the walled chateau.

From the gates a road ran straight into the countryside spread out behind the chateau, creating a far more important aesthetic perspective than the tiny clutter of the town huddling below its imposing frontage. Once, when sprinting from the gates as a carriage came thundering out onto this road, I broke away from my panting companions just in front of the monastery and ran down the hill into an orchard. As the hullabaloo of the chateau's groundsmen chasing my friends disappeared in the direction of the road, I made my way quietly through the trees, choosing my footing as carefully as my desire for speed would allow as I made my way down the steep slope that led towards the town.

You will think it an invention of an overly pious old man's memory if I tell you that, just as the bells of St Procopius began to toll out the hour right above my head, one of my hasty steps came within an inch of a shiny black snake slithering through the fallen apples. But this instant stands clear in my recollection, all the more so because it brought me to a standstill – at least, that was my intention. Instead of my heels digging into the earth, though, they bit into a mat of half-rotten apples which sent me skidding wildly forwards. I crashed headfirst into a tangle of fruit, leaves and branches and must, I suppose, have hit the trunk of a tree against which I found myself resting moments later.

It could only have been moments, for the bells were still ringing when I came to. Even when they fell silent, the resonance of one note – no, nothing that definite, some overtone, perhaps, some mysterious conjuncture of chime and echo shaped by the hills surrounding my home town – still seemed to vibrate all around me. It was then, for the first time, that I disappeared. With the air itself reverberating like a giant bell just struck, it was as if – how can I put this? – my very self began to melt away. From an intense consciousness of who and where I was, born first of fear and flight and then of shock and hurt, my identity began to lose its boundaries and fade into a sense of everything around me – apples, grass, moist ground, the light warmth of the day, the reverberations of the bells – and then beyond this, through leaves and branches and filtering sunlight into the glare of the sun itself, and through this again into a boundless sense of all being.

This was not a confused state, but clear and sure, more clear and more sure than anything I remember up until this point in my life, and it was infused with a sense of transcendent happiness, utterly beyond words. It was as if my whole being was disappearing into a blinding light, a light so bright that I fell into it like a spark falling into the sun. I think I cried out as I surrendered to this blissful radiance of nothingness and everything. Just as I gave myself completely to it, it gave way, suddenly, to total blankness.

I have no idea how long it was before I became aware of surfacing from this void. I re-emerged into a world from which all sense of inspired well-being was utterly gone. In its place was a whirlpool of distorted images and ideas into which I felt myself sinking like a tiny vessel in an enormous storm. There was no temptation this time to surrender to this overwhelming sensation. It was filled with a premonition of impending doom, and I fought my way back to a surface made of a rush of memories that, no matter how confused and deformed, were at least recognisably my own.

When I came back to myself I was standing, hands limp at my sides, blinking into the ordinary light of an autumn day. My head ached and I felt nauseous – symptoms of the blow to my head rather than the state I entered after my fall. For something like this mysterious state would come upon me on and off at different stages throughout my life without any attendant ill effects. Throughout the rest of my childhood I would simply slip seamlessly into it, enveloped in a warm glow from which I would emerge confused and struggling to find myself in relation to the things about me. I gathered from my parents and teachers that I appeared to be daydreaming or just staring into space at these times. On many an occasion I returned to find

67

a teacher's ruler being applied with some force to my hands or shoulders, or even that I was being slapped about the head, but I would always be too uncertain of where or who I was to try and explain.

I was afraid to share my experience in the apple orchards of the Kalnoks with my parents, given the illicit nature of that expedition. They were more indulgent about my "absences" as they chose to call them, and put them down to my simply being a dreamy child. As for my schoolmates, they found my tendency to sudden abstraction a cause for humour – never more so than when I was seen gazing blankly at nothing as a ball I was meant to catch fell right before my feet, or when I would stop dead in the middle of an account of some adventure and then not remember at all what I had been talking about. One of the boys in my class even managed what I am told was a fair imitation of my appearance during these momentary states: apparently my eyes would blink rapidly and there would be a slight rhythmic movement of my facial muscles, if his mimicry was anything to go by.

No one, not even myself, as I remember, seemed to notice how often I would slip into this state of being when the bells of St Procopius rolled over our town; this was an association I would make, to my extreme cost, only many, many years later. At the time my moments away, as I would think of them, simply became a part of the Eden of my childhood, shaped as it was by the powers that shaped me.

Yes, I am old now and aware of the skin around my eyes sagging in on my vision, the frame of my mortality a constant peripheral reminder that I see all now through the gravity of the years that draw me inexorably towards my end. But I still hear, in the silence that has claimed me and will probably damn me in this far and inexpressibly foreign land, the thud, thud ... wait ... the thud of the falling apples of Letovice.

~

You may say that I left Letovice by degrees. First I was sent to the Piaristen-Unterschule, a renowned junior school in the region. This was in the nearby and slightly larger town of Mährisch-Trübau. Here I did well enough (despite my dreamy spells, which, in any event, became less and less frequent as I grew older) to be allowed to go on to an academic high school. And so began the steady movement south that brought me, ultimately, to what seemed to me then the very edge of the world. The first step was small enough, although at the time it felt breathtakingly large: my parents decided

I should go to secondary school in Brünn, the major city in Moravia, which lay some fifty kilometres south of Letovice.

Throughout my time in Brünn nothing would please me more than being able to escape out of the town's tiny streets into one or another of its public squares and look up and see, perched on Petrov Hill, the towering shape of the Cathedral of St Peter and Paul or, on the hill next to it, the looming spectacle of Spielberg Castle. Not only did this give me a grander version of my familiar home setting but I thrived on the religious inspiration of the one as much as I did on the thrill of the frightful legends of the other.

But you could not afford to be sentimental about the past in Brünn. As a schoolboy dodging around its streets and squares between school and my lodgings it often felt like I was negotiating a vast building site. The dust of demolition regularly filled the air, with a Gothic chapel here, a Renaissance palace there, yielding to a vivifying spirit of moving forward and opening up. Everywhere theatres, banks, squares, and the houses of the new industrialists were rising up in place of the faded elegance of tatty Baroque and Rococo palaces and a maze of cobbled alleys.

The progressive spirit of the times permeated the school at which I was accepted. Neither my family nor my academic background were quite good enough to get me into the classical secondary school, but my father was not interested in my studying a lot of dead languages, as he put it; he was more than happy with my being at the Unterrealgymnasium, where mathematics and the sciences could prepare me for the new world that was clearly breaking upon us.

As for myself, I could still depend upon disappearing into any number of churches in Brünn and losing myself in their cool heights in summer or stuffy warmth in winter. Gilded naves, high to the point of giddiness, impressed me then, as did the false perspectives of frescos and the life-like appearance of painted terracotta statues. Most of all, for my sins (and I can say that in all seriousness now), I was drawn by the Jesuit church very near our school. Of what was once a massive Jesuit seminary that took up several blocks in the new town layout there remained only one of the most, for me, special churches in Brünn.

Two things made it so. The first was that P Jacobus Kresa, rector of Madrid University and eminent mathematician (he was the author of the Logarithm Table), was buried in its crypt, having died in Brünn while passing through on his travels. The second was the peculiar beauty of the altar

69

immediately to the left when one entered. This was dedicated to the missions and was surrounded by wonderfully carved figures representing those territories still waiting for the chance of salvation. Asia and America were done well enough, but the figure of Africa, a Nubian of extraordinary grace – his fingers sheer poetic filigree on his upheld hands, his limbs combining delicacy and strength in perfectly balanced proportion, his glistening blackness capturing the onlooker's distorted reflection in its mysterious depths – absorbed me more with every visit I paid to the church. Or, as increasingly became the case, just to this figure gracing one of its side altars.

Dreams of being a famous mathematician or missionary are legitimate enough for a growing boy, but I know now the sin of hubris that lies behind so much of the actual achievement of such status. Moralising aside, I know now, too, the temptation that Africa represents, the seductions that unknown sculptor, who in all probability knew nothing of Africa, nevertheless caught so well in dreaming and crafting that continent into a human shape.

Yes, there was much to prompt my eager young imagination in Brünn. Still, I could not help but recognise that much of this was merely a copy of the city upon which the town was so actively modelling itself. Brünn was already being called a suburb of Vienna. The new ring road cutting a swathe around the town, the parks that led off this, and many of the buildings going up were virtually exact replicas, on a minor scale, of the same developments in Vienna. Often the same town planners and architects worked on both cities, but one always knew that a building that was four storeys in Brünn was five storeys in Vienna.

I was thus overjoyed (as were my parents) by my doing so well at my studies that I was promoted to Oberrealschule in Vienna. I was beside myself with a mixture of delight and nervous excitement at the thought of going to the metropolitan centre around which our provincial lives revolved.

~

To arrive in Vienna for the first time was a kind of homecoming. To behold each of its major sights was to remember them from books and pictures rather than to see them, although the numerous modifications in progress since Joseph II's first rebuilding commissions gave a certain disjunctive quality to each of these visions.

It was as if these landmarks floated up at one out of a new and shifting landscape, but for this much at least Brünn had prepared me. As in

Brünn, the ancient city walls of Vienna had recently come down before the trumpet of the modern. I easily recognised the broad circular boulevard replacing them, even if not quite completed, as the ideal of which Brünn's incipient version was the platonic copy. The incomparable imperial palace, however, rose from the spaces being cleared for new buildings and parks with a grandeur Brünn could never emulate, and the stone lace spire of St Stephen's Cathedral sailed above the changes that surrounded it with a serenity no church in Brünn could match. These now became the landmarks that would catch my eye wherever I went, making my way in this glorious, effusive bustle of old and new.

And make my way I did. My excellent academic progress earned me an internship in the offices of the Imperial and Royal Austrian Lottery. My parents were overjoyed; my elder brother was well set to take over the bakery, so to have one's second child's future independently assured within what seemed to them to be the exciting new world of administration was truly something of which they could boast. "Exciting" was not quite the word I would have used for the rather mundane clerical duties of my new position, but I certainly felt well placed within the tight hierarchies that continued to govern Austrian life even as it was modernised. I was slotted in at a respectable level and adorned with a suitably impressive official title: Praktikant an der K. & K. Lotto-Direktion, Wien.

"Respectable" is not always a word used in connection with lotteries, I know. I must tell you they are of ancient origin, nevertheless, and were once a standard part of the entertainments of the Roman emperors and the feudal princes of Europe. Lotteries went on to become an important part of raising royal revenues in more recent times: France, Italy and England had all introduced State lotteries, attempting to absorb or suppress the many informal lotteries that were flourishing everywhere. The rationale for the appropriation of private lotteries was the frequency of fraud in their operation, but by the nineteenth century the State lotteries acquired something of a similar reputation and were discontinued in many countries, certainly in England and France.

This should give you some sense of just how seriously my offices were taken in Austria where the Royal and Imperial Lottery was maintained – the Empire was becoming increasingly expensive to run – despite the disrepute into which lotteries elsewhere had fallen. Our administration had to be seen to be entirely trustworthy in its governance of the world of chance, a contradiction that may best be explained by saying that we exerted maximum control over a certain area of affairs so that luck could take its free course within that realm.

Speaking for myself, I must say that I was glad that, as the executors of fortune, my colleagues and I were forbidden to live in the infinitely small but reciprocally powerful hope it offered. For me there was no sacred geometry of chance, no arcane wisdom of luck; when I chose to think of the medium over which we presided as anything other than an administrative problem, it was with a vertiginous sense of its sheer contingency. There could be no purpose or design here, just conjunctures of the most infinitely random kind, and it was to preserve this complete absence of logic, reason or faith that we laboured so meticulously.

My internship proceeded smoothly and by 1865 I had every reason to play the part of a confident young man about town, with a little money in my pocket, opportunities for amusement aplenty, and my future assured. If anything I underplayed this part, being of a retiring nature, and I was modest in my explorations of what Vienna had to offer someone in my position.

The city was an explosion for the senses. Whenever I stepped out of my rooms – which, extremely modest though they were, cost me over a quarter of my income – I was met by a profusion of spectacle and consumption: the shops and houses of the better areas were built in a jumble of styles, as if Vienna had no style of its own, and regardless of design they were smothered in decorative arabesques. On the few occasions I was invited into private homes I was overwhelmed by gilt and stucco, tortoiseshell and multicoloured glass; I felt lost in the rococo mirrors that casually refracted one into the infinity of their multi-paned surfaces. Once I was shocked to bump up against a life-size wooden Negro, glistening like the altarpiece in my favourite church in Brünn but nowhere near as delicate or refined. I did not know enough then to recognise all this for the garish display that it was. My provincial tastes were in no way equal to such a task, and so I simply indulged – indulged as a voyeur, as my means dictated.

It was in the coffee shops that I was able to participate eagerly in the excess all about me in, perhaps, its purest form, the massive layers of whipped cream, chocolate, custard, crystallised fruit, marzipan and who knows what else that adorned the mountains of confectionery under which the city seemed to be sinking. I took part with gusto in the religion of the four o'clock break for coffee and cake, and joined the throng of the entire Viennese workforce as it worshipped punctiliously at the altars piled with gateau and torte.

72

Of course I knew there were other sides to Vienna: proletarian quarters in dark regions that the city kept secret and I never had reason to think about in those heady days, let alone enter. Occasionally their presence permeated the world of gay overindulgence on whose fringes I so modestly lapped. I would sometimes see ragged bodies piled in the parks, tattered men sleeping upright in doorways, even whole families deposited on manicured lawns, dully awaiting the ever present force of authority to move them on. For Vienna was nothing if not an ordered place, and one felt the hand of Habsburg power behind everything.

In much greater proximity to me was another hidden side of Vienna, the invisible but insistent world of carnality. Never spoken about, one was nevertheless constantly aware of its silent, potent throb. My age made me an obvious sensor for this deeply veiled dimension of the city's excess, but given that it was one of the most intimate ways in which those who had fed off those who had not, continuous hints of its existence could be glimpsed by even the most modestly averted eyes. One's embarrassed gaze was never turned away quite fast enough to miss some good burgher negotiating with a shabby working woman just off a main street; one's ears were never deaf enough when whispered arrangements were made by factory girls to give themselves to bankers or lawyers just for a bed.

My innate prudery – like my income when it came to the other indulgences of the metropolis – kept me at a decent distance from this aspect of Vienna's simultaneously suppressed and flaunted sensuality. The act of procreation hardly seemed to attend the prosperous and shiny middle-class families abroad of a weekend, despite the multitude of well-organised offspring gathered about them. It was the good wives buried in clothes so cumbersome that it is certain they could not get dressed without assistance to whom I aspired, I would say, rather than to whom I was attracted.

I was young and, it turned out, underestimated the attraction I presented to others making their way through this world; before long, I somehow found myself caught up with a certain young woman. Perhaps her official designation (girl, as in "sales girl") is more accurate, for M was barely out of school. You must forgive the abbreviation; modesty is I am sure not necessary after all these years, but even today her name in full wrecks the composure necessary for the telling of this story.

~

M worked in a shop that specialised in fine paper. She possessed a sure and instinctive feel for the product she sold, and was promoted more rapidly than usual to front of house. She never ceased to amaze me with her knowledge of the varieties of paper available: laid, linen, smooth, matt, embossed, she could reel off the types and the ranges produced by various manufacturers with ease, and make insightful suggestions as to their uses.

I dealt with reams of paper every day, but for me, until I met M, it was an invisible medium important only for the way in which the symbols of my profession – the endless play of numbers, dancing with each other in the incalculable possibilities of chance – took shape on it. It was an absence really, at best a surface for the lifeblood of my day-to-day activities: ink, ink, and yet more plain, black ink, spelling out the tortuous web of administrative detail necessary to guarantee the deadening banality of luck.

Once I came to know something of the abundance of weights, textures, and colours available, I began to be offended by the plainness and coarseness of the paper with which I worked, and to resent the way in which the rich art of paper is generally reduced to sheer functionality. Even today, I suspect that if the quality of the paper available to me here in this far-flung colony of a foreign country were not so execrably poor, I may have been content to leave for you only gleaming white sheets, the physical embodiment of the purity of silence. Living now as I do in the reality of the world to which I have been exiled, where the medium to which I must entrust the fullness of my confession is as rough and shoddy as that reality, I find I have little choice but to adorn it with words.

M and I first met at St Stephen's Cathedral where she happened to attend the same Mass to which I went quite regularly. The religious habits of my youth still clung to me, but I think my routine appearances at Mass had more to do at this time of my life with some vague idea that the order and predictability of the litany would offset the void of chance that was the concern of my working hours. Even the mysteries of the Church – the Trinity, the Eucharist, the Incarnation – while above reason were never contrary to reason, and so had in them an immanent logic that defied the complete absence of reason that it was my job to preserve. There was nothing very definite in all this for me, and so another reason for my going to St Stephen's was for the social life it offered. I began making some acquaintances there, and I certainly attended church gatherings in the hope that these acquaintances would at some time include members of the opposite sex. This hope was to find its incarnation in M.

Like St Augustine himself I must confess to lusting after a girl during the celebration of God's solemn rites within the very walls of His house. I am afraid I must admit to being attracted at first to several of the young women who shimmered in the sea of twinkling devotional candles beneath the ornate images of the Madonna; for some time, M did not stand out particularly. Then, one Sunday, while I stood outside the cathedral ostensibly admiring its multicoloured, ceramic-tiled roof but actually running through the possibilities of attempting an introduction to one or two of the more attractive women, this girl – for she was too young for me to see her as anything else at the time – appeared before me from out of a crowd of very similar looking girls and announced herself with a forthright stare.

The frankness of that look, which I was forced by its very frankness to return, made it difficult not to exchange some words on the next occasion that we met, and before I knew it we were considered something of a pair at the various church-oriented activities we attended. M soon began to wait for me at the doors of the lottery offices as I left for lunch, often with some special delicacy that we would eat together in one of the new parks nearby.

In the mix of peoples making up a city that was the centre of an empire that sprawled over many, many nations, I found M's faintly exotic looks both attractive and comforting. Her Slavic features suggested that her family was but a few generations away from regions close to those of my birth, but this in itself was enough to ensure the disapproval of my thoroughly German parents. I was a long way from home, though, and just adventurous enough to allow myself to give in to the temptation of this, at first merely titillating, difference between M and myself.

What I did not count on was just how addictive I would find those extraordinarily arched cheekbones, dark olive eyes, and slashed plum of a mouth. Nor, as our meetings at evening church gatherings extended to time alone in the green darkness of the park, did I have any idea how quickly kisses could move to the mysteries of female dress, and my discovery, as if for the first time in the history of the world, of breasts milk-white in the moonlight, warming the inside of my hand as the slight chill of an early summer night pressed in upon us. Further experiments with meeting places and the art of negotiating each other's clothing led to the opening up of whole new realms of the empire of the senses. M became for me a hymn of all the differences brought together by the Habsburgs.

I continued to attend Mass, but now in a feverish cycle of transgression, confession, penitence, absolution – and transgression again. The Canticle of Canticles (the one book in the Bible in which God is not mentioned by name) became the only book I was fit to study. I could feel my face suffuse with blood when sections of it appeared in the feasts of the Virgin Mary or the Holy Women. "O that you would kiss me with the kisses of your mouth" rapidly lost all of its officially allegorical meaning for me as I learned the tangible truth of breasts like clusters of the vine, breath like the smell of apples, and kisses like the best wine that goes down smoothly, gliding over lips and teeth.

Night after night I unpacked the realm of metaphor that is the Song of Songs, discovering with Solomon the reality that inspired the lines:

> Your rounded thighs are like jewels,
>   The work of a master hand.
> Your navel is a rounded bowl
>   That never lacks mixed wine.
> Your belly is a heap of wheat,
>   Encircled with lilies.
> Your breasts are like two fawns,
>   Twins of a gazelle ...

How my staid words crack to remember this, how my story strains beneath such memories. How, too, does my guilt give way before the years of sacrifice I have laid on the altar of that sweet sin, whose incense still wreaths around me in the years of my loss. M lingers to this day like the trails of smoke from a candle just extinguished ... "O that my left hand were under her head, and that my right hand embraced her".

As for M, well, she was always much more prosaic in her love, if love it was. Although love it certainly seemed, with a flurry of small gifts for any occasion or no occasion at all, faces warmed as they met for a kiss or a whispered intimacy over tables loaded with Black Forest cake and steaming with hot chocolate on winter afternoons, hands clasped through the autumnal tumble of the city as we rushed back breathless to our places of employment after meetings that always seemed too short.

And yet I never sensed in M the flights of imagination she inspired in me. I do not mean the poor and purple prose I scribbled in my vain attempt at keeping a diary in those days. It was that she so clearly lived her love in the physicality of the moment, not just the slidings into and enfoldings, although the way her eyes rolled back and fluttered in the peaks of her ecstasy spoke of heights that I, in my hardness and pourings forth, never quite seemed to attain. But in all things she was so completely of and in the world. She seemed thick, somehow, in its very materiality, in a way that always struck me as foreign to my experience. If you will forgive my making a metaphor of the simple fact of her profession, it was as if she were the paper and I the words, she dense with texture, weight, colour, shape, and I attenuated into the tortuous twists and turns of signs.

And it was then that I began to suspect that I was, in some essential way, a man of words — made up, that is, of words, living through the word not the thing. It was as if words came between me and even that small, lithe body, beautiful beyond words as it twisted and turned beneath me in the dim light of some secluded spot. At one and the same time it seemed to become part of me, warm and slick under my hands, and to remain absent in its very indescribability. Was it this that came between us even as we came together? Was this the distance that we both began to feel, I sick and desperate at the first hint of its appearance?

"I opened to my beloved, but my beloved had turned and gone" says the Song of Songs, and one day, too soon, forever too soon, I found my-self alone again in the city, wandering like the singer through its streets and squares, asking of the watchmen, "Have you seen her whom my soul loves?" When I saw her young friends — erstwhile friends perhaps, for she no longer joined them — it was all I could do not to say out loud, "I adjure you, O daughters of Jerusalem, if you find my beloved, that you tell her I am sick with love."

But she was gone. And I had to endure that most ignominious season of youth: "I am my beloved's and my beloved is not mine." Oh, I did it all: the standing in various forlorn poses under street lights on routes I suspected she might take home after evenings out with whoever had replaced me; the feverish visions haunting my bed of what we had done now being done with someone else; and worst of all the endless composition of speeches of explanation, accusation, protestation, each of which collapsed, one way or another, sooner or later, into pathetic begging.

These last I committed to a rich array of papers, creating letters which, despite their increasing intensity, fell lifeless at the door of M's heart. She tried, briefly, to work up enough energy to respond to something which was for her simply finished, done with, and then did the only other thing she could in all honesty do – ignore me. As kindly as possible at first, and then with a growing irritation that was harder to hide. Suggested meetings were turned down, my letters were returned unopened. And so I slowly submitted again to lonely lunches and evenings, and watched with a kind of horrified helplessness as paper relentlessly became again for me a mere passive element in the world of administering other people's luck.

Where else then was there for me to go but back to the arms of the Church? The world of my young male colleagues held no attraction for me – the drinking, the boasting, the brash play, the harsh laughter and loud, empty words all repulsed me. No, what comfort I could find in the emptiness that was life without M came to me most when I was enfolded in the warm, rich, dark mystery of the cathedral. At first I felt myself to be only a tiny soul lost in a cavernous silence that no intoning or recitation seemed capable of penetrating, and the pathetic monologues, self-pitying and sterile, that made up my prayers fluttered around me like so many lost birds. But eventually I found my way back to faith and grace in the depths of the confessional.

Here, in the sacrament of penance, my soul soared free of M, and in agonising slowness my body and mind began to follow. Step by step, the erotic imagery that so possessed my faculties floated free from M's lovely form and became attached instead, after the example of great writers of the church from Plotinus to Augustine, to the beatific vision. My all too corporeal love, embodied in my carnality and its rising up to M's insistent physicality, gradually transmogrified into the adoration inspired by the rich iconography of the Church. Ravished by the Virgin's chasteness, taken by the Bridegroom at his coming, I went forth, like St John of the Cross, into the "dark night/With anxious love inflamed" for the Lord, not some simple girl. M was no longer Magdalene now, but Mary.

~

In the Church, as I began to re-establish contact with other people, I found a new social life. I allowed myself to be drawn into activities suggested to me by confessor and pastor, partially in penance but also because, practically speaking, in these I found a structure and order that could take over my own bruised and battered will, my almost complete loss of initiative.

This was the case at first, but steadily I found within myself a deep enthusiasm for the exercises of religion, particularly prayer, or rather – and the distinction is important – meditation. In a truly meditative state, I felt I had nothing to say but, strangely, was still able to say it. I felt I was in a dialogue of silence, a communion made of not speaking. Here I found the beginning of the experience that was to hover just before me as it drew me further and further into the religious life in which I wished to lose myself – no, not so much lose myself as find myself without words.

Oddly enough, what came back to me now as an ideal was my boyish talent for mathematics and the ghost of the desire fired in the Jesuit church in Brünn to aspire to the status of that long-dead inventor of the Logarithm Table. I harboured no real aspirations in this direction, of course; my career in numbers and symbols had blunted any real ability I may have had in this realm, but I longed again for the kind of clarity I once knew there. Mathematics was a kind of language that struck me now as chaste and true, cutting through the excess in which Vienna was drowning and in which I myself so nearly went down. It was a language into which I longed to translate all the uncertainties of my life and the falsehoods I saw all about me.

Vienna was a place in which nothing was as it seemed: I was sick of butter knives shaped like Turkish scimitars, ice buckets like Prussian helmets; marzipan effigies of every figure under the sun adorning cakes that were otherwise the only forms allowed to be true to themselves. The literary language to which love – false too, all false – made me aspire billowed extravagantly about me in journals and books that looked to me like so much cream whipped up into a frenzy of pretension and already beginning to drip down the walls of the libraries and academies as a prelude to a mighty implosion. The whole city tottered like an over-aesthetic confection the consumption of which would produce only so much flatulence. Words, in their flattery and self-delusion, could no longer talk this away. In contrast, mathematics became for me a kind of monastery in which one could live in the full knowledge of the only things that mattered, those things of which one could not speak.

But the sacred space of numbers was by now forever closed to me, sullied by the illusion of wealth built around it that I in my daily labour did nothing but help perpetuate, and that the population of Vienna clung to feverishly as the reality of an impending collapse of some sort became obvious. And so before me now I saw no longer figures but only the figurative mysteries of the Church through which one reached, in the end, a consecration to silence. Perhaps at the point where words gave out, truth could briefly flare up – as it promised to do in my seizures – and then fall away, done with words forever.

~

It took some time for me to work my way towards this spiritual understanding. The more overt features of the religious life claimed me first, and I became known for my enthusiasm for prayer and ministering to others. I was guided towards the Congregation of Mary, an organisation something like the Third Order of the Franciscans, in which one lived the life of a Religious within the secular world – without celibacy, although God granted this to me, as St Augustine feared for himself, sooner than I wished.

Steadily this organisation became my life, and I became increasingly alienated from my activities at work. I moved through the machinery of chance like a ghost, as if I was in a medium there that I could not touch and could not touch me. My distraction never told in the carrying out of my functions; if anything, I perfected them in a clarity born of almost complete abstraction, performing my duties in a secular trance of meticulous accuracy. It was only a matter of time before I would enter the new reality that claimed me.

No one in the Congregation of Mary overtly disapproved of my work in the State lottery. As far as the Church was concerned, the national game of chance met the conditions that made it a morally justifiable contract between all its participants: the stakes were small and, as far as anyone knew officially, belonged to those who gambled; no fraud or deceit was involved. There was an equal risk and equal opportunity for everyone, and there was certainly no prohibition by the civil authorities. So, while the Protestant churches railed against gambling, including the Imperial Lottery system, I, deep in the heart of a thoroughly Catholic empire, stood professionally on firm civil and theological ground.

Still, even if adjudged an acceptable form of contract by the Church, gambling was in the Church's eyes technically a contract of a special kind – an aleatory contract, as it was put, reliant upon the throw of a dice and hence dependent on uncertainty. This sat increasingly oddly with my return to certainties newly wonderful to me as I rediscovered them through the mists of passion and pain in which I had lost them. And there was increasing surprise amongst some of the members of my new community of friends that someone of my spiritual gifts should spend his days working in the realms of chance, helping to generate expectations so tenuous as to be false and dealing with people who put greater faith in an unlikely ticket to material wealth than in the wafer of certain spiritual hope.

At a meeting of the Congregation of Mary at this time, word came of the Trappists at Mariastern. Looking back, I am uncertain now whether my hearing again of those passing Trappists did not have as large an element of chance in it as the good people of the Austro-Hungarian Empire were prepared to accept in their Imperial and Royal Lottery. As my faith flickers and flares along with this poor colonial lighting, I wonder if it was not the memories of my fall from grace that warmed my heart and fired my conviction that this was what I should do, where I should go. If not for the sheer luck of their passing through as I was still caught up in the exquisite pain that only the mix of hope and hurt that is rejected love can produce, would my soul have leaped as it did when we were asked to pray for them? And would our discussion as to how we could raise funds and other material support for them have been enveloped in such an effusive glow if my mind was not, that very night, filled – despite every reluctant attempt to cast them out – with the secret corners of M's body? Who can know, now that the time has passed, and what I have done is at the mercy of my memory?

In any event, as soon as my imagination had been inspired by the Star of Mary hanging in the Turkish night, reasons aplenty rushed in to give support to my epiphany. Bosnia was much in the news then. The double monarchy of Austria-Hungary had been angling for administrative rights over this crumbling outer edge of the declining Ottoman Empire for some time, and it would be good, I felt, to be in the advance guard of those reclaiming for Christendom lands lost to the Turk for over four hundred years. An exotic mix of peoples lived there – Catholic Croats, Orthodox Serbs, and Slavs who converted to Islam during Ottoman rule – and Banjaluka, the town that featured in our instructions of how to get our contributions to the Trappists, was already famous as the scene of many Austro-Turkish battles.

My friends and superiors in the Congregation of Mary encouraged me in the sense of vocation that rapidly overwhelmed me, and almost before I realised what I was doing, I had resigned my position in the lottery administration and was on my way south to the Trappists, armed only with a letter of recommendation from the Prefect of the Congregation.

5

I arrived at Mariastern amidst such celebration as the harsh circumstances prevailing there allowed. The celebration had nothing to do with me, of course, arriving unannounced and accidentally on the evening before the tiny founding community was about to make its formal entry into the first completed building of their new monastery. Despite the flurry I was given a warm welcome and made as much a part of the next day's festivities as a postulant could be. I was given the most passing of introductions to Father Franz, who peered up at me through the twilight from an excavation for the foundations and cellars of the next building, already begun. He acknowledged the celebrations in a rather perfunctory fashion, and the moment they were over switched his attention back to the preparation of the ground for his new building.

I was taken in hand by Fr Bernard, who had joined the monks just after they left Rome. He was the closest thing to a novice Franz had received while Master of Novices at Mariawald, and had now himself been appointed Master of Novices. Fr Bernard began with what was intended as a stern and thorough questioning of my intentions. This interrogation was constantly interrupted by his having to respond to the rapid orders and incessant demands of his wiry red-haired leader, who seemed to be everywhere at once as he bustled around the site for his foundation. This clearly irritated Fr Bernard, and it was almost immediately apparent to me that all was not well in the fledgling community that I had travelled so far to join.

My own status was not long in question and I remained outside the community for only a week while my application was considered. On the 14th September 1869 I was received into the community as a novice, a fact recorded in the original *Klosterbüchern* which is still kept at Mariastern as a much revered commemoration of the pioneers of the monastery.

The reasons for the simmering discord I sensed from the first were not hard to discover. Fr Bernard and Fr Robert, the other professed monk from

Mariawald who had left to join Franz, were clearly put out that the new community was not moving more quickly towards the strict regularity of Trappist life. As far as their leader was concerned, it seemed that this simply proved they were unsuited for the business of forming a new foundation.

It is difficult to deal with facts when they turn, as they invariably do, into figures. You may think that I am forcing a point here or, worse still, trying to turn an actual event into an allegory, but the truth remains that when later – much, much later – I dared inquire into the dissension, I learned that the first sign of it really had come in the shape of an apple.

The winter before my arrival was intensely cold, but it was also comparatively dry. By the time spring was well under way, the region was in the grip of a severe drought. The Verbas far below ran sluggishly at best, and up in the forested hillside there was virtually no water to be had. Even the small spring on which Franz had placed his hopes when choosing the site of his foundation would sometimes run dry. This not only frustrated his first attempts at planting, but also often left the community thirsty. The plum trees that they were clearing in the course of building were not yet bearing fruit, but here and there the odd apple tree had sprung up, and by the beginning of Lent these were substantially laden with firm, crisp, moist fruit.

Unfortunately, the usages of the Order forbid the eating of apples during Lent, a circumstance that led Franz to grant the first of the dispensations he considered necessary under the circumstances. Fr Bernard and Fr Robert were indignant at this breach of the Regulations. The situation became so bad that the two monks actually left the foundation, only to return somewhat chastened, if not entirely crushed, when they discovered how defenceless they were outside the protection of the Order.

I must make it clear that from the beginning Franz never departed from the broad outline of the Rule in establishing Mariastern. As for apples in Lent, the Rule of St Benedict allows for certain dispensations from time to time. For the rest, the community kept exactly to the daily schedule of the Rule. They went to bed at seven in the evening and awoke at two in the morning, and said the Breviary at the regular times. If, to the horror of the two Fathers, Franz required the monks to observe the Liturgy of the Hours in the orchard during the working part of the day rather than return to the single building that served as a chapel as well as everything else, he was technically within his rights as a Superior.

When, however, as became increasingly necessary, Franz had to go to the Turkish Pasha or the Austrian Consul to deal with some matter or other, or even into the city to shop, Fr Robert and Fr Bernard began to complain openly again about their Superior's failure to live the regular life. Interruptions of this nature had soon become a common feature of the running of the new foundation. For much of the day Franz was to be found, dictionary in hand, conversing with the locals upon whom the community still depended, or directing workers from outside the community, or instructing the sick who had already begun besieging Mariastern's single building. On these occasions the two Fathers wandered about grumbling at the disturbance and loss of monastic tranquillity. Franz, for his part, could often be heard muttering that such religious hotheads caused him more trouble than the Turks with all their threats.

Franz initially intended to himself serve as Master of Novices, but the two Fathers objected to this, arguing that Franz looked after the novices too little. Fr Bernard so often complained that the novices would not learn any order or regularity under such conditions that Franz was left with no choice but to appoint him Master of both white and brown novices. When I arrived the community had one of each: Brother Gallus, a white novice, and Brother Fridolin, a brown. In Franz's opinion both were endowed with exceptional qualities for monastic life – they were quiet, diligent, obedient, humble, and happy in every situation. There was nothing else to look for in a novice as far as he was concerned, and he would have been happy to let them be. A fiery, young, and inexperienced Father – Fr Bernard was only twenty-five at the time – could only do damage to novices of this character, he felt. All he would say to his new Novice Master, through clenched teeth, was, "You will surely see to it that your people learn regularity."

My introduction to Trappist life was then, from the outset, a divided one. I came to the community for the silence and stability Fr Robert and Fr Bernard argued for, but I also recognised that no such community was yet in place at Mariastern. Nor would such a community come into being without the kind of energy and volatility that my new Superior represented. I was, however, entirely in the hands of my instructor in the religious life and was exposed directly to his views.

Thus, if our Superior was not present at every canonical hour, or if he worked one or two extra hours into the evening, this was held up to me by Fr Bernard as an example of a worldly attitude and lack of religious spirit. And when the call came for the end of work in the afternoon, I was expected to join Fr Bernard and Fr Robert in downing tools exactly at 3.30 p.m. in order to be at Vespers exactly on time, regardless of the state of the job at hand. Our Superior's frustration at the degree to which our work would be set back by being left for the next day was clear to me, and I often tried to give an impression of wishing to complete the work before me even as I demonstrated the obedience required of me by following the Novice Master in all things. I am afraid I came out of this simply looking flustered and ineffectual to both sides in this dispute.

On the one hand I saw little wrong in what appeared to be the largely insignificant deviations from the Rule our Superior introduced, but on the other, with each day that I lived St Benedict's Rule and learned the Trappist Regulations, I saw less and less reason for ever departing from either. As I discovered for myself the sweet logic of their discipline and made my home in the comfort of their rigour, I came to resent more and more the tiniest alteration in their observance.

My initial sense of Franz was, to say the least, a mixed one. Looking back, it was a composite picture, a collection of images cut out of a blur of motion. Franz was not an attractive looking man, but the sheer energy vibrating in each of those images had a magnetism all its own. His flaming hair may have been cut to regulation length and was invariably hidden under the practical broad-brimmed clerical hat that topped his robe and scapular, but his pebbly eyes bored into you as he preached, and his mouth, already framed by the forked tangle of the beard that was to become his most striking feature, burst out at you as commands issued from it in a stream of qualifying directives. It was difficult to separate the man from the haze of activity that surrounded him, just as it is difficult, but so very necessary, to distinguish his greatness from his achievements.

I admit it to you willingly here and now: none of the sins to come, those of which I will accuse Franz and those that I committed against him, can erase the relief, the joy, the intoxication of first being caught up and carried away in that man's intensity, of giving in to the flow of his passions and surrendering to his strength and vision. This is more than attraction; this is and was – I must put it before you in its naked honesty – love. Love as physical and all-consuming as any I have known, but burning now with a holy zeal and enveloped in the glow of faith. It was Franz, yes, who took me along my last faltering steps from Magdalene (forgive me, dear M) to Mary, there beneath the shining star of the Holy Mother.

85

Not that this was an easy process. I was repulsed at first by his crudity and gruffness. The very smell of his strength offended me, fresh as I was from the delicate ordering of numbers, the ornate arrangement of chance, let alone the city and its refined pursuits. From polite conversation in the elegance of a Viennese coffee house to barked orders in a freezing Bosnian ditch seemed not so much a long way as a translation into another state of being – which was exactly what I wanted.

By the ninth or tenth meal of beans I truly had to struggle with keeping at bay visions of spicy black pudding, bubbling beef goulash and freshly baked strudel, but that too passed (although I have never quite been able to suppress a deep if distant longing for just one more slice of Sacher's famous torte – one of the more worthwhile and enduring results of Prince Metternich's reign). The very intensity with which Franz lived his particular interpretation of the Rule tested my vocation to the limit in the shortest possible time, and then sealed it for all eternity.

~

It was soon clear to me that much of Franz's infamous brusqueness was generated by the tension between his commitment to his Order's observation of silence and his frustration at feeling he needed to tell everybody what to do. In this I was one of his worst recruits. Whereas Franz discovered with each day more of the talents and abilities his father had found wanting in him (by now he was coming into his own as administrator, handyman, farmer, carpenter, architect, builder and engineer), I learned just how poorly equipped I was for the second half of the Benedictine motto. My abilities at prayer were proven, indeed had led me to this place, but work, when it was real work and not some metaphor for the spiritual life, flummoxed me. And the only meaning work had for Franz was skilled physical labour. He had no time for those who obscured the distinction between prayer and work in saying *orare est laborare, laborare est orare*. For Franz work was work, and prayer, prayer – even if, as was obvious if one watched him closely, the strict round of the Divine Office was for him the real drudgery of his day. In this sense only, the hours spent in Choir were for Franz very much what Benedict called them (although not in the sense Benedict intended): work, *opus Dei*.

For me the Liturgy of the Hours was sweet bliss. Here in the set form of prayers, hymns, and readings sanctifying the various hours of each day, prayer took on its real meaning for me; here my words could disappear into those of the ancients, my doubts give way to their understanding, my self be lost in the communion of saints. The Gregorian chant that, for those accustomed to the tricks of modern music, may be monotonous, for me was full of an infinite variety subtle in its very simplicity, despite the few and cracked voices of the community I had joined. I was never happier than in the long sad chant that accompanies the adoration of the Cross. Certainly much less so than when I struggled over some simple physical task and Franz out of kindness or frustration (more, I suspect, the latter) kept giving me simpler and simpler tasks.

One would have thought this disability would have distanced me from him, as indeed I often felt, in my early days at Mariastern, that it did. I think I can identify, for example, the moment when my religious name was sealed. I had only been at Mariastern some four days when Franz gave me detailed instructions as to how to go about a particular assignment – I cannot remember what exactly but it involved a hammer – and came upon me some time later staring into space, hammer hanging at my side, the nails strewn upon the ground before me, the job not done. I am sure his first reaction was to lose his temper with me, but instead he called me back to earth with a loud laugh and said, "Today is the day of Joseph of Cupertino in the Calendar of Saints. When the young Joseph was caught up in his ecstatic visions at school, the other children, seeing him gape and stare just like you, lost like you to all things about him, gave him the sobriquet 'Bocca Aperta'. I am afraid you too shall be known amongst us as the Gaper, so let us at least sanctify you as such."

The truth of the matter is that, for whatever reason, with my adoption of the daily life of the Cistercians of the Strict Order my "absences" returned. I could find no association between the two; all I knew was that, as is to be expected, I was extremely tired throughout the period of adjustment to the Trappist lifestyle. The early hour of retirement, for one thing, was strange to me, and for weeks I would lie awake for hours in our common quarters listening to the sounds in sleep of the other five monks, finally only falling asleep myself just before I was awakened with a start by the 2.00 a.m. call for Matins and Lauds of Our Lady's Office in Choir. Somewhere out of this daze of exhaustion, usually later in the day, the old familiar warmth would envelope me, take me away, and then deliver me back to the world, confused and uncertain as to where I was or what I was doing.

Again, I was unsure how to share the resurgence of my episodes with anyone else, let alone my Superior, and I was content to suffer whatever title they conferred upon me, as in my school days. If anything, I found quiet consolation in my moments away, for they now seemed suffused with an ineffable sacred presence. I was more than happy to let my self dissolve and fade into the embrace of the holy and eternal, and the confusing and sometimes terrifying return to self and reality taught me how unfit I was for this world and how much I should look for my comfort in the next. And so it was, upon receiving my habit a few days after I arrived, I happily took with it a religious name not every monk might have welcomed. None of the versions of the history of which I am a part – except my own – give the full form of that name; even the single account that accords me a few pages to myself calls me "Father Josef Eduard Biegner". For my part, I shall always hold by the name Franz gave me, and it is as Father Joseph Cupertino that I bring myself before you now.

This gives you some indication of how I came to be Joseph Cupertino, but not *Father* Joseph. I went to Mariastern intending simply to join the band of Brothers, but Franz soon decided that I was intended for priestly office – or that I was not fit for anything else. He chose, in other words, to recognise my ineptitude as a vocation, and from then on my primary "work" at Mariastern was to study for the priesthood, a privilege Franz extended to no one else during the founding stage of the monastery. Much to Fr Bernard's irritation, Franz personally undertook my training as a priest, stealing, as he must have seen it, valuable hours from his own labours for this purpose.

In return he earned my complete devotion, the more so because I could not understand what he saw in me that would prompt him to do this. The other monks presumed some sort of special friendship between us, and so began the myth of "Pfanner and Biegner, one Heart and one Soul, Friends until parted by Death" – a myth worked into reality now by historians and hagiographers alike.

There is some truth in this myth, as there is in all myths. Equally, there is some deep mystery, something beyond the story the myth expounds. Something of this mystery resonates in my religious name. Why is the source of this name suppressed by everyone but me, as if it was rather embarrassing? And, more to the point, why did I suspect something of Franz's ambivalence towards me coming through in the name of the saint he chose for me? Well, "Joseph Cupertino" is not a common religious name for good reason: we pray to him when we lack confidence in ourselves or when others belittle us because he is said to understand these things only too well – this saint is, after all, also known as "The Dunce".

~

Joseph Desa of Cupertino was born in 1603 into a miserably poor home. He was a sickly child, ugly and extremely dull. At school he was an object of mockery. He was absent-minded, he was awkward, he was nervous; a sudden noise, such as the ringing of a church bell, would make him drop his schoolbooks on the floor. He would sit with his companions after school hours and try to talk like them, but each time his conversation would break down. He could not tell a story to the end, no matter how hard he tried. His sentences wandered on interminably and then stopped in the middle because he could not find the right words. All in all, even for those who pitied him and wished to be kind to him, Joseph was something of a trial.

Nobody wanted Joseph, not even his mother. Joseph learned this very early in life and accepted it. He did not seem to want himself, or to know what he wanted. Often he scarcely seemed to know what he was doing. He was so abstracted that he would miss his meals; when this was called to his attention, he would shrug and reply, "I forgot." Studying, then, was an impossibility for him, although the thought never troubled him. But so, too, was any more practical occupation. He was apprenticed to a shoemaker but never managed to mend a single shoe.

One day some mendicant friars came through Cupertino, and Joseph thought that surely he could at least be a friar and go about begging his bread. Intelligence was not needed for this, and he was strangely fascinated by the idea of such a life. But gaining entry into any of the Orders proved almost impossible for him. He applied at one convent, but the door was closed to him at once; at another, and was told it was quite hopeless.

Eventually he found a community that agreed to take him on trial as a Lay Brother. But it was no use; despite their best intentions, the brethren found him a test of their patience. Not only was he very slow and difficult to teach but his fits of abstraction made him quite unbearable. He had a way of suddenly standing still in the middle of doing something and forgetting everything. He would drop to his knees in the most unlikely places, utterly oblivious of all around him. He might be washing dishes in the scullery, he might be carrying food into the refectory, and then one of these bouts would come upon him and whatever he was washing or carrying would crash on the floor. In the hope of curing him, bits of the broken plates were fastened to his habit and he carried them about as a penance, as a humiliation, as a reminder not to do the same again. But he did not improve. He could not be trusted even with serving the bread because he would forget the difference between brown and white.

It was decided that Joseph's remaining in the monastery could serve no material or spiritual purpose. His habit was taken from him and he was told to go. That day, he said later, was the hardest day in all his life; it looked as if everything in heaven and earth conspired to shut him out, and he never forgot it. He used to say that when they deprived him of the habit it was as if they had torn off his skin.

Back in the world, Joseph was as exposed as a snail without a shell. He was beaten and robbed, suspected of being a thief himself and punished. He was rejected by everyone, even his own family, as he looked about desperately for shelter. Eventually his mother, ashamed to have her son wandering about in such a condition, begged the Franciscans to take him. This they eventually agreed to, after much persuading, but on condition that Joseph be given only the habit of the Third Order and be employed as a servant. He was appointed to the stable and made the keeper of the monastery mule, a duty he carried out with complete acceptance, asking nothing for himself and doing whatever he was asked with genuine pleasure. Since it was now clear that he could never be a Franciscan, he was overjoyed that at least he could be their servant.

Gradually the friars began to notice the joy emanating from the stables and appreciated the welcome they were always given there by the keeper of the mule who seemed so glad to serve in this humble capacity. In his free moments Joseph went out and begged for the begging friars he had been unable to join, and it was noted how trusted he was in the town, and how he was welcomed amongst the poorest of the poor.

Some began to ask whether he might not make a Franciscan after all. The matter was discussed in the community chapter, and his case was sent up to the provincial council for consideration. It was decided, not without some qualms, to allow him another attempt to enter the Order. But once he was admitted, the problem of what to do with him surfaced anew. As he was useless at work of any kind, his Superiors set him to study, hoping that he might learn enough to be ordained, even though this too seemed hopeless. He barely learned to read, let alone write, and he could never expound upon the Gospel satisfactorily.

One text, and one text only, seemed to take hold of him, and on this alone he could always be eloquent. Luke xi, 27 *Beatus venter qui te portavit* – inspired his thought and speech and, through one of those mysteries of grace, this was the text the Bishop's eye fell upon when Joseph was examined (as a mere matter of form) for entry into the priesthood. The lyrical flight of Joseph's discourse on "Blessed is the womb that bore Thee" amazed everyone present. There was no question about his being ordained.

Soon it was not only the outcasts of this world who came to realise the wonderful simplicity and selflessness hidden beneath Joseph's odd ways; a few began to discover that the secret of his abstractedness was that he was lost in the labyrinth of God. This did not prevent his remaining a problem for the more practically minded, and to the end of his life he had to endure many a scolding from them. Others were offended by his constantly slipping away, despite his priestly office, to do the work he did before, washing the dishes, sweeping the floors, or attending to his mule. He would look out for the jobs others tried to shirk, and when some protested that such work did not become a priest, his only reply was, "What else can Brother Ass do?" And when he got Brother Ass alone in his cell, he would beat him to make him work harder.

But, as I say, the real reason for Joseph's absent-mindedness was his gift of seeing God in everything about him, and becoming lost in the wonder of it all. It seemed easier for him to see God dwelling in His creation than to see creation itself. He would spend whole days lost in its fascination, and only an order from his Superiors could bring him back to earth. Out of nowhere the eyes of God would look at him, and he would see the hand of God at work in nature, disposing all things. Joseph would then stand still, exactly as the vision caught him, fixed as a statue, insensible as a stone, and nothing could move him. The brethren would use pins and burning embers to recall him to his senses, but he would feel nothing. When he did revive and saw he been pricked or burned, he would hold no resentment. "What else can my Brothers do?" he would ask, and laugh, as he so often laughed.

As time passed, his ecstasies began to intensify, and many eminent witnesses testified to the particularly strange form that they began to take.

Joseph would rise from the ground, and move about in the air. He might be in the refectory, in the middle of a meal and suddenly float into the air with the dish of food still in his hands, much to the alarm of the brethren at table. In chapel, especially, he began to levitate regularly. He would fly from his place towards the altar, or to a shrine on a special festival, and hover over it. But even when he was out in the country begging, he would often unexpectedly waft up into a tree, or ascend to the top of a church tower. The smallest thing would suffice to bring about this act: a word of praise for the Creator and His creatures, the beauty of the sky or of the trees on the roadside, the sound of a bell or of church music – and up into the air Joseph would go.

Miracles began to be attributed to him, especially amongst the poor. He would touch blind eyes and they would see; he would lift up a sick child and it would be cured; he would write out the benediction of St Francis and it would work wonders as it was passed round a village. Naturally his fame began to spread, but with this came a deep resentment, especially amongst several of his brethren. Many refused to believe the things attributed to Joseph; not only were these events incredible, they said, but Joseph was not the kind of person to whom such things could happen. He had too many faults to be a saint, and lacked all the traditional virtues.

He was reported to the Vicar General as a troublemaker in the community, an impostor who "stirred up the people", and was called to stand trial before first the inquisitors of Naples and then the General of the Order in Rome. Joseph refused to say anything to defend or explain himself on these occasions, remaining silent and totally submissive. Nothing could be proved against him, but it was decided he must be kept, piously but firmly, in safe custody and in the strictest seclusion. For a moment, when he heard the sentence, Joseph shivered. "Have I to go to prison?" he asked, as if he had been condemned. But in an instant he recovered. He knelt down and kissed the Inquisitor's feet; then got into the carriage, smiling as usual as he was carried away.

For the next thirty-five years he was not allowed to attend Choir, go to the common refectory, walk in procession, or say Mass in church. Under pain of excommunication he was forbidden to speak to anyone, except the Religious around him. He was not permitted to write letters or receive them; he might not leave the convent enclosure; all intercourse with the outside world was cut off. He was ordered to remain in his cell in one lonely house or another of the Capuchins or Franciscans for the rest of his life. And so he was left to himself, and he lived, this dull man whom no one could teach and no one wanted, almost continually wrapped up in the vision of that which no man can express in words.

Joseph of Cupertino died on the 18th September 1663, and those with him at the time said that in his final moments, the old laughter came back into the face that had quietly grown ever sadder over the years. He was beatified by Benedict XIV in 1753 and canonised in 1767 by Clement XIII, but it was to be nearly a century and a half before a suitable cause could be found of which he could be made the patron. This came about only when man by material means managed to emulate one expression of this man's saintliness, and I, who have lived long enough to hear of men taking to the air in machines (although I have never seen such a wonder), now proudly bear the name of the patron saint of airborne travellers and aviators. It is as if I, like Joseph of Cupertino, had to wait a long, long time to come into my own.

Franz was not to live so long, and for him, I suspect, right until the end, I was the Gaper, the Dunce, the Holy Fool.

~

In those early years, however, I did justify Franz's faith in whatever abilities he believed me to possess. I was consecrated as a priest in the Cathedral of Banjaluka in 1874. But I also made myself useful at Mariastern, in my way, earning the reputation of "mother of the house" as I became known for mending clothes, tending to the sick in our community, and decorating the chapel with such flowers and foliage as the Order allowed.

In the three years between my arrival and consecration, the Trappist General Chapter declared Mariastern an independent house and admitted it into the Order as a Priory, with Franz, of course, as its Prior. This came about in 1872, when all the basic conditions the Regulations demand of a Trappist house had been met. Our community had grown to thirty in number, with postulants still joining us almost by the week. Three wings of the monastery-to-be were completed, and work on the church, which formed the fourth side of our cloister, had begun. This gave us the enclosure necessary for our prayer, but the developments required for the work that made us self-sufficient were in place well before then. Near to the enclosure stood an impressive array of farm buildings, workshops, a flour mill and a saw mill. Sufficient ground to support the new community had been secured, and, most important of all (mainly as a result of Brother Zacharias's tireless fund-raising efforts), everything was paid for.

Through all of this, Fr Bernard and Fr Robert still challenged Franz whenever they felt he was infringing the Rule. To Franz it seemed almost as if they were seeking no less than the Pasha of Banjaluka to frustrate him. A case in point was the sawmill. At one stage in its construction, while Franz was away on other business, Fr Robert dismissed all those working on this building on the grounds that a sawmill was too worldly for a Trappist monastery. On Franz's return Fr Robert was taken aside and spoken to, most firmly, I have no doubt, and work on the mill began again. It was only just completed when the Pasha protested at its operation. Franz reminded him that the Turkish High Court had given him permission to build the sawmill. "Ah, yes," said the Pasha, "but not permission to saw!" A protracted lawsuit had to be concluded before we were able to cut our own boards.

Irritations of this sort continued for years, but Mariastern began nevertheless to prosper rapidly. With prosperity, however, came another set of problems, chief amongst which was the acquiring of manufactured items. Few of these were to be had in a country so alarmingly primitive despite its being right on the doorstep of Austria. Everything we could not make ourselves at Mariastern had to be imported from Austria or Germany. This meant that we had endless problems at the border, with duties levied on each and every item we brought in, from boilers and mill wheels down to every nail.

The Turkish customs officials had no idea what duty to charge on such things, and simply invented an amount on the spot for anything not included in their table of tariffs. We had learned to become quite inventive in dealing with people who were so simple that they believed the devil hummed overhead in the telegraph wires and had attacked the workmen who were erecting telegraph poles on their land. How did one explain machinery to people who could not be induced to mount the "fire-car" that rode the shining rails bringing the new Europe to them?

Franz, of course, issued the greatest challenge of all. "What is a church," he declared one day when we were well into our construction of this building, "without a bell?" It was not only illegal to import such a thing, it was against the law to ring bells if they were already in the country. Nevertheless, Franz decided that it was unthinkable that his monastery should be without bells.

After all, it is the bells of the dormitory, refectory, chapter and church that dominate the whole life of a house of La Trappe.

It was Brother Zacharias who came up with a plan to deal with the situation, a plan worthy of any smuggler. He bought a cask of poor wine in Altgradisca, emptied it, and packed a bell carefully inside before resealing it. At the border he happily paid the duty owing on the wine, and arrived triumphant with the first of our bells. "Not only has it arrived safely," Franz commented as we retrieved the bell from the wine, "but it has been christened already!"

A second, larger bell reached us through the innocence and ignorance of one of our new Brothers. Not realising this was illegal, he simply packed the bell along with a number of other goods into the hay wagon that was our standard means of transport from the border to our foundation. When he crossed the border, he declared the bell – in German. None of the Bosnian officials understood him and he had no idea of the risk he was taking. The officials did not discover the bell, and in holy simplicity our Brother brought it to the monastery.

The smaller bell was placed in a small turret on the roof of our house, amidst much furtive celebration. It was not only concern for the Turks that dictated so modest a placing. While bells are necessary for the structure and organisation of monastic life, one of the ways in which the original Cistercian houses of the twelfth century reacted against the over-elaborate Benedictine churches was by doing away with large bells mounted in bell towers. In our desire to reinvigorate the Cistercian return to the strict Rule of St Benedict, as Franz well knew from Mariawald, Trappist houses usually observe this feature of Cistercian architecture.

The larger bell, then, was hung on the underside of our roof, in the opening of the yet unfinished gable. At first it remained unused. Franz ordered only the smaller of the bells to be rung, and then only softly and at night, gently chiming our way through those Offices carried out in darkness. In this he followed the Regulations perfectly: "We use only two bells to ring for the Office," says de Rancé, "and they are never rung together." The founder of our Order also quite clearly limited the size of the bells to be used. "They are to be such," he stipulates, "that each of them can be rung by one Religious alone."

Our new bells fell within this requirement and became a great pleasure to me, adding beauty as they did to the solemnity of the monastic night. I had grown to especially love Matins, that longest and most ancient of the Offices which takes us back to the Vigils service of the early Church, and the accompaniment of the smaller of the bells through invitatory, psalm, hymn and lesson was particularly beautiful.

But the bell-ringer at Mariastern grew more daring with each night, and with Franz's encouragement the ringing of the larger bell was added to our celebration of Lauds. The dawn Office sees in the rising sun a symbol of the Resurrection, and its *laudates* veritably shout our praises to God, a feature that our bell-ringer increasingly took to heart as he swung on the bell rope that hung down into our chapel house (then a part of our refectory) with a vigour that grew with each morning that passed. Soon both bells were brought into play for the remaining Hours of the Divine Office, and the bell-ringer was joined by the Sacristan in ringing these as loudly as possible in broad daylight.

I own to being concerned about this, but it was not my place to challenge our Superior regarding his interpretation of the Regulations and I remained silent. For a while we thought that the Turks, too, chose to ignore the reverberation of our bells across their landscape. But Franz was summoned before the local court soon enough, as he was on each of his many real or perceived infringements of Bosnian law. At court the Pasha demanded to know how he dared to install a bell on his roof and "molest the people", as he put it, by ringing it out loud. Franz's response that he had to use the bell as his Brothers could not call each other by using words was enough to settle the case.

Our not being brothers in the flesh, our not marrying, and our working in the fields regardless of rank were a real source of concern for the Turkish authorities. The issue of the bells now forced Franz to display in court one of the oddities that most provoked local sensitivities, that is, our living in silence. It also provided a clear instance of our having broken the law. The verdict Franz brought back to us was unambiguous: the bells had to come down.

Franz left the court saying that he would have the bells removed, but instead he simply ordered us not to ring them for some time. He felt especially sorry about what this meant for the few scattered Catholics in the surrounding region. Some had told him that on hearing the first bell for Matins, they too rose and began to pray. Moreover, for the first time they knew what time it was at night. None of them owned watches or clocks,

and they had never before heard a bell ring from a tower. Their only indic-
ator of time was the sun, and at night or during bad weather they had no
idea what time it was – "like the poor souls in Purgatory", as Franz put it.
"I cannot let them be robbed of that consolation," he announced.

A month went by, and then another, which took us well into the next in
a monotonous series of droughts. As the drought worsened, the various
religious denominations of the region began to hold public processions
to invoke Divine intervention. Franz observed the shaky holding aloft
of a variety of garish icons that emerged at alarming angles through the
clouds of dust sent up by hundreds of stamping feet, and he was taken by
an original if dangerous idea. He arranged to see the Pasha and suggested
that his "servants" add their prayers to all the others being sent up for rain,
adding that in order to encourage them to pray all the more fervently,
however, he would have to ring the bells. The Pasha, who was in a general
state of despair, agreed.

I would love to say, as several of the books dedicated to Franz's life do:
"The monks prayed, the bells rang, and the rains came." The rains did come,
but not before the inhabitants of the region had had more than enough time
to get used to the ringing of our bells. No one was convinced of the greater
effectiveness of our prayers over theirs, but by the time the rains fell (and
we rang out our jubilation over this for much longer than was strictly necessary), the bells were no longer an issue in the hills around Banjaluka.

I must confess that somehow their ringing echoed falsely in my soul, and
whilst the other monks praised Franz's guile in overcoming the heathen,
I found it difficult to accept such an extravagant display of our bells and
our prayers. My vow of obedience obliged me to suppress such thoughts,
and I was rigorous in this, but my body, heart – or, some might say, my
very soul – burst forth in protest.

~

None of the many accounts of Franz's victory over the heathen Pasha records
that, as the full chiming of our bells echoed through the spectacular scenery
of Banjaluka for the first time, one of the monks fell to the ground in a
rigid faint. The extremities of his body began to twitch and jerk and spittle
frothed around his mouth. In terror, a Brother ran for the Superior, signalling frantically. Seeing that what the monk wanted to convey was beyond
his signing powers, Franz gave him dispensation to speak; seconds later

97

Franz was by my side, telling those who were trying to revive me to desist. Over the next few minutes, while waiting out the seizure, he explained to the monks that I had suffered an epileptic fit. "No, no, no," he told me he had said as some of the Brothers started pulling away from me, "seizures are not contagious! That is merely a superstition, one amongst many I am sure you have all picked up – and I shall rid you of!"

And so I came to, dazed and confused, to find my Brothers gathered about me as I lay on the ground, with my Superior educating them on my condition. In no uncertain terms Franz was informing them that seizures had nothing to do with demons invading a person's body or even with proof that one had been touched by God and given mystical powers. If they wished me to be healed of this affliction it would be better to pray instead, he was saying when I was able, awkwardly, to find my feet and stumble off.

Franz was nothing if not modern and scientific in his medical views, which were extensive, if unconventional, and strongly held. Indeed, within a relatively short time of his arrival in Bosnia he became known throughout the surrounding regions as the *Velik Hedschim*, or Great Doctor. The sick were brought to him on horseback, in carriages, and even on primitive wooden sleds, often after days of travel. Whenever Franz himself went abroad, the ailing and crippled were brought to him on the roadside.

This did much to earn respect for our foundation and our religion, but Franz himself was brusque and matter of fact about the whole business. Once he said to me, "They see me standing in front of the monastery gates consulting my books after examining them and they say, 'Look, now he prays.' Well, they may attribute their healing to my prayers, but the truth is I now never leave our buildings without my homeopathic pocket dispensary!" He was to become increasingly knowledgeable and dogmatic on matters medical as the years passed.

Certainly at Mariastern he was already beginning to feel that he knew more about medicine than all but a few doctors. In general, they were members of a profession he held in very low esteem. But if anything to do with health irritated him even more than the average medical practitioner, it was the primitive beliefs of the general populace – as my Brothers had found out whilst they stood around staring at my fallen form.

I did not become a shining example of the efficacy of prayer, I am afraid. The seizures continued, although I learned to recognise a certain sensation that I would experience as a forewarning of them. This was familiar to me from my early episodes: again it would feel as if the very air was resonant with a sound not so much heard as felt, and I was disappearing into its reverberations. Often this was juxtaposed with the ringing of our bells, but not always – I do not know what conditions would bring about that strange conjuncture of tone and overtone that would seduce me away from the world. But I knew when I felt myself melting away into that sound beyond sound that a seizure was at hand, and that I was on the edges of a different atmosphere in which all knowledge and sensation were suspended and a whole new realm of possibility awaited, even if always beyond me.

This state would usually allow me just enough time to get my ponderous and leaden physical self out of harm's way before the seizure took hold, although I must say that it was not always followed by a full-blown seizure. Sometimes I would hover in this aura – the best word I can find for an experience so beyond words – and then, as with my childhood absences, return to the normal world of definite dimensions and density. I always felt strangely robbed at these times. I do not wish to sound overdramatic or, heaven forbid, inflate the importance of my – as Franz stressed again and again – simple medical condition, but it was as if the possibility of understanding something of enormous importance about the very nature of all things was held out before me, then snatched away.

With only my Superior to talk to about these things (and I knew his view of my condition all too well), I found my way to the collection of books kept in an out of the way corner of our by now quite substantial monastery. This once meagre library was constantly being added to as those joining the monastery donated books they thought appropriate. Amongst the primarily religious works I quickly found Franz's thick and much-consulted medical encyclopaedia and, to my surprise, several pamphlets specifically on my condition – one even to do with Bielefeld-Bethel, Germany's most famous epilepsy "colony". Did Franz add these after my condition manifested itself? It would warm my heart to think so, but it was the less scientific side of my condition that I longed to learn more about. And this I did, though from one of the more unlikely sources – an account of the experiences of Joan of Arc in one of a number of works on the lives of the saints in our library.

From the age of thirteen, I read, Joan reported ecstatic moments during which she saw flashes of light coming from the side, heard voices of saints, and saw visions of angels. While I could not claim such overtly spiritual manifestations, the Saint is reported to have said of her blissful experiences that, while in them, she "felt that the secrets of the universe were about to be revealed to her". It would be nothing short of laughable to compare the ecstasies that drove her on to become a heroine, martyr and saint with my moments away from reality, but from what I have told you, you will recognise that I had grounds for some small affinity with this sensation.

Perhaps more to the point, St Joan's mystical experiences are reported to have been triggered by the ringing of church bells. Again, my seizures were not as directly linked to this phenomenon. Franz's bells could at times peal out as loud and long as he wished while I carried on in my mundane world as humbly and ordinarily as I usually did – and I have no wish to reduce a saint's communion with God to my medical condition – but I could not help but notice those elements that coincided with mine.

Still, if one is going to allow for some similarity between the holy condition of the saints and my experience of (allow me this little irony) the "sacred disease", Franz had diagnosed the correct spiritual connection from the first. The saint whose experiences most closely resembled mine was the one for whom most practical work was an impossibility; the one who tested the patience of those about him (never more so than through his inability to tell a story directly to its end); the one to whom we pray when we lack confidence in ourselves or when others belittle us: Joseph of Cupertino – the Gaper, the Dunce, the Holy Fool.

Holy I have been far too little, but foolish I have been far too much, and much more so than I could blame upon my illness. But if the truth of this digression in which I have taken you too far from Franz's story is to be known, through all my foolishness, I would not exchange the brief glimpses of bliss my illness afforded for all the joys that life on this earth can give. One must, after all, as I have learned in my old age, take one's transcendence where one finds it.

~

As for Franz, the evidence of his achievements was all around us. Roads ran through the forest, two bridges spanned the Verbas River, a factory with a steam-driven spinning jenny churned out cloth, a brewery produced beer that was kept in an ice cellar, and acres and acres of crops glistened in the sun. It was impossible not to bask in the glory of Mariastern, shining testimony to our Superior's energy and vision. And it was impossible while in Franz's presence not to feel the seduction of his power, and in the sway of this to give him, so easily, the love demanded by his authority.

Looking back, it may have been possible to commemorate Franz in silence if his story had ended in Bosnia. With his foundation firmly established, Franz returned to the letter of the Trappist Regulations. To his credit, with fewer reasons for granting dispensations of any sort he went about his business of extending the work of Mariastern by more traditionally sanctioned means.

It was not my place to even think of approving or disapproving of the material development of the monastery, although I was becoming aware of its disruptive influence on our contemplative life. As it was, the remote site chosen for our foundation was changing rapidly. Austria occupied Bosnia during this period, opening up the area to German immigration, and set-tlers and speculators were pouring in. Mariastern became their invariable first port of call and Franz was consulted constantly on everything from trading rights to land purchases. In his desire to see the region won for Catholicism, he responded unstintingly, although this cost him dearly in terms of effort and time and meant that he was frequently away.

Not that the monastery did not benefit from the opening up of Bosnia as well. Postulants too poured in, and before long our community numbered nearly two hundred. Franz was becoming the Superior of what amounted to a small town rather than a monastery. Building never ceased, new devel-opments sprang up almost overnight, and more and more property came into our possession. Our range of crops was expanded, a cheese factory, a tannery, and a textile mill were set up, and – to my private and silent concern – an orphanage and school were started.

These latter developments came especially close to threatening the character of our Order. Such active works were directly contrary to the Cistercian spirit and vocation, but Franz found a way of accommodating them. Since Trappists could not undertake pastoral work outside their own buildings, he asked the Bishop if some of the Sisters of Mercy in Agram could come to Banjaluka. This was only acceded to when he offered to meet all the costs involved, which the flourishing of Mariastern enabled him to do. Part of the debt here resided in Franz's conscience; he never felt easy about the way in which he had fled to Mariawald from the boredom of his life amongst the good Sisters.

Franz did not stint, then, in establishing them in Bosnia. He bought two houses in Banjaluka for the Sisters, and set them about developing first the school and then the orphanage. Both were much needed in the region, and grew rapidly. Soon the boys' section of the orphanage was moved to Mariastern, and it did not take long for an agricultural school, in which the monks were to be the main teachers, to develop from this association. The line between teaching and proselytising is a thin one, particularly for monks, and I watched with real fear as this new activity threatened what our Statutes call our "hidden mode of apostolic fruitfulness".

By this time I had been made Master of Novices at Mariastern, and so was able to keep well away from the temptation that the teaching of the orphans presented for some supposedly committed to the contemplative life. I did my best to instil this sensitivity in our novices, but I found it almost impossible to keep up with the numbers joining us. Postulants were not screened carefully enough, in my opinion, and so novices came before me who were not always suited to the exacting conditions of a house of the Order of Cîteaux. The point of our history was lost upon them, which was not surprising, as all about us was the excitement of growth and development and responsibility.

Who could refuse needy children, peasants cut off from their land by speculators, Catholics seeking to develop this land for Christendom? That I even write of such things is an indication of how porous our enclosure within the monastery had become. It was as if the world we renounced reclaimed us constantly through its woes and needs. And it was our perceived success in the world that brought this upon us. We became the largest house the Cistercians had had anywhere since the Golden Age of the Order. But our size was no asset; we were simply too big, and our size itself attracted still more postulants to us. Even supposing they all had genuine vocations (and my experience was that they were increasingly lacking in this respect), more than a hundred Religious are too many for one Superior in the contemplative life, especially when that Superior is often elsewhere or otherwise engaged.

As Master of Novices I could not convey the intricate network of tiny details that make up a life of contemplation to the large groups that came before me. I stuttered and stumbled, lost their attention, finally lapsed increasingly into silence. It would have been difficult enough to maintain respect under these conditions even without the embarrassment of my seizures, but as things were I could feel myself becoming something of a joke amongst the novices. Each day I felt more like the Gaper, and certainly when it came to the most exciting developments at Mariastern (whirring machinery, bursts of steam, the clatter and chatter of productivity) I was, without doubt, the Dunce.

I tried to teach that the value of a monk's work does not lie in the products that result from it, however good and necessary those products may be. The monk works well only when his hands are able to make things out of silence, for he thus concentrates nature by the dynamic effect of his own silence. So I would say, and lower my eyes at the stark incomprehension I saw before me. I felt lost in my own monastery, which had become too crowded and full of bustling activity for life to keep flowing smoothly and quietly through the proper channels.

In short, I was soon nostalgic for our early years of isolation and struggle, and the hardships that gave meaning to work and prayer alike. The only way to return to such a life now would be to participate in the founding of another house, and it was this desire that smoothed over my growing frustrations with life in Franz's all too successful foundation. I was still able to appear, as always, in total accord with his wishes, his most faithful and loyal helper, and he, meanwhile, had already begun to look about for a second foundation.

To the astonishment of the Bishop, Franz announced that he had been attracted by a beautiful property owned by a Turkish Beg – "Earl" or "Lord", if you prefer – situated about a mile outside the town of Busowac. The Beg was only too happy to sell up and move out as the Turks were leaving in their hundreds from a region that was now only technically still theirs. The Bishop approved the sale (more or less a fait accompli in any event), and Franz named the site Mariannaberg.

You may remember that Mariawald is situated in the Marianne Hills. It had not taken me long to discover how deep Franz's resentment ran over his treatment at the house in which he had become a Trappist. I am not even sure how he felt at the news that reached us in 1875 of Mariawald's being closed down under the terms of Napoleon III's dissolution of the monasteries. We heard that Mariawald's buildings were extensively damaged during France's war with Germany, and its stained glass confiscated and sold to the British Museum. Franz did not appear to be moved by this news although it must have filled him with deep and mixed emotions. It had been difficult for him to accept the decision that, when Mariastern was declared an independent Trappist house and joined to the Order as a Priory, it was not declared to be a daughter of Mariawald. To the end of his life Franz remained convinced that, as he dictated to me in those final dark years, "Mariawald should have been and should have remained my motherhouse, for it was in Mariawald that my Trappist cradle stood. Although the Abbot of Ölenberg – who was *not* our Prior – closed the doors of Mariawald to me, it made no difference. For even if a mother throws her child out, she cannot deny being her mother."

The General Chapter viewed the matter differently and gave our monastery to, as Franz put it often and vehemently, "another mother who had as little to do with Mariastern as the woman in the famous argument who demanded the living child but according to Solomon's decision did not get it". The monastery to which we were given was, to add insult to injury in Franz's view, a French one – "despite the fact that Mariastern was founded solely by German brethren, built with German money, and still was supported mainly by German alms!"

Port du Salute, situated in western France, was probably chosen by Chapter because it is regarded as one of the strongest Trappist houses and, whatever else Franz achieved, he had not overcome the Order's view that he needed to be kept under firm control. As it was, he made one, and only one, hasty trip to the monastery to present himself as, in his words, "its legitimate [illegitimate?] son" and accept the Abbot of Port du Salute as the Pater Immediatus of Mariastern. He would only return once to the monastery of Port du Salute, and then only for the most formal and general of occasions. He certainly preferred this strange relationship, however, to Mariawald's Abbot becoming – as would normally be the case in such a troublesome succession – his immediate father. Although no longer the Vicar General of the Trappist Order, Abbot Ephrem was still the Abbot of Ölenberg, and it was he who had shut Franz out of Mariawald.

This was the history that was written into Franz's choice of Mariannaberg as the name for his next foundation. He could thus inscribe his origins as a Trappist into his new house without tying it to Mariawald. After all, he came to define his vocation and his spiritual vision whilst chopping away at the trees that covered the hills in which Mariawald was set, rather than from his experiences in the monastery itself. Clearly, if he had had enough confidence in his ability to found such a successful house in Bosnia from the first, he would have used the name of the place in which he was able to be the kind of Religious he wished to be. It was in the Marianne Hills that he had his only truly happy first experiences as a monk, and if "hills" was not quite an appropriate term for the mountainous region in which he now found himself free to pursue his vision, then the Mountain of Our Lady and Saint Ann it was to be.

Or so Franz thought. Suddenly, unexpectedly, a sharply worded letter arrived from Rome. The Bishop had clearly turned against Franz's expansionism; he accused Franz of buying up Bosnian land cheaply for wealthy Germans and Austrians (no doubt out of a confused sense of the relation between Franz's assistance to other speculators and his own developments), and said that he was always up to something he had not cleared with his Superiors. His application for a new foundation was turned down unequivocally, and the letter informing him of this ended with the stern wish that the Prior would restrain his unruly spirit.

~

It was thus a chastened Franz who prepared to set off in 1879 for the annual gathering of the General Chapter of the Trappists in Sept Fons. The night before his departure he came to me and said, "I often ask myself what St Francis de Sales or St Vincent de Paul would have done in my circumstances. Would they really have put up with it all? Would they not have resisted? Would they not have got involved in any sort of conflict?"

I remained silent, but he must have sensed something of a rebuke in this. "I accept that sometimes I am at fault," he added quietly. "If I were a saint like St Francis or St Vincent I would not have done everything so hastily. I am always in a hurry. If I was asked to create the world I would have wanted to do it in one day instead of seven, and so I would have quarrelled with the Lord God Himself."

I have no doubt, however, that as he left his creation in the pre-dawn of the next morning, Franz looked back up at Mariastern shining now like a whole constellation of stars in the hills and regretted nothing. Anything that could not be done in a day, I suspect, he thought was not worth doing; there were, after all, other worlds to create. And so it was that within months, and more unexpectedly than I can ever express, I was to find myself in another world altogether, huddled along with thirty-one other Trappists on a dock under the burning sun of the south-east coast of Africa.

MARIANNHILL

6

W<small>E LANDED</small> at Port Elizabeth on 28th July 1880. Three hundred and ninety-two years earlier, a little further round Algoa Bay, Mass was offered for the first time at the southern tip of Africa. Bartholomew Dias erected the last of his padrões on a rocky islet there, known thereafter as the Island of the Holy Cross, before yielding to the decision of a council of his senior men that they should give up their search for a sea route to India and return to Portugal. For us, too, our landing would prove something of a false start.

Despite the fine weather of that July day – doubly strange for us in this inverted world where it was mid-winter at the time of our mid-summer – we huddled together on the jetty. The crowd that gathered to witness our arrival continued to chatter and point while the Bishop who had recruited us in Europe and returned with us on the ship gave what was clearly a lively address, not much of which we understood. His heavily accented, rapidly spoken English was beyond the abilities of the French priest whom Franz had recruited as an interpreter at the last minute, none of us having any grasp of English.

Père Etienne managed part of the Bishop's opening line: "This is the last and greatest deed of my life …" which he attempted to put into French for Franz, who then tried to hand-sign it on to us. The Bishop's eloquence soon outran our convoluted attempts at interpretation. Eyes on the ground, we stood there and let his words wash over us. From their tone if not their sense I could not help feeling that the Bishop, despite his hearty self-congratulatory air, was glad that his laborious and embarrassing task was over. For us it was just the beginning – the real beginning of Franz's story as far as his hagiographers are concerned.

One thing that was clear was that the Bishop loved a ceremony. But we were not in a celebratory mood. We burrowed into our cowls, hands thrust further into the sleeves of our habits than is required, eyes fixed more than is required on the ground. Peripheral vision meant, however, that we could not avoid seeing the gorgeously attired group that formed the centrepiece of our welcoming party – seemingly a religious fraternity although their grand regalia was utterly unfamiliar to us.

Père Etienne, who was still straining his interpretive abilities to the full, managed to pick up something of the nature of this group and nodded towards them while stroking his cheek. This is our sign for "green", which we also used to indicate Irishmen; we were thus reminded that Bishop Ricards, the very Irish Bishop Ricards (for it was he who was speaking), had originally hoped to bring Irish Trappists back with him or, failing that, a French branch of the Order. The Austrian Prior based in Bosnia had taken the Bishop, as well as the whole of the General Chapter of the Trappist Order gathered at the Monastery of Sept Fons, by surprise when he stood up and announced, in his German-accented French, "If no one will go, I go!"

Bishop Ricards' celebrated oratorical skills were restricted to English (why is it that so many of a missionary disposition are, like their patron saint, St Francis Xavier, inadequate linguists?), but even his limited French was enough for him to understand that this was the only response he was going to get to his plea for Trappists to come to his vicariate in the Eastern Cape colony and establish a base there for missions to the Natives. And so here we stood, banished from our observance of silence yet unable to understand the Babel into which we had fallen.

A rising wind whipped the Bishop's words away and brought the awkward ceremony to an earlier halt than we could otherwise have expected. We were then herded from the jetty up the steep hill from which the town overlooked the bay. Once in town, we and the St Patrick's Society (identified now by their snapping and flapping flag) and the rest of the Bishop's welcoming party entered St Augustine's Church. Here a solemn *Te Deum* was sung and the benediction pronounced in a service far too ornate for our observances. It seemed to me that the relative plainness of the church itself, soothing to our group as it may have been, was more the result of its location in this distant colony than any aesthetic expression of the Bishop's spiritual sensibilities.

It is difficult to describe how we, children of stability and silence, felt on landing amidst the spray of that foreign dock, walking up that wind-whipped alien hill, entering that church the architecture of which was like a mocking echo of the ones familiar to us. It was as if the walls of our enclosure had been torn down, the silence that was the very texture of our life ripped to shreds. We who clothe ourselves with silence in a world of noise were naked now to those who love their own clamour and are impatient of everything else. We were at the mercy of those who fear us for our silence because it accuses them of their own emptiness.

I was numb with the sights and smells and sounds that had pressed in upon me with no respite for every instant of the time since we had left Mariastern. There I had known the noise of industry, yes, and the disruption of too many eager young noviciates, but the one marked the borders of our enclosure and the other signalled, for all its irritation, the vibrant growth within it. Ever since we had left, the blare of life had engulfed us. By now I was desperate for the walls of our withdrawal from the world to rise up again around me, enfolding me in the rigours of the routine that denied me any choice except the choice to love God beyond the indecision out of which speech and thought itself are born. *Lord, I have loved the habitation of Thy house, and the place where Thine honour dwelleth.*

At last we were led to a hall in the cathedral grounds, and left to ourselves and whatever efforts we could make to reconstruct the prescribed procedures of our observances. In deadened disarray, we fumbled and bumped our way into some sort of order. Our places made for sleep, we pulled our travel-stained habits around us and entered the Great Silence of the night.

~

Throughout the stormy and unpleasant voyage to Africa we were to all intents without a Superior to speak for us. Franz was prostrated as much by seasickness as by the embarrassment he felt at this weakness. He felt thoroughly disinclined to use his linguistic intermediary with the Bishop, Père Etienne, and claimed that he could not talk because his tongue would not move as a result of the strain of his illness. Thus we remained isolated from Bishop Ricards and the warm conviviality he shared with the other travellers – some Irish clergymen and even six French-speaking Sisters of the Congregation of the Holy Cross who threw themselves into the humour of the Bishop's linguistic limitations while the misunderstandings lurking beneath our translated circumstances festered.

Rattling in the holds, amidst the machinery and tools we were bringing with us, was clear evidence of these misunderstandings: an enormous crockery set, each piece emblazoned with the inscription DUNBRODY ABBEY,

SOUTH AFRICA. Franz resented this frivolous extravagance, presented to us when we reached England on the first leg of our journey. He wanted a printing press and, in defiance of the Bishop's wasteful gesture, used some of the limited funds he was able to raise before leaving Europe to purchase one. This, along with a complicated pile of photographic equipment, was also stored below deck. Franz even went so far as to include in our party a printer, the only lay person recruited for this enterprise.

In any event, all of our party found the name chosen by the Bishop for the foundation we were to establish both foreign and inopportune. Quite apart from the fact that we ourselves were barely a community yet, let alone a community likely to be elevated to the status of an abbey, it was presumptuous to give the new venture even the appearance of such a status when there were as yet no abbeys at all in the southern African colonies.

As far as "Dunbrody" was concerned, this was no more than a sentimental association on the part of the Bishop, who enjoyed representing himself as a "child of the old Western Island of Saints". Certainly the original Dunbrody Abbey was Cistercian, but the more immediate association in the Bishop's mind was its location in County Wexford, where he was born and lived before coming to Africa. There the great ruin of Dunbrody Abbey squatted, a casualty of Henry VIII's dissolution of the monasteries, which had slowly, over three centuries, taken its place as a natural feature of the countryside – a pile of echoing and empty stones that Ricards, as a child, delighted in clambering over. It is unlikely that the "farm" he had bought for us in the Eastern Cape was by happy coincidence already named Dunbrody, although this is what was put about at the time and may still be found in several accounts of our arrival.

~

It soon became clear to us when we were dumped there that there was nothing worth putting any name to at Dunbrody. We had boarded a train for the site the morning after coming ashore, accompanied by the Bishop and a number of his priests. The clergy of Port Elizabeth were in a happy mood. We suspected that our own peculiarities were the object of their clerical jokes, but would not have been able to ascertain this even if we had wanted to as their informal English was beyond the powers of our translator.

The further we travelled from Port Elizabeth, the more forbidding the scenery became. It is difficult to believe now, but in our ignorance we really had come with a vision of the jungles of Africa enfolding us in a lush dense green embrace. Instead, before our eyes now stretched low hills bare but for straggly bushes, some sort of tall dull-green succulents, and strange, flat-topped, woody growths barely worth the name of tree.

The weather remained surprisingly fine – we would soon learn to dread the high, clear, light-blue sky of the dry winters in this region of summer rainfall – but it was cool whenever one was not in direct sunlight and a chill wind came through the windows of the coach, kept open in anticipation. Franz attempted to cheer us by remarking that the scenery would surely become more appealing before we reached our stop, but Bluecliff Station brought no improvement. We climbed down from the train into a barren landscape strewn with rocks and strangled by a low, rough tangle of brush. The bark of the flat trees was a ghastly greenish-white, and their spectral branches were covered with long, white, and very sharp black-tipped thorns such as we had never seen except in the more graphic representations of the only crown Our Lord was to wear on this earth. Thorns were the chief feature of the region's vegetation: the succulents proved to be cacti covered with clumps of particularly spiky thorns erupting out of a fine hair of thorns, and the tangles of brambles that pushed up everywhere were weighed down with thorns almost too heavy for their branches. Wherever one looked, needle-sharp points were lifted up from the sand by the gusts of a cold wind.

The train carried a number of horses and a small bus for the Bishop and his clergy. Franz, Père Etienne and I (the only priests in our party of monks) were asked to join them whilst the rest of our Brothers marched off across the hard land in the direction of Dunbrody Abbey. My down-cast eyes took in nothing but dry, dead earth. Occasional furtive glances let me know we had entered a low, flat valley, its edges marked by a long row of crumpled black-green hills. The valley floor was barely covered by a threadbare carpet of dull growth, broken here and there by fissures and rumpled mounds. Dust drifted up between every break in this coarse cov-ering. It puffed up from our wheels on the poor track, where the hard, flat light caught it as it fell away behind us. Momentarily lit as if from within by the sharp morning sun, the dust hanging in the still air was suffused with bright gold – all too brief a beauty that served only to envelope and choke our marching Brothers as we passed them.

We crossed a wide sandy depression, so shallow as hardly to justify the very basic bridge spanning it. Franz – head high, eyes darting this way and that over this new land he had to master, impatient questions as always at the tip of his tongue – asked what this was. "This is the Sundays River" was the interpreter's phrasing of the Bishop's reply. Assuming his question or the response to have been misunderstood, Franz asked where the river was. The Bishop glanced at the translator, but made no answer. In the wake of this uncharacteristic lack of response, we were left to wonder that such a broad, flat furrow should be called a river.

Finally the bus lurched up an incline, brambles screeching against its sides. On this slightly elevated spot stood a crude corrugated-iron structure, not much more than a shed, standing forlornly in the midst of a wilderness of sand, thorn and sky. Père Etienne shouted for the benefit of Franz, "*Voilà l'Abbaye du Dunbrody!*" All the clergymen laughed and Franz laughed too. I maintained my silence (you will remember that *coarse jests* and *words that move to laughter* are subject to *a perpetual ban* according to the Rule) as the Bishop and his clergy alighted. Franz remained frozen in his seat and asked, "Are you serious, My Lord?"

Irritated in his embarrassment, the Bishop repeated, "This is Dunbrody Abbey."

"*Da haben sie mich alten Esel aufs Glatteis gefürt,*" muttered Franz.

"What does he say?" asked the Bishop quickly, stiffening visibly when Père Etienne used his small grasp of German to explain Franz's reference to a donkey that was induced to dance on ice.

We stepped onto the brown grass that turned to powder beneath our sandals and awaited our Brothers, who were moving rapidly across the desolate land in the hope of finding something more encouraging where we stood. Again I heard Franz murmur, this time to himself, "What did you leave behind Father Francis, and what do you find …?"

~

Virtually oblivious of the Bishop and his clergy as they left in a cloud of dust, Franz tried to see in the shabby shed before us the hut that had been the kernel of Mariastern. How easily, it seemed now, had that hut in Bosnia given itself up to Franz's inspired energies. One of the reasons the assembled Trappist leaders at Sept Fons were so shocked at Franz's announcement that he would take up Bishop Ricards' invitation was that he had been informed that very morning that he was to be made abbot of the flourishing complex of monastery and church, mill and dairy, workshops and orphanage, fields and roads he had built up in Bosnia.

If it was difficult to hold together in one thought the pulsing energy of the newly founded abbey of Mariastern and this desolate hut, it was still more difficult to imagine any physical association between Dunbrody Abbey, County Wexford, and this site chosen for its African reincarnation. For those of us expected to carry out the actual transformation there was no association at all. The whole enterprise, including our presence, was the product of Bishop Ricards' ever generative way with words, and this alone. We who strip ourselves of words, it turns out, originated out of a book, one of the Bishop's books, his celebrated, much reprinted and variously translated first book, *The Catholic Church and the Kaffir*. To this day I have kept my copy, obtained some time after we were ensconced at Dunbrody. It is subtitled "A Brief Sketch of the Progress of Catholicity in South Africa and the Prospects of Extensive Missions on the Point of Being Founded for the Natives of British Kaffraria".

Had the Bishop limited himself to "the Progress of Catholicity in South Africa", his book would have been a very short work indeed. *The Catholic Church and the Kaffir* is nothing but an extended apology for the lack of missionary success in the region, Protestant and Catholic alike. "It is not too much to say," writes the Bishop, "that even the best and most earnest of the missionaries, who have laboured amongst the native races, have felt and acknowledged their work on the whole to be a failure." Those few Natives they did manage to "convert" invariably fell back into the carnalities of paganism – which is why, I assume, he refers to them as "Kaffirs" in his title; he explains that "the name was probably first given to those who bear it by the Arabs, and means 'infidel' or 'unbeliever'".

On one of his trips to Europe Ricards had read a report of a visit by the French Emperor in 1868 to an agricultural colony set up by Trappist monks in Algeria in the town of Staouëli – "land of the saints" in the old Arabic, as this most Irish of Bishops gleefully notes. In this he found support for a similar idea that had been brewing in his own mind for some years, the idea that, where other missionaries failed by preaching and teaching, Trappists could succeed by silent example.

A Trappist monastery, in the opinion of the Bishop, would prepare the Natives, through the model of devotion, kindness, self-denial and prayer set by the monks, to receive missionary priests with some respect and with some notion of the supernatural character of our Holy Religion. "The monks, it is true," he writes, "are not missionaries; but after a time the monastery will become the centre and the home whence missions will radiate through the whole Tembu population. The material prosperity of the model farm, its hospital and its *hôtellerie* cannot fail to exercise a salutary influence on the surrounding Natives; and the young missionary priests, who are burning with ardour to throw themselves into the work of Native missions, will, besides having a house of retreat and a home in illness, share in the prestige of the good monks."

There are only a few passages describing Native life in the Bishop's book. Like his patron saint in this endeavour, he was fundamentally incurious about the foreign world in which he found himself. He followed St Francis Xavier in depending on his writings to inspire a missionary vocation in others. This did not stop his imagination, however, from calling up our presence and the reaction of the Natives to it well before we actually arrived: "The Kaffir is essentially a practical observer", he asserts with all the confidence of ignorance. "The choicest and most keen-sighted amongst them may at first wonder at the poverty and mortification and long prayers of the monks, and set down to folly the rising at midnight to sing the praises of God, and their vegetable diet and ..." – one can feel the Bishop's own uncertainty growing – "their grave silence." He adds, however, with a confident rhetorical flourish, "But a time will come."

It is at this point in the Bishop's writing that one can sense his entering the oral mode for which he was already renowned. One sees a secretary scribbling furiously as the Bishop paces his study, gesturing before an imaginary congregation, and declaiming in ringing tones: "The Grace of God, drawn down by the prayers of the pious monks, will fall like the blessed dew over the thirsty land on hearts so disposed to hear the word of God and keep it; and the soil once rank with foul and carnal superstitions will bring forth fruit a hundredfold under the culture of the ..." – at last we have it – "... missionaries."

In one slip of the tongue our contemplative life is collapsed into that of the active apostolate. In one word our vows and observances are simply erased and in their place is raised the voice, the mighty voice of the Bishop himself, ventriloquising through his imaginary "missionaries", irrigating metaphorically the dry land he so literally left us to make productive with our silence.

In the beginning was the Word ... I have resisted this most obvious of openings for my story. Now I find I have no choice but to engage on their own terms those who exemplify that awesome reversal of God's creation that is the genius of man: the flesh become word, so that it may live beyond itself, eternally, if you will. *In the beginning, then, was the Word.* For if ever a story began – and ended – in words, it is mine.

The simple but deeply ironic truth of the matter is that we Trappists, consecrated to silence, were seduced into Africa by a man whose very essence was words – Bishop Ricards, at the time the most famous preacher and celebrated religious author in South Africa. Small wonder then that I seek our genesis in the words that brought us forth. In the time that has passed since Franz talked himself to the edge of the grave, I have been haunted by the echoes of those who once ruled my world with words even after they melted away, one by one, into the final silence. And now I have the chance to hunt the Devil in his lair, to float like the spectre I have become through those ghostly labyrinths of phrase, sentence, paragraph, chapter and book, seeking the traps he laid for us in the most secret of his hiding places.

And there I find the origin of my story and my sins – the story that is my sin, no less than Franz's – in the personal history of that ultimate verbal artificer, the charmingly eloquent and ever articulate Bishop Ricards. A diversion into that biography, then, is no indulgent digression; it goes to the heart of this story. So let us leave Franz gaping for a while longer, gaping no less than his ever reliable right-hand man, Father Joseph Cupertino, at this tumbled down hut, the second in his career. As the sea of the Bishop's eloquence withdraws and Franz stands staring for the first time at the stark reality of Dunbrody Abbey, let us see if we can find, somewhere, flashes of the Bishop himself in that infinite medium of which he was such a master.

~

The book that brought us into being appeared in print just as the Bishop arrived in Europe on his recruiting trip and, in between his efforts in this regard, he was very much caught up in the promotion and distribution of his first serious literary endeavour. The letters he wrote while on this trip – yes, I have used our historian well, even as he has been under the impression that he is using me – are filled with the progress the book is making, the number of copies ordered, the translation about to be finished, which influential person to send a copy to next. Augsburg, 11th November 1879, will do as an example: "The German translation will be ready tomorrow. Bishop Pancratius says that the translation is very well done and it is got up nicely. I hope to send you a copy next week. I have just signed a letter – translated from my copy by Canon Soratroy – to the Queen Dowager. It will go to her majesty with a nicely bound copy through her great friend and advisor, Bishop Pancratius."

"I hope to send *you* a copy next week ..." The relationship between the Bishop and the person to whom this letter is addressed must be brought into our story, for it is in these letters that the Bishop consummates the act that was to result in our birth. The "you" in question is one Sr Marie-Gertrude – "My Dear Sister Gertrude" to Bishop Ricards – or, as she was born into this world, Josephine Amélie de Henningsen. If all speech is, finally, a dialogue, then she is the one constant listener to whom all Ricards' words were addressed, regardless of the many and varied audiences before which he was to appear in his time.

When the young subdeacon James David Ricards came to the Eastern Districts of the Cape Province as the recruit of Dr Aiden Devereux – recently appointed Bishop of the region but once a teacher of classics at the college where Ricards excelled as a student – he found himself one of a party Dr Devereux had drummed up on a particularly productive European recruitment expedition. Ricards left London along with two schoolmasters and a mechanic, and at Antwerp they were joined by seven nuns of the Assumption, also recruited by Devereux, of whom Sr Marie-Gertrude was the leader. Devereux was concerned to raise the standard of education in his vicariate, and the Assumptionist Sisters were a recently formed congregation from Paris that specialised in teaching.

In Sr Marie-Gertrude he found – as the astonished James Ricards soon discovered on his passage to Africa – more than a run of the mill schoolmistress. Striking and sophisticated, she belonged to the international aristocracy that had survived the various revolutions in Europe. As Josephine Amélie, she was brought up in the cultivated and diplomatic world of Brussels until she was fifteen, and thereafter moved with her family to London. Like many of the young ladies of society of those days, she received a thorough and good education, and she took part enthusiastically in the literary and scientific pursuits popular in the social life of London in the 1830s and '40s.

As I was to learn for myself later, Sr Marie-Gertrude had attended the public lectures of the great physicists and chemists of the time, and heard first-hand the opinions of Coleridge and Byron on literature. Once her religious vocation was embarked upon, she found friends in the resurgence of Catholicism in England in personages no less than Nicholas Wiseman and John Henry Newman. When preparing for her work in Africa, she had consulted directly with the ageing Alexander von Humboldt himself (despite his notorious dislike for female company), whose seemingly endless writings about his expeditions in South America made him the most famous traveller of the time. Not forgetting the level of education that she would be concerned with, her superiors had also sent her to gain experience in the schools for the poor in Paris.

Ricards majored in Natural Philosophy (particularly Physics and Chemistry) along with Theology at the College of Maynooth and, in addition, harboured the literary ambitions I have touched upon already. While Sr Marie-Gertrude's experience in these things seemed to extend infinitely beyond his, the poetic amalgamation of religion and science at the centre of these two souls became the medium for their personal intermingling. The mysteries of the religion that they shared we may take as something of a given, but the revelations of the scientific discoveries then absorbing the educated classes was another sort of alloy altogether, one that would prove equally important for the generation of our story.

The urbane nun and the bashful young subdeacon met for the first time at a grand dinner hosted by the Dhanis family in honour of the soon-to-depart South African missionaries. I myself heard her tell, as she must have on many, many occasions over the years, how he first came to her attention. "*Mr Ricards*," she would say, stressing his lowly title at that time ever more strongly the higher he rose in rank and stature, "fresh from Maynooth, was seated near myself and Minnie Dhanis. Minnie was pressing him to eat as he appeared shy and out of his element, to which he replied, '*Je n'ai pas de femme*.' I nearly burst into laughter, but Minnie, ever the poised hostess, replied, 'That does not matter, my dear, eat all the same.'"

"We were on the ship for some weeks," she would continue, "before I dared explain to him the difference between '*faim*' and '*femme*'! At the time he was aware only that he had made some sort of a mistake and looked much confused, the poor young man! In an attempt to make up for this he accepted Minnie's offer of some lovely ices on the table, pink and shaped like sponge cakes. Not knowing anything of this delicacy, he put an entire dessertspoonful in his mouth at once, and you may imagine the agony this caused him – and us, too!"

It may have been Ricards' social vulnerability that first won Sr Marie-Gertrude's attention, but their mutual affection was formed under far more rigorous conditions. The voyage out to South Africa proved a hothouse for the making or breaking of friendships: the drinking water went bad, the food spoiled, and the captain used his vessel's other function, that of a whaler, in an attempt to remedy the situation. The chase and harpooning were exciting enough, but the sustenance resulting from the cutting up of the whale was hardly worth the unpleasant experience the passengers had to endure, huddling away from the scene of the slaughter, the decks awash in blood between mounds of flesh and fat that huge sea birds attacked through a stench that not only enveloped the tiny vessel but permeated the air for miles.

Such circumstances showed the young Ricards off in his best light. His practical assistance with fainting nuns and vomiting priests, and, more especially, his determined efforts at keeping up the spirits of those with slightly stronger constitutions, won the appreciation of all the passengers, Sr Marie-Gertrude's in particular. A wisecrack went a long way in these conditions, and Ricards' ability to amuse was tested to the full for the whole distance of the voyage.

When, after a passage that encompassed near mutiny, violent gales and several abortive attempts to land, they reached their final destination, it was nothing like their expectations. Nestled in a hot bowl between dry, bare hills, Grahamstown was a wholly English nineteenth-century cathedral town. The bizarre contrast this created was such a relief to the newcomers that they welcomed even the very Anglican thrust of the spire of St Michael and St George which dominated the setting. Far from being some sort of clumsily put together settler muddle, Grahamstown gave the impression of always having been solidly established. It exuded a sobriety, propriety, and decorum that resisted its recent and fraught origins. In this very proper atmosphere, Bishop Devereux appointed Ricards as his personal secretary, while Sr Marie-Gertrude set about her task of founding a Catholic school that would raise the standards of colonial education to those worthy of the universal Church.

These tasks, along with their respective positions, separated the two most of the time, despite their geographical proximity. And so the relationship that continued and developed their seaborne intimacy was carried on through an ongoing flow of letters that began almost immediately and remained uninterrupted for many years, regardless of how near or far the one was from the other. These letters were no less than a marriage that took its shape in words and words alone. And, after a proper period of time, the idea of "Dunbrody Abbey" appeared as one of the most cherished fruits of this union.

In one of these letters, written by the Bishop to Sr Marie-Gertrude during a year's leave of absence abroad some eight years after his arrival in the eastern province of the Cape, we read:

New Ross, County Wexford
Ireland
7th June 1858

I have just been told again that there is no prospect of any missioners for our barren fields. I tried twice in Maynooth, but all in vain. Neither will the Trappists come. The resolution of their last Chapter was: No new foundations for the present. The usual response – no subjects to spare, God's time has not yet come for the conversion of southern Africa.

This afternoon I decided, despite the risk of the weather, to make my way out to dear old Dunbrody, in the hope that this would clear my head of such news. The desired effect did not seem likely, as the first thing I received was a short soaking at the hands of a squall. As the rain began to sting, I made my way towards the grand pile of Dunbrody at an increased rate. Its mass stood out against the sky with a kind of solitary grandeur about it not readily found elsewhere, and I made my way quickly into the space below the great central tower. Here I gratefully accepted the protection of the huge ruined arches, still magnificent in their height and noble in their proportions, while I waited for the storm to pass.

As suddenly as it began, it was over. Light poured out in the wake of the stately passing of the mountains of dense black cloud, and the ribs of that long-gone greatness in which I sheltered were illumined. The ruins were so lit up as to become not so much the remains of a glorious past, but the shape of a greatness waiting to be completed and a grandeur still to come. In the magic of that moment I knew that here was a name, among and above other such names, to conjure with: St Aidens, Glendalough – Dunbrody!

Old Irish names dear to so many in the old country may plead for us in the new!

I decided then and there to invoke all this magnificence in my search for priests and missionaries in the Eastern Vicariate. Dunbrody Abbey, here a ruined relic of the past, will become again the outpost of the future, a Christian future in a pagan land ...

I remain, My Dear Sister Gertrude,
Yours most sincerely
J D Ricards

Ricards' trip had included an audience with Pope Pius IX, during which, almost in passing, his notion of members of the Trappist community serving a kind of preparatory missionary function came up. His youthful excitement was, I am sure, infectious, and the Holy Father saw fit to respond in a benevolent if, it would appear (for nothing was documented of this audience), rather non-committal way.

However small the actual support for Ricards' somewhat curious idea was, he certainly had enough imaginative fuel for it, as his letter to Sr Marie-Gertrude shows. And so began the dream in which we were expected to become the Bishop's players. Words, words, words, filling the space left in love.

~

For all Ricards' visionary aspirations, it was Sr Marie-Gertrude's presence that was at first felt most forcefully in their new circumstances. Her educational efforts flourished spectacularly from their inception. Her acquaintance with the best in contemporary literary, scientific, and religious opinion could not be matched in any other school in the colony, and Catholics and Protestants alike were only too eager to send their children to the Grahamstown Convent. All the more so after they heard of her leading her nuns and children, during one of the frontier wars, into the safety of the fortified church armed with a cavalry sabre that she claimed to have learned to use in her early days.

Such wars regularly punctuated frontier life and during each of these Sr Marie-Gertrude – sabre aside – tirelessly led her Sisters in the nursing of the sick and wounded, the laying out of the dead, the visiting of widows. It was when she assumed responsibility for the many children left parentless after the Christmas Day massacres of the 1850 frontier war that her care and concern earned her the name she was to be known by to the end of her days: Notre Mère.

But words have a way of finding their own place in the world, as the young Ricards was soon to discover. Although things had improved considerably from the days when, as one Huguenot fiercely informed him shortly after his arrival, "a Romish priest passing through this country would be shot as readily as a wolf", Bishop Devereux still found enough reason to establish a weekly newspaper in Grahamstown, *The Colonist*, to respond to fairly regular attacks on the Catholic religion.

This publication, along with some help from Sr Marie-Gertrude, was to prove the making of Ricards. From the moment when, after his ordination in Cape Town, he was made editor of *The Colonist*, his career soared. The Bishop had given him this position only on the advice of Sr Marie-Gertrude, for whom he maintained the highest regard. His own feeling was that Ricards was too young and socially immature for the job – the man indulged constantly in puns, after all! But Ricards revelled in a professional association with words from the first, emerging as a man of great powers of persuasion and appeal in ink no less than in the flesh, and in no time made *The Colonist* very much his own paper.

The newspaper, and Ricards as its editor and chief contributor, achieved a prominence amongst Catholics that was not surprising in a country with a long history of anti-Catholicism. Many who came to South Africa, especially the Dutch Calvinists and French Huguenots, saw it as their duty to exact revenge on Catholics for the massacre of St Bartholomew, Alva's rule in the Netherlands, or the dragonnades of Louis xiv. *The Colonist* carried the South African Catholic response to these stories, and those on the Inquisition, the Gunpowder Plot and – certainly the most popular feature of anti-Catholic sentiments at the time – the scurrilities springing up in the wake of Maria Monk's "awful disclosures" of immorality and sadism in a Canadian convent. Even though Maria Monk herself was judicially proved a liar and punished by the civil courts in Canada, such fables had a long start, and often the disproof never caught up with them, especially in the more far-flung reaches of the colonies.

Ricards' career went from strength to strength as he took on such challenges, matching them word for word and dispatching them with great panache. He went on to earn the degree of Doctor of Divinity and the reputation of being the best preacher in the colony, as well as that of the best lecturer on the scientific subjects then of great popular interest. The mere announcement that Dr Ricards was to lecture was sufficient to attract a substantial crowd at any kind of gathering. From the telescope to the microscope, he could be trusted to encompass his subject in the most amusing way: in the middle of a lecture on "The Electric Telegraph", for example, he was handed a telegram (arranged prior to the event) from Cape Town which began, "Forgive me for interrupting your lecture ..." Oh, he was shameless, no trick being beneath him in winning over an audience, seducing a crowd, maintaining his friendship with a nun.

And then there was his habit of ending with a reading from some popular work of fiction. As one historian – not Fr Adalbert I hasten to add – puts it, with just a hint of disapproval: "The Eastern Vicariate had a lecturer-priest in Fr Ricards, who became popular for his talks on physics and chemistry, and for his readings of Dickens and Lever and Moore, which would not normally lead by a swift path to the marks of the true Church."

It was not uncommon to find Ricards, himself rather short and stout, exaggerating these features of an evening in some church or town hall in imitation of Dickens' Mr Justice Stareleigh – "all face and waistcoat". He would roll onto the platform provided for his performance and, having brought Stareleigh to the flesh, would switch into the role of the chemist pressed into jury duty in the famous trial scene from *The Pickwick Papers*, becoming – as much as his own physical attributes would allow – the tall, thin, yellow-visaged Thomas Groffin interrupting his swearing-in to beg the court's pardon but may he be excused from attending. "On what grounds, sir?" Ricards would demand as Mr. Justice Stareleigh and, without missing a beat, would answer as Thomas Groffin, "I have no assistant, my Lord."

"I can't help that, sir," Ricards would reply, reddening as much in his imitation of Stareleigh's anger as from his exertions in the sweltering colonial heat. "For Mr Justice Stareleigh's temper bordered on the irritable," he explained in a rumbling aside to an audience desperately homesick for the characters behind these caricatures, "and brooked not contradiction."

Sweat running in rivers from the impressive dome of his already much-receded hairline and disappearing into his clerical collar over the several chins he had begun to develop while still relatively young, Ricards' attempts at reassuming the full length of the chemist would bring the now-expected response from the audience. He struck an exaggerated stance of resignation and paused until the laughter subsided. "Then there'll be murder before this trial's over; that's all," he announced as the audience hung on his every word. "I merely wanted to observe, my Lord," he went on into the expectant hush, "that I've left nobody but an errand boy in my shop. He is a very nice boy, my Lord, but he is not acquainted with drugs; and I know that the prevailing impression on his mind is that Epsom salts means oxalic acid; and syrup of senna, laudanum. That's all, my Lord." With this, Ricards would compose himself into the "comfortable attitude" of the tall chemist and freeze into that pose whilst the house came down around his ears.

Or so I imagine, reading as I did once in an old and rather battered issue of an Eastern Vicariate circular, that "laughter truly held both her sides when Fr Ricards gave the trial scene from *Pickwick*".

~

I find, more and more, that without such imaginings, the ability to understand events from the past that have brought me to my present position eludes me. And it is important for you to imagine with me now that in Ricards' audience on that occasion, or, rather, at the rear of that audience or perhaps even outside the building, peering through a window or hovering near the door, were a few representatives of what Ricards, some years later in *The Catholic Church and the Kaffir*, would call the "impossibly difficult neighbours for the colonists of the frontier", the Tembu people.

We must imagine that every so often, Ricards would catch a glimpse of one of these black faces, and shudder inwardly, not at its colour, or the shape of its nose, the thickness of its lips, the tight springs of its hair, but at the frank incomprehension it registered regarding his performance. While some of his broader physical exertions may have occasionally provoked a response, even a humorous one (if not of the most approving sort), what must have frozen Ricards to the core was the way in which the hilarity of his text and his expert bringing of this to life fell dead before such a face.

For it was humour, finally, that measured the presence or absence of any common ground between him and another, and that was the vital element without which his many other talents could not take root. The success of his lecturing, his preaching too, and the excellent relations he enjoyed with his congregation, not to mention his considerable success with the settler community at large, all turned upon the perfect sense of wit in which he took much pride (even as he castigated himself – wittily – for such pride). From the broad jest to the clever aside, from the unexpected association to the outrageous contrast, from the acute compression to the extended conceit, in this terrain he was master. Ricards could make the oldest punch line work anew, invent a new one perfect for any occasion, make even his delight in puns win approval.

His comic gifts, dependent as they were upon a shared set of manners, needed a common social sphere in which his wit had purchase and his erudition sufficient scope. He was never more at a loss than when one of his quips was not appreciated, especially through a lack of understanding of just how clever it was. His deepest fear was of circumstances in which his comic turns and learned forays alike collapsed before simple incomprehension. He knew of no way to recover from rejection of this sort. Quite simply, he did not know how to relate to those who missed his jokes.

Which is where we Trappists came in. Our silence was meant to fill the space created when the Bishop's punch lines began to fail.

~

And fail they did, with regard to Dunbrody, from the first. On that inauspicious day when the Bishop attempted to address the Chapter General in his appalling French, his request for Trappists to come to his mission fields was met by a forbidding silence. None of the Abbots present showed the least interest in the project of a man who knew no French and in any event was proposing something so alien to the Order.

It is true that the scattering of the French Trappists during and after the Revolution led some of their houses to adapt the Rule to the needs of the time. This included, in a few instances, some limited mission work (the foundation in Staouëli that so inspired the Bishop being the prime example), but a concern for the prescribed regularity of the Order, which engagement in missionary activity could only mitigate against, was already beginning to reassert itself amongst the Generalate.

The Bishop's vapid assertions that Pope Pius himself supported the idea of Trappists undertaking missionary work in South Africa – the Pope had died the year before and left no written instruction to this effect – carried small weight under such circumstances. Even the letter of recommendation Ricards managed to secure from the new Pope in an audience he had been granted whilst on his way to the General Chapter, a letter in which

Leo XIII asked the Trappists "to do justice to the best of their ability to the wishes of the Apostolic Vicar", was not specific enough to penetrate the negativity emanating from the assembly.

I have heard it said that it was out of pity for the Bishop, sitting there flushed and uneasy in the stillness that followed his dreadful performance, that Franz rose and said – those dramatic words again, variously formulated and translated in their repetition in account after account of Franz's life and work and immortalised now as the signature of his fame – "If nobody else is willing to go, I shall go".

Other reasons for Franz's leap into this silence will emerge, but all in good time. Let us note for the present that Franz, despite his inability to speak English, had been appointed as Bishop Ricards' interpreter at Sept Fons. This was because Herr Max Anton Fraundorfer, a German Catholic from Port Elizabeth who had learned English while trading there, accompanied the Bishop to the General Chapter. The idea was that Bishop Ricards would present his opinions to Herr Fraundorfer in English, Herr Fraundorfer would pass these on to Prior Franz in German, and Prior Franz would make them known to the congregation of Trappist leaders in French.

This meant that the Bishop had explained his plan in detail to Herr Fraundorfer, and Herr Fraundorfer had communicated this to Franz well before the Bishop's disastrous presentation. It was Franz himself who had prepared the script Ricards stumbled through before the General Chapter. So much, then, for his celebrated "spontaneous" outburst; it was as calculated an intervention as Franz ever made. As he stood there straight and alone amidst the welling scuffle and sibilance of a chamber full of holy men whispering and gesturing to each other in surprise (yes, he was to be made an Abbot that very day), he was thinking of Mariannaberg, the foundation in Bosnia that his Superiors snatched away from him before it could be begun.

Mariastern was a success, yes, but to a large extent an accident of his own energy; he had not, in some way as yet unknown to him, made of it the kind of foundation that truly embodied the idea of religious life of which he had intimations when working alone and in exile in the hills around Mariawald. With the Bishop's command that he "restrain his unruly spirit" still stinging his eyes as it had when he let the letter of rebuke fall to the floor at Mariastern, he stood now before the General Chapter in secret protest. If he could not raise up the Mountain of Our Lady and Saint Ann in Bosnia, then perhaps South Africa was far enough away, and in its way exile enough, for that as yet unformed but dearest wish of his heart to come into being.

The Bishop's offer, by the time it reached Sept Fons, had become – on the surface at least – a very generous one. It certainly appeared so to Franz, fresh from dragging Mariastern into existence out of nothing. In the course of preparing Ricards' address to the General Chapter, he learned that the Bishop had started out on his tour prepared to offer the Trappists (so central to his vision) only the farm he had procured. As his search for real monks to give substance to those he so energetically imagined became ever more futile, he steadily improved the material nature of what he was prepared to offer. Ironically, the further he got from the kind of monks he originally had in mind – he never really recovered from being turned down by the Irish Trappists – the more he was forced to offer in his efforts to win anyone over at all. Sept Fons was, in effect, his last chance of convincing the Trappists that there was a place for them in the special conditions presented by the South African mission field.

And so, by the time Bishop Ricards put his appeal to the General Chapter (each term of which Franz went through in detail as he rendered it into French), he was prepared to announce that he would not only give his whole farm but provide at his own cost the necessary buildings for the monastery as well as the farm. Furthermore, he would for the first three years supply the clothing, food, tools and seeds that the monks would need. Before Franz had burst out with his famous "If no one else will go, I will go," the Bishop on his own volition had offered, in addition, to pay the passage of the monks from London to their destination.

Franz, meanwhile, had thought of another way to make use of the Bishop's clearly generous resources. As the General Chapter tried to bring itself to some sort of order by establishing the terms upon which they could confirm this startling offer, Franz added that he could only go if the Rt Rev. Bishop Ricards would also undertake to pay the balance of the debts still owed on Mariastern. He would require at least 25 000 florins to meet this, he said; otherwise he could perhaps send his Sub-Prior, although he would rather go himself.

If anyone had been paying attention to the Bishop at this point, they might have seen his eyes glaze as he mentally converted the florins into sterling (it came to £2 000), and perhaps even heard the beginnings of his willingness to settle for the Sub-Prior. The preferences of the General Chapter – not to mention the Bishop's inability to make his case in French – overwhelmed his chance of taking up the cheaper of the options before him. To be at a loss for words at the very moment that his book was springing off the page and into life must have been one of the great frustrations of his career, but there he stood, speechless, as his words took material form before him. The material form of a strange-looking, strange-sounding, very foreign foreigner with whom he could speak only through a translator.

As for Franz, he was exceptionally pleased with this last upping of the Bishop's offer. If the amount he put forward exceeded the needs of Mariastern, well, the Bishop gave the impression that his resources could easily accommodate this generous figure. Thus Franz neatly wrapped up his past, and could part cleanly and honourably from his first foundation.

In response to the General Chapter's enquiry as to the number of monks he would take with him, he rather hastily answered that ten (a cipher really to himself, empty as far as the actual men he would choose) should suffice. He asked that he be given leave to return to Mariastern to inform his community of these developments and prepare for departure. This was granted and so, in a shower of kisses of peace, Franz was sent off from the heart of his Order. To work, in effect, towards the destruction of everything that it stood for.

Bishop Ricards left the General Chapter just as promptly. His last words to Franz, after the two had agreed on a date to meet in Augsburg for the settling of the final details of their agreement, were a reminder that he should collect as many alms as possible for the new foundation. The Bishop himself was off on a frantic fund-raising tour, each step of which must have made him more appalled at how much he was forced to offer to win over the Trappists. He could not have been much comforted by Franz's parting words: "I go with my brethren as your leader and builder. Your Lordship shall be the paymaster and general provider."

~

Returning to us at Mariastern, Franz had announced that Mariastern now had not only a daughter but a dowry too. In the eyes of the community, the oddity of the Bishop's plan for a Trappist mission amongst the African heathen was only partially offset by the generosity of his support for it – until, that is, Franz revealed that he himself would be leading this new venture. At this, the community, the younger members especially and the novices in particular, grew as animated about the proposal as Franz himself.

Outside the Chapter Room, where the community was gathered to hear about the bright, sunny land of South Africa (a place where one might live for God only and in so doing work for the salvation of souls), the first hints of winter were in the air. As Franz broached the touchy issue of who would be selected to accompany him, he was forced to temper the ardour with which virtually the entire community put itself forward. No delicate persons could come, he said, looking around sternly and, grasping the first example that came to mind, he stressed that no one afraid of being sunburned could possibly be selected. The sight over the next few days of shoemakers, tailors and other brethren whose work at Mariastern normally kept them indoors applying themselves to the task of getting their skins tanned by the sun at every opportunity – cowls off, sleeves pulled back, even the odd habit raised above the knees – became something of a threat to the dignity of the monastery.

The very silence of Mariastern (whatever silence, that is, one was able to maintain in the busy monastery) vibrated with excitement about the new enterprise. In the midst of this, Franz left again as suddenly as he had arrived, heading off to meet with Bishop Ricards and Herr Fraundorfer in Augsburg. Here Franz's characteristic confidence in his ability to overcome all difficulties came up for the second – and by no means last – time against the reality of the babel out of which his new foundation was to emerge. With no idea as yet how fatally flawed they were, he threw himself into establishing the practical details of the broad agreements entered into at the General Chapter, with his usual disregard of the finer points.

Admittedly, by the time the three met again, Herr Fraundorfer's dislike of the impulsive German Trappist had become a significant addition to the translation process. This was not helped by Franz's abrupt opening announcement that he now wished to take twenty-five men with him (it had been difficult to dampen his own infectious enthusiasm at Mariastern) or by the Bishop's ready acceptance of this alteration. As the person really in control of the finances of the Church in Port Elizabeth, Herr Fraundorfer must have been all too aware how much even the original terms the Bishop agreed to threatened their slender means.

The meeting, then, despite its apparently expansive air, was frustrating.

Not that Franz shared this with the rest of us. As with so much of this story, he kept it to himself and we are forced to find out what really occurred by peering and squinting through the haze of years. And so, here again, I am left to play the historian, scrabbling through dusty old papers lost in the past they record or pouring over more recent publications, if only to measure how far they deviate from what I know or guess to be the truth.

Some of the work allocated to me later in life, as you will see, lent itself to this endeavour, and I have been able, in the last few years, to call upon that new Father, a fine man in his prime, who has set himself up as our historian proper. In my meetings with Fr Adalbert I cling for the most part to the ways of silence now done with by his generation (a nod or a mild sound of assertion is sometimes all he has to work with), but he is generous in sharing with me excerpts of his work in progress, although he is often, I can see, rather disappointed by my reactions. It is clear that in his opinion I missed the significance of most of what was going on about me, and as far as his general account is concerned, he is, I am sure, correct in thinking this. But I remain quiet, and leave him to inject his idea of life into the history of what is now, partly through my own efforts, dead and gone.

In this he is often extremely useful, as in his recreation of the meeting between the Bishop, Herr Fraundorfer and Franz at Augsburg, although it requires no stretch of the imagination to realise just how much each, sometimes quite deliberately, misunderstood what the others had to say.

To Franz's eminently practical question regarding wood and water and livestock, the Bishop, according to Fr Adalbert, made only the haziest of replies, always rounded off with the words, "Don't worry, Father, it will be all right." By the end of the meeting, Franz was most uncharacteristically reduced to confused acquiescence, accepting each of the Bishop's responses with the only English phrase he knew, purely because he had heard the Bishop use it so often. "All right," he would say, not knowing whether to be more uncertain about what the Bishop had just said or the increasingly obvious, if mysterious, hostility behind Herr Fraundorfer's attempts at clarification. By the time Franz did come to understand the businessman's dislike of the proceedings in hand, it would be too late to salvage the damage that was being done as he and Ricards struggled towards the murkiest of agreements.

The Bishop himself, for that matter, did not make plain his real feelings regarding the arrangements they were making. Here Fr Adalbert is at his most helpful, sharing with me Ricards' diary entry for 17th November, 1879: "Met Prior Franz and Mr Fraundorfer and arranged all. No other chance of obtaining a community of Trappists now on any other conditions. Agree."

7

I wish that the thirty of us who finally made up Franz's party could have reported a similar air of resignation when we surveyed the actuality behind the Bishop's casual assurances. Instead, each of us in his own way fought back a rising sense of despair. We could take in our new situation at a glance. Dunbrody stood just slightly higher than the encircling mass of thorns, and was bounded on one side by yet another dry riverbed. No sign of life was apparent in the immense expanse that stretched in every direction to the distant encircling hills.

Franz walked to the door of the shed, turned and said: "Each of you, according to your trade or calling, look about this place and report to me." Then he disappeared into the dim solitude of the shed. Those of us who began "looking about" soon put aside any sense of our trade or calling and simply concentrated our efforts on searching for a water supply; some of our number just sat on the ground forlornly, ignoring everything around them.

As evening drew in, we regrouped. In the gathering darkness Franz, who had not ventured out, stood at the door of the shed, awaiting us. There was nothing encouraging to report. One Brother asked, "Reverend Father, will you stay here?"

The question fell into the emptiness as much inside as around us. Franz let it echo there for a few long, silent minutes, and then burst forth: "*Sit gloria Dominin in aeternum, et laetetur in operibus sui. Ubi abundat peccatum, abundat et Dei misericordia.*"

The spiny cacti and the spiky thorn were God's work, he told us. Even if only as a punishment for laziness, He let them grow *et laetetur in operibus sui* – and He delights in His works! Therefore we should not be angry when they spread over our fields, or complain when they penetrated our skin or our shoes. Instead we should investigate what uses the sap and meat of these strange looking plants might have. If this meagre fruit was so refreshing, he said, producing an opened one from the sleeve of his habit, we could imagine how wonderful the fruits would be that industrious and intelligent hands planted here.

Since he had such hopes in this land of thorns, he went on, we should know that the resolution he was about to make was firm and unshakeable. "On this last day of July in the year of Our Lord 1880," he intoned, "here in your presence under this African sky, on this African soil, I resolve never to leave this piece of land, but to live and remain here until death."

Whoever did not have the courage to stay here with him, for whom this land had too many thorns and the cacti too many spines, should say so now, he said, staring hard at each of us in turn, and that person would be put on the train the very next day so that he could return to the fleshpots of Egypt – or at least to the onions of Bosnia.

Here some amongst us even smiled, and one could feel the whole community's spirits reviving. But Franz would not have been Franz if he hadn't backed up his inspirational words with something more practical. And so he ended this, his first address to the Trappists of Dunbrody, South Africa, with a numbered list of the advantages we had here in comparison with our start in Bosnia. He began with the support of the local clergy, the Governor, and the population of Port Elizabeth, and moved on to the land we had been given for nothing and the promise of financial support from the Bishop. In Bosnia he had had to begin his foundation with just three Brothers and one priest, none of whom was suited to the work they had to do. Here we were a community of over thirty, hand-picked by himself, and representing almost every trade we would need.

As for the site, although water was clearly a problem, the soil was fertile, and if the climate was dry and hot, at least we should suffer no fevers. And if we lacked the free use of timber the rich forests of Bosnia allowed us, the land about was full of stones, the riverbeds promised good brick clay, and – he reached down and picked up a handful of the sand at his feet which he let run through his fingers – the soil was of a kind that when mixed with only water would substitute for lime.

And there, in this closing combination of keen observation and practical application, you have the power of Franz Pfanner. As the sand sifted from his hands into the cold evening breeze, he was like a magician creating life out of the very deadness of the ground beneath us. Comforted, the community ate a rather strange meal that had been arranged in honour of its arrival, disposed itself for sleep, and woke to find the thorn bush's service as a figure in an inspirational oration well and truly over.

"Clear the bush!" was the command on the first day. And every day for the next nine months.

~

Under Franz's direction, one of the first tracts we cleared revealed a pool of water in a sharp bend that the otherwise apparently dry river had cut into a steep bank. This was evidence that the river, the White River (so named, we assumed, after the dry white sand gleaming in the sun that was all that we could see of it), had a small and largely subterranean flow. While we were discovering this, either through sheer luck or, as it appeared at the time, as a result of Franz's magic, the steam pump that the Bishop had promised us arrived.

Our initial amazement and joy at this coincidence soon gave way to our first real observation of settler life. During our brief time in Port Elizabeth, we had been surrounded by a religious community – a secular community, perhaps, but a religious community nonetheless. Now, at the Bishop's insistence, two mechanics from Port Elizabeth were sent out to assemble the pump. If we needed encouragement in returning to the self-sufficiency and enclosure that defines our Order, these two crude and disreputable looking young men provided it. They insisted on calling each other "engineer" – a term that in our European experience implied very different qualifications and abilities – whilst putting the pump up near the muddy pool in a leisurely and not particularly efficient manner. When they were done they departed in a self-congratulatory mood awash with pompous assurances that everything was in order, leaving us to discover that what they referred to as "the pulsometer" did not work at all. A bucket tied to a cable saw us through this disappointment, bringing water up to the "Abbey" pretty successfully. Those clearing the plots marked out for our agricultural endeavours carried on with their work in quiet desperation.

And how we laboured! Building was, for the moment, out of the question; the first thing we had to do was clear a space for ourselves amidst the thorns. In any event, a built enclosure seemed superfluous in an empty wilderness with nothing and no one to isolate ourselves from. Enfolded only in the reassurance of our holy routine, we launched ourselves at the bush. All of us, priests and Brothers alike, kept the hours of the Lay Brothers, working more and praying less; there was no logic to the life of a Choir monk here. And so, brown and white habits alike could be seen bobbing amongst the bushes, slowly beating back the sea of thorns. Even our observation of the Hours often took place right where we were working, as it had in our early days in Bosnia. Awake as always at two, we could be found ahead of the thin dawn, taking to the bush with our axes. We began by clearing not just fields but two roads, one from our tiny monastery to the fields and the other to a railway station closer to us than Bluecliff.

The labour was not only backbreaking but deadeningly monotonous. Perfect as this was for meditation, it was difficult to draw inspiration at the end of the day from the small patches of bare sand we won from the bushes. Still, the weather remained mild for a time and the food promised by the Bishop arrived every Tuesday and Friday – carrots, turnips, potatoes, beans, salad, beet, and onions. It was a rich and varied repast and ensured our strength for each day's battle with the desolation that engulfed us.

~

I did not share with the others – let alone Franz – my main difficulty at this time. Our desolate surroundings, as I have called them, simply did not animate me in the way Franz would have wished. Do what I would, this landscape resisted my inner life. The contemplation that was our chief business here on earth seemed, in my case, sealed off from this particular corner of the earth. It was not that I, virtually a founder of Mariastern, was unused to battling in work and prayer with the wilderness; it was just that this kind of wilderness utterly failed to kindle my religious enthusiasm.

It was not wild enough, in one sense, nor extreme enough, in another. Perhaps I expected something more exotic, having left the comfortable hills and neat fields and orchards of Letovice to find God in the wilds. My spirit aspired to high, craggy peaks, mist-enshrouded, and echoing water-falls and thunder. To dense, dark forests even, where one could be lost for weeks in dripping green and black. Or, at the opposite end of the scale of the sublime, to the deserts of the early saints: endless dunes with the sand blowing constantly over their surface, where one prayed through cracked lips while staring into the searing sun until blindness itself became sight. Anything but this numbingly mundane world of flat bush and low hill, not far enough from anywhere to give the thrill of isolation or close enough to warrant the struggle for seclusion. This foreign place all too quickly surrendered itself to ordinariness. I could feel no mystery here, no hidden world of the soul, no visionary immanence in the landscape.

I came to the Church haunted by a sense of the miracle behind all things, out of the sense that for some – not for me, perhaps, in my unworthiness – but for others, the secret behind reality, the secret that gave the slight surface of the world its depth and significance, would break through the commonplace and illuminate it forever. Even my illness confirmed this. For what else were the auras that presaged my seizures but the assurance of a meaning to all things lying just behind their appearance? And if I could not experience this first-hand, except in the hints given in the grip of infirmity, I could become part of the history of those who lived in its reality on a daily basis, and perhaps even share my life in some small way with those who still did.

As it was, the blank emptiness of Dunbrody was brought home to me by a strange inversion of sorts – in short, good health. Weeks and then months went by after our arrival without my suffering a single seizure, or even a hint of the sensations that sometimes foreshadowed them and sometimes came over me of and by themselves. Franz, of course, noted this with high pleasure and overtly – of course – I celebrated with him. But you with whom I have shared so much already of my secret history will guess how much, for all the disorientation and inconvenience they involved, I missed those moments of high portent, when the gateway to my fits seemed like the gateway to His presence. So what if I emerged again from those gates in chaos and confusion? At least, as I passed through them, I was assured of the promise of His presence if not the thing itself. In this way my auras joined with my prayers in becoming raids on the unspeakable. Their absence could not be compensated for by all the strength of the words by which I was taught to pray.

Perhaps this is the reason – although not the only reason – that, no matter how much I reminded myself that God is everywhere, I could not feel His presence in Dunbrody; He seemed distracted, His mind somewhere else. I blush even now at this blasphemy, but the memory of Dunbrody prevents me from denying the force with which I felt it.

~

Franz entered this wasteland like Adam. His answer to its blankness was to name it. Where my imagination failed, he mapped; where I felt remote from this place, he claimed it for his own. Not technically, of course: we

Trappists own nothing, and our houses we give, by tradition, to Mary. And so, within a month, Franz had renamed Dunbrody Abbey. He ended his first sermon at "this most distant point of this continent, at the outermost part of the inhabited world", as he called it, with the announcement that his new foundation would now be called – in an act of most seemly compromise (rare enough with him) – Maria Dunbrody. Standing over our kneeling forms, he looked out from our low hill and divided up his world. The limestone ridge along the large meadow we had cleared he called Mariaberg; the large lowlands near the ridge, Marienwiese; the field we created between the monastery and the Sundays River, Mariafeld; the pond, which was a quarter of an hour's distance north of the monastery, Mariaquelle; and, finally, the projected monastery enclosure north and east, what else but – Mariakaktus.

Thus he domesticated his wilderness – or so he thought. As far as I was concerned, the more one looked into its bland features for visionary possibilities, the more sullenly it stared back. One could sense, even as Franz spoke, that the names he gave would not stick, would be shrugged off soon enough or lost in the usual muddle of settler names. As for the indigenous names for the features around us – not that we would have paid much attention to these – there was no one to tell us what they may have been. We seemed to have been dropped into an entirely empty landscape.

When Franz asked the Bishop where the Natives were, Ricards waxed eloquent about the wars fought here earlier in the century between the settlers moving up from the south and the indigenous peoples coming down from the north. There was some amusement when he told us the name of the local inhabitants we were meant ultimately to encounter. Much distortion of the mouth and tongue into strange clicking and clucking sounds occasioned this – but we were not here to learn about them or even, in the first instance, to communicate with them. We were here to be seen by them, enacting a way of life that would in no way bend to local circumstances or alter in relation to a different context. We carried our way of life with us like a turtle carries its casing, just as it has been carried unchanged through hundreds of years of history. Distance was as meaningless as time for the perpetual way of life to which we were silent witnesses, and it was our business to begin recreating that shell around us as soon as possible.

In one way and one way only was I eager to encounter at least one of the natives of this land in his natural state, but the black figures we had seen at the harbour, twisted beneath loads or listlessly awaiting another load, did not even approximate the extraordinarily graceful Nubian in the altar of the Jesuit church in Brünn to which I had returned again and again in my days of youthful infatuation with the missions. By this time my image of the African had been modified somewhat – by the four black figures on display in the Museum of Natural History in Vienna, for example; skinned, stuffed, and enclosed in glass cupboards, rather pathetic additions to the rows of exotic animals alongside which they were exhibited as further examples of the taxidermist's art. I still trusted that there was some truth in the representational power of sculpture, and that the people who once lived here could be brought to life even out of this determinedly mundane landscape. But, I wondered, what would bring the finer creature I hoped for to this dreary expanse of bush?

Unknowingly we had already encountered as indigenous a character as we could wish to meet, although he could not have been further from the figure I had in mind. I have mentioned that a meal was ready for us on our arrival. This was prepared and served, after a fashion, by a strange little man who put the food before us in a rustle of clicking sounds interspersed with some – English? – words before disappearing into the background. I am told his wife was shooed off Dunbrody before our Brothers could be made impure by coming into contact with her, and the wizened clay-coloured man of slightly oriental aspect retreated to another location as well, returning occasionally to perform some service or other. We were well able to do without his continued culinary skills, but we did need him as a guide now and then. On such occasions he seemed to know exactly when to materialise out of the apparently empty landscape.

I was used to such natural servants from my childhood in the Czech lands – people who were invisible until a pair of hands was needed, or who performed those basic household functions that seemed to just happen by themselves. In Letovice I had belonged, if only just, to a social class that took it for granted that it would be served. As Catholics and German-speakers this was our right, and it seemed only right, too, that the Czechs perform this function. Their very language – part of the landscape but not of its government – marked them out for peasantry and servitude. It seemed entirely unnecessary for us to learn that language, apart from the odd word or phrase of instruction with which to hurry along a particularly slow menial. Communication took place in whatever they were able to learn of our language, the language of culture and civilisation and of the wide world beyond their rootedness in what would have been, without our presence, an insignificant backwater.

In similar ways, then, for myself and my brethren – mostly citizens of a modern empire and members of a strictly hierarchical ancient Order – the strangely proportioned mud-textured man in his tatty approximation of European dress was invisible. We never for a moment considered him to be the audience before whom we had come to put our living example of the contemplative life. We never learned his name – he was referred to simply as "the Hottentotte", for this was the only introduction to him we ever received – or recorded his existence, except when his presence was noted, by accident as it were, at the edges of some event for which we required his services. Or so it seems to me now, all these years later, as I remember our first supper at Dunbrody and the odd trip to one of the other struggling settlements in the Sundays River valley. Looking back, I see that while we waited in vain for the noble savages to gather about us and wonder at the lives of those who loved God to the exclusion of all else, the one witness to the futile struggle of our time at Maria Dunbrody was more silent and self-effacing than we were ever to be.

~

And futile it was, as some of us admitted to ourselves from the first, despite Franz's declarations to the contrary. Still, our Rule requires that we offer not only our obedience but our obedience with a good will, and this most of us did as best we could even when things began to conspire against us.

The mild period that continued for a few weeks after our arrival soon gave way to bitter cold. Although there was only a dusting of snow on the mountains in the distance to the north, the winds came down directly from them into our valley, icy, dry and cutting. The ground turned to iron, the picks provided by the Bishop bouncing off it as we tried to break it. The bushes dried to an inflexible hardness, tearing at our hands as we tore at them. Only the thorns continued as always, though they felt harder and sharper in the freezing air.

Fortunately, Franz by then had turned his attention from clearing to his main passion, building. As soon as there was enough space on our modest rise, he had us add to our shed a room for himself, which, as our Superior, he certainly needed. Following Trappist tradition, the next priority was accommodation for visitors, few though these were likely to be, and we set about providing this before embarking upon a smithy, workshops and a Chapter Room.

These structures were built of raw brick and in a style suitable for the climate – the beginnings of our colonial cloisters were evident in the wide verandas Franz ordered us to construct around each of the buildings. Commencing on the "Abbey" itself was a source of contention from September, when Bishop Ricards came to Dunbrody and was shocked to see how far the buildings were progressing in contrast to the fields. Acutely aware of what it was costing him to feed us (Herr Fraundorfer no doubt made sure of this), he had supposed our priority to be cultivating the ground so that we could feed ourselves. Franz, on the other hand, understood the agreement struck in Sept Fons and Augsburg to entitle him to build a suitable monastery while we were provided with food and equipment by the Bishop.

We were beginning to suspect that the Bishop's resources did not match up to the liberality he had extended while wooing us to his vision. The pedigreed bull he had promised never arrived and, virtually without exception, the items handed over to us by the Bishop were collected by none other than Notre Mère, as we too now took to calling Sister Marie-Gertrude. Whilst the Bishop flustered and blustered she quietly delivered the few articles of any real use that we were to receive, having gone before our arrival to the entire community of Port Elizabeth, particularly its farming districts, collecting on our behalf. Her own experience had taught her how difficult first beginnings were in a strange country and her initial struggles made her sensitive to what was most needed.

When, in the course of his attempts at piecing together the grand tale of our victories over adversity, Fr Adalbert showed me a school exercise book that he found preserved in the archives of the Missionary Sisters of the Assumption in Port Elizabeth, I must say that tears welled in my eyes. For there, on the first page, written in Notre Mère's own elegant hand, were the words: "Result of my four days' begging for Trappists. 2nd July. Our Lady's Visitation. 1880." The pages that followed contained lists of the gifts she elicited on our behalf, with the names of the donors: Catholics in a column on one side of the page, Protestants on the other. There were over five hundred items – household goods and agricultural implements, bowls and kettles, hammers, hoes, picks, rakes, and so on –

that allowed us to carry on with the one half of the Trappist motto without which the other was meaningless. Certainly Ricards had prayers enough to offer us, but if we had been left with only our bare hands, the ability to work would have been denied us. And it was Notre Mère who filled those hands so lovingly with the instruments that connected our prayers with the material world.

Not that the Bishop did not try, in his way, to assist us. The local newspapers, I discovered later, featured prominently the eight horsepower Fowlers traction engine he purchased with the bulk of the single, generous donation he received before leaving Europe. The Duke of Norfolk would have been proud to know that his five hundred pounds were invested in such a progressive and practical item – until it was clear that it could not work without coal (a resource entirely absent from this part of the colonies) and it was left lying like a mechanical whale beached on the Port Elizabeth quayside. And so we entered the public records of our new home, an ancient Order floundering in its attempts to become a part of the modern world.

The Bishop did manage to make one delivery of a sort more typically associated with an endeavour such as ours, one that gave him and Franz equal pleasure. Towards the end of August he arrived with two bells, which he consecrated before we hung them in a primitive wooden bell tower – forerunner, Franz stressed, of greater things to come. He and Franz shared one of their few moments of closeness as they stood together listening to the bells ringing out for the first time over the valley.

"It gives me a thrill of delight to hear them," the Bishop said as he surveyed what could have been a prehistoric vista. "Just think, such sounds have not been heard in this place since time began."

At this I clutched the hammer I was using on some singularly uncooperative nails more tightly, and turned away.

~

On a cold bright day in early October, the Bishop arrived unannounced at Maria Dunbrody. Franz broke from his labours and, barely bothering with a formal greeting, burst into an account of our work. The Bishop had learned by now not to be startled or offended by his protegé's abruptness, but he was startled by the awareness, which took some moments to sink in, that he was being addressed in English – of a sort.

"We have work as the lions," Franz was saying excitedly, "and when we all days till the New Year so hew down the spines, we shall arrive at Kor-nei."

The Bishop should have been prepared for Franz's vocal exercises by the letter he had recently received from him, the very first our Superior tried to compose in the language of the colony. This, too, Fr Adalbert has exhumed from the pile of letters concerning Dunbrody in the archives of the Cape's Eastern Vicariate and, all these years later, I still remain impressed by how much English Franz had mastered in so short a time. Ricards, I am sure, was more taken with the opportunities for humour at Franz's expense that the letter offered. I can hear him now, reading an irresistible excerpt aloud to one of his staff, no doubt with the thought that a touch of humiliation would not go amiss in his dealings with this stubborn Trappist.

"Yesterday your servant Isaai with an helper has brought the three cows which you, my Lord, had the kindness to send," he would have read. "The Brothers have burnt the mark in them, but one was so wild that the Brother could not stop her. She became furious and ran through the door of the yard into the bush in a few moments. The cows are so savage it is dangerous to come them near and particularly to milk. I do not know are they so wild at Grahamstown? Or they have the apprehension of the habit of the Brothers? She slinged one of the Brothers who would milk her down. If you do see her when travelling back and forth, the cow fugitive has the mark of Dunbrody and she bears a cord about."

With Franz now before him, he said slowly and deliberately, "I have not, in my travels out here today, seen the 'cow fugitive'. Are your brethren unused to bovines in Germany?"

Franz was embarrassed enough by the agricultural ineptitude of his monks, but the Bishop's tone made it quite clear that his attempts at English were not much better.

"Excuse, my Lord, when I speak so faulty," he said. "I beg my Lord to correct me and say me the faults in return ..."

At this Bishop Ricards found his opening and, for once in his career of rhetorical excess, made the blunt pronouncement he had come to deliver. "Prior Franz, I am unable to subsidise the monastery any longer," he said. "The resources of the vicariate are at an end. From now on you Trappists will have to manage on your own."

Even I could understand Franz's response. After a stunned moment he grunted "All right" and turned away. Despite the irony implicit in its parody of the Bishop's liberal assurances at Augsburg, this brief reply was marked by great dignity, especially in the silence that followed it.

But dignity of any sort disappeared when Franz suddenly exploded into speech, insisting with as much force as Père Etienne's translation allowed that the Bishop continue at the least to give us seed for our crops, and some potatoes in the meanwhile. Moreover, Franz said, he needed more monks for the extra work and the Bishop would have to pay their passage here.

There was no chance of this last request being met, even though a belatedly recruited novice had already asked to leave Maria Dunbrody and further dissatisfaction was brewing. Over and above the difficult and uninspiring nature of our situation, Franz's strict adherence to the Rule was beginning to take its toll amongst those without the true Trappist vocation. Franz had put down such mutterings as he heard with the authority that came so easily to him, in his usual confidence that the situation was thus settled. He was totally unprepared, thus, for what happened when he threw down his demands to the Bishop.

Without even bothering to attempt an interpretation, Père Etienne fell at the Bishop's feet and begged to be allowed to return with him to Port Elizabeth. Confused by the imploring priest clutching at his soutane, Bishop Ricards sputtered some noncommittal sounds to the scattered tableau of equally confused onlookers and turned to leave, Père Etienne in tow.

Franz hurried after them, berating Père Etienne into translating as his anger exceeded the small grasp of English he had worked so hard to attain, and in this undignified scurry the new terms of our tenure at Dunbrody were established. "As Abraham bartered with the Lord over Sodom, so I continued pestering him" was the way Franz put it later, which was fair enough as he came away almost as empty-handed.

The Bishop stopped, and in real pain and defeat turned towards Père Etienne and said, "Tell Prior Franz that my resources are exhausted. I am exhausted. All I can give him for a short while is beans, bread flour and dried fruit." With that he turned back and pressed some cash on Franz – "for the writing of letters" – and left.

We were never to see Père Etienne again although word of his wanderings filtered back to us occasionally. Cut loose from the anchor of his vow of stability, the world lay before him, but it was clear that he was simply lost before such endless possibilities. At first we were told he was to take a steamer to Madeira; later we heard he was undecided between going back to Europe or heading for Australia. And so, like the wandering Jew, the monk who leaves his community must forever after be at the mercy of his freedom and blow before the winds of chance and circumstance.

~

And we of Maria Dunbrody? Even as the evening breeze began to sigh through the bushes we had yet to conquer, Franz turned to the brothers gathering around him, lifted his hands in the air, and shouted, "You, O God, are the share of my inheritance! With the Psalmist I say, It is You who will restore my inheritance."

Then he explained our predicament, and why he had agreed to the Bishop's abandoning us in this wilderness of thorns. "This is not the end of Maria Dunbrody," he went on, almost choking on the Irish part of the name that always came so awkwardly off his tongue. "No, I am only now convinced that it is really begun!"

And so it was that Maria Dunbrody became truly a Trappist house, entirely self-sustaining. We Trappist Brothers went back to our assault upon the vegetation with the renewed energy of those who knew that from now onwards we would have to feed ourselves. This meant that the building operations had to be cut back drastically, although two new rooms were given priority. One was to house the printing press Franz had stubbornly brought along against the Bishop's wishes, the other the photographic equipment he more or less smuggled into our baggage.

The corrugated-iron roofs were barely mounted on these buildings before the press was set up (the Bishop's crockery set remained forgotten in its crate in a corner of the main shed), and the camera and its accoutrements were unpacked from their straw beds. The energy spent on the latter was wasted, we were to discover, as the chemicals for developing that we brought with us had gone off. But that one layman Franz had insisted on including in our party, a printer by the name of Julius Henry Seibels, soon found his fingers, clumsy after some seventeen months' layoff, busy with typesetting.

This was Franz's solution to our predicament, as he called it – a pamphlet that could be published on a regular basis and circulated to friends and benefactors, "informing them" (so the first issue of what he decided to call *Fliegende Blätter von aus Maria Dunbrody* announced) of "the activities of the Trappists in Africa, their well-being and the progress made in their work of civilisation". Funds would come in more easily, Franz reasoned, if contributors not only knew about us but were rewarded with some sense of how their money was being spent. This, however, was in a future as yet far from decided. It would be some time before Franz's "Flying Pages" reached Europe whereas the end of our sponsor's support came into immediate effect. With the Bishop's small protection removed, we were now completely exposed to our new circumstances.

As if to drive this home, the weather, which had quite rapidly modulated from bitterly cold to pleasantly warm days with refreshingly chilly evenings, soon gave up any pretence at moderation and turned into a continual baking heat that burned us in our as yet unplanted fields and baked us through the corrugated-iron roof of our chapel. Through the good offices of Notre Mère, who continued to support us in whatever way she could, we were able to exchange the single thick and coarse habit, which was all we had for outer clothing since leaving Europe, for the thinner and lighter ones allowed by our Order. She had these made up for us, but they too became soaked with sweat as we prayed indoors. Within moments of stepping back outside they became tinder-dry, especially if the wind came up, which it often did with frightening force.

"One needs to have plenty of beans in one's stomach not to be lifted up and blown yards away by those blasts," joked Franz in his *Fliegende Blätter*. He used the fact that none of us came down with the common cold after getting wet and dry in this way several times a day as proof of how healthy the Trappist lifestyle was.

Franz ordered us to shave our heads completely, almost certainly in direct response to the concern the Bishop once expressed about sunstroke after seeing us in the fields without hats. "Our heads turn as brown as walnuts as the wind, rain, and sun have their wholesome effect on our pates," he wrote. "Maybe the vegetarian Trappist heads are less likely to be sun-struck than the soft heads of those in the world spoiled by all kinds of artificial lotions."

Wind and sun, perhaps, but at the time the rain was only a rhetorical flourish that had as yet had no chance to test the toughness of our bare skulls. By the end of the year, the drought had settled in earnest and everything around us except, of course, the skeletal thorns – which simply grew more cutting and cruel as the bushes that bore them gave up any pretence at foliage – withered and died. By December it was clear that we would be forced to rely on artificial irrigation and, as our much-vaunted "pulsometer" was still not working, Brother Barnabas, by trade an organ builder, put his joining skills into erecting a windmill of his own design. This was meant to raise water from the rapidly drying White River onto our fields, but the hot and fitful winds that gusted the powdery dirt around us were either too unsteady to drive it or so strong as to threaten to destroy it completely.

We concentrated our efforts on the pump that had defeated Port Elizabeth's finest "engineers" and discovered that it was in its positioning that the fault lay. It had been placed in a way that asked too much of its modest powers. Once we adjusted its height to its abilities, we were able to raise enough water from the river to irrigate a small field. But, at the first sign of our crops bearing fruit, flocks of birds descended and devoured the results of our labours, tempting some Brothers into running about and waving, one or two even into shouting, to drive them off. The Brothers were soon called to order, but it was difficult to concentrate when we were gathered for our religious activities, knowing that as our prayers flew heavenwards so too in greedy beaks did our crops.

Worse were the baboons. A large troop appeared from nowhere and hovered near our pathetically small field, dashing in and tearing up our straggling plants at the slightest opportunity. We watched, day and night, beating drums at all hours to keep them off – an activity that not only interrupted our Masses and meditations but also the little sleep we were allowed. Despite our best efforts, hundreds of baboons continued to disport themselves less than fifty paces from us even while we were working and, in their disturbingly human scratching and cartwheeling, gambolling and barking, courting and cuffing, seemed a mocking echo of the intrigued observers our silent life was supposed to attract.

As we acted out our rituals in the empty theatre of this barren valley, both our work and our prayer came to seem more and more like a performance for which no audience had turned up – although most of us, I am sure, amidst the failures and frustrations that marked each day, were quite relieved not to have to enact an exemplary role, especially when it came to farming.

~

In this fashion we struggled on towards the first anniversary of our arrival at Dunbrody. As we approached this date, the austerity of our religious life began to feel more like simple destitution. We reached the point where Brother Shoemaker announced in Chapter that there was no longer any fat to grease our shoes. Franz had already told him there was no money to buy leather for new shoes and, if we could not take good enough care of those we had, we would soon have to walk barefoot – something even Franz could not compel us to accept on ground covered with thorns up to eight inches long. Indeed, Franz himself confessed that he was appalled at the thought that the next Sunday would be the first on which he would observe the Lord's Day without newly greased shoes.

It is one thing to renounce wealth, another to be trapped in penury, and the small issue of our shoes brought home the reality that the penances of our Order were beginning to make no sense in an existence made up of nothing but penance. Despite this, Franz would not for a moment consider relaxing the requirements of the Rule. If anything, he became ever more severe and strict in its interpretation, to the degree that some of our Brothers secretly conveyed a complaint to Bishop Ricards.

As a result the Bishop sent an emissary to our monastery on a visitation and, although it was decided on the basis of his report that the general feeling was one of support for our Prior, the dissension was considered serious enough for four of the dissatisfied monks to be ordered back to Europe. Their leaving, followed by that of two novices (who announced they could make a better living as tradesmen in the colony), was another serious blow to the already low morale at Maria Dunbrody.

Franz responded by writing to Mariastern – of which, you must remember, he was still the legitimate Superior – asking for more monks to be sent to his new foundation. This resulted in the Sub-Prior at Mariastern, Fr Bonaventura, protesting to Rome that "his" monastery was being weakened by Franz's demands. His protest reached the Congregation for Propaganda at almost the same time as a complaint from Bishop Ricards. He reported that Franz was neglecting the cultivation of the soil at Dunbrody while indulging in the raising of buildings, and was bringing more monks to the foundation than agreed to in the original contract.

~

For Franz it must have felt as if the old antagonisms of Mariawald were gathering about him again. But the person upon whom all of this was to have the most terrifying immediate effect was – forgive me – myself.

The greatest blessing of living in a Trappist community was, for me, the organisation of every minute of our lives into the exacting detail of our daily timetable. I loved the Regulations, and the prescriptions of each of its one thousand eight hundred and two paragraphs that kept at bay all choice except the choice to love God. I depended on the certainty that the Rule refined all other cares out of my life, and that any decisions concerning the community were entirely in the hands of my Superior. *The first degree of humility is obedience without delay* states the Rule, and no words in the Rule were sweeter to me than those that begin the section on obedience: *This is the virtue of those who hold nothing dearer to them than Christ; who, because of the holy service they have professed, and the fear of hell, and the glory of life everlasting, as soon as anything has been ordered by the Superior, receive it as a Divine command and cannot suffer any delay in executing it.*

I chose to live in a monastery precisely because I wanted to walk entirely, as the Rule says, by another's judgement and command. I would have been alarmed even at the general notion that I was Franz's right-hand man if Franz's authority was not so complete that the responsibility it entailed was erased from all except himself. When, then, barely a month after the muted celebrations that marked the end of our first year in Africa, Franz announced abruptly in one of our assemblies that he was going to attend the General Chapter of the Trappists in France in order to "clear his name of calumny" and that I, as Sub-Prior, was to be acting Superior in his absence, I was shaken to the core.

The obedience I delighted in meant I could not refuse the authority thrust upon me, although at its announcement my entire body, despite the stultifying heat of the day, broke into a cold sweat. In shivering compliance I accepted that from which I could not even pray for release. All I could think of were the words of Thomas à Kempis: "Love to be unknown and to be esteemed as nothing."

When we were alone, Franz produced a series of letters giving me his authority on certain issues. While packing he fired off commands as to how I should handle the daily routine. This was unnecessary as there was nothing in the Regulations or the Rule with which I was unfamiliar, or the way in which Franz interpreted these in his running of the monastery. Embodying his natural authority in my timid and retiring manner seemed increasingly impossible with every order he gave regarding the orders I would have to give. I must have cut a lonely figure, gazing forlornly after his cart disappearing into the far perspective our location afforded us.

I turned back to find the entire community of Maria Dunbrody, gathered for Franz's leave-taking, staring at me. No words of St Benedict ever struck me with more force than those I recalled then, directed to the Superior of a monastery: *Let him understand also what a difficult and arduous task he has undertaken: ruling souls and adapting himself to a variety of characters*. Nothing was clearer to me than my own uncertainty before that task, reflected as it was in the eyes of the variety of characters before me that day.

Fortunately the signal for Divine Office was given at that moment and the group broke up to *hasten to the Oratory with all speed*, as the Rule requires. Once inside that humble structure of tin and brick, the glory of our ancient rituals and practices took over and I was lost again behind tightly closed eyes in their resonance. This was only for the duration of our prayers, however. As we stepped back outside, I felt the full force of the responsibility for all these souls lost in this dry, deserted valley.

~

As it turned out, the few decisions I made were forced upon us by necessity. St Benedict tells us in his Rule that in any community thorns of contention are likely to spring up, but the actual thorns that hemmed us in had at least the advantage of keeping us focused on the common issue of survival. My brethren honoured me with the respect due to my rank, and I aimed at being clear and exact in my responses to the steady succession of inexorable events that overtook us.

The gravity of our story shifted in any case with Franz to Europe; whatever significance our isolated battle with the elements possessed did not reside in our day to day scratching at the surface of this forsaken corner of the earth. The enormity of both our effort and our despair may easily be shrunk to a paragraph or two. There is not much to add to the simple fact that our Turkey corn, watered regularly at ever-greater effort, remained but stalks, or that when we did succeed in keeping the birds and baboons at bay from our cabbages, insects invaded and spoiled them. Weeks were spent damming the White River as its stream shrunk beneath the level at which either the pulsometer or the wind pump could operate, but by the time the wall was in place its small flow had ceased altogether. This put our drinking water at risk and we were reduced to tracking down small stagnant pools in the gleaming white sand of the empty riverbed.

One blessing remained to us: Mother Marie-Gertrude. Once Franz left, Bishop Ricards took to visiting Dunbrody again, albeit irregularly and in a rather shamefaced and apologetic manner. This he attempted to hide behind a more than usual degree of bluster. Sometimes he would bring guests with him, to whom we were hard put to show the kind of hospitality traditionally extended by Trappists. If Notre Mère was included in the party, we were always assured of a serene understanding of our position and a deep sympathy that was usually expressed in some sort of timely and useful donation.

She was particularly friendly to me, on each occasion finding me after I retired from the ceremonial welcome I was required to perform. I did not mind the interruption – she was always sensitive to our routine of work and prayer – or the way she would draw me out about my thoughts and feelings. As Superior, I needed no dispensation to speak and, given her fluency in German (Bishop Ricards could never complain about misunderstandings when she was there), I suppose I have never spoken as much as I did in those private moments with Notre Mère, certainly not on the subjects she broached. But if I did speak more than usual on these occasions, it was only because she was in no way afraid of stillness, and respected my reserve. The sheer comfort of her presence as we surveyed, often in complete silence, the shimmering heat of the valley or some shrivelled growth on which we had poured such loving attention, remains with me now as one of the few blessings of Maria Dunbrody.

Once – it must have been the first time she entered our receptoria, in her charity accepting our small pretensions to architectural grandeur that so angered the Bishop – I saw that she was immediately taken with a lithograph Franz had pinned to the wall. It was a portrayal of St Boniface bidding adieu to his monks as he was about to leave on his famous foreign mission. When we were alone I asked her why this attracted her attention.

"Oh, that same picture hangs in the community room of the convent in France where I was a postulant," she replied. "I've gazed at it for hours, thinking that, of all the trials St Boniface suffered on his travels, that moment of leaving his community and his country must have been the worst. It tells me more about the reality of religious life than the grand pictures of St Boniface cutting down the sacred Oak of Thor on Mount Gudenberg or clutching a bloodstained book to his chest as he is hacked to death by pagans."

I thought the picture was a poor choice for our reception room. Regardless of the veneration due to St Boniface, it seemed to me wrong to introduce ourselves to visitors under the emblem of one of the Church's most famous missionaries, particularly here in the mission fields where we, as a contemplative community, were such an anomaly. Again and again in those days at Maria Dunbrody I would repeat to myself the words from Constitution number Thirty One: Fidelity to the monastic way of life is closely related to zeal for the Kingdom of God and for the salvation of the whole human race. Monks bear this apostolic concern in their hearts. It is the contemplative life itself that is their way of participating in the mission of Christ and his Church …

I was touched by Notre Mère's understanding of the depths of the bonds of community and the value of stability even in the life of one famed for his wanderings and proselytising. I had no hesitation in reaching up for the lithograph and presenting it to her. She received it with quiet gratitude, without pretence of polite refusal. As we stepped back outside into the dusty heat, she breathed into the baking air the words of the Psalmist: "In a desert land, and where there is no way and no water: so in sanctuary I come before Thee to see Thy way and Thy glory."

I had never heard the vision of Maria Dunbrody put so perfectly, and for a moment I was able to look out over that sea of thorns like a sailor who is sure of the ship that carries him.

8

Port Elizabeth, 1st April 1879

My Lord

I feel not well and at times very much depressed, which often makes me quite unfit for business. I am thinking of taking a run home shortly; it is my intention to take the children home with me and stay six to eight months. I must have entire rest and not be engaged in business, to recover my strength; I have been falling off of late and cannot get my night's rest; the least noise disturbs me and keeps me awake for hours, sudden fears overcome me and I am shaking all over, without any cause; such is the case and I cannot explain it in any other way, but that I am overcome with cares and anxieties for my family and business. I hope to God, it may soon change for the better, as it is really knotting me up altogether …

Yours most sincerely
M A Fraundorfer

If Dunbrody was born of the letters exchanged by Notre Mère and the Bishop, the end not just of Maria Dunbrody but of all Franz's ambitions was to emerge from the letters that passed between the Bishop and Herr Fraundorfer, the second most constant of his correspondents. Fr Adalbert is in the process of collecting and organising these (sharing them with me in the meanwhile), but thus far Herr Fraundorfer has never appeared in any of our official histories. Who would admit that our holy work could be jeopardised by a mere layperson, an upstanding Catholic layperson at that, living thousands of miles away at the time of our defeat?

You will remember Herr Max Anton Fraundorfer from his presence at the first negotiations between Franz and Bishop Ricards. This solid German had worked his way up to becoming one of the most prominent businessmen in Port Elizabeth, a good friend, indeed one of the best, of the garrulous Irish priest who was busy making his way up the ecclesiastical ladder at the same time. Despite their intimacy, Herr Fraundorfer's respect for the Church would never allow him to relax into informality; in all their contact and correspondence, he remained Herr Fraundorfer to Ricards and addressed Ricards by the appropriate term for his rank. When Ricards was promoted to Bishop of the Eastern Vicariate, nothing but "My Lord" would do, even in the most personal of exchanges.

And much of a personal nature was to pass between them. Although his business ventures had prospered, Herr Fraundorfer's private life suffered a severe blow with the death of the wife who had given him four fine young children, all girls. This occurred not long before the Bishop was about to embark on his extended trip to Europe in search of Trappists to give body to his rather idiosyncratic missionary vision. Herr Fraundorfer's presence during the negotiations between Franz and the Bishop was a direct result of the distressed state he was in at the time. Just after the Bishop set off on his voyage, he received the letter telling him that Herr Fraundorfer, too, was on his way to Europe. We must travel back two years to the time of the writing of that fateful letter, the first in Fr Adalbert's collection, if we wish to have some idea of the wreck that befell us just as I was beginning to feel some small sense of being in command of Maria Dunbrody.

Herr Fraundorfer and the Bishop met up in Paris, and made their way to Sept Fons together where the fatal deal was struck – Herr Fraundorfer apparently the invisible medium for the exchanges both there and in

Augsburg. By the time of the later meeting, as we know, his translation was already beginning to colour the way in which the relationship between Franz and the Bishop was developing. What we did not know was that the antipathy he displayed towards Franz went beyond his sharp sense of the Prior being crude and of a lower class.

Granted it was he who had to deal with the ever-increasing number of monks Franz wanted to add to the party; the travel arrangements which kept altering as a result of this, the weather, and Franz's rapid changes of mind; the decisions as to which items to buy in Germany, and which in England or South Africa; and even the extra underwear the monks would need if they travelled, as Franz felt they should, in just one habit while the cloth for the extra habit was sent on ahead as baggage. This in itself would have been enough to generate a high degree of irritation.

The proliferation of correspondence over these and many, many more details grew so large and sometimes so heated that Franz at times in a fury gave up writing to Herr Fraundorfer on certain issues and told me to take over the correspondence. Still, there was something more at stake in the aversion Herr Fraundorfer was unable to contain by the time we left London for the Cape, an aversion quite obvious in the letter he wrote to the Bishop after he finally saw us on board ship. I leave you to make what you will of his reference to one Fr Joseph Cupertino, but here, written in Freiburg where Herr Fraundorfer had set up his new home, is a plain example of his feelings regarding Franz and many of our party:

Freiburg i/Baden, 26th October 1880

My Lord

I am afraid the Prior strained a point to swell the number of his company and was not over particular in the choice of his companions.

I am glad you are pleased with the Trappist priests: Fr Joseph Cupertino especially is a man I took a great fancy to before I ever met him. He is so clear and exact in his letters, straightforward in his dealings, a man on whom you can depend in need. May God give this community grace to fulfil their duties as Catholics and monks faithfully, and all will be right!

By all means do not allow the Prior to send forth his scribbling without your sanction; his language at times is not select and may do no good here nor at the Cape. Keep him strictly to his mission work and check his trips to Port Elizabeth as well. There is much good in him, but his greatest fault is that he believes more than actually is the case, and often borders on a line which is dangerous: I mean he does things which cannot be reconciled with our religion and duties as Christians.

You may depend upon it that I will always take a lively interest in everything concerning your mission and the various establishments. I am now most anxious to hear of their arrival at Port Elizabeth and Dunbrody ...

And hear of us he did, and not only through the Bishop. He had received no more than a couple of letters from Ricards, one saying we had arrived, the next telling him of our absconding novices (which confirmed everything he thought of Franz's choice of men), when up popped an article by Franz describing our journey to the Cape which was repeated in the major Catholic newspapers.

"Prior Franz seems very fond of writing," Herr Fraundorfer wrote to Bishop Ricards, adding in a note tinged with alarm, "he speaks of his printing press having arrived and soon publishing a small paper. I hope he will be guided by you: especially I would recommend him to be more select in his expressions."

At the very moment he was posting off this warning, Ricards was busy noting in his diary the delivery to Dunbrody (along with "two bags mealies, one bag rice, one bag and half beans, cask of split peas, one 50 lb bag flour, one bag of dates") of two reams of printing paper. And within a few weeks the Bishop was noting in his Chronicon, "I read a translation of the 'Fliegende Blätter' printed at Dunbrody: take no notice of exaggerated descriptions of poverty, etc. Tell the Prior that I mean to write shortly to the Vicar General on the present state at Dunbrody."

This letter was indeed written, and was amongst the reasons for Franz's leaving for Europe. Before sailing, however, Franz would find something even more deserving of his immediate attention, in person, in Europe. With a day or so to spare in Port Elizabeth, he took the opportunity to look into the precise nature of our financial affairs as recorded in the town's records. Here he understood for the first time not only how dire these were but the source of much of Herr Fraundorfer's hostility to the whole Trappist endeavour. The Bishop had paid only £1 000 against the £5 000 purchase price of Dunbrody, Franz was horrified to discover. He was not, therefore, the real owner of the property; it was to Herr Fraundorfer that the mortgage actually belonged.

As if this were not enough, Bishop Ricards also chose the moment of Franz's leaving for Europe to bring up the matter of the £2 000 paid to Mariastern to release Franz from his debts there. This, too, it turned out was raised as a loan from Herr Fraundorfer and, the Bishop now declared, should be repaid by the Trappists.

Mysteries were not something Franz had much time for, and he was never happier than when cutting through them to the material explanation he was always certain lay behind them. Herr Fraundorfer could not have been pleased when, just two days after Christmas, he and his whole family were disturbed at a most uncivil hour in the morning by a determined battering at the door of their home in Freiburg. One does not have to be overly creative to picture their servant, on opening the door, being almost knocked down by the extremely vigorous monk demanding to see Herr Fraundorfer. The servant was no doubt surprised to see anyone coming off the streets in religious dress, as this was still the unhappy time of the Kulturkampf (which will always be a disgrace to the German nation), let alone someone confident enough to burst in and scatter fresh snow from his white habit all over the entrance hall.

When Herr Fraundorfer joined Franz in the study, he "hardly had the opportunity to say a word", as he reported in his next letter to Bishop Ricards. Franz, he said, "was talking away like a steam engine", informing him not only that he intended to expand his new community to at least two hundred monks but that he had come directly from the General Chapter of the Trappists in Paris, where it was confirmed that the £2 000 paid to Mariastern to free Franz for the Dunbrody enterprise "was solely a present and not a price to be repaid". If the Bishop could not keep his promise to support the building operations at the new foundation, then Franz was given permission "to have recourse to the charity of the public". He would therefore be in Germany for some time, collecting funds and recruiting postulants for his foundation.

After this defiant declaration he spun around and left. Herr Fraundorfer must have felt as if a whirlwind had swept through his house as the swirl of Franz's habit set the papers on his desk fluttering and the door to the street closed with a slam. I can imagine him now, settling his papers with one hand and picking up his pen to write to the Bishop with the other.

~

Franz made his way from Freiburg to the provincial town of Linnich in Aachen. There he agreed to meet with a certain Dr Oidmann, who had come across some of Franz's publications and had written to him asking him to visit if ever this was convenient. It was Franz's passing comments on the Trappist way of life – in particular, his declarations on the value of a vegetarian diet – that had caught the doctor's eye.

Although his particular preoccupation was to promote the more moderate consumption of salt, Dr Oidmann had for some time been recommending the abolition of flesh from the food intake of his patients. At the smallest opportunity he would expound at length on this topic, and he was becoming well known for the public lectures in which he claimed salted foods were the source of drunkenness and the cause of moral depravity. The two men took to each other immediately, finding that their views on diet complemented each other perfectly as part of a programme of procuring health by natural means. They joined forces on their lecture tours, mixing the cause of Dunbrody with the promotion of a general philosophy of living more in accordance with nature. So at one with each other did they become that, when Franz's punishing fund-raising schedule made it impossible for him to keep an engagement, the good doctor was able to fill in for him.

Everywhere Franz went now there was a cry for overseas colonies as Germans woke up to the fact that other nations had already divided up pretty much the whole world between them. At first many in Franz's audiences took an aggressive interest in the tiny corner of the distant land he had come to speak about. But as soon as they sensed the lack of opportunity that was obvious behind even his most enthusiastic accounts of the area in which Dunbrody was situated, they lost all interest beyond, perhaps, giving a small donation to the struggling foundation. This was a region clearly as desolate in terms of commercial interests as it was bereft of the trees and forests and mountains that for them gave nature its value.

Franz was left to fall back on health as his strongest line of appeal, reinforced as this was by his association with Dr Oidmann. I have had occasion enough to hear Franz expounding on the virtues of our diet of bread, beans, fruit and potatoes, but I gather that on this tour he added a new twist to this, one brought on by the location he was trying so hard to promote. "Not by what enters the mouth and then the stomach does our body flourish but by what enters the ... *nose!* The air that we breathe! Man does not live by bread alone, he lives also by air, and down in the south of

Africa the air," he would say, aware that this was the only advantage left to him with which to sell forlorn and isolated Dunbrody, "is excellent."

This was not much with which to win over an audience, and Franz was certainly no Bishop Ricards when it came to selling an idea made of little more than thin air. Still, the illnesses caused by the heavy German winters and those now rampant in the heavily polluted areas of the country gave him quite a lot to work with. Many a colonial became a colonial out of the quest for an atmosphere that suited his or her delicate or even tubercular lungs, and Franz's attitude to health allowed him to make even broader claims for the dry winds of Maria Dunbrody. As evidence he could produce two Brothers who had been cured of asthma and a prize exhibit – myself – now freed of epilepsy.

Franz was careful on this tour not to venture into the other enthusiasm to which Dr Oidmann had introduced him. Well, encouraged him, really, as the doctor's recommendation was scarcely necessary to bring the parish priest of Wörishofen to Franz's attention. The fame of Fr Sebastian Kneipp, the great "Water Doctor", had already spread throughout Germany. His success in curing ailments attracted wide attention from the time when, whilst still a curate, he began to practise a form of hydrotherapy for the benefit of the poor in his parish. People from neighbouring areas, rich as well as poor, flocked to him for treatment. This was some years before his famous book *My Water Cure* – a copy of which I, even now, always keep about me – was published. It went into many editions and translations.

Fr Kneipp's system consisted of the strict regulation of daily life. His general rules were: early to bed and early to rise, a walk in the dewy grass on bare feet, simple meals, no stimulants, not too much meat, an abundance of cereals and the plentiful use of cold water internally and externally. By the time of Franz's discovery of this hero of the *Naturarzt* community, many of the recommendations of cold water popularly attributed to him were exaggerations. Since Franz, given his general distaste for moderation, would not become one of the more moderate followers of Kneipp, it is perhaps fortunate that in the years to come he turned to someone as tentative as me for help in developing water cures à la Kneipp.

Our circumstances in 1881, in any event, severely militated against anything that required the extensive use of water. Even as he embraced the theories of Kneipp whilst he was in Germany, all the healing power of water made Franz think of was the drought that was Dunbrody. Think, but not say;

of some things it is better to remain silent. And if Franz was not always good at working out precisely when this was the case, on this occasion he did realise that, whilst extolling the virtues of Maria Dunbrody's warm and dry air and proclaiming the health of his community, he should say nothing of that place's aridity and dust.

Franz's lectures would end with an appeal not only for funds but for postulants. He was more successful with the latter than the former, for although a significant amount of funding came in, interest in going to South Africa amounted at some meetings to a minor flood. Some would say that Franz's examination of the impulses that lay behind this interest was not nearly rigorous enough, but Franz was enormously encouraged by the large number of candidates who, in his opinion, were worthy of his destitute new house in the wilderness.

~

Freiburg i/Baden, 18th March 1881

My Lord

The Prior is an excellent beggar with a certain class of people. Where you and I and many others would not get a penny, he gets £10 to £15 with ease. You may really say, there is no accounting for taste. There is no doubt too that his style of writing suits a certain class of his countrymen better than does mine.

But as long as it is a means of obtaining assistance for Dunbrody let him have his way. I look more cheerfully now on the future of this undertaking, if only because the Prior will do his utmost to say: I managed without the aid of the Bishop. In fact, he knows his reputation is at stake.

It appears that Franz's progress on his lecturing tour of Germany was followed with obsessive interest by Herr Fraundorfer who, ever since his return to Germany, had seen himself as the official representative of and chief fund-raiser for Dunbrody. This perception was certainly supported by Bishop Ricards and generally accepted by the Church authorities. Herr Fraundorfer's painstaking efforts towards fund-raising had, on the whole, followed the more conservative routes of tapping money for the missions: a few written appeals in the local church magazines, the odd fund-raising event arranged by the ladies of a particular community, perhaps the occasional address to some small gathering. As he reported to the Bishop, Franz's methods quickly eclipsed such efforts.

The indulgent attitude Herr Fraundorfer was prepared to adopt in the first few months of Franz's tour soon gave way to irritation. This grew worse once he was instructed to send all funds he collected for Dunbrody directly to Franz who, as Superior, was responsible for everything to do with the foundation, including its finances. By May, Herr Fraundorfer was writing to Ricards:

> Today I am remitting to Prior Franz through the Standard Bank £200 collected from different parts of Germany. Up to the present I have no acknowledgement of the £197 I sent a month ago, and I told him that unless I do receive this, I would hold back any further remittances.
>
> I find that the Prior is a man of everlasting trouble. He wants to meddle in everything. His giving a presentation at Würzburg without first asking the Bishop's permission shows very bad taste indeed. No priest, particularly a monk, should forget himself so far. I sent a letter to Canon Soratroy; he says he will give the Bishop of Augsburg an outline of it and felt very much annoyed at the liberty the Prior wants to assume. I am of the opinion that whatever you may do and put up with, the Prior will not come to reason unless he gets a severe castigation from his Superiors. I never met with a monk who has such queer ways about him.

And so the formal complaints to the Church authorities picked up pace again. Franz survived the first round of criticism made to the General Chapter by Bishop Ricards and his own Sub-Prior at Mariastern. The instigator of this next round may have been only a lay person, but Herr Fraundorfer was slowly gaining a very sophisticated sense of church politics, and steadily cultivating his relationships with those who had real influence and power. He also missed no chance of finding out more about what Franz was getting up to, and reporting it to Ricards.

Freiburg i/Baden, 28th June 1881

My Lord

On Corpus Christi I met Brother Zacharias in the Cathedral; as he did not recognise me, I spoke to him and made an appointment with him for the afternoon. From him I learned valuable information of the collection he is making for Dunbrody.

I thought it just as well to get all the information I could from him (although he is a man of few words, and one has to draw him out carefully); it may be useful to you.

I told him that I had heard a rumour here that Prior Franz was to return to Mariastern and be made Abbot there. He said this was not likely. He explained to me that the Sub-Prior whom Prior Franz appointed in his absence, Superior Bonaventura, is a Frenchman, and since the departure of the Prior he has been most favourable to his own nationality. Brother Zacharias seemed very sensitive on this point, so I did not touch on it again.

It is strange now, after all the years that have passed, to read a report of my old friend, he who opened the gate to Franz that fateful day at Mariawald, he who supported Franz in his break with the house where they both joined the Trappist Order, he who suggested that they seek out a new foundation where they could live by the Rule in harmony ...

And he who now, unwittingly, gave Herr Fraundorfer and Bishop Ricards the crucial information that could enable them to bring their unruly protégé under their control. The knowledge that Franz's power base at Mariastern was shaky was to prove most useful to them. Franz's authority at Dunbrody depended after all on the fact that he was still technically the Superior of Mariastern. To undercut him there was to contain what he could do at Dunbrody.

~

Not long after Herr Fraundorfer ran into Brother Zacharias, Franz wrote to Herr Fraundorfer offering to pay part of the mortgage (he mentioned a figure of £1 500) in annual instalments if Bishop Ricards would transfer Dunbrody to him. Herr Fraundorfer's suggestion to Bishop Ricards in response to this was that the Bishop and the Prior share the debt between them, as this would allow the Bishop to maintain some financial control over Franz. The problem with this suggestion was that his own fund-raising was by now going very poorly indeed, what with Franz himself sweeping the country and snaffling up like a bloodhound every penny that was likely to go the way of Dunbrody. I must admit to a moment of mild amusement when I read in one of his letters to the Bishop the true measure of his desperation: "My tickets all have failed, not a single number of thirteen tickets was lucky, but I have always a chance in the future and if successful I will always remember your Mission …" How typical that even our dour Herr Fraundorfer would play the Devil's own number in an attempt to win luck over to the Lord's work. But it was strangely comforting that the Imperial and Royal Lottery was still inspiring wildly superstitious stratagems, even if this was in the hope of buying us out of our place of sanctuary.

I must also admit that this entirely unexpected and most passing of references to my former place of employment caught me off guard. Even in my old age I was forced to return to the Regulations and read again the paragraph that states: "We never tell any story about the sin of impurity, nor even speak of it. We say nothing which might bring it to mind, either directly or indirectly. We should have so great a horror of it, that we ought not even to know that such a sin exists. Or if it is known" – alas, dear, dear M – "we should still lose all memory of it …"

How thankful I was then that I had chosen an Order famous for its penance.

~

If Herr Fraundorfer's fund-raising was going poorly, his campaign against Franz gained strength by the week. In this his greatest ally (not unexpectedly) was Franz himself, who managed to alienate the Superiors of whatever region he was in at the time with almost unerring accuracy. In early 1882, Herr Fraundorfer could report as follows:

We travelled from Augsburg to Ratisbon, Amberg, Metten, Deggendorf, Prague to Vienna, but wherever we came, archbishops, bishops, priests, and even laymen inquired about Prior Franz and some very hard things were said about him; even the Nuncio here, Archbishop Vanutelli, put a question to me.

I will not repeat any of the reports circulated about Dunbrody, promises made and not kept, etc. etc. I have always put the matters fairly before the parties high and low, protected your name and honour as bishop, and I believe with some success. The Bishop of Ratisbon said that Prior Franz must be very careful in his diocese, in fact, he has not shown up there for some time. Abbot Maurus OSB at Prague said as much, that Prior Franz was a man you could never depend upon and his doings were very queer. In

Augsburg, at one of his addresses a Canon left the hall; he could not stand the language made use of by the Prior.

All the persons we have met are getting tired of the Prior's travelling lectures and his influence in Germany, Bohemia and Austria is declining.

I doubt now that this man can be brought to reason. Surely he owes obedience to his Superiors and especially the Holy See! The Abbot of Meten OSB said: Mr Fraundorfer, do you know what is the great fault of Prior Franz? I replied, No. He said: With all his good qualities he has no humility: there is always a selfishness about him. This is an old and experienced prelate.

You can depend on my doing all I can to assist you.

The collecting trip is fairly going on, but we have at times great difficulties to get to the proper channels. I will give you a full description when I return ...

It did not take Franz long to decide that Herr Fraundorfer was the cause behind his declining fortunes. From encounters such as at Ratisbon, where Franz had once been well received and now no longer was, he had discovered that Herr Fraundorfer had been accusing him of not keeping his contract with Bishop Ricards and obtaining money under false pretences. When Franz wrote to Herr Fraundorfer in the strongest terms, declaring this "a mean calumny" and Herr Fraundorfer "a malicious slanderer", Herr Fraundorfer protested again and again that he had said nothing overtly against Franz. He blustered on about legal action against the Prior and insisted that, although he would prefer to remain above an affair it was beneath his dignity to engage in, Franz would if he went to the newspapers "get an answer there, short and sweet, with the concluding remark that any other publications of his will be treated with the contempt they deserve".

Herr Fraundorfer was soon complaining to the Bishop that:

Prior Franz has again most rudely attacked me, and continues to make all opposition and trouble he possibly can. I am now so far advanced that it is my firm belief that as long as such a man without any conscience, without humility, without a true missionary spirit is at the head of affairs at Dunbrody, there can be no blessing from the Almighty. If it is the call of the Trappists that the Superior travels about over a year through Germany to circulate false reports and to run down the Mission at the Cape, the sooner he exchanges his habit for something else the better.

~

Things in Europe were clearly coming to a head and, whether he knew it or not, Franz's command of the situation was slipping. Perhaps, as usual, he had taken on too much, and his association with Dr Oidmann was not helping. Excited by the early success of the "International Mission of Health Vigilance", which Franz had helped him set up, Dr Oidmann was eager to convert his next preoccupation into an organisation of a similar kind. The able physician was in touch with a growing body of people increasingly united in their opposition to the vaccination of young children against disease. He soon convinced Franz of the rightness of this cause, and so yet another theme was added to the addresses Franz gave on his collecting tour. As a founding member of the local branch of the "International Union of Anti-Vaccinationists", Franz could now be heard thundering forth against "the fatal, heathenish superstition concerning a malady which must be expelled from the body by poison".

No matter how much he directed his opinions regarding vaccination against the State, this particular enthusiasm further damaged Franz's standing with the Catholic authorities (who did not come out against vaccination). Meanwhile, his decisions regarding the community of Mariastern, although technically correct, had not come across well. While in Europe, Franz did not even visit what was, after all, still his foundation, and his fallout with the very Sub-Prior he had appointed was by now well known. One of the complaints Franz put before the General Chapter of Trappists he had travelled to Europe to attend was that Fr Bonaventura would not sanction his request for a further six Brothers and a priest to be sent from Mariastern to Dunbrody. As this was clearly a case of simple disobedience (Franz's "request" in this case having all the effect of an order), the Chapter General gave its support to Franz – upon which he promptly demanded ten monks in the place of the six he had originally requested.

The ten were packed off to Dunbrody, but after they left it became clear that the reason for the Sub-Prior's reluctance in obeying Franz – Fr Bonaventura argued that Franz was seriously weakening the Bosnian foundation to prop up his new and ailing South African house – had real merit. All the more so, it must be added, when Franz's success in attracting postulants became known and reports of other large parties already on the way to Dunbrody were received. In this light Franz's victory seemed thin and his actions mean and petty.

~

I am afraid that I was not doing much to support things at my end, other than maintaining our modest achievements. I attempted to produce a third issue of *Fliegende Blätter aus Maria-Dunbrody*, but this was not a great success. I lacked entirely Franz's talent for lively description and managed only a heavy-handed appeal for financial support within the stark overtones of a sermon. Even as I laboured over the thing, it simply lay before me refusing to come to life, much like the sermons required of me as Sub-Prior. The latter at least my Brothers forgave, appreciating even, I think, the restfulness of my delivery after Franz's energetic poundings. But my attempt at writing was not worth much even as an historical document. All it recorded of significance was the arrival of some of the postulants who were, entirely unbeknownst to me (or everyone other than a few at the centre of this tale), the cause of Franz's next near-expulsion from the Order.

It is hard for me even now to believe that the addition of twelve bedraggled boys, their extraordinary variety of shapes and sizes linked only by the almost luminescent whiteness of those body parts protruding from their rumpled brown habits, could so nearly have proved the final hurdle for a foundation even as weak as ours. From the thin, gangly and startled to the profusely sweating, fat and stunned, all twelve blinked at our huddle of a house exposed before more sky than they had ever seen, in a disbelief not yet entirely cured out of those of us who had laboured here for nearly two years.

However, this was nothing compared to Bishop Ricards' fury at their turning up. Aware that we were still barely able to keep ourselves from starvation, he unceremoniously deposited the new arrivals along with two large bags of haricot beans. He left immediately, inspired by every lurch of the carriage and spray of dirt to ever further heights of displeasure in the letter of complaint he was composing in his head in the miles between Dunbrody and Port Elizabeth.

For my part I was disappointed that he had not brought the vine cuttings I had requested. In all honesty I must report that my meetings with the Bishop were generally quiet and pleasant; he had seemed rather taken with the modest proposals I dared submit in Franz's absence, the establishing of a small vineyard being a case in point. But when the postulants shared with me the news that another eight were following hard upon them, with yet more soon to come, I could understand how the detail of a few vines might have slipped his mind.

~

Franz was, of all things, sitting for his portrait when the blow fell. The time had finally become ripe for the Bishop's complaints to be registered in their full force and with the right authorities. Herr Fraundorfer's strategic nurturing of avenues of influence was beginning to pay off and, with Franz's base within the Trappist Chapter General severely eroded by his behaviour concerning Mariastern, it seemed that Herr Fraundorfer's prediction that "this unscrupulous man will soon be rendered harmless" was about to be fulfilled. And so it was in June 1882 that Franz, who had retreated to his favourite haunt of Linnich for a period of quiet consultation with Dr Oidmann, first came to realise the degree to which he had been outmanoeuvred by Herr Fraundorfer.

Dr Oidmann, it turns out, had a more than amateurish interest in the arts; apart from his medical practice, he was also the owner of three large stained-glass factories, one situated in Linnich and the other two in Brussels and Berlin. From these factories church windows were dispatched to all parts of the world, including missions in China and the Philippines. Dr Oidmann discussed with Franz the possibility not only of sending windows to Dunbrody but also – in an extra burst of enthusiasm typical of the two men – of setting up a glass-manufacturing industry there. It was while he was making a sketch in his studio for one of the windows intended for Dunbrody that it occurred to Dr Oidmann that this was a good time to execute a portrait of Franz. Franz protested, but the doctor was insistent. He was in any case, he said, making an album of each of his colleagues in his latest venture, the International Pioneer Society for the Protection of Persecuted Minorities, of which Franz was – of course – a founding member.

Even though their plans concerning the most beautiful of the Catholic arts were to come crashing down at the very time the portrait was being painted, it is this likeness of Franz that has come to be the one by which he is known. The reason for this is not so much its compelling accuracy (others were to capture the intensity of those eyes but none were to show them set in lids red-rimmed with the effort such intensity required) as that Franz was so taken with it that, when in later years photographic portraits were made of him, he insisted on the identical pose and expression.

It was on one of the first days of summer, when Franz was just becoming comfortable with Dr Oidmann's efforts at portraying him, that a large and imposing envelope was delivered to the doctor's door, addressed to

Fr Francis Pfanner. Opening it, Franz found in his hands a decree from the Congregation of Propaganda in Rome removing him from his position as Prior of Dunbrody. A brief covering letter announced that the Vicar General of the Congregation of Rancé was to send a French Prior out in his place.

There was no room now for the kind of manoeuvring Franz had entered into when he had received the letter from the Abbot of Ölenberg advising him to return to the world. Franz was stunned, and it was just as well the lineaments of his face were firmly in place on the canvas, for if ever a face fell his must have now. Even so, to this day that framed face, reproduced on the wall of many a mission, stares into the future in the full awareness of the suffering that awaited, as if the very glow in which it is highlighted is suffused with threat. It does so with no hint of resignation; if there is a tinge of sadness, it lies well behind the stubborn glare reinforced by every fold and line worn into it. Even the straggly beard, neater here than in any of the photographs to come (if already beginning to lose the blaze of its younger redness), cannot hide the set of that jaw, clenched in confrontation with everything that would resist it.

Franz would need every inch of this determination. For it was not just Propaganda that had begun to doubt him. Of late he had received a number of queries as to why he was staying so long in Europe, in all likelihood from donors supporting his South African foundation. He had been forced to conclude Issue No. 4 of *Fliegende Blätter* (which he had wisely taken back into his own hands and wrote himself from Europe) with an "Answers to correspondents" section. In this he had written the following: "To Mr B V in M: Why do I stay so long in Europe? I can only answer by word of mouth."

Actually, he had not been neglecting his South African concerns. He had continued his negotiations with Bishop Ricards even if he had broken all contact with Herr Fraundorfer, and had, in fact, asked the Bishop for permission to obtain another site for his foundation if the Bishop would not let him purchase Dunbrody for himself. To this the Bishop replied that he would not countenance the Trappists buying any site in his Vicariate.

~

The effect of all this was to devolve directly on me. My duty, as I understood it when I was made Sub-Prior, was to maintain as steadily as possible the work we had undertaken at Dunbrody. We had begun with the fencing

Franz had planned before his departure and, dry as our land was, it was suitably marked off for some miles. Dead the land may have been too, but this did not stop us progressing in faith and hope with our basic farming operations. We not only cleared many an acre of bush as Franz commanded but took on the really hard work of digging up the roots and stumps that would hamper the ploughing we hoped to begin when the rains for which we prayed so earnestly came.

In our chapel of corrugated iron, on the packed earthen floor of which I spent much of my time alone and prostrate, I had deal desks set up for our great tomes of ritual from which we sang our praises to God day and night. Our simple wooden altar now had a plain stone step before it, and I was happy with the sanctuary this simple building gave us from the endless landscape and endless sky that emptied out formlessly all around us. The borders to our valley, which I now knew as the Zuurberg and Winterhoek mountains, were too low and too far away to give a meaningful shape to the place we inhabited, although their names ("sour mountain" and "winter corner") took on a severe appropriateness, especially in the second of the waterless yet freezing winters we had just come through.

I was walking, book in hand, through the small area set aside for my vines (still not forthcoming from the Bishop) when a telegraph from Franz was given to me. In it I was ordered to send two Brothers to the next region in which there was an established Catholic presence – to Natal, a port further up the coast upon which we had disembarked. It was the first hint I had of a departure from Franz's resolution never to leave this piece of land, to live and remain in this place until death.

With the words of his solemn declaration ringing in my ears I sent off, as ordered, Brothers Barnabas and Paul to explore the possibility of our resettling elsewhere. We were sorely tested by one practicality before they were able to leave, not being sure, despite the efforts of Bishop Ricards, of the response to Catholics outside our immediate area and how they might be received in a province we knew to be predominantly English with a small Catholic presence, French at that.

We decided, therefore, that the Brothers should travel in civilian dress. Franz, I am sure, would have derided our concern, but I was able to put together a rough ensemble for each of the Brothers after searching through the collection of cast-offs and leftovers our tailor (never too sure where our next batch of cloth would come from) had squirrelled away. They left in this rather unbecoming dress on the first of the crude but effective wagons we had made while Franz was away.

Some weeks later they returned with an extraordinary tale with enough good fortune in it to make us willing believers. We were later to learn, somewhat to our cost, the harsh reality behind their story. The two excited Brothers reported that the Bishop of the region was initially hesitant about our inquiries but his objections were overcome by the miraculous intervention of a kind Sister of one of the local Orders. We were now welcome in a land that appeared to them to be a lush, green heaven after Maria Dunbrody.

This was information upon which I understood I must act quickly but cautiously. I did not want to risk running into Bishop Ricards or one of his representatives in Port Elizabeth, so I set off for more distant Grahamstown in order to telegraph the news to Franz. Even my unsubtle mind understood that the Bishop needed us resident on the farm he had purchased, if only to retain the confidence of his creditors. It was for this reason that I had felt obliged to send our Brothers to look for land in another vicariate without the Bishop's knowledge. I knew that the positive response we received from Natal must be communicated to Franz with even greater discretion.

Much as my surreptitious behaviour pained me at the time, it has amused me since to hear of the air of mystery that I, the plainest of men, created with my attempts at secrecy. In the course of his historical investigations, Fr Adalbert asked me to explain the following letter written by Bishop Ricards:

St Augustine's, 9th August 1882

My Dear Sister Gertrude,

It is dreadfully close today here in Port Elizabeth. Last night we had thunder and lightning and I was in hopes the drought was beginning to break up. It is still very dry at Dunbrody. I sent a lot of things there yesterday. I must make Fr Joseph understand – if this is possible – that he must provide for the number of postulants and Brothers Prior Franz is sending out.

I cannot make out the object of Fr Joseph's time away from Dunbrody. He is a man who never travels, yet it appears that recently he went with the wagon to Bluecliff station and on his return told the community he had been to Grahamstown. This was told to me by Mr Terpend, neighbour to the Trappists. Terpend also tells me that Fr Joseph had the news that Fr O'Brian was in Uitenhage and was to remain there for a week. He expresses wonder at who could have told him this at Bluecliff, and treats it as evidence that Fr Joseph had indeed gone as far as Grahamstown ...

How typical, you may think, that everyone knew of my secret journey, and how odd that the actions of one so ordinary should be scrutinised as if they made up the plot of some thrilling romance. Still, to this very day, none but Franz and myself have ever known the exact nature of the exchange entered into on that excursion.

Franz's reply to my message did not come by telegraph; it came in a well sealed envelope that was delivered to me some weeks later at Dunbrody. At that moment, the entire history of the Trappists in South Africa lay in my hands. I need not tell you how much those hands shook or how much I have wondered since if I should not have just let it fall, let our whole sad enterprise shatter upon the hard, drought-stricken earth of Dunbrody and been done with it all there and then. But I opened Franz's letter and, for once, acted cleanly and clearly in the way he would have wished.

Franz began his letter with the blunt announcement that he had been removed from the office of Prior of Dunbrody. It was with a hollow, faint feeling that I read on, trying to take in the reality that Dunbrody was withdrawn from the power of his jurisdiction. He could give us no orders, he wrote; but he did have some suggestions to make to me as his representative at Dunbrody, and he trusted the future of our community to my response. His "suggestions", typically, took the form of an ultimatum that turned on a single fact his enemies had overlooked. Our Superior – for so I would always think of him, until just before the end – had studied the forces ranged against him with great care and found that he could overturn the entire offensive with one strategic decision on my part.

As his letter explained, Franz was no longer our Superior only as long as we remained at Dunbrody; outside of Dunbrody we remained his subjects, for we belonged by rights to Mariastern and, even if Mariastern had no wish to see him return, he was still technically its Superior. Three options, Franz wrote, were available to us: our community could stay at Dunbrody, in which case "he would have nothing to do with us any longer"; or we could return to Mariastern "where we had vowed stability and whose legitimate

Superior he still was, and to which place he himself would return"; or we could go to Natal, where he would join us and "dare a new foundation together there with us".

Franz's ultimatum arrived on 30th August, the day before Bishop Ricards was due to make one of his regular disapproving inspections. As usual, the Bishop joined us in Chapter, but before he was able to speak I presented myself to him and declared, "Since you have taken the Superior from our community, there can be no question of our staying at Dunbrody."

Short as this was, I had thought long and hard about how I should phrase the statement proclaiming my response to Franz's ultimatum. In retrospect this was, perhaps, not the best way to express it, but the public face later put on our leaving Dunbrody differed so much from the real circumstances that it does not matter much. Unfortunately, my attempt at careful and judicious phrasing so as to avoid alarming my brethren threw them into confusion. I had to quieten a rash of shuffling and whispering after my pronouncement, in the midst of which it became obvious to me that Bishop Ricards knew perfectly well what I was saying. It was possible that he had already been informed of Franz's dismissal.

It had struck me in the middle of my announcement that Bishop Ricards' counterpart in Natal must have been in touch with him before agreeing in principle to our resettling there. In the event, this was borne out by Bishop Ricards having been accompanied on this visit by a Fr Weld of the Jesuits. The Jesuits, I discovered the next day, were interested in taking over Dunbrody.

It was important to let our community know as little as possible about the absence of authority that threatened us. I understood that they did not see in me a figure capable of real command. They had been kind enough to suffer my ineffectual ways as long as I was standing in for Franz, but there was no question of my leading them to a new promised land. Without the presence of Franz behind me I was nothing, barely a shadow, unless I was a shadow he cast.

As far as both history and the general public of the time are concerned, the drought was more than enough reason for us Trappists to leave Dunbrody. Certainly Bishop Ricards wanted no further scandal attached to what was quite clearly by now the failure of his much circulated and celebrated idea of establishing Trappists in the mission fields. He was, within minutes of leaving Chapter, walking around our farm, pointing out to Fr Weld the potential behind its rather sad features. In Chapter he had simply given us leave to do as we saw fit, and he ignored me as I walked past him whilst he was demonstrating the pulsometer to the Jesuit. I could not help feeling a lurch of affection for that stubborn machine that we had coaxed into working order when the best mechanics in Port Elizabeth could not – or a moment of irritation that all our efforts were erased in the Bishop's presentation of its fine operating condition.

By evening, accompanied by Fr Arsenius and Brothers Robert, Henry and Pius, I had given Bishop Ricards formal notice of what I presented as Prior Franz's order to our community to leave Dunbrody. This I felt I could do as, in reaction to Franz's ultimatum, I had decided that (as far as I was concerned) all authority over our community now devolved back to him. *Exi de Terra Tua* was the way I put the command I invented as coming from Franz, to give it something of his own flavour. "Leave your Land!" Never since the Jews left Egypt had a command been so welcome. At last we had the opportunity to shake ourselves free of the dust of Dunbrody – which in truth remained a desert despite our almost superhuman efforts – and find a new and more fertile place in which to take root in Africa.

We did not know, as we set about in the weeks ahead eagerly preparing for our exodus and anxiously awaiting word from our Prior, that back in his study in Port Elizabeth Bishop Ricards was jotting down our future in his diary: "A command received from Prior Franz on the 31st ult. ordering Fr Joseph and all the Brothers to leave Dunbrody. To avoid the miserable scandal of their leaving for Europe, and considering that I am likely to dispose of the farm more advantageously than I had at first thought, and that the Trappists have done a good deal to improve the property, I free Bishop Jolivet from all responsibility for its payment. I never meant the Bishop of Natal to be responsible for the £2 000 I lent Prior Franz; this I will insist must be repaid by the Prior ... Hence I allow the Trappists to leave my Vicariate and consent to their settling in the Vicariate of Natal without asking the Bishop to undertake any pecuniary responsibility ..."

In this entry lay the seeds of the Bishop's final victory over the troublesome Prior he had conjured up. By the time they came to fruition, however, the Bishop's nerves had given way. His biographer dates his first breakdown to the period in which he was most concerned with the Trappists in Dunbrody (something kept completely hidden from us), and suggests that his lectures from this period on lost their sparkle. Whatever satisfaction he received later from gaining the advantage over Franz would rapidly be lost in his failing health. So much, then, for the war of words out of which we were born in Africa, delivered from Dunbrody, and born again in the most appropriately named province of Natal. Out of each birth, a small death: and for me, the far greater question of the final silence which will swallow us entirely – except for the echoes we leave whispering in our wake, taken up by other mouths, surrendered into other ears.

More prosaically, the legal and public face of the Bishop's diary entry reached me in the form of an account. This was to be delivered through me to Fr Franz, and was laid out in stark and simple arithmetic:

Money lent	£2 000
Support of Trappists in Dunbrody	£3 000
Money owed by Trappists	£5 000

Over 50 000 florins! I had no idea how Franz would react to this entirely unexpected claim upon us and no time to ponder its fairness or implications. With virtually not a penny left to us, I arranged (without letting our already desperately demoralised community know anything of this new turn of events) for the most condensed version possible to be telegraphed to Franz: NATAL LAND GRATIS, RICARDS OPPOSED, PAY DUNBRODY. I hoped that from this he would understand that the condition upon which we were to be allowed to leave was to acknowledge what the Bishop saw as our "debt".

~

For myself, all I knew was that for the moment I was the leader of a community that had received into its weak arms another twenty postulants the day before it was due to leave Maria Dunbrody. These bewildered newcomers had barely a few hours' rest before we rose at three in the morning in utter darkness. A darkness far deeper than usual in the early summer of November that glowered into a dull purple of low cloud and spitting rain as we clambered clumsily into our rough carts.

And so the Trappists departed from Dunbrody under the guidance of their Sub-Prior, Father Joseph, "while the lowering sky wept the tears denied us in all the time we were there". Or so I was to express it in my first humble account of the life of Franz Pfanner, poetry creeping in, I suppose, in his absence. Nothing further needed to be said then, nor needs to now, of our stealing away from the Sundays River valley in the pouring rain, or of our leaving Port Elizabeth. No pomp and ceremony this time, just our silence amidst the gulls and the wind. The only thing I noticed out of the corner of my eye as we headed down the quay was the hulk of our traction engine lying forlorn in the rain which drummed upon it as if it would never cease.

<h1 style="text-align:center">9</h1>

The four days it took us to sail from Algoa Bay to Durban gave us our first exposure to the peculiarly English hostility towards Catholics that we were to find common amongst the settlers in Natal. I tried as far as possible to maintain our separation from the world as we journeyed out into it. In order to assist my Brothers in their observances, I engaged a traveller – German, at least, if not Catholic – to transact our business and speak for us. For with the Psalmist I said, "I will guard my ways, that I may not sin with my tongue. I will bridle my mouth, so long as the wicked are in my presence." Our translator soon forced me to continue with the psalm, admitting with David that although "I was dumb and silent, I held my peace to no avail". Wiry and well dressed, like an ermine in its winter coat, he weaselled his way past my earnest protestations and, with evident delight, let me know what the other travellers thought of us. Whenever the exigencies of our situation necessitated my communicating with him, nothing I could do deterred him from departing from the basic issues at hand and filling my ears with the passengers' opinions.

"They say you are afforded special protection from *mal-de-mer*," he whispered to me conspiratorially after a day at sea, a rough day during which our party had, remarkably, been free of seasickness. "But still you do everything possible to make everybody miserable – not speaking a word, gazing steadfastly all day at your boot tops, wearing strange apparel, eating nothing but vegetables. And they are fascinated that despite your strictness you allow your men to drink!"

"Only one glass of beer a day, as a special travelling indulgence," I caught myself answering. And, before I knew it, I had slipped into explaining away another point that the other passengers clearly found odd about us. "We sleep on deck," I said, more in irritation with myself for trying to explain our behaviour than with those who criticised it, "because there is no suitable space below for communal withdrawal." I could have gone on about the heat and our habits and the example Franz set for us on our voyage to South Africa, which would have made far more sense to our detractors than my brief and oblique references to our way of life, but I spoke in the hope that a few blunt statements would end the special attention paid to us.

Of course they did not, and I was reminded forcefully what an error it is to try and explain the mysteries of our vocation. In a matter of hours our layman was back at my side telling me that people on board were of the opinion that the way Trappists could hold their tongues made them the most eligible genus of missionary Natal could have. On the last day of our brief voyage one of the more senior men on board went so far as to try and address me directly – through, that is, the translating powers of the intermediary I was by now thoroughly sorry I had employed – on the topic of "the holy and good la Trappe" of whose beliefs he pretended to have some knowledge.

"It must be regretted," he said, "that his followers today, generally men of iron will and rectitude" – and here we Trappists were indicated with a generous wave of the hand as if there were no insult in this – "should now, so many years since his advent, still be promulgating the old world superstitions." Had la Trappe lived in these enlightened times, I was informed from the elevation of his florid and corpulent worldliness, the honesty of his intellectual perceptions would have led him to cast away these antiquated beliefs.

I gazed out to sea, attempting only an ambivalent smile in response, and thought how fortunate it was for the speaker that he could not attempt to engage Franz in a similar dispute. How often in the years ahead was I to feel my face freeze into that fixed smile that did so much to earn me my reputation of kindliness when in truth it was the surest expression of my discomfort in the world. Still, it was an effective aid to silence and, even as my jaw and lips clenched into what was to become their characteristic form, I was grateful for the way those who engaged me in speech inevitably read whatever suited them into the quiet smile almost lost in my beard.

As for the speaker who prompted that arrangement of my features on this occasion, his opinions were sufficient to remind me of how sad it is that those who have nothing to say are the ones most compelled to say it. Like nervous gunners, they fire burst after burst into the dark, illuminating nothing and hitting nothing, except by accident.

~

It wasn't raining when we anchored off Durban, but it might as well have been. Sea and air merged into a single sultry medium and the closer we came to shore the further it receded into a hot grey haze. You could almost grasp a fistful of the dull breeze and squeeze the moisture from it.

For some time our ship had been sailing alongside a steep bush-clad promontory running along the coast. This suddenly dropped off to reveal a large and perfectly formed bay. Between the curve of the beach that encircled the bay and the landward side of the large outcrop we had just rounded was a narrow opening, on either side of which were piers made of piles of stone that gave definition to a waterway. A pilot boat came alongside us and guided us over a hazardous sand bar and through the waterway into what surely must be one of the best natural ports anywhere in the world. A tranquil sheet of water perhaps six miles in extent was embraced by the promontory on one side and wavy tiers of foliaged hills on the other. The hills were dotted here and there with the distant glint of tin roofs and the shimmer of whitewashed walls.

We disembarked at the public wharf into a ceaseless commotion: the jangling of chains, barrows rumbling over the quay, sirens hooting, locomotives screaming as they pushed and pulled their long-bodied wagons into position, the grinding of winches, the ho-hoying of sailors, and the Natives – streams of Natives – chanting some monotonous refrain as they laboured semi-naked in the broiling sun. I wiped the sweat from my eyes and looked again at the toiling ones, and suddenly, there before me glistening through the added blackness of his coaling, was my poetic Nubian of the mission altar in the Jesuit church in Brünn.

He appeared fleetingly, only to blur back into a partly clad labourer. But he emerged again for a moment elsewhere in the crowd of workers and disappeared again. And for what can only have been seconds he was multiplied over and over, shovelling coal in a truck or moving up a gangway in a slow and single file with a basket on the distended muscles of his powerful neck, his fingers knitted gracefully into its dirty filigree. His voice the low call of the desires of my youth, he came alive around me even as he vanished into the reality of his strangeness.

Bishop Jolivet, Vicar Apostolic of Natal and Ordinary of the Missionary Oblates of the Immaculate Conception, awaited us in the midst of this noise and confusion, attended by some of his priests. Bright, bird-like eyes flickered over us from a neat, sharp face, smooth-shaven as if to emphasise a tight, determined jaw. He gravely accepted the Trappist greeting of touching first one shoulder and then the other, but seemed very aware of the attention our party was attracting. The small crowd of settlers on the dock were particularly taken with the peculiarity of our dress. The Bishop brusquely ushered us onto a ferry that carried us over the channel between the spit of flat land on which the wharf was located (with the substantial town of Durban straggling behind it) and the dramatic rise of the natural wall between port and ocean. Quiet, virginal and green, this was known as the Bluff, and on it was situated the mission station of the Oblate Fathers.

A Breton, short and spare, Bishop Jolivet spoke no German and clearly was hostile to all things German. His translator let me know before we landed on the other side of the short channel that while the Bishop would provide quarters for us, he could not provide rations. My Brothers were, in any event, to stay only a matter of days at the Oblate station. I was to leave immediately to inspect a station eighty miles from Durban that the Bishop intended to hand over to us.

And so the story of Natal that Brothers Barnabas and Paul brought back to us in our desperation in Dunbrody began to be revealed to us for what we should always have expected it to be: too good to be true. We were to be suffered in this place only under very specific conditions, as was quickly made clear to me by the Bishop. It was some time before I learned that his sensitivity about our arrival lay in the rumour – a rumour some say was enshrined in a town council document – that the Port Natal settlement would admit no Jews or Catholics. It did not occur to me at the time, despite my recent exposure to British prejudice, that there was a firm (if never openly expressed) reason as to why the Oblate community was hidden away on the seaward side of the bluff we had just climbed and crossed, out of regular contact and even sight of the business community buzzing around the port. More to the fore, however, were Bishop Jolivet's own national prejudices.

The French and the Germans were not likely, he announced to me within an hour of our arriving at the mission, to work peacefully together. He admired our remarkable loyalty to the Holy Church during the Kulturkampf, but it was his task to avoid friction in the work for the salvation of souls, and the general opinion in his vicariate was that Germans were hot-headed, pedantic, critical and convinced of their own superiority.

If a quiet and kindly smile is the surest sign of my discomfort in the world, an over-earnest appearance of wanting to please comes upon me before all authority. I have never known which I dislike more about myself, and as the Bishop spoke I could feel my whole body adopting a pose of obeisance – not just the submission required of me by my vows, you understand, but something beyond the religious. This overwhelming desire to ingratiate has nothing to do with what the Rule calls the first degree of humility, which is *obedience without delay*. It is a kind of physical and mental cringing that I know must inspire in others the irritation I feel myself even as I do it.

On this occasion, standing before the Bishop with my body hunched in an attitude of self-abasement, I did make a small effort at rising above this weakness. "Austrians," I said quietly.

"What?" said the Bishop, surprised at any interjection from a Trappist, let alone so subservient a Trappist.

"Austrians," I repeated, reluctantly but with the sense that I owed our reputation this much. "Our Superior and most of our community are Austrians, while I myself am from …"

"Austrians, Germans," he burst out impatiently as my sentence tailed off, "*toute la même chose* – for my people here they are all the same, and apart from anything else there is the language problem. Therefore we have decided that you Trappists shall have your own separate project."

Franz, of course, would want nothing less, and I indicated our agreement with an inclination of my head.

"There is a mission on a Zulu reserve inland from Umzinto, a place down the coast from here," the Bishop continued as, to my consternation, a rider approached us with two horses. The question that rose up out of my gut against all that my vow of obedience could do was, fortunately, caught in my mouth as the Bishop said, "There are no carriages or coaches, I'm afraid. Indeed, there is no road to St Michael's."

The Bishop then went on to tell me something of the history of St Michael's. It was the first mission his predecessor, Bishop Allard, had tried to establish, making it the oldest Catholic Native mission in Natal, and perhaps the whole of the country. It was started in 1855, somewhere further inland, but was attacked and its buildings destroyed by hostile tribes barely eight months after they were built. Bishop Allard had withdrawn the two missionaries there despite having been severely reprimanded by his Superior General for this decision and, in its place, had selected less ambitious territory that had been set aside as a location for the Zulus. Within a year he abandoned the outstation again. "The Kafirs," he had written to Bishop Mazenod, "have refused the Divine seed."

St Michael's had stood deserted ever since. The sole revenue of that isolated farm came from the raising of pigs, something none of Bishop Jolivet's priests appeared willing to do. According to Bishop Jolivet the site was more suitable for a hermit than a priest. "I told my clergy that in you Trappists we had hermits of a sort," he said to me, "and we should give you St Michael's. And thus it is that you have been welcomed here with open arms. So, off you go!"

~

From the moment I mounted my horse in mute obedience to this command all I remember is a sodden green blur of great discomfort. Speech was not a problem on our journey; my guide was not so much silent as surly to the point of being mute. I clung to my great sweating beast and followed him as best I could. We had to proceed on foot much of the time, in any event – myself more often than my guide – as we skidded endlessly down steep slopes to rivers cutting their swollen way through the tangle of bush that constantly surrounded us and then had to haul ourselves back up.

I would normally have considered walking a relief, but as my shoes slipped and slid on the wet undergrowth, or got caught in great roots, I had to hold onto my horse as tightly as if I were riding just to keep my balance. Mounted or dismounted, our faces were whipped by vines and scratched by thorns, and I was thankful for the thick cloth of my habit over the rest of my body, despite its being drenched with perspiration. The sound of crashing waves was always in our ears and now and then we would burst into open spaces with sweeping views of the sea. I am not sure which was worse, the blazing heat of the open sky or the dank broiling shadowland of the bush. The insect life remained constant, buzzing and biting and getting into one's eyes and ears and mouth. At times I felt I was suffocating in humidity and insects.

Eventually we turned away from the coast and began to climb. The heat was severe, but as we crossed patches of comparatively open grassland the travelling became easier. Any pleasure I took from this was balanced against the awareness that it was clearly the result of the landscape's becoming drier and drier. We were soon following the spine of a long ridge, with fingers of smaller ridges running off both sides. Occasionally one saw signs of Native habitation at a distance down some of these smaller ridges. Beyond this, in every direction, rolled a vast crumpled land.

"Hlatenkungu Hill," grunted my guide, nodding at a particularly knotty knuckle on the main ridge. I caught the name properly only much later, but it was at this point that we turned off to the right and descended a short way down one of the thicker fingers. Quite quickly we reached a deserted and ruined chapel. Beyond this, squeezed onto the very tip of the finger, was a small jumble of buildings – nothing like the neat layout of one of our houses but not unpleasant in design. These buildings were as deserted and dilapidated as the chapel.

I knew Franz would not be concerned about what constructions there were on the site; his eye would be a farmer's. He had learned by now, in practice as much as in principle, how important it was that we be entirely self-sufficient. In this respect, St Michael's was clearly hopeless. The soil immediately around the buildings was poor and there was no water supply. The land below the ridge looked more fertile, but the one riverbed running through it was nothing but a scar of sand. This was thorn country, and broken country at that – a land of dry rivers, hilly terrain, heat and low rainfall. It would be extremely difficult to farm, and the lack of roads and bridges would make it almost impossible to bring in supplies and materials.

Dunbrody all over again, you may think. But there was something else about St Michael's Mission, something more disturbing. Was it the few pigs I saw snuffling at the door of the chapel, with the saint himself carved above them, sword raised to kill the demon? Surely this was going too far, but in years to come everything I sensed that day at that abandoned mission would declare itself in the most terrifying way. Something I can only describe as malevolent hovered around the edge of its loneliness – not emptiness, no, there was too strong a sense of presence in its desertion, something that seemed to inhabit the very air that moved about the place and claimed it for its own. No matter how I tried, I could not shake off this feeling, which I was certain had more to do with St Michael's being deserted than any question of unreceptive Natives or lack of luck in raising pigs.

A sense of dread filled me as I surveyed the new home intended for us. I could not bring myself to investigate the buildings in any detail. The landscape alone had written all over it the kind of failure we had just escaped and, as for the rest, I was quite sure that this place of pigs would extinguish what little spirit we had managed to keep alive in escaping from a place of thorns.

All I could do was turn around, indicating to my guide that I had seen enough and that we should start back immediately. He did not appear in the least surprised although the blank expression he wore throughout the journey made it difficult to establish what he was thinking. He simply wheeled about and set off at a pace that for once I did not find difficult to match. I bounced my way awkwardly after him as we returned to the Oblates on the Bluff, repeating in reverse the dreadful journey.

~

The situation on the Bluff had deteriorated in my absence. Somehow, word had got about in our tattered community that Franz had been dismissed and that a Frenchman was to be made our new Prior. Bishop Jolivet had no time for our confusion and simply wanted us on our way to St Michael's as quickly as possible. Indeed, he had begun arrangements for a number of heavy ox-wagons to be loaded with our luggage for the journey. How he expected these to reach a mission only just accessible on horseback I had no idea (no one had told me as yet of the longer inland route to St Michael's, which followed more or less usable roads). All we owned had been sent down by rail to the terminus of the line at Isipingo, just south of Durban, and was being transferred to the wagons.

My own position was intolerable. I owed the Bishop full obedience and so continued preparing our community to leave for St Michael's, but Franz had made it quite clear that we were to remain in Durban until he arrived. When this would be, or whether he would arrive at all, was uncertain. For all I knew, there may have been some truth to the new rumours circulating. Trying to re-establish authority over our community in Franz's name under these circumstances was practically impossible However, my dithering proved to be just what was needed.

Our circumstances made it difficult to remain quiet in any meaningful way, and between the rumour-mongering and bickering that surfaced continually few of my vague orders regarding packing for the journey were carried out with any efficiency. And then, in the midst of this formlessness, word suddenly arrived that Franz, like the Spirit of God Himself, was moving over the face of the waters. More prosaically, a telegram from Franz was received at the Bishop's house in Pietermaritzburg, announcing his imminent arrival at Durban harbour. I was to leave my Brothers loading the wagons for St Michael's and go immediately to meet him.

The relief was so overwhelming that I almost wept. Never have I mounted a horse so joyfully, and no amount of formal restraint could hide my delight when Franz stood before me. Without a word I reached out and touched each of his shoulders, and he mine. Then that gruff voice came, asking me what all this was he had been hearing about St Michael's and why no one was referring to him as Prior.

Stumbling over the details, I told Franz of the station intended for us – just the physical particulars, he would have been impatient with any metaphysical speculations. I explained that the wagons were due to leave for this site first thing the next day. More reluctantly I told him of the confusion regarding his status as our leader.

Still tired and weak from the seasickness that, as usual, laid him low for much of the voyage, Franz nevertheless leapt up from the chair he had been occupying on the veranda of one of the harbour buildings and demanded to be led to his community. None knew of his secret arrival, but as we approached our temporary quarters on the Bluff, two or three Brothers recognised Franz at a distance and came tumbling down, rushing to greet him. One plunged, socks, shoes and all, through a stream, throwing himself at Franz in the most unseemly fashion. Breathless surprise was all about us as we rode into the camp, and not a few tears. A few hard words followed too – most of our community soon accepted that Franz was still our legitimate Superior, but two amongst us were opposed to this.

A furious controversy broke out, the upshot of which was that the two who had lost confidence in Franz's authority took his advice and left almost immediately to return to Europe and join a monastery there. Franz led the rest of us in Vespers and Benediction, and then announced that we would not be going to St Michael's. He would see Bishop Jolivet in the morning, he said, and sort out with him the momentous question of where our new home would be.

And so the wagons did not leave that next morning, but they did stand poised at Isipingo Station, as per the Bishop's orders. Brother Barnabas was left in charge of them, with strict instructions not to set off until Franz himself gave the order. Meanwhile, Franz and I prepared to head up by rail to the Bishop's residence in Pietermaritzburg, about fifty or sixty miles inland.

~

After my months of muddling, the return of Franz's leadership came at a dizzying pace. What is more, confidence and purpose seemed to attract good fortune. Just as we were getting ready to leave for the station to catch the train, a Native arrived carrying a letter in the cleft of a stick and looking for "Herr Pastor". Our amazement at his being able to speak some German was met with the explanation that he worked with Lutheran missionaries in a place just north of us that was actually called New Germany. The letter was written in German, and its unusual salutation made it clear that its author, one Rev. C W Posselt, did not understand that we were Catholics. "Dear Mr Missionary," it began, and went on to tell us that a Chief Manzini in the Shozi Reserve near Dassenhoek in the neighbourhood of a town called Pinetown had asked for missionaries to come and "teach his people the book". As the Reverend had no available staff he directed the request of the Chief to us, having heard of our recent arrival.

It turned out that Pinetown was one of the first villages we had to pass through on our journey by train to Pietermaritzburg. And what else should Franz discover on the front page of a newspaper he had picked up to peruse on our journey but that there was to be an "Important Land Sale" in the very area Rev. Posselt had drawn to our attention. A "valuable freehold estate" known as Zeekoegat was to be auctioned the next day, the advertisement announced, and the description of the property was most encouraging. The estate was well watered, with a large quantity of thorn wood on it; and was situated at an easy distance from Pinetown railway station. The land was described as very suitable for growing tropical produce and the property afforded hut rents of 20s per hut. There were 43 huts and their tenants, according to the advertisement, were willing to pay double or treble the rent to stay on the land.

"This is the finger of God," exploded Franz, and he could hardly contain himself as we passed through Pinetown Station, his head out the window, looking about as if ready to put in an offer to the next person we saw as the train pulled out of the station and we continued on our way.

~

We arrived at the capital of Natal, Pietermaritzburg, at about 2.00 p.m. and Bishop Jolivet called Franz into his office immediately. I could see from the Bishop's face that he had heard a lot about Franz, not much of it good. I was asked to wait outside, but whenever the low rumble of their exchange was raised a tone or two I could hear what was said quite clearly. Soon the Bishop was asking with some exasperation how a man as poor as Franz would not take St Michael's as a gift, and whatever Franz answered was met with the sharp retort that the Bishop would not allow anyone to get into debt in his vicariate.

As I sat there, quietly thankful that Franz was handling things so coolly, one of the Bishop's staff hurried up to me and, thinking that I had some authority in this business, asked if he could interrupt the meeting with a telegram for Franz. I indicated that he should simply try knocking for admittance. He made his delivery and had hardly begun to leave when I heard Franz ask permission to open the telegram.

"What does he mean, must the wagons continue waiting? Didn't I tell him expressly to do just that!" Franz shouted, stamping on the floor. He roared at the Bishop, the messenger, and anyone else for some distance around with ears to hear, "*Una stultitia facta est. Nolo aliam!*"

I cringed in my corner. What was the Bishop, who had given us St Michael's and on whose orders our wagons were to leave for that place, to make of such an outburst? The door closed abruptly and a hush settled. Slowly the rumble started again, to my surprise in a remarkably restrained tone that modulated into what I can only call agreeable.

Over an hour passed by. Some time was clearly taken up with our experiences at Dunbrody, and I gathered much was said regarding Franz's credentials. Points regarding land and farming were firmly put, and I could easily fill in our concerns with roads and access to railways and the port. I heard the words "silent example" and "savages" and "postulants" a number of times and, even through the Bishop's solid walls, I could feel Franz's vision beginning to take shape.

Suddenly the door burst open and the messenger was called for; it had just been remembered that no reply had been sent to Brother Barnabas. I heard Franz dictate the telegram to him loudly in the presence of the Bishop: "*Das Ganze halt! Zurück nach Durban!*" and knew that in this curt directive lay our salvation from St Michael's.

When Franz and Bishop Jolivet came out a short time later on openly friendly terms, I dared hope for even more, and indeed, once I was alone on the train with Franz, I learned that all we could have wished for had been accomplished. It was a miracle, Franz told me. Once he had lost the temper he had been so carefully holding in check, it was as if the Bishop suddenly saw that he was dealing not only with a man of fire and energy but one who had been frustrated for too long by unrealistic formalities.

The Bishop had not been entirely surprised at our negative response to St Michael's but believed we did not have the resources for any other option. Franz, nevertheless, had got him to agree that if someone was prepared to sell us land on credit, then he should place the same confidence in us. "He now recognises," Franz said in conclusion, "that he is dealing with a trustworthy man. A man, in short, who knows his own mind and is able to carry out his plans successfully."

It was then that Franz let me know that he had returned from Europe with enough backing to serve as a basis for credit. My happiness at this was, as always, tinged with surprise, for Franz rarely prepared one for such announcements. On this occasion, though, it was also shaded by anxiety, for this was the first moment that seemed to me opportune to discuss Bishop Ricards' letter of debt. Franz had not raised the matter of my cryptic telegram, and so I simply held out the account, which had remained in the pocket of my habit from the day it arrived at Dunbrody until now. He took it from me rather brusquely, scanned it, and tossed it aside.

"This is just nonsense," he said. "We owe nothing of this. He should be glad for not having to pay *us* on top of these amounts!" He put his head as far out of the carriage window as he could, scanning the world of his new prospects with a hungry eye and I was left to align myself with his mood, filled with a sense of energetic anticipation as we passed through Pinetown on our way back to the Bluff. Still, I did take the liberty of picking up the Bishop's somewhat crumpled bill from the dirty corner of the compartment, and returned it to the pocket of my habit.

~

One soon learned how rapidly anticipation for Franz became actuality. The next day he and Brother Barnabas (now forgiven as his impudence in sending the telegram had had such a fortunate effect) rode out to Zeekoegat. They were accompanied by Mr Grant, an agent from the Land Colonisation Company, and Julius Schultz, a local doctor who was Catholic and German and fluent in English. Franz and Brother Barnabas, assisted by Dr Schultz, who also owned a farm in the area, carried out tests on the plants, the soil, the trees, the river and even the rocks in the river – which they established was now free of the hippopotami that had earned the estate its name.

They were well satisfied with the results, and finally Franz stood back and said directly to the land agent in the language he was determined to master, "Is it allowed that I can stand under that tree and pray?" I imagine Franz did not wish to encounter in Natal the difficulties he had with the Turkish authorities while building Mariastern. A rather perplexed Mr Grant, finding he needed a translator as much for Franz's English as his German and wondering why he had been asked to give permission to a monk to pray, turned to Dr Schultz. The doctor (a man we were to get to know well in our early years at our new foundation) explained that what Fr Franz really wanted to know was whether there would be any hindrance from an official source to the Trappist way of life, a life of work and prayer. A relieved Mr Grant, anxious only to conclude the transaction, opened his arms to the whole terrain and assured Fr Franz that he could pray anywhere he wished on his own property.

On the 21st December 1882 Franz put in an application to the Land Colonisation Company for purchase of part of the farm. This was granted directly. And so Franz became proprietor of an initial 745 acres (he was soon, bit by bit, to buy up the whole estate and much, much more) and landlord to "eighteen Africans and sixty women", as stated in the deed of purchase.

Franz called our community together and, before any other business, circulated a document from the Bishop stating that he was legitimate Superior of the Trappists at the Bluff and that the community should render him canonical obedience. This, he said, must put an end to the vicious slanders circulating about him even in our own community, slanders that had thrown our very future into danger. We must return to silence and obedience, he stressed sternly. Then, when the group was suitably chastened, he switched tones and announced the entirely unexpected triumph of our new home.

The stillness changed in an instant from subdued to stunned, with relief flooding through the community as the news sunk in. And then our hearts surged as one to our Superior as he stood before us, firm, composed, every inch our leader. Brothers rocked in mute delight, clutching their hands within the sleeves of their cassocks. Here and there tears rolled down faces etched through their beards by the hardships of the last two years.

In this joyful hush Brother Barnabas signalled for permission to speak. This granted, he told us the Isipingo station master's comment when he heard that our Superior had ordered us not to proceed with the wagons to the mission intended for us. "That's a smart man you've got there to refuse to go to St. Michael's without even going to look at it," the railway man, a German himself who had been in the colony for some years, had said. "Only a fool would think of farming at that place."

~

The spectre of St Michael's was never quite to leave us. After passing a spare but elated Christmas on the Bluff, we set off for Pinetown on St Stephen's Day. Just as we approached the gates of the Oblates' property, one of the French priests came up to the wagon in which Franz and I were riding and accused Franz of having obtained permission to enter the Natal vicariate under false pretences.

"You were supposed to go to St Michael's," he said, "and now you have let us down. Who will go to that desert and, like the prodigal son, take care of the pigs there? Father, we are disappointed and I wanted to let you know this."

To my horror I heard Franz answer in his most formal voice: "I am sorry, but at present it is impossible for us to take over St Michael's. Yet I promise you, Father, that one day that mission will be served by one of our Fathers, and if it is God's will this will be soon."

This promise darkened for me our leave-taking of the Bluff and the Oblates. For a moment the upside-down medieval world of St Stephen seemed to open up before our party and a vast blackness threatened to billow out and swallow us. But then the dejected priest turned away, and the ordinary world of snorting animals, creaking wood and sweaty habits closed back in. From the safety of the mundane my heart went out to the priest so obviously under orders to make his way to that land of Legion down the coast as we made our hopeful way up into the hills.

~

At Isipingo Station we loaded ourselves and our goods, such as they were, onto the train and headed for Pinetown. The first steep ascent out of Durban is known as Jacob's Ladder and we, even without the dream's white-winged visions of loveliness, took this as a personal confirmation of God's gift of our new land to us. We then passed through a pretty line of villages making up the suburban territories. Their names alone, such as Sea View and Bellair, spoke of the more stimulating climate of the vistas over the bay that the journey out of Durban afforded. Hillary and Malvern were equally

186

attractive halts, situated amongst the pretty undulations and billowy hills of the land between the port and Pinetown. We saw a good stone quarry from Pinetown Bridge, where we paused while the engine took on water, and soon set off at an ascending pace over the river, passing thick arching lines of elegant bamboo, graceful palms and tangles of wild banana.

At Pinetown we reloaded everything we owned onto heavy ox-wagons, and set out on the last stretch to our new home. We had already left the station when it occurred to us that we did not know the way. Franz had gone on ahead on horseback, assuring us that the road was obvious. We found ourselves presented with a vague array of tracks leading off in many different directions from the station.

As was usual when we were out in the world, a curious crowd, of mainly Natives on this occasion, gathered around us. Their gestures indicated that they were commenting on our gowns and beards, but their language was entirely foreign to us. Leader as I was of this contingent of our community, I gave the dispensation for speech to one of our Brothers. No one in this gathering had even a smattering of German, however, and our Brother's stammered attempt at a few words in Latin and then even in Bosnian had little effect.

One or two in the crowd responded in what I recognised as English, but none of us spoke that language. We milled about at a loss until a man of European origin came along who spoke Italian. In response to the queries we put to him in our ecclesiastical Latin, he pointed out the road to "Het Zeekoegat Farm" and then asked one of the young African men (whose language he spoke) to lead us in the direction of Manzini's Reserve. The young warrior gave his weapons, which we had been eyeing with some alarm, to another man, took the rope of the first span of oxen, and shouted something that got the lead ox moving.

Slowly our whole procession creaked into motion and the oxen strained into their yokes as we rumbled across a rivulet that marked the outer reaches of Pinetown. We moved off to the north-west, heading towards some hilly country to the left of a dramatic rise in the land ringed with an almost perpendicular wall of rock. From my journey with Franz to Pietermaritzburg I knew that this was the next in a succession of abrupt upsurges in the rumpled landscape that one met as one proceeded inland. I was relieved we did not have to attempt in our wagons the long and exhausting pull that had taken the train around and over it.

~

We did nevertheless have to crest a number of lower hills and a pretty substantial ridge to reach our destination. I spent some of the less taxing moments of our journey trying to align the Native boy leading my wagon with my mission-altar Nubian, an exercise to some degree frustrated by having to take into account my sense of smell, not previously part of my poetic vision. The sun was setting by the time we had hauled ourselves up and shadows were already beginning to steal over our new land as it lay before us. Our guide set off confidently down the slope on the other side of the ridge, the wagon gathering speed with each foot of the descent.

My attempts at guiding the huge weight beneath me rapidly proved futile. Franz had described our destination as a hill perhaps a half-mile further on, but we had been led too far to the right. Instead of cutting across the slope that fell away from the ridge, we jolted almost directly down it at ever greater speed. With the oxen being pushed forward in complete disarray, we rumbled straight down the hill until the front wheels of my wagon sank into the marshy ground at its foot. Behind me I heard the second wagon being drawn inexorably towards the same fate.

Darkness was coming on and the wagons were stuck fast. I sent word for the other wagons to remain where they were, and stood there taking in the quiet of the green hills around us as they gave up their light. Soon enough Franz came galloping into our disaster. There was no question of getting the wagons out of the mud that day and disappointment filled the air.

Then Franz did something that took us by complete surprise. "Unload," he said. "We will stay here for now. This spot will be our temporary mon-astery. The hill can wait." We stared at him in complete incomprehension. We had never known our leader to give in to contingencies of any kind, let alone pure accident. "Unload," he repeated, irritated at our blank expres-sions. "It is God's will."

Did he understand then the precise nature of God's will? For to this day our monastery still stands, rooted now beyond all moving, at a loca-tion decided by the error of a young Native boy and the misfortune of some waterlogged ground. I cannot say that my poor aptitude as a leader and bad record with animals did not have some hand, too, in our build-ing upon a mistake, but as the records are content to overlook this, let us leave it be. Even that first evening was sultry enough for us to long for the cool breezes of the higher ground ahead, and for years to come any who had to pass a summer in our monastery had good cause to question its positioning "down in the hole", as I so often heard it put.

This complaint was an exaggeration. Lower down than intended we may well have been, but the land still fell away all around us, especially to the north. Once Franz had ordered us to shift towards a northern overlook, we were out of the wet clay and on a low, flat table of the most solid rock. We would learn later just how solid when trying to hack into it the cellars of our buildings.

Below us spread a flat expanse of what looked like extremely promising farmland, with a small but steady river winding through it. This pastoral scene was ringed by soft hills that stood ready both to frame our solitude and lift us up to new vistas. For a few moments we simply stood, gazing out in quiet satisfaction. After Dunbrody this was a veritable Garden of Eden, and we were all gladdened to hear our leader say, *Hic dormiam et requiescam.*

Sleep and rest had to wait, however, while we unpacked the baggage from the two wagons. Once we had stretched a few pieces of tarpaulin over some of our larger pieces of luggage and curtained the sides with blankets, even the hard ground was a comforting bed. When I awoke upon it to change position in the night, it reminded me that we had come through the mire into which I had led our community. Along with the Psalmist we could say, "It is good to be here, let us make our tents here." And so, reassured, I fell back into a deep sleep on our first night on the site of our new foundation.

~

The next day, the feast of St John the Evangelist, Fr Franz celebrated Mass for the first time on what had been Zeekoegat Farm. In the morning light we could see ahead of us the higher ground Franz had chosen for his monastery, and we were only too glad not to have to haul our belongings that much further just then.

Around mid-morning a small group of us walked with Franz up to the top of the incline. The view from there was truly spectacular, a vista of hills so gentle in a shimmering haze that you felt you could reach out and stroke them. Beyond these, to the east, was the broad gleam of the ocean. Looking back, nevertheless, I could not but feel that there were advantages to the temporary site we inhabited as a result of my failure to control my oxen. Lower it may have been, but it nestled neatly against the rising ground behind it, protected from weather and undue observation alike. There the hills seemed to enfold us, taking us into their arms in a welcoming embrace. From there, too, we could easily see the full extent (at least so I, in my limited vision, thought) of the land that would preoccupy us, the cloistered world we would make out of our work and prayer. What had we to do after all with vistas beyond our sanctuary, the place to which we had sworn our stability?

And so, as we stood there gazing out over this new world, it seemed to me that the temporary location into which we had stumbled by chance was more in accordance with Trappist principles than the elevated spot on which Franz had first set his mind. The instructions regarding settlement are clear and exact in the Regulations: our resignation of the world is to be reflected in our avoidance of spectacular sites on mountains or near lakes and seashores. The very names of our greatest houses in Europe – Clairvaux, Chiaravalle, Marienthal – spoke of their positioning in remote valleys that had to be cleared and subdued before they could be inhabited. A small river was considered the only necessity, given the important role of water in Cistercian life. And there below us was one, running close enough to the humble position of our unplanned site to serve both practical and spiritual purposes.

Did Franz think of the Rule or our Regulations as he turned away from the site that had initially tempted him? I only know that he turned away from the magnificent view reluctantly, with a single comment: "This is a place of visions. Right now, let us get back to work."

And so we walked back down, watching the rest of the wagons make a more orderly descent than I had done the day before on the opposite slope. By two o'clock they had arrived amidst tremendous rejoicing at the place where mishap had brought us. Temporary it was meant to be, but somehow I had the feeling that we were finally home.

10

The first shape our new Trappist house took was a corrugated-iron roof supported by discarded packing cases with tarpaulins hanging at the sides. From one of the packing cases Franz had the photographic equipment exhumed; it had lain dormant throughout our time in Dunbrody. He had obtained fresh chemicals before we left Durban, and so we have, captured in an instant of its creation, a picture of the primitive camp that was the genesis of our foundation.

From that instant time itself changed for me. Whereas the building of Mariastern stays with me as a story made up of a succession of obstacles met and overcome, and Maria Dunbrody as a tale running out in a desert of sand and thorns, the coming into being of our Natal home bursts into my memory in flashes, instants cut out of time and enshrined in some more ethereal record. If we came to South Africa on a flood of words, and nearly drowned in that flood, for a while at least we arose triumphant out of that patch of Pinetown mud in a series of silver, silent, frozen moments.

It was Brother Othmar, our long-frustrated first photographer, who aimed and opened the lens of the camera obscura and then hurried with that latent image on its glass plate into the deep shadow of our tent. There, the negative of its form swirled up to him from the plate in its chemical sea. Then he opened a flap of the tent and let the sunlight burn through the plate onto paper he had specially prepared and placed below. Slowly, a shimmering inversion took place and a true reflection of our work began to appear on the paper. And so, for any eye that cared to see, we emerged out of the void of time, and our work took shape in the flow of change that had already bypassed it by the time it had come into being. "Good, good," said Franz as he studied the first of Brother Othmar's prints. Since then many hands have performed the same small miracle of light and dark to illuminate our passage into history, as our archives will attest.

In those first days the Monastery at Pinetown, as it was provisionally known, was a blur of activity. In its swiftness it constantly defied the slow eye of the camera, which demanded periods of absolute immobility to capture its subject. Like an anthill in the sun, our new home was full of scurrying life; old and young alike, without noise or shouting, hurried back and forth in their work. In one sweep of the eye you could see through the high grass the building of a baking oven, the digging of a well, the preparing of a garden plot, the unpacking of yet more crates, the washing and mending of clothes, the cooking of food, the raising of tents, and the construction of a smithy. Here one was cutting wood or using a plane, there another was busy with masonry, and others were digging, writing, drawing, or simply setting the table. All this took place on the stretch of open ground where the Choir Religious said the Divine Office, studied and, in the hours of labour allotted to them, took part in the work of the community. Work and prayer blended into a single current of Divine contemplation.

At first Brother Othmar found prayer to be the easiest prey for his lens, simply because of the regular stillness it required. But the photographs he took of the Religious generally turned out to be amongst his least successful. A monk who had unconsciously assumed an attitude that radiated the spiritual would stiffen imperceptibly as soon as the camera was turned on him, his pose becoming that of a puppet, meaningless and absurd. Either this or he would become so self-consciously holy that the image would be too sugary and sentimental to be of any use.

It may seem strange to you that we monks allowed ourselves to be photographed. Surely those who have chosen to lead a secret life with Christ in God should not be tempted into such a public display, you may feel, and I must admit to sharing these feelings at times. For Franz, though, the quickest and best way to give our friends and supporters in Europe a vivid sense of where we worked and prayed was to present a picture. He had seethed under the inability to represent Dunbrody in this way, all too aware that a Rhenish missionary on the west coast of the African subcontinent was already using photography as a major feature in his fund-raising.

"Everywhere I go in Germany," he would complain, "it is Schroeder, Schroeder, Schroeder. And why? Because the Rhenish Missionary Society has always understood the use of propaganda! With them it's pamphlets and tracts all the time, monthly and even weekly! And now they send this man Schroeder to the mission fields 'with Bible and camera' as they say, travelling everywhere with huge amounts of chemicals, the proper paper, even a special darkroom tent! And what am I given? *A dinner service!*" I should mention here that Bishop Ricards' gift to Dunbrody remained lost somewhere in an unpacked case, never again, to my knowledge, to see the light of day.

Franz believed that Germany would soon colonise the south-west of Africa and one reason for its success would be Schroeder and his pictures. He had seen on his German trip how popular this new mode of communication was, with everyone getting landscape pictures of their travels and sending copies to their friends to show where they'd been. Those travellers, he said, wrote the silliest things in the worst possible way about their journeys, barely literate accounts, often using any old polite formula. They knew they could rely on pictures to say it all to their friends.

Franz's dearest wish was that we could press actual photographs – as he had heard was being done by some new process in Germany – into the newsletters recording our progress that he sent out with unremitting regularity. As it was, he had several of the Brothers working on etchings made from hand-drawn images of our more spectacular physical locations and achievements; their imprints adorned the *Fliegende Blätter* from its earliest issues.

Soon enough Franz would get his wish, and our foundation and its community would find its way into books extensively adorned with pictorial evidence of our accomplishments. By then some of us would harbour the deepest doubts about what we had achieved, but there is no doubt that much of the success of Franz's projects lay in his understanding the importance of letting our supporters know what shape their money was taking in distant corners of the world. To this end he insisted that copies of our photographs become a regular addition to the letters and pamphlets we sent to our more important contributors and our motherhouse.

~

I would have cause, as our story went on, to think much about photographs. About the way in which the photograph, in seeming to tell the truth about what it revealed, quietly erased interest in everything it did not reveal; how it framed a vision of the world as you wanted it to be seen, and then presented this as the whole world. Each in his own way, Franz and I fell victim to this optical illusion.

For Franz, the photograph was the ultimate verification of his work, irrefutable evidence of the truth of what we were doing; for myself, my fascination with photographs lay in the kind of fantasy they could conjure up, for the way they could capture an enigma beyond language. I saw in them an almost miraculous possibility: could it be that in this most modern of technologies lay the potential for fulfilling our most ancient purpose?

Did not the apostolic secret of our silent life lie in being seen, after all? Who has not noted the miracle that takes place amongst those well-meaning but aimless sightseers who are constantly to be found visiting monasteries these days? Even when the formal tour is over, they hang about as near the cloister as they can, hoping to catch a glimpse of the monks we so carefully keep out of their way. If one should come into view, they invariably end up saying that he embodies a world of peace. The more insightful add that it is impossible to see a monk without realising how devoutly he believes in God.

Yet what have such casual visitors actually seen? Only the most fleeting hint of this or that aspect of the religious life, disconnected from its depth and flow. Still, the most trivial daily task of a monk is so charged with meaning when undertaken in accordance with the monastic Rule that the Divine and mystical presence is visible in the slightest gesture; spirit is so closely allied to flesh in this that even the least receptive and sensitive outsider is filled with awe.

If such visitors as these become quiet with reverence, why could we not give God to the world through images of those moments when, in the figure of some monk, in one of those humble objects used by monks, He is so unmistakably manifest? Why could photographs not be taken of monastic life that captured and recorded perceptible elements of the Divine? Why, in short, should photographs not tell all that matters of our story – without words?

Through this reasoning I became increasingly caught up in our photographer's work. Whenever time allowed, I was to be found watching Brother Othmar treating the collodion-covered glass plate with silver nitrate and hurrying to expose it to light in the camera before the film of viscous liquid dried, or coating the photographic paper with silver chloride ahead of burning the image onto it. I was caught up in the process by which our deeds were brought to light to the point of going with Brother Othmar into the tent we used as a darkroom as often as I could.

I surprised even myself in this because the developing and fixing process was by no means a safe one. Collodion, as our photographer enjoyed telling me through his teeth as he struggled with the different elements of his craft (we could not, of course, sign in the dark), was nothing more than guncotton dissolved in ether and alcohol, inflammable and highly explosive. Many a photographer had blown up his darkroom, some even their entire home and others themselves as well, Brother Othmar would warn me if I bumbled around too much in his tiny realm of blackness. And he favoured potassium cyanide over the salt of soda others used for fixing the pictures, primarily because this could be more quickly rinsed from the final product and thus used less water – as always an uncertain resource even in our comparatively well-watered new home.

Between the risk of explosions and poisoning, the history of our house took its bright silvery shape in a world as black and white and grey as our surroundings were green and brown and blue.

~

I remained absorbed for some time in the procession of images of our work and prayer that came out of that tent. I could easily believe, as I heard was later done, that if you flashed these pictures before the viewer at anything like the speed with which our new house rose from its marshy ground you would have the whole story of its coming into being flickering before you.

The picture of our camp amongst the packing cases, for example, quickly flickered over into a large house, some eighty feet long, with timber supports, an iron roof and canvas walls. No sooner had Brother Othmar taken a picture of this than we added a small corrugated-iron building that doubled as the "priory" and goods store. This became one of the most famous pictures of our early days, indicating as it did our Prior's humility and practicality. The first prints of this were hardly dry before our photographer was trying to get a picture of the hand-press we also managed to squeeze into the priory. This was in celebration of the first issue of *Fliegende Blätter* that was, within a few weeks of our arrival, already rolling off the press.

Not much more by way of building was to take place for some time, and the hungry eye of Brother Othmar's camera had to hunt elsewhere for our history. It found the corners of the big house where the tailor and shoemaker made little places for themselves; it caught us eating, praying, studying, and writing too under the iron and canvas when it rained (which it did often in this topsy-turvy world in the midst of the summer's heat). We purchased some oxen and, even though we settled too late to make use of the current year for farming, our work in the fields – or at least our work of making fields out of the mostly virgin land that was Zeekoegat Farm – began right away.

Soon enough then the camera was framing not only Brothers in their brown habits as they worked the soil but also the glare of the Fathers, their white habits standing out particularly well against the shades of grey into which the photographic process translated the rich earth. Quite apart from the good photographic subjects we made, we Fathers understood that our hours of physical labour would again, as in Dunbrody, have to match those of the Brothers if our ideal of physical self-sufficiency was to be reached soon.

For this reason we accepted that, for the first two growing seasons at least, our primitive living quarters would have to remain as they were while we concentrated on cultivating the land. Here, unlike Dunbrody, the land was alive with promise, producing even in its wildness fruits both tempting to us and a test for the Trappist Rule. We planted patches of sweet potatoes, round potatoes, monkey nuts (which produced a very fine cooking oil), and a most exotic and exciting crop of pineapples. But it was our own grain that Franz wanted us to produce in the shortest possible time; for the present the bread that was the staple of our diet had to be purchased from the bakers in Pinetown. This bread was too fine-ground and not, as Franz put it on our behalf, "to the Trappist's liking". Some of us may well have preferred the taste of the finer bread, but it did not provide strength enough for work, he would say as he swung a hoe with us at twice our speed. And, he would add, it cost twice as much as it did to make flour.

This meant that the construction of a mill was our next priority, a project that would involve damming the river that flowed through our lands. All of this was quite as it should be according to the Rule. *The monastery ought if possible to be so established that all things necessary, such as water, a mill, a garden, and various workshops may be within the enclosure, so that there may be no need for the monks to go about outside of it, since that is not at all profitable for their souls*, states Chapter LXVI.

Once work towards this end was under way, the camera began to leave us alone during our prayers. As our scurrying about settled down into more sustained forms of labour, our work produced more impressive images in its visible effect upon the landscape. These were perfect backdrops for Brother Othmar, who would regularly stop us and pose us against a cleared break in a field, say, with some of us frozen into position with a pickaxe, others apparently pressing a spade into the ground. Another favourite scene of his was the wall of rock near the river from which we were busy hewing huge blocks; the light fell most effectively on the stone, and our chief mason – an impressive-looking man with a shock of white beard tumbling over his special apron – did not mind standing with hammer poised over chisel biting into stone for whatever length of time it took for Brother Othmar to get the picture just the way he wanted it.

At the time these tableaux appeared natural enough, although every now and then we'd catch the shadow of Brother Othmar falling into an otherwise perfectly composed scene. I would be reminded then of our artifice. Did Aristotle not say (yes, there have been many times I have fallen into the temptation of regretting the Trappist rejection of scholarship, although I agree with the founder of our Order that it has a physical ease and a mental enjoyment unbecoming for a monk) that when you change the form of a thing you change its purpose? The purpose of our work was to create sustenance and to build, but what then was the purpose of the photographs of our work? At an obvious level, as I have said, it was to support our work through commemoration and propagation, but this process became part of a shift, almost imperceptible at first, in the very purpose of our community. No one has learned more than I that when you write about an experience you cast it in a new form and therefore furnish it with a new purpose. It is impossible to tell the truth of an experience in words because words are of a different form from experience.

The danger, too, is that when you represent experience in another form, experience may well come to follow that new form. This I am afraid became all too clear in the series of pictures emerging from the darkness of our photographic tent. From the start we became through the lens in those early days, perhaps quite understandably, a work-oriented community. Although on the whole we kept to our regular routine of prayer, there were occasions – rare at first but ever more frequent – when the urgency of our physical work meant that we Choir monks were yet again stopping for our more minor Offices right there in a field or on a building site instead of gathering formally at the big house.

~

In the midst of these efforts to establish our community, several Brothers came to me to report a strange phenomenon. They complained that while their eyesight was perfectly good during the day they were totally blind at night, even when the moon was shining or the lamps lit. In the course of five days seven men reported that they were unable to locate doors and passages and had to be led about. They could no longer see their neighbours during Mass or the dinner plates before them at meals. This blindness set in at dusk and lifted with daybreak.

Amongst the minor ailments I had then been treating (sores on the leg were especially common but responded fairly well to the remedy of aloe juice a settler had shared with me), sunstroke had already afflicted two or three Brothers. Despite the warnings of several visitors, Franz maintained the policy adopted at Dunbrody of having our heads shaved regularly so that we would get used to working bareheaded in the sun as quickly as possible. But, along with the heat, the light in Natal seemed to me particularly strong. I do not know if it was because of my pale blue eyes, which have always been sensitive to light, but I found colour here more dense and vivid than in Dunbrody, where everything appeared washed out and weak in the harsh, dry glare. Perhaps it was the extra moisture in the air, which seemed to glow with the richness of nature's palette like a deep oil painting after the thin watercolours of Dunbrody.

This was the only cause I could find for the blindness that some of our Brothers were experiencing at night, but Franz dismissed it out of hand. After consulting, against his own principles, an experienced physician from Pinetown, he eventually agreed that this might be the case and, on the doctor's advice, provided the Brothers in question with tightly plaited straw hats and eyeglasses with tinted lenses.

As pictures of us taken towards the end of our first year in our new home show, the hats quite quickly became a regular part of our dress (even Franz's), but the mystery of the night blindness remained. The condition of those suffering from it improved with the quite racy addition of the glasses and hats to their costume, but the blindness would return after about ten to fifteen days.

Franz quickly added the failure of the doctor's advice to his list of evidence against conventional medical practitioners. It was, perhaps unsurprisingly, Brother Othmar who maintained a particular interest in the phenomenon. Franz even allowed him to include an appeal – of the sort Franz himself would never make – in our next issue of *Fliegende Blätter* for advice from European doctors on this "night shadow", as he had taken to calling it.

That the photographer rather than a medical specialist or the Superior should have to put this request would appear strange only in a community not run by Franz. I found it fitting that it should be the creator of the bright pictures of our progress who should be the most concerned with the darkness hovering at their edges.

~

What the camera's hungry eye did not find was any sign of Chief Manzini or, as far as we knew, any of his people. This was no Dunbrody, however, and people had come running down the hills from everywhere on our arrival. They were, at first, mostly curious youngsters who squatted by our huts and crates and watched the strange things we unpacked and what we did with them in amazement. Franz noticed that men in their prime did not often join our audience, but grisly and gnarled old men would sometimes stand around, mute and solemn. Later, shining brown women, with uncovered breasts like clock weights, would also gather to stare at us as their naked children played in the sand and raced through the grass. Even from the distance they chose to maintain – cautious or respectful, it was impossible to say – our nostrils registered the mingled smells of smoke and body odour we came to associate with hut dwellers. It drifted over to us at work and prayer, pungent beyond the familiar odour of our sweat-soaked habits.

Some more responsible members of the villages did follow, although none appeared to be of chiefly rank. Their main concern, it transpired, was to find out if their homes stood on our property or not. This they conveyed in a mixture of broken English and much creative hand-signing, both of which Franz was able to match. When he showed them the white flags that marked our boundary line those who fell within it were overjoyed and shouted out happily at least twenty times in succession "You my father!" The faces of those outside our boundary dropped, and the best explanation Franz's inquiries could elicit was that, in keeping to the hut tax originally set in the advertisement for Zeekoegat Farm, we were undercutting our land-owning neighbours quite considerably.

As we watched the household heads hurrying back to take the good news to the huts that looked down upon us from the surrounding slopes of our property, we eagerly anticipated the spreading of the message of our presence to the other groups of huts dotted about the natural arena in which we had set ourselves as the focal point. And so we waited to become the objects of silent example in work and prayer, which was as far as our practical purpose in the world extended.

As it was, the fact that we worked our own fields and building sites was clearly a cause for much surprise, even awe. I could sense some suspicion, too, in the loudly shared comments of our audience. It was not our place to acknowledge our spectators, in work or prayer, but I could not but notice that with them our prayers were the object of equal attention. Viewers were always at hand, at least during daylight, to see us line up in two's on the open grassy plain and listen to us chant and recite our psalms as the

Breviary demanded of us. Whether any lurked about in the pitch dark when we rose for our Night Office is a question, but when we bowed reverently in unison under a glaring sun, our white clothes amplifying our white skins, we were watched in amazement. And when Franz ordered one of our bells to be freed from its cage and mounted on two large crates so that it could be rung for the Feast of the Epiphany, the general wonderment reached new heights.

"I am not too sure what they will think when they hear it ringing at two o'clock in the morning," Franz muttered to me as he observed this. There were, of course, no scattered Catholics as there had been in the Bosnian countryside to take secret comfort from the tolling that in the dead of night marked our strict keeping of religious time. Nor was our new home in a landscape in which time of the sort we measured had much place at all. I was not certain, thus, in what spirit Franz added with a grimly deliberate air, "I am sure that such a nocturnal peal will make a powerful impact upon them."

Clearly, some order had to be brought into this general display and its reception, and soon enough Franz explained that those who wished to observe us would have to wear clothing, at the very least a shirt. This thinned numbers considerably for few in our audience could come up with even an upper garment as the price of admission. Franz had in any event decided that, in order to set up the correct relationship between us and those for whom we were to be an example, something of a more formal distance should be established. Calling in Mr Grant, the Land Colonisation Company agent, and the ever-desirous-to-help Dr Schultz, he gathered together the eighteen heads of families settled on our property and took down their names and the number of their wives. One man had nine wives; the others had fewer, but the total number of wives did come to the advertised number of sixty.

This occasioned a considerable expense for our tenants, for tradition demanded that the husband must build as many huts as he had wives and the Government of Natal required a tax of 14s for each hut or wife that made up his homestead. Those African families that had no property of their own – which, as far as we could make out, was generally the case in Natal – leased land from settler landowners, paying their landlords two English pounds per wife. In return they could collect sufficient firewood and building material for their huts, plough and plant wherever they wished, and graze their cattle. The Natives let us know that they considered the levies far too high.

Through Mr Grant, Franz told our tenants that we would ask only one pound per wife in tax, on condition that they withdrew their households to the opposite side of the river from our foundation. This was greeted with much delight, and even the stricter work requirements that Franz insisted would go along with this new arrangement did not dampen the general happiness. Few actually listened as Mr Grant conveyed Franz's instruction that the trees and shrubs that had been left standing in the middle of ploughed fields, or at most cut down to knee height, would from now on have to be entirely uprooted. If they missed this announcement at the time, our tenants were to be reminded of it quite forcefully when ploughing began for the next season.

As far as we were concerned, the new spatial arrangement was necessary for us to begin to claim our legitimate succession in the line of great monastic houses of Europe. As with our medieval forbears, the solitude of our cloisters would take centre stage in the amphitheatre of the hills around us, and from this our silence would resound and bring order and decorum to the wild land. With our audience moved back a proper distance, the ancient design that guided all we did would make itself manifest. Our monastery would become the centre from which a sort of colony or range would spread out, to be settled by those whose labour at first would be modelled on ours, and eventually their prayers too.

Then our lives would again become secret and, beneath such outward activities as our work in the fields and celebration of the Liturgy, we would return to our daily participation in the Cross of Redemption. Our aspirations towards a heavenly existence would be lived again, as the monastic life ordains, in the silence of inner solitude proper to sinners. We would continue to consecrate ourselves to God in penance and austerity and renunciation, living out our solemn and perpetual vows in the wilderness that is the very nature of the call to a monastic vocation. And, here in the new wilderness granted to us, we would descend by prayer into the empty spaces of our spirits and await the fulfilment of the Divine promise: "The land that was desolate and impassable shall be glad, and the wilderness shall rejoice and flourish like the lily."

Or so my Brothers and myself may have put it. For Franz, we would find, the challenge was to take this romantic picture out of the past and translate it into a vigorous, lively, modern institution, albeit in Africa. He wanted to show that medieval laws and customs had a present purpose and utility. There was no contradiction here: from the bogs we have reclaimed to the wool we have produced, Cistercians have always changed the material lives not just of the communities about them but whole regions and nations. We did not do this by looking outwards, however, and seeking to understand or meet the needs of those about us. No, it was the secrecy of our lives along with the productiveness of our silent ways that attracted people to us. Throughout time, men have no sooner renounced the world than the world rushes after them, avidly contemplating those who have vowed to contemplate God alone.

~

As yet, of course, we had no cloister to hide us, and our solitude lay open to the world like the centre of a split fruit. Our monastery of tin, wood and canvas gave us sleeping quarters and a few workspaces but not much more. We had no place to worship except under the greatest dome of all, the sky. And, cupped in God's hands, we had only the surrounding ring of hills to echo back silence and chant alike.

As such, we were an open picture of our faith, something that Brother Othmar exploited to the full with his camera. Quite properly, his lens remained concentrated on us and not on our exotic observers, who were not yet part of the picture we wished to project – nor should be until they belonged to the life we had come to create. But the limits of the lens were already becoming clear to me. A camera may frame and focus, but one thing it cannot do is name. A name is something that must be given to a picture, and without a name a picture does not naturally take its place in any story. A picture, after all, is all surface; its depths are only an illusion created by light and shade. I had hoped to see our story emerge from those gleaming surfaces; I wanted their glistening silences alone to speak. But the names we bring to things, even the briefest caption identifying the location or subject of a photograph, come from the mouth, not the eye.

After work, naming is the first expressly human attribute God gave man. "Out of the ground the Lord God formed every beast of the field and every bird of the air, and brought them to the man to see what he would call them; and whatever the man called every living creature, that was its name," the Book of Genesis tells us. The Rule of St Benedict is our Order's only interpretation of the Bible, and I hope I do not stray from it in saying that this passage has always struck me as some kind of a test for man. As far as naming is concerned, God abdicates his power to man to see what he will do with it, and follows man in what he does without comment. Franz understood this intuitively, as I registered when I took the religious name he bestowed upon me.

Animals and birds were not unnamed in Natal by the time we arrived, but the more naked the landscape, the more ready Franz was to name, as he had proved quickly and decisively at Dunbrody. I wondered, as the first weeks went by, why he seemed so hesitant to name the fine property he had acquired. Clearly "Zeekoegat" had to go, but the first Natal issue of *Fliegende Blätter* (still emblazoned with the subtitle *aus Maria-Dunbrody*) went out with no more than the "Monastery at Pinetown" as our foundation's name.

Again and again the question of a name came up. Our very identity was at stake in this crumpled landscape where, on the one hand, indigenous names resisted us in their awkwardness and, on the other, new names given by the settlers were scattered about and took root like weeds. The river that ran through our farm was known as the Umhlatuzana and any other name we tried to give it was met with blank incomprehension by Native and settler alike. And the area only recently dubbed New Germany kept stubbornly to this designation even as settlers of other nationalities moved into it. Pressure grew on Franz to give our monastery a name and many suggestions were put to him, but he refused to be drawn into any debate on the matter. Finally, when yet another period of sanctioned discussion on this topic had come full circle, Franz, who uncharacteristically had not said a word, suddenly stood up. "Mary Ann Hill, we will call it," he said, and then ran the words together: Mariannhill.

There were some mumblings to the effect that although we were amongst hills we were not in actuality on a hill, and that the name did not link us in any way with what was still, after all, our motherhouse, Mariastern. Franz dismissed these objections by stating bluntly that all our monasteries were dedicated to the honour of Mary, and that St Ann, mother of Mary, was our dear grandmother. "We add hill," he continued, indicating the promontory before and above us, "because our monastery will eventually be built on a stately hill from which we can see our entire property, the surrounding neighbourhood, and even the Indian Ocean."

His reference to the hill surprised a few amongst us. Our present site was already beginning to feel quite naturally the place to be, and with every alteration we made it seemed more so. We remembered then that

Franz still spoke insistently of our structures as "temporary" and, looking about us again at the bits of wood and metal and canvas we had erected, we recognised with something of a shock just how temporary they looked. As for "Mary" and "Ann", well, Franz's manner indicated that he would not enter into further deliberation regarding their invocation, and soon enough the combination of the three words assumed that sense of rightness of all place names in regular and common use – regardless, as is often the case, of their accuracy or appropriateness. In any event, immediately after Franz's pronouncement, the pages of our *Fliegende Blätter* flew *aus Mariannhill*, and the same name came to be inscribed in white on the bottom right of Brother Othmar's shimmering photographic prints.

Franz would later declare that a further reason the monastery should be called Mariannhill was "to honour a noble benefactor who gave a donation for the new foundation". This was what he published as something of a fulfilled prophecy in *Fliegende Blätter*, but there were layers of secrecy behind Franz's uncharacteristic reserve over the naming of his new foundation, some more innocuous than others, that did not come easily to the surface. Much later, when the duty of dealing with the finances of our house fell upon me, I learned from our records that this donor was actually Franz's stepmother; it was her financial support that allowed him to put in the offer to buy Zeekoegat Farm. Clearly he was embarrassed that his initial fund-raising had only found success so close to home, and I found this a natural enough reticence.

Some of us already knew that Maria Anna, by strange coincidence, was the name of both Franz's mother, who died giving birth to his second sister when Franz was still very young, and of his father's second wife, the stepmother Franz had come to love as much, even more, than the mother he could barely remember. Despite her own contribution of seven children to the surviving four of his father's first marriage, she appeared to have made no distinction in her affection for them all, except perhaps to show a quiet but particular fondness for Franz. I was to write down at Franz's dictation many of his loving memories of the second Maria Anna, everything from her doing away with the endless beetroot his aunt (housekeeper between the two Maria Annas) served for dinner to the new buildings her substantial dowry enabled his father to add to his property.

Most of all, Franz took comfort to the end of his life in the memory of her appreciation of his courageous spirit and hard-working disposition.

She it was, he told me, who stood with him early on that morning when he was to leave the farm for the first time to go to school in Feldkirch. Who understood his choked-back words and cried his tears for him and said "Be brave". These more sentimental "unofficial" reasons behind the naming of Mariannhill became less of a secret as the years went by, and on the whole the community was happy with, even took comfort in, the maternal spirit informing the name of our house.

I was the only one who knew something of the darker logic behind that holiest and prettiest of names, stemming from the frustration of Franz's plan to establish a second house in Bosnia which was to be named, you may remember, Mariannaberg. I knew, too, that Mariawald had found its seclusion in the Marianne Hills, and I was already beginning to get an idea of how unhappy Franz had been in the monastery where he became a Trappist. All his religious ideals were formed outside the cloister of that house, in the hills surrounding it, where he worked in solitude after his authority had been stripped from him.

I cannot remember how much I knew then, and how much I learned as I scribbled away to the sound of Franz's voice – that voice which, as his body weakened, seemed to become his entire being – in the long days and nights still far ahead. But I felt even on the day our name was announced that its logic, as inevitable as the result of an equation correctly completed, cut through religious form and domestic affiliation to a darker part of the powers driving Franz. "Why leap ye, ye high hills? This is the hill which God desireth to dwell in" I could hear him say with the Psalmist. Here, at last, he had found his hills again, and was free to be the kind of Religious he believed he should be and to create in this likeness a house around him.

All this the camera – in its vistas of our hills, its portraits of our prayers, its staged scenes of our work – could not portray. And so it was that I first began to learn just how important it is to relate what lies outside the frame we give to our life to what we conceive as its centre; how that clumsy apparatus, the camera, can only tell a certain truth about its subjects, and how a picture cannot be entrusted to silence. Brother Othmar's photographs might have appeared to take us to a reality before words that was fixed forever in time, but I have lived long enough now to see how those pictures have floated through time, gathering words as they inexorably drifted free of us.

I have surrendered then both my own and Franz's hopes for those black and white witnesses of our very work, physical and spiritual. They depict neither observable fact nor spiritual essence, empirical evidence or holy mystery. Instead, they, like everything else we have done, whirl and spin in our wake during our time on earth. And what else is time but the measuring out, syllable by syllable, of the one long sentence we hope will spell out the meaning of our lives? I am all too aware that in thinking this I, an old, untutored man, am wandering into a terrain forbidden us Trappists: "We take our readings only from the Holy Scriptures and some other works of the Holy Fathers," say the Regulations, "works composed more to warm the heart than to enlighten the mind." And de Rancé instructs: "We banish all matter taken from scholastic theology, from disputed questions and from everything capable of drying the heart." But where else am I to look for the secret of our sins but in the lair of words, wherever it extends, now that my heart is so cold and dry a thing?

~

Barely two months had flown by at "Mariannhill" when Franz informed us that he must make another journey to Europe. He needed to fetch at least ten more men from Mariastern, he said, and buy some machinery and building materials. To me only he added that he intended to offer his resignation as Prior of Mariastern and announce his new foundation as a fait accompli.

The urgency behind his trip lay in this quiet aside. Although he had convinced our community and Bishop Jolivet of the legality of his status as our Prior, Franz had just received a decree of deposition. This had been decided on in Rome, sent on to France, and forwarded to Mariannhill by the Vicar General of our Order. The subtleties of the options Franz put to us regarding his remaining our leader after Maria Dunbrody were clearly lost upon the higher levels of authority in the Church. In their view he was, quite simply, no longer our Superior; we, then, were no longer considered to be under proper Church authority. Rumours were rife in Europe about the "illegal activities" of the Trappists in South Africa.

In ignorance of this, our community believed that the decision we had made at Maria Dunbrody and the ensuing mêlée in Durban had settled the matter of Franz's leadership and our legality as a religious body once and for all. In this atmosphere of confidence (shared by everyone except myself) I, as Sub-Prior, again became Superior. Hugging my knowledge of the true reason for Franz's journey to my heart, I prayed that I might be capable of the authority required of me. Franz clearly guessed that I needed support and had revived the full leadership structure as set out in the Regulations; I was to be assisted by Fr Arsenius and Fr Henry. The three of us were privileged by the Rule to converse with each other and the other members of our body, but the obvious nature of the work laid out for us did not leave much open to discussion. My preference for leaving as much as possible unsaid was in any event deepened by the secret I had to keep, and my hope was that we could simply proceed in solitude and silence with the projects already planned or begun by Franz.

~

We had been settled into our natural rhythm of work and prayer for barely a month after Franz's departure when the porter interrupted me in my duties with the announcement that someone from Durban wished to speak with me. The visitor turned out to be a reporter for the local newspaper who wished to publish an article on us in his tabloid. With some reservations, and after consulting Fr Arsenius and Fr Henry, I invited him on a tour of our foundation. Only a few days later – on Friday 18th May 1883, to be exact – a copy of his newspaper, the *Natal Mercury*, was hand-delivered to us.

At the time I found it extremely interesting to see how we appeared to an outsider. Despite some of its more obvious errors, such as the year we arrived in Natal and some of the details of our observances, the article was accurate enough. The reporter did describe the monastery as consisting "simply of a few wood and iron sheds of the roughest construction", but he was quick to add that "this can be done without any disparagement of the mechanical ability of the builders, who seem to care little for personal comfort, and do not pretend to grandeur in their edifices". His lack of understanding regarding our avoidance of speech ("there is no gaiety," he wrote, "and not even the smallest detail of commonplace conversation is allowed to enliven the monotony of the constant toil. Some of the men have not spoken for a great length of time …") did not bother me; it is something every Trappist must simply accept as part of his observance of silence. In any event his claims regarding the "oppressive stillness" of our monastery were belied by the "contented appearance" he attributed to us. I was more concerned at how Franz would react to our exposure to the public, especially during his absence. I had no idea how he would take to any account of his community other than his own, and I would have to wait two months to find out.

We were not idle in this time. We extended the wood and iron buildings already in use and covered their sides with white-painted corrugated iron. Within, we made dividing walls by dipping horsehair blankets in tar and hanging them. We also erected some small new buildings made of dry bricks, and smeared the outsides of these, too, with tar to make them weatherproof. We even managed to fulfil our first printing contract, producing a small catechism in the Basuto language that Bishop Jolivet commissioned for the well-established French Catholic missionaries in a mountainous country inland from us. It is difficult now to remember our quiet satisfaction at this particular achievement; when I think of it now, I am all too aware how even the smallest touch of pride prevents one from seeing the sin one is holding up in one's hands to God, expecting His praise.

Dr Schultz remained a firm standby, and generously donated various plants from his farm in Westville so that we could experiment with those crops that were most suitable for our agricultural purposes. We had to travel by cart to his farm to collect the seeds and young trees and were served there with cool drinks by his young daughters after our dusty journey. Unfortunately these girls insisted on our shaking hands with them after they had treated us to this kindness, and then turned away giggling as we wiped our hands vigorously on our habits to rid them of such contamination.

On one occasion Mrs Schultz, who was accompanying her husband to see the progress we had made with our new buildings, caused us even more disquiet. When we reached our sleeping quarters on the tour, we asked her to remain outside. The good lady persisted, however, in following the inspection party, not realising, I am sure, the full implications of her curiosity and impetuosity. As soon as the party left the building I ordered the fumigation of our dormitory, so that any influence she may have left behind to disturb our rest would be fully eradicated.

Such were the risks of our exposure to the world, and many were the mistakes we made in stumbling about in it. For example, Dr Schultz gave us pineapple suckers, orange trees and banana plants to cultivate; the bananas in particular grew extraordinarily well, far outstripping the citrus plants, and we lavished much attention on them. They were by far the most successful of our first crops, and a magnificent array of trees laden with this fruit was ready for Franz on his return.

I must admit that I waited eagerly for Franz's commendation of this long, yellow-skinned addition to our meals, and that something of my relief at his return from Europe in July was taken away by his swift dismissal of the banana as a part of our diet. It was too rich, he said, and would, like meat, overheat our blood; this would not only affect our health but cause sensuality. Remember, he lectured me as I stood forlornly by my trees on the day he arrived, that food and drink have a moral impact. Neither our physical constitutions nor our Rule, therefore, could tolerate the banana.

~

Franz's return was, nevertheless, glorious. On his travels he had looked neither to the right nor left. The Holy Spirit was his guide and led him safely along the correct path, to the place marked out for him by Divine providence. Mariastern may have succeeded in frustrating his plan of a second monastery in Bosnia, but nothing it seemed could prevent a new foundation succeeding in South Africa.

By May Franz had finished with his business at the first of the monasteries he had built up from nothing, and his journey back through Austria and Germany was nothing short of a triumphal procession. Eleven professed monks, twelve novices, eleven postulants, six Sisters of the Holy Cross and four German settlers sailed with him from Hamburg to Southampton, and then on to South Africa. Mariastern, at that time a community of over one hundred souls, largely as a result of Franz's hard work, had at first resisted giving him the ten men he requested for Natal. By then, however, Franz had not only convinced his Superior, the Vicar General of the Trappist Order, that his deposition should be set aside but had won his support for the whole South African enterprise.

The Vicar General himself intervened at Mariastern, sending a strongly worded letter that rejoiced in the success of the monastery in Natal and supported Franz's claims upon the community of his first foundation. It was difficult not to read some pique into the manner in which these were complied with: in addition to the ten monks requested, they threw in a bonus of an eleventh – a sickly man of no use to their community, intended I am sure as an unspoken comment on Franz's frequent assertions regarding the health-promoting nature of the South African climate as well as the Trappist life as he believed it should be lived.

Freed now of Mariastern, a fully legitimate Superior in his own right at Mariannhill, and far from the watchful gaze of the Order, Franz was finally able to create the house of his wishes. His monthly reports and the photographs he had sent had done their work well and his collections in Europe on this trip were remarkably successful. Franz could now meet Bishop Jolivet's condition of full responsibility, *suis tamen impensis*, for all costs that he incurred. Once this worry was off the Bishop's mind, he was content to maintain a friendly but distant relationship with Mariannhill and Franz could again work with a free hand.

And work he did.

~

Franz was, I could see, rather taken with the newspaper article written about us in his absence, but he was also put out at how shoddy an impression our buildings had made on the reporter. A disregard for personal comfort or religious grandeur was one thing, but the appearance of near destitution was quite another. And, after striding again through the echoing stoneways and arches of Europe, Franz himself seemed shocked at the very rudimentary accommodation he had ordered at Mariannhill. He was determined to turn our plans for buildings, roads, crops, mills and dams into reality as soon as possible.

This was a strange time to dream of expansion. The meagre contact I had had with the settler community in Franz's absence left me with the distinct impression that they were depressed and disappointed. They were bitter about the return of a Zulu king to Zululand, which lay just northeast of us. This was an area that had recently been conquered after severe reverses and more trouble was expected from that quarter. As members of the British Empire, they had been humiliated by their military loss to the Dutch settlers inland, and the establishment of an independent province north of the Vaal River was yet another threat to their safety and comfort. But even more immediate were their economic woes. Franz himself came back from Europe on a wave of bad financial news that was about to wash over the colonies.

The epicentre of this news was my last secular home. It turned out that my instincts about Vienna had not been a matter of mere romantic disappointment and personal revulsion – a spectacular commercial crash had finally come. Rumours of whole families being ruined and hordes of citizens being driven to suicide had reached us at Mariastern, but lost in our own world we left that city to the waltzes and whipped cream that seemed to be its luxurious last wishes. Now, Franz reported, the woes hidden for so long under determined frivolity were bursting the banks of the deliberate ignorance that had kept them at bay.

However, it was not an international financial crisis barging in on our isolation but a few lonely nuns who would serve as the next strand in the web in which we were eventually to be entangled. Yes, six Sisters of Mercy on the high and remote hills of Kaffraria were to set that sticky thread of destruction vibrating, waiting just for the first step of the unwary.

It began simply enough. Franz's travels were made possible on our limited means because he applied for grants-in-aid from the European Land and Immigration Board. The members of this body in Durban, amongst them some of the leading businessmen of the town, were impressed by the rapid improvements we had made to our property. They extended free travel to Franz and drastically reduced fares to the new members he brought to our community. Clearly they saw us as useful settlers in our own strange way.

Franz perused the local newspaper on a regular basis after our first appearance in it (although all such publications were still rigorously forbidden in what passed as our cloister) and found many more mentions of us, mostly concerned with our building and planting. "Heaven knows," he would say as he snapped the poor newsprint over to another page, "little enough else happens in Pinetown!"

Now the Regulations are quite clear on the kind of news Franz was reading to us: "We never tell a story from the outside world under the pretext of being able to draw some instruction from it," says de Rancé. "There is to be an absolute ban on anecdotes from gazettes, on current news from the world, on talk about the royal court or about our school days. Such things cannot but indispose the soul and cast it into dissipation and memories of things we ought to forget."

From the moment that Franz first read the account of us in the *Natal Mercury*, he seemed to forget this regulation completely, as if it were as obsolete as its reference to royal courts. Within days he was sharing with the whole community in Chapter an article by a local settler who expressed the opinion that "it will be both interesting and instructive to observe how far it is possible in this country for a body of European men – by dint of their own personal exertions, by the use of their arms and heads – to feed, shelter and sustain themselves upon our soil and beneath our skies".

"This unfortunate glimpse into the lives of our neighbours shows how poorly they are doing," was Franz's response. "After years of effort and constant complaints about the lack of cheap labour, they are not able to match our achievements here in a few short months!"

In the April of that first year at Mariannhill, the *Natal Mercury* announced that "another German newspaper", *Das Kapland*, was to be published in Cape Town. "Abbot Franz," Franz read to us quite casually, "is to be a contributor." We were more shocked at the time at the error in Franz's reported rank than anything else. Our Superior had only just been fully reinstated as our Prior, and none of us – well, all but one of us perhaps – had any aspirations to the status of an abbey for Mariannhill. This turned out to be a misguided concern, one that blinded us to other complex forces at work behind this apparently simple announcement.

In his contribution to *Das Kapland* (translated in full in the *Natal Mercury*) Franz took on nothing less than the whole "political economy" of settler society. His argument was aimed at "the taking from our own colony, and then the returning into it of our own productions", a practice he condemned as "a most expensive mode of business". Claiming that the "science" of political economy was not unknown to Trappists, indeed that their grasp of it "is of no modern date, coming as it does from the fifth century", he invoked St Benedict's Rule concerning our practice of manufacturing our own clothing as a basis for his position.

"And this Rule we in South Africa intend to observe," he went on, listing the roads, bridges, tannery, oil press, waterwheel, and the flour, saw and cloth mills we constructed, as evidence of the extension of the Rule to all aspects of our "economy". As a result we had cheaper corn and oil for our own community and for the Natives on our property, he told a readership he was sure would be impressed by such things. "And," he added, "we shall make out of colonial stuffs our own clothing, as well as shoes, thus again giving to the nude Kafirs a chance of obtaining a cheap woollen covering."

In building up to his conclusion, Franz informed his audience that it was because of our material success that the Government granted us reduced rates of passage. He underlined the labour potential of celibate monks as against "emigrant fathers with families" and, in a final flourish meant to spread confidence in his argument as far as he could, he brought up the plight – see now the web, intricate, beautiful, floating directly in our path – of "the Sisters from Switzerland, lately settled in Kaffraria".

Franz was outraged that, despite the Sisters' operating as we did on the basis of self-sufficiency, and sharing the benefits of this in the same way we did, they were denied assisted passage on the grounds of being unmarried. "Although they work their gardens and fields without any assistance resulting from a married state," Franz ended off with a flourish, "I believe these labouring Sisters are more fitted for Kaffraria than those lady-missionaries who go about with long trains and sunshades."

~

I was not in a position to judge just how bad the *Natal Mercury's* translation was of Franz's original German, but his English was coming on just enough for him to take pride in seeing his ideas in that language. The *Natal Mercury* had published brief summaries of material from *Fliegende Blätter* before, but this was the first time they chose to translate Franz verbatim and at length. The effect was explosive.

Up to that last line, Franz might have got away with his opinions on settler society. Even if his article had remained within the pages of *Das Kapland*, or in the German language, or in the Cape colony, some security in solitude may have been left us. As it was, Mercury – in his proper Roman form as god of commerce, not the Greek messenger of the gods – delivered the article to our doorstep, translated into the language of our neighbours. And so the web caught us and the spider sprang.

I am too melodramatic, my metaphor too strong. The good lady who chose the nom de plume of "Mina" for her sharp response to Franz's article was, I am sure, a respectable woman, quite un-insect like and, judging from the nature of her response, perfectly, even extremely, refined. "Sir," she wrote to the editor of the *Natal Mercury*, "Prior Francis seems to despise our lady missionaries with their long trains and sunshades. I would tell him through your paper that if a female missionary wishes to do good to the Kafirs she must gain their respect, which the long trains and sunshades have done; but it is very doubtful if a Sister dresses in short petticoats and shoeless feet, a white rag on her head, and a hoe on her shoulder, with three pumpkins on the back, it will convince the Kafir of the style to be approved of."

The three pumpkins were a bit much – the shoeless feet and white rag too, I am sure – but Franz's article clearly stung her more than she herself was capable of stinging, spider or not. Or so it appeared from her reference to a Sister who was assaulted "near Umtata … which never happened to our missionary ladies, in spite of the long trains and sunshades which Prior Francis seems to disapprove of". Her letter ended: "He has got his work cut out to produce all that is enumerated in his letter, but he has got 80 single men to help him, and there will be no long trains and sunshades to check their ambition. – I am, &c., MINA"

Franz, of course, could not let things be and allow the eloquence of our work to answer in its own good time. Nothing would do but that he must immediately rush to his desk and begin: "Sir, Once more I turn to take up my pen to address your readers, and to explain to them that 'Mina', who on the 6th replied to my article of the 4th, is in error when she writes that I despise the missionary ladies with their long trains and sunshades …"

Would we never have enough of long trains and sunshades? Not if Franz had his way. In this exchange he demonstrated his absolute determination to meet any public criticism publicly, to match point for point, letter for letter, word for word. The good Mrs Mina got as good – no, as would always be the case from now on – much, much better than she gave in her linguistic assault. In wit, in logic, in image and phrase, and, beyond all else, in sheer length, our Superior came back to her with mighty sweeps of the pen. From differences in fashion and culture to the practicalities of working attire, to allowances for all classes according to their occupation, to the means of gaining the respect of the Kafir, he overwhelmed her with a steady barrage, complete with Latin turns of phrase, German proverbs, Biblical allusions and exegesis, and illustrations from his past in Bosnia and the present at Mariannhill. He ended by graciously allowing Mina her "rich trains, &c." but exhorted her "not to trouble about the ill-treated Sisters in short dresses, who set the world such a glowing example".

Somewhere in the deluge Franz poured upon his pithy antagonist there was an attempt to clarify his original point regarding assisted passage for the Sisters, despite their being single women. I am sure Mina, whoever she was – and whoever she was, she knew her Bible, her pseudonym having been carefully chosen from the parable of the servants who invested their master's money wisely – had no idea what she was about to bring down upon her head when she shot off her pointed comments. But she learned her lesson well and never bothered the letter columns of the *Mercury* again.

~

Trappists, preferring nothing to the love of Christ, make themselves stran-gers to the actions of the world. One could argue that Franz's energetic presentations of those actions in Chapter, where the crackle of the broad pages of the newspaper sounded as strange as the news he broadcast, could be taken as a necessary part of the guidance he owed our community as its Superior. Our Statutes can be interpreted as allowing for this, *as long as the special character of the contemplative life is safeguarded*. And even as he shared with us those aspects of life beyond our enclosure that he believed were of concern to us, Franz maintained for the rest of the monks *a careful formation in the discipline of separation from the world*.

But it was in the nature of Franz's character to be not so much a reader as a writer. Writing was for him a way of dealing with idleness – he first began to write at length at Agram, where he grappled with the boredom of being the Convent's spiritual director by preparing for publication the discarded history he had discovered of the institution. This he never completed, but the routine of writing took hold and, before he became a Trappist, he kept an extensive and detailed diary. This was lost (stolen, Franz insisted) just before he entered Mariawald, something he grumbled about constantly in those long days and nights towards the end of his life when he was trying to recreate these years through me.

At Mariawald the regime of Trappist life left scant time for reading or writing. In his Regulations, de Rancé is unambiguous in his dislike of books in general. "No one may go to the library without the permission of the Superior, and it should be given very rarely, because nothing is so common with Religious as succumbing to the temptation to pick up some learning and to read out of curiosity," he directs, telling us, too, that "we do not carry a book to work with a view to reading there". Franz went further: he even found the books that were read aloud in the refectory an irritation, sometimes because he thought they were badly written, sometimes because he flatly disagreed with them, but mostly because they did not deal with topics he believed to be important.

As for writing, not much is said in the Regulations of an activity that has so small a place in one of de Rancé's houses: the only clearly expressed rule regarding writing is that the desks and common tables in the cloister are to be used for this purpose. "It is only holy things that we write in the cloister; if someone happens to have orders from the Superior to write a letter," de Rancé stipulates, "he does not do it in the cloister, but in his cell, or in the place designated for this by the Reverend Father Abbot." In the first flush of his contemplative enthusiasm, Franz had no trouble keeping to the four private letters a year allowed a Trappist, and even found some relief in abstaining from the growing interest in writing he experienced at Agram. At that time he began to think that there was something about the whole business of writing that tends to corrupt the purity of one's spirit of faith.

But in establishing a Trappist house of his own, Franz soon abandoned such thoughts, treating them as an indulgence a man of his new responsibilities could not afford. He returned to writing with a vengeance. It began with the flood of begging letters that poured out of his calf stable in Bosnia, and developed with the positive responses he received, some of which made a point of commenting on his style. One Ludwig Auer in particular, a youth educator who ran a publishing house for the instruction of the Catholic laity in Donauwörth, commended Franz's "graphic, creative, and gripping" prose and sent Franz a small hand-press. It was intended to save him time in his correspondence but was of use in an increasingly wide range of publishing endeavours at Mariastern. I have told you that Franz went far out of his way to make sure that Dunbrody was similarly equipped, and the more substantial press he purchased as the proper gift for a new foundation (in place of Bishop Ricards' gift of crockery) was rapidly given pride of place at Mariannhill.

The press was so valued a feature of our house that Franz at first actually slept next to it, housed as it was in his tiny and primitive "priory". Within a matter of months its accommodation was given precedence in our building programme and we created a special brick-floored printing room, twelve by twelve feet in size. This in turn became the cradle for everything the publishing house at Mariannhill is today. The recognition Mariannhill has won as the home of the famous St Thomas Aquinas Press comes back to the dictum Franz often repeated – paradoxically, ironically, misguidedly, who is to say? – that "it was as a Trappist that I came upon the real value and importance of the press".

I am not sure if his ever active soul saw this impulse to write – no, this vocation, as compelling, as it sometimes seemed, as anything he undertook in the religious sense – as an aspect of his manual labour or his contemplation. I must report that it was mainly in the time set aside for private prayer that he wrote (not even his writing was allowed to intrude upon his commitment to the physical work required of us). As long as he applied himself to spiritual topics to be published in organs for religious propaganda, his writing, I suppose, could be seen to fit well in the periods dedicated to contemplation in the daily life of a Cistercian monk.

His first well-known composition – the amusing forty-one-page booklet *Are you a Chimney Sweep?* – was clearly aimed at winning vocations, and his openly propagandistic account of his experiences with a seeress in Alsace, entitled *Something for Unbelievers*, could fall within the tradition of religious meditative writing. Our Order saw fit to support, and the Catholic *Pressverein* to publish, a history he wrote of Mariastern. Even *Fliegende Blätter* kept its true course in the arms of the Church, raising both the image of Christ's work in Africa and the need for material support for this work.

~

After his encounter with Mina, Franz seemed unable to stop his forays into the public arena. Within weeks a brief court report of a "Serious Charge Against An Ex-Trappist" earned three full columns in response. The case concerned one of the many postulants already pouring into Mariannhill from Germany, one Hermann von Grueber, who was clearly never meant to be a Trappist and had been dismissed. After being turned out he was arrested on a charge of stealing from a German settler farmer and his case had come up for trial. Franz was "surprised and annoyed" to see a failed postulant referred to as an "ex-Trappist" and desired to put a "brief but correct explanation" before the public. What followed was anything but brief, and turned out to be nothing less than an apologia for our whole way of life, especially "one of the strictest and most important rules of our Order: silence", the breaking of which was the fault for which von Grueber was ultimately expelled from our monastery.

I cannot help saying that I cringed at this display of our deepest mysteries in the grubby form of ink and cheap paper. Apologies and explanations have, as I have had occasion to put before you previously, no place in our vocation, and it is in resisting them that much of the charisma of our silence resides. Once this has been surrendered, it is possible to see in the insistent flurry of letters to come, as well as publications of all kinds – our "Flying Leaves" were soon to gather into articles, newspapers, magazines, journals, calendars, books of every type, illustrated and otherwise, a mountain of shuffling and shifting paper – evidence enough for the titles of "Apostle of the Press" and "God's Trumpeter" that Franz was to earn.

Soon enough Franz's pen found a topic that would truly cut to the quick of our spirit and vocation. Whatever exposure we endured before the settlers of Natal through the medium of the press, little could be found to fault the way in which our house prospered and grew. On our own ground, we were entirely focused upon establishing ourselves in such a way as to make it possible to live strictly according to the Holy Rule of St Benedict, as reformed by St Bernard and modified by de Rancé. Here anyone was welcome to watch our silent work and prayer towards that end and, indeed, throughout our first year at Mariannhill our being watched in this holy endeavour was the essential nature of our relationship with those nearest to us, the Natives.

Sometimes I could not help but wonder what they saw in us, kneeling for hours apparently doing nothing, and then suddenly beginning to toil away with what must have seemed like gratuitous energy and speed. And what did they think when we rose up from our labour in the fields, formed into two rows and bent down deeply as we intoned "Glory be to the Father and to the Son and to the Holy Ghost"?

I would cut such wonderings short with great firmness, and remind myself that what they thought was beyond my concerns as a contemplative. We were as yet completely ignorant of the Zulu language, and they of English, which Franz was learning at a rapid pace. But the lack of communication between us was not just a by-product of our mismatched languages; it was, rather, the proper expression of our commitment to both God and the world. We were dedicated, after all, to seeking God, not to seeking souls for God.

There was one major anomaly in the progress of our building. Franz seemed to be in no hurry to raise up the walls of our foundation. With no language available to us other than laying ourselves open to the gaze of the Natives, he feared that the solid barriers of a monastery would rob us of our "apostolic fruitfulness". Until now, he would tell us, the Natives had known nothing about an invisible, omnipresent and omniscient God. Our kneeling in prayer seven times a day, whether at a plough or up on scaffolding, at the washtub or at the anvil, showed them that this invisible God was indeed everywhere. Thus every Brother hoeing a field or herding the oxen had become a missionary to them, and his example taught more about praying than all the learned debates about perfect prayer.

Hidden apostolic fruitfulness was the full phrase, I reminded myself silently while Franz spoke. And there were times when even Franz had to admit that our uncloistered state presented special problems for our way of life. As when, one day, Brother Cook came running up to Franz, signing furiously. In irritation Franz gave him permission to speak, and was told that two women trying to trade with us had placed themselves and a flock of children right in front of the kitchen door.

"Why don't you just chase them away?" Franz asked. "I have given you permission to use the Zulu words you know to buy milk and maize or sell bread and sugar."

"Yes, but I don't know how to say 'go away,'" the flustered Brother replied.

Franz strode off to the kitchen and there indeed were the women with half a dozen bags, baskets and bundles full of maize spread on the floor, ready for inspection and sale. They had draped blankets about themselves, but enough flesh was on display to remind Franz of why he had issued and publicised a strict ordinance forbidding women to enter the grounds of the monastery. He had even relocated the old road behind the site of our temporary monastery so that women would not walk in sight of our living quarters. And here were two women right on our grounds! In a fury (or, as he would call it later when he related the event for our edification in Chapter, "in holy wrath because it concerned the house of God"), Franz stammered a few words in Bosnian which even I recognised would shock anyone who happened to speak that language. When this had no effect, he resorted to what he called "the universal language".

Snatching a handful of ropes that lay amongst the bundles and bags on the floor, Franz had taken a swipe at one of the women. "In addition to this rather expressive sign that even dogs can understand," he added, "my eyes, too, signalled that my amiability was quickly deserting me." The blows, though, seemed to have been enough to scatter the women and children, who grabbed for their baskets, scattering maize in all directions as they fled. The larger of the two women appeared to have lost the most because she tried to grab all her baskets at once, he told us, while attempting to keep her blanket about herself and dodge the flailing rushes at the same time.

"Maintaining silence to increase contemplation does not by itself rule out communication," Franz said. "We Trappists after all use sign language to express ourselves to each other, but we must remember that it is a language that is spoken on all continents when nothing else will work. The blows I directed at those women showed the expressive force of a single sign. A long sermon in Zulu could hardly have matched it."

~

And so Franz's point was made, and our perpetual silence defended. But no outward form of our silence, be it the rituals of our work and prayer or our hand signs and the limited sanction of speech, seemed to inspire a curiosity strong enough to draw the Natives closer to the meaning of that silence. Despite our ending our first year in Natal with one hundred and eighty-eight acres of waste land made arable, three and a half miles of road completed with as much again half-ready, and buildings that covered one thousand three hundred square yards, even the most meticulous accounting of our achievements would find only one baptism recorded at Mariannhill. And this baptism was, according to whatever theological concept one brought to bear, more than doubtful.

The truth is that the first Zulu drawn to Mariannhill was a dead one. He was also, what is more, brought to us by the Lutherans – indirectly, it is true, but the truth is that faith of any kind had very little to do with our first baptism.

What transpired was this: the young man who had brought the message to us from the Lutheran pastor that led to our finding the site we now occupied had not forgotten us. He came to observe our progress quite regularly, and we came to know him by his name, Fotsholo Dube. One day he arrived and asked us to cure a sick neighbour of his. Franz's dislike of formal medicine was as strong as ever, but with a land full of people outside our – metaphorically speaking – doors, his homeopathic pocket dispensary came back into play. The comparative abundance of water in Natal enabled him, too, to indulge his interest in Fr Sebastian Kneipp's Water Cure to the full, and he was only too ready to experiment with this on anyone who seemed in need. We were, therefore, slowly regaining our reputation as healers that we had earned in Bosnia.

On this particular day Franz was far too busy with a building project to be led off into the surrounding countryside, and thus ordered me to see to the matter. My own reputation for tending the sick within our community remained intact throughout our travels, so much so that I was alarmed to find myself referred to in more than one of the newspaper accounts written about us over the years as "the physician for the monastery". One even claimed I was a "Doctor of Medicine", a total fabrication strengthened, I suppose, by Franz's absolute refusal ever to call upon any of the local medical fraternity to deal with illness or injury in our community. I am afraid that I would be the one to seal this prejudice forever, the cost of which I would learn within a few short years.

At the time I had begun adding to my rather primitive self-acquired medical skills a number of Kneipp's practices, a recourse that resulted in strengthening Franz's trust in me as a healer to a remarkable degree. This was largely based on the testimony of the first of my patients, who had been suffering from severe headaches and loss of appetite diagnosed by a medical practitioner as a collapse of the nerves. The practitioner's powders had produced no relief and, as the afflicted Brother reported to Franz in writing, that was when he was started on the Kneipp cure. "To begin with," he wrote, "I was immersed in a warm herbal bath for twenty minutes, then I was given an ice-cold washing down and made to move about in the fresh air. After that half a big bucket of water was poured over the top part of my body, and the other half over the lower part. Then I was given steam baths in regular succession, alternated with warm baths. The results were optimal. The pain in my temples ceased, I could sleep again, and my appetite came back. For all this I have to thank Fr Joseph."

And so it was that I found myself following Fotsholo out into the hills just beyond the borders of our property. There, in a ramshackle hut set amidst neglected fields and surrounded by mangy dogs, I found an old man clearly near his end. I did what I could to make him comfortable physically, but he passed away just as I began to pray over him. Entirely at a loss as to what to do next, I baptised him *in articulo mortis* and set off back to the monastery. I lost the path briefly, although not in any uncomfortable way, and took the opportunity to enjoy the quiet of the hills offset by the wind blowing about them whilst I forged a path of my own through the long grass.

As I came up to the monastery I was quite astounded to find a group of people standing around Franz with the body of the old man I had left not so long before laid out on the ground in front of him. Apparently the dead man's household felt that we should be responsible for his burial as I had put him to rest. There was, we gathered, some concern about my having put him safely amongst the *amadlozi* – Fotsholo translated this for us as "the spirits of the dead" – and banishing him firmly to the world below so that he would not come back and trouble his relatives, or bring disaster to the community.

We buried this most tentative of Christians according to Trappist custom in an area hastily designated as our cemetery. The ceremony took place in full view of the much thinned ranks of curious observers who still made up something of a daily audience, augmented on this occasion by those associated in one way or another, we assumed, with the deceased. They watched without comment as our entire monastic community turned out in full formal dress to convey the dead man to the grave. We had clothed him in the roughest habiliments of our Order, as we would have one of our own, and carried him on a board with a bolster of straw beneath his head. As we walked we sang penitential hymns, and when we reached the grave one of our brethren put the capuch of the Order over his head.

We then lowered the man into the grave without a coffin, as is our practice, and burning coals from the censer were poured alongside him. After this the Brothers took turns to fill the grave slowly with earth while we priests and the Choir Fathers went down on our knees and bent almost to the ground as we prayed for the repose of the soul of our first Native Christian. From the corner of my eye I noticed that as we did this our audience also ducked to the ground, reaching out with their hands to the sand before them and apparently praying in their own way. As we stood to sing the *Miserere*, I could not help but wonder what those watching us thought of us – we who never talked to the living but suddenly took so much interest in the dead.

Again I arrested this thought as quickly as I could, but as I did so I realised that as long as we lived openly under the gaze of the eyes of those around us such thoughts would continue to insinuate themselves. The pure contemplation of God seemed impossible when the nature of our relationship with our neighbours was so very porous, and I felt myself beginning to miss the spirit within Franz that so infuriated Bishop Ricards. What had happened to that concern for building that the Bishop had accused Franz of putting before all else, even our most basic material needs? Something had changed here in Natal, some new spirit was struggling to be born, and within myself I became aware of a hint of fear of this child of a very different wilderness.

We had not had the chance to offer our first convert the full comfort of a Trappist death. There was no time for us to gather about his bed of straw and support and console him with our prayers, as we would do only a few months later when Brother Barnabas died, the first of our Brothers to enter his final agony in Africa. Kneeling gently before Brother Barnabas, I had stroked the hands trained to build instruments that sounded out in all their musical glory the greatness of God, hands that had instead been turned, without a single complaint, to our most mundane problems with wood – a bend here, a join there, even a whole structure, like his brave attempt at a windmill at Dunbrody – and had found their way to silent worship in the humble ingenuity needed to solve them.

Even in death, with unseeing eyes wide open to the timber angles of his own devising in our dormitory roof, his mouth open and working as if in soundless song, he elected silence. And we respected this although it meant that he did not, as is required of a devout Trappist who feels his last hour is approaching, ask his Superior for permission to die. Franz came to him with the traditional offer to break the seal that had held his tongue throughout his Trappist life so that he could, while he yet had strength, address us, his brethren, from the brink of that eternity to which his soul was hastening. But he chose not to speak to us, be it of our holy calling or his life that was past or of that which is in the future; he simply kept to his song that offered up his breath alone, with no word or melody to harm it.

~

It is doubtful, I suppose, that we would have offered our first convert the dispensation to speak from the brink of eternity. Would we, given the opportunity, have allowed that he had anything to tell us, I wonder? And yet it was his silence in death that spoke more eloquently to our daily witnesses than all our display. His burial, it turned out, had the most profound effect on our Zulu audience of any of the rituals we followed. We were totally unaware that the solemnities we offered him – apart from the water and smoke and murmuring at intervals – had much in common with the Natives' own manner of burying the dead. The Trappist custom of interring the body without a coffin was, we were to learn later, a crucial point of similarity with Zulu customs and sparked some interest in our strange practices.

Did this mean that the Zulus left our tiny cemetery preoccupied with the immortality of the soul, in its existence separate from the body? Did

223

it provoke thoughts about their ideas of a "high God" and ours? I do not know. I only know that when they did come to us it was not for the Word Incarnate but, quite simply, the word.

Only one Zulu of rank had come to inquire about us since our arrival. This was just a few days after we had set up our camp, and while he may have been a chief, our guess was that he was a fairly lowly one. This we surmised from his mode of dress, which consisted of a shirt and a short jacket but no trousers – his nether regions were covered instead by a piece of cowskin. He did, nevertheless, sport spurs on one ankle and rode up on a beautiful horse. After some convoluted and quite tortuous meandering on his part, we finally managed to make out that he wanted to know if this was a place where his people could "learn the book". It was clear that this was his expectation of a "mission" – no doubt raised by the Protestant missionaries in Natal – but we were in no position to offer such learning, nor, strictly speaking, was it our aim ever to do so.

Still, Franz immediately jumped in, hurrying the interpreter along to let the chief know that we intended to educate both his and all Native children in the crafts. Perhaps Franz's careful distinction regarding what we were able to teach was lost in translation, but when the answer was conveyed in the affirmative the chief, if such he was, jumped in the air several times in delight. Then he stopped suddenly, mid-flight, and with a darkening face inquired how much it would cost. When Franz told whoever was interpreting that day to reply "Nothing at all" and to add that we would also feed and clothe his children if they behaved and obeyed, the chief was clearly overjoyed. He positively leapt on his horse and headed off with the news to his homestead, which, although at a considerable distance, was one of those that looked down upon us from the surrounding hills.

Franz had put his reply to the chief with perfect correctness. As he said on more than one occasion, "The Catholic Church has a great many religious Orders, each of which has its own objective. Our objective is to teach the uneducated classes agriculture and handicraft, for which our lives must serve as the first example." In Franz's view, we were pioneers who had to precede the other Orders so that they, in turn, could educate, teach, take care of the sick and do mission work and other works of charity.

Franz, myself and Julius Seibels, our printer, had been busy trying to assemble the printing press when the chief arrived. As our eyes followed our visitor's meandering passage back to his home, Seibels – a layperson, you will remember – sighed and remarked, "Such a fierce ambition to read. How wonderful in their eyes must be those rows of curious little black figures, twisted and turned into every conceivable form, and stamped so regularly on every page of a book. What untold delights, what concealed mysteries they must imagine these could unfold to them!"

Or words to that effect. I am an old man now trying to re-imagine things long gone, and such quaintness of expression is possibly all my own. Still, what I do remember strongly, and I think accurately, is the way Franz expanded on this passing thought. "Yes," he said, "but as for spiritual values, other missionaries tell me the Natives have scarcely any vocabulary for them in their language, and therefore no desire for them has entered their minds as yet. There can be no wish for unknown things, and so we must use this desire for literary advancement to point towards higher things. In the end, I am sure, we will have to use the incentive of the book to lead them beyond their earthly aims."

He turned back to the crate of metal and oil and type as I stood there gazing out into the haze. It was then I first began to wonder if the Africans could only become Christian when we gave them the language in which to be Christian. What did this say of a God of silence? Many times in the months and years ahead, when we tried to cross the barrier of the languages around us, it occurred to me that in propagating God He ceases to exist outside the language in which He is put into words.

Even at the time, Franz's comment worried me. There was a thin dividing line here and it was one that we had stood in danger of crossing before, as when the Immigration Board approved Franz's appeals for assisted passage for new members, rapidly expanding the size of our community. Approval was granted on the basis of our agricultural and building achievements but also because, from the first, Franz stressed that we worked "in the supposition that the monks, by cultivating and tilling land after the best principles and newest inventions and by teaching the savages agriculture, industries, and a quiet home life, will render an essential service to the English Government".

I had been concerned about the word "teaching" in this letter to the Board that we drafted painfully in English soon after our arrival in Natal, and on this occasion I dared express my disquiet. "It seems to me too direct a way of expressing our role as silent example," I ventured to say to Franz, but he dismissed me out of hand. "You are quibbling," he said, "and quibbling about a word in a language you do not even speak." According to Franz the intricacies of our Order would have to be put not just in English but in a manner that could be easily grasped. He reminded me that we had found ways to have schools before – remember Mariastern! – and would no doubt find ways again.

I remembered Mariastern all too well in this regard and my disquiet remained. Soon enough Franz was in touch with Bishop Jolivet, asking if we could introduce an Order of nuns, very much like those Sisters in Kaffraria who had so unwittingly brought a tumble of print down upon us. They had founded a school in Umtata but, as Franz foretold, the international financial crisis affected us all "down to the last Sister of Mercy in Kaffraria". Fewer and fewer settlers could afford the tuition, room and board of the school, but the intrepid Sisters simply became a better example in Franz's eyes when we heard that they coped with these new circumstances by taking up the farming that had so offended Mina's sensibilities. It was women with just such spirit that he hoped to introduce to Mariannhill. Ultimately he was looking for a congregation of nuns who could carry out the pastoral work forbidden to us as Trappists.

However, the Bishop was adamant in his refusal of Franz's request for Sisters of Mercy from Agram, the branch of the Order Franz had both fled from and retreated to. Whilst he recognised that Sisters could be of great value in Natal, he insisted that they must be of a French congregation, as were all the other Religious of his vicariate. More specifically, he told Franz, he had given the French Sisters of the Holy Family sole care for the work in Natal, and no other Sisters should be imported from overseas. This did not suit Franz and so he decided our work would have to go ahead without nuns. How we were meant to pursue it, forbidden as we ourselves were from participating actively in apostolic activities, was an open question. And we were still grappling with it when the answer, for good or ill, was heading towards us on the new road we had built from Pinetown directly to our gates.

~

I had grown both tired and wary of the strangers who endlessly came knocking. As we grew more self-sufficient we had less and less need of Pinetown, and the town itself had fallen into decline with the departure of the large military contingent that had been stationed there during the recent wars with the Zulus. Nevertheless, the road between the monastery and Pinetown – much praised in the local press along with our numerous improvements to the surroundings (not least our unique bridge-building method) – had the unfortunate effect of drawing people from the town to us. These were usually people with only the most salacious interests, who, after enjoying our hospitality and the by now standard tour, would stand around pointing and chattering, mostly on the subject of our refraining from speech.

One morning, a rather light-skinned Native speaking fluent French approached our porter. The flustered monk ushered this confident and prosperous-looking man before Franz, leaving our Prior in turn to be startled by his excellent French. His name, he told us, was Benjamin Makhaba, and he had received his Christian education in the Mission School of Roma, in Basutoland. He himself was from that high and remote land that lay above and behind the dramatic range of mountains to the north of us, and he had been trained as a saddler by the Oblate Fathers.

He had encountered what he called "unfortunate circumstances" at this station and had, as a result, come to Durban where he worked at his trade and learned Zulu. (Franz respected his reticence on the subject, but we too had heard reports of flaws in discipline regarding, especially, liquor and marriage for cattle). By dint of steadfastness and industry Benjamin amassed a small fortune and invested this in the acquisition of three eating houses for Natives in the town. For a while prosperity turned his head, he had told Franz in his overly formal French, and he forgot his religious obligations. But after three years he returned to the consolation of his faith and, on the advice of a priest in Durban, had come to us to apply for the post of catechist.

What is one to do when the hand of the Lord seems so clearly writ upon a person? From the moment he heard the word "Zulu" coming out of a black Catholic mouth, Franz had barely been able to hold himself back from appropriating Benjamin in some way, his mind filled with the tumbling options he was dying to put to this portly, well-dressed and finely mannered man. When the word "catechist" was sounded, Franz virtually pounced. "Of course, of course" filled the air as Benjamin was only too gladly accepted. This new member of our community set off for Durban at once, with a view to settling his affairs there. In a matter of days he had sold his three "hotels" and returned to the solitude of the monastery.

Franz was ecstatic. "The son of the right hand," he reminded us when speaking of Benjamin, regaling us with Jacob's joy at the birth of a son despite Rachel's death during their travels in the wilderness. "The one who assisted with the repairing of the walls of Jerusalem," he went on, quoting now from Nehemiah even before Benjamin's return, "a person of distinction returning from captivity!" As it was, we found Benjamin's tribal surname difficult and it was as "Benjamin the Basuto" that he was always known amongst us.

II

Benjamin's first task was to make good on Franz's promise to the junior chief who had approached us on the day after our arrival. We were not in a position to meet the offer of training Franz extended on that occasion primarily because of our total ignorance of the local languages, although this was not for want of trying. When, on seeing some of our more prominent structures, our tenants had asked us for help with building we were able to respond – so long as they built proper, or "human" as Franz called them, houses: square with a flat roof and at least one window and a door, and a table and chair inside. In this we had managed with just signs, a feature of communicating without a common tongue that suited us well, and a more positive application of Franz's theory regarding a "world language" than his driving off the women.

Indeed, Franz was so confident that our Order's signing abilities could be turned to good secular effect that he believed no other language was necessary to teach the Natives how to work or learn a trade. Signs were sufficient for teaching beginners many things, he believed, and beyond that our mere presence and the example we set of hard work would be both school and sermon for the children of nature amongst whom we had set ourselves. Still, nothing in our lexicon of hands and fingers had managed to convey a world beyond the earthly one at which we could gesture.

One African decided to visit our church and we made him welcome, along with three others who joined him (properly attired, of course) over the next few weeks. They would sit there all day long and play with the unblessed rosary beads we gave them and seemed to listen attentively to our chants, but eventually they drifted off like smoke from the grass fires we would sometimes see burning in the distance.

228

Benjamin was now asked to found a school where the Word could take hold, and with it He who is beyond all words. He began by visiting the kraals in the vicinity of the monastery to drum up scholars, and immediately met with some success. "Perhaps it is his big black face and sparkling eyes that steal the hearts of the people," Brother Zacharias said as we watched the first catch of two little boys fearfully entering the room we had set aside for a schoolroom. Our faithful collector was visiting us after one of his fund-raising trips in Austria and Germany, and I must confess that I thought his success in playing up for Europeans the more colourful aspects of our neighbours in Africa was showing too plainly.

For myself, I wondered how the boys' senses were reacting to the new space they were entering. The schoolroom must have seemed so enclosed to those used to the open hills, the smell alone oppressive. By now we were building with green bricks of our own manufacture but were still covering the walls with tar to prevent the sun-dried clay from eroding too easily. Even though Franz had ordered that the walls should not rise all the way to the roof, allowing an eighteen-inch opening to serve as a source of light and ventilation, the newly daubed rooms reeked of our construction methods. Topped off with white corrugated iron, our black-walled buildings must have looked stern and stark amidst the waving grass. I can remember clearly the pungent smell of the tar that burned my nostrils in the midday sun.

I tried hard to imagine what was passing through the two young minds but abandoned the effort in a crisis of indecision as to whether it was proper to my contemplative vocation to think in this way. And if we did not know what the boys were thinking, we received a clue as to the thinking outside our enclosure when we asked Benjamin to tell us the meaning of their names: Mazamani was beyond his interpretive abilities, but the name Kantolo expressed all too well how we were perceived beyond our enclosure: its meaning, in Benjamin's translation, was "jail".

Later that afternoon, as was common at that time of year, a surprisingly cool rain swept in and I caught sight of two wondering faces peeping out at the dripping damp from what must now have seemed the cosy environment of the schoolroom. Once the rain eased off they sallied out, the dress in which they were attired for the great occasion now more appropriate for the weather.

My heart went out to the two small beings, their heads almost lost in tattered hats of no mean age. Their spindly bodies were naked under an abandoned soldier's jacket and a mighty greatcoat respectively, each drawing the scum of two feet of mud along with its bearer as he struggled past. My work did not involve any contact with the boys, but I watched from hooded eyes as more and more of them cautiously came down to join those first two.

We had soon discovered that it was not so much Benjamin's talents that drew our scholars in as a command from the mysterious Chief Manzini whose absence so bemused us. He lived, it turned out, some eight miles from where we had settled in our expectation of finding him and had, it seems, been watching us carefully since our arrival. Our future relations would make it clear that he had no interest in our making his people Christians; he wished only that we should teach them to "hear", as he put it in one of his early messages, "what the paper had to say". Chief Manzini considered himself too old for this kind of learning but ordered that every kraal under his jurisdiction send at least two boys to our school, no matter what their age or inclination. All six of his male children attended regularly at his insistence.

Benjamin the Basuto threw himself into his appointed task with startling vehemence. Nonetheless, his every effort with letters and numbers failed, and the incessant din of alphabet and abacus filled the air around the schoolroom – by his own admission – in vain. He was adamant that this was in no way because of his failings as a teacher, and it is true that his story-telling appeared to be effective and inspiring. One of his young pupils, for instance, could report with ease what God had done on the six days of creation although (to the embarrassment of his teacher who was translating for him) he also informed us that on the seventh day "God took rest and made porridge for all men"!

Franz soon began to suspect that Benjamin's enthusiasm for education outstripped his talents. The "Basuto" was employed, after all, as a catechist rather than a teacher, and whilst the subject matter he taught was distinctly confessional – for basic literacy was conveyed to the boys through the medium of a Catholic education – Franz and he fell out over his method of teaching it. The crux of the matter was language: Benjamin chose to follow the prevailing custom of the land, which was to teach Native children to read in their own tongue first and to continue from there in English. Franz felt a far more pragmatic approach should be followed.

This difference came to a head one sultry afternoon, the lowering clouds and humidity pressing in on the schoolroom where Franz had requested my presence. I would be in charge whenever he was away, and this included overseeing the school. Unfortunately the debate ensued in French, the only language the two antagonists shared to some degree and one in which I was most uncertain of my expression even if I could understand enough of it.

I did not, in any event, have strong feelings about Franz's argument that the pupils should be taught in English from the beginning. The whole issue of teaching, as I have indicated, seemed to me entirely outside of my calling, the question of language thus superfluous, even distasteful. In the words of the Psalmist, "To Thee silence alone is fitting by way of praise" and I was more than happy to stand aside, staring at the floor as the voices of the Prior and the catechist raged around me.

"The boys want to receive help to get *along* in life," Franz was arguing, smacking his hand into his fist with each emphasis, "which, for the ambitious boy, means going to *town*. To do this he needs at least a smattering of *English*, and this is why he has *come* to school. Zulu, no matter how highly developed his proficiency in it may be, will lead him *nowhere*. There are simply *no* positions in which it will be of any use."

Franz's approach to language may well have been purely pragmatic, but Benjamin's contrary conviction was based upon something even more fundamental that Franz did not seem to grasp. The fact of the matter, beneath all sophistry and rhetorical effects, was that Benjamin's knowledge of English was extremely limited. Hence his teaching depended on his ability to communicate in the Bantu languages. Perhaps he was too proud to spell this out, and his apparent stubbornness led Franz to turn unexpectedly to me. "Well, what do you say, Father Joseph, considering there so earnestly?" he asked and, faced with my open-mouthed surprise, turned back to Benjamin. "Do you see?" he continued. "There is the miracle of silence! We call those things miraculous that seem inexplicable to us and how Father Joseph can remain silent before your obstinacy is certainly inexplicable to me!"

Then, in a manner that permitted no opposition, he announced, "English is the language that is best understood in the towns and on the farms, so it is in English our boys will learn."

Stillness reigned for a few minutes, and then slowly, quietly, in his best formal French, Benjamin said, "I wish to tender my resignation as teacher."

A new development in our community allowed Franz to accept this with just a touch too much alacrity. He was about to turn away, when Benjamin, son of the right hand, he who helped rebuild the walls of Jerusalem, spoke again. "And I wish to become," he said, each word hanging in the warm, tar-filled air, "a monk."

The miracle of silence fell then on Franz, his mouth working in his beard as he gasped, whether for air or words I am not sure. The beginnings of a sentence began to take form and then collapsed. He was now speaking in German anyway, and was still muttering in this language as he went out of the room, leaving Benjamin and me to stare first at each other and then, as if by mutual agreement, at the floor.

~

This was the first time Mariannhill was confronted with the problem of admitting a Bantu to our community. A special Chapter was called, with free dispensation for everyone to speak. By its conclusion Benjamin's request was rejected, on the grounds that the Trappist Rule was too strict for the African. Our rising at two o'clock in the morning, and spending seven hours a day in prayer, meditation and Mass; our nine hours of hard manual work before retiring at seven in the evening; our food of fruit, vegetables and water, with meat and wine and beer strictly forbidden; our dress of shoes and long brown habit with cowl or – even more unthinkable – white habits with black scapulars; our prayers and chants in Latin and, above all, our silence, the silence that is never broken except in the case of absolute necessity, and even then only with the permission of the Superior … We solemnly reminded each other of each and all of these things, and decided that the native people of South Africa, at their present stage of development, were unsuitable candidates for this rigorous life.

Benjamin the Basuto took our decision with quiet dignity. He remained with us as a catechist for a while, although he spent more and more time amongst the Zulus in our neighbourhood. Having lost his schoolroom, he treated the growing number of kraals around us as a great school over which he presided. Working in our fields in the morning, I would watch from the corners of my downcast eyes as he strode off. Fotsholo sometimes went ahead, an hour or so before, to announce the approach of the evangelist, and in the evening I would see the two of them plodding wearily home together.

On cooler days the pair would assemble a small circle of potential converts, Benjamin altering unbecoming postures, arranging extra bodily coverings, and generally disposing the listeners to the better reception of his good tidings. It was clear though that when there was "a bull of a sun", as Fotsholo would say, the temptation of the great gourds of beer that stood in every kraal became too much. Benjamin would then return no longer the proud hotelier but the wasted patron, bleary and red-eyed and mumbling to himself about something or other.

~

It is another of the sad ironies of Mariannhill that the teacher who re-placed Benjamin came from that country over the seas to which our first catechist later attempted to travel, in the hope of finding there at last his true spiritual home.

Franz had passed through London on his trip to the European continent in 1883 and made use of the opportunity to advertise our new foundation. His presence was announced in the *Tablet* and the *Catholic Times*, and a young student of history and languages from Birkbeck College, whose interest in the Zulus had been aroused by the pictures filling the newspapers during the Zulu War of 1879 – pictures of ferocious savages, adorned with flow-ing plumes and leathern girdles and brandishing assegais whilst swinging striped shields – went to hear the unusual missionary give an address.

The student, not even twenty years old, was Alfred Bryant, born in London, the son of a printer. "I really cannot say what moved me to present myself," he wrote of this occasion, "as I had never for a moment entertained any thought of a missionary life or any desire to leave my country. Before I knew it, however, we had come to an agreement whereby I should go out and be made some use of."

Bryant's published account of how he came amongst us has achieved a certain amount of fame, and I have it here with me. In it he tells how he immediately spent £30 of his own money on a ticket for the good ship *German* of the Union Line, which took passage for Natal in August 1883. The voyage still took thirty-five days, even though the ship's sails had been supplemented with a steam engine. He arrived in Durban in September, and found a town consisting of only two streets, inches deep in sand, with an assortment of shops on either side of each. He managed to get a lift on an ox-wagon to the station and from there followed our route by rail, alighting in Pinetown to find a largely deserted military camp – so much for those brave and tragic figures in khaki he had seen depicted in the papers in heroic engagement with the Zulus – and a public house.

Commonly known as "Fort Funk" because the local residents had re-treated to its confines in fear during the hostilities of 1879, the Wayside Inn was a far cry from his favourite haunt at Birkbeck, the Friend at Hand in Russell Square, but he took a half-pint there by way of refreshment and a farewell to such indulgences. In similar vein he had picked up a copy of the *Natal Mercury* where he could not have found much to compensate for the sacrifices that had brought him so far. (All "Our Own Correspondent" had written for that month was: "Very little of interest has happened in the village lately, so I have not troubled you with a letter.")

Having, unlike ourselves, no trouble in asking for directions, he had set off at once at a brisk pace to walk the three miles from Pinetown to Mariannhill. The road, he writes, put to shame anything like it he had seen in Natal thus far, and the closer he came to the monastery, the more he was encouraged by the evident improvements to the countryside: our stone bridge built ingeniously without lime, the acres and acres of land under cultivation where members of our fraternity were working in the fields, none raising their heads as he passed or showing any sign of curiosity.

I still find his first impressions of us interesting. Coming up to what he assumed was the monastery, he had walked tentatively to the entrance of something that could only be called a yard. Within, monks could be seen flitting about silently. Most turned their backs on him as he tried as self-effacingly as possible to attract some attention, but eventually one paused long enough for him to inquire if it was possible for him to have an audience with the Prior.

The monk did not answer, but beckoning with a finger bade him follow. He was soon transferred to another monk, to whom by a single gesture was communicated an intimation of what the visitor wanted. This monk knocked at a door and communicated with a third, again with hand-signs only. He then went across the yard and approached a small square wood and iron structure over the door of which was painted – fortunately, for Bryant would never have guessed – "The Priory". Underneath this notice was a smaller one, bearing in English and German the words, "No Receptions". The monk knocked on this door and, without the slightest communication with the person within, hurried the visitor across the yard to a construction of wood, iron and tarpaulin on the other side.

Here he was shown into a subdivision that made rather a neat room, and the monk left, bowing low to him as he did so. A few minutes later – and I will confess to finding this section of his account particularly interesting – a tall man with shoulders hunched as if to make himself less imposing, but impressive still with his substantial beard and in the garb of the Order, entered. His inquiring look intimated that Bryant should speak. Taking it for granted that he should do so in German, Bryant asked whether he was addressing the Prior and was treated to the single prefix "Sub". Self-consciously he dealt with the lack of further response by introducing himself and explaining his intentions.

The Sub-Prior (yes, this was indeed myself) nodded and signalled to a monk hovering at the entrance to the room, who brought in refreshments of which Bryant partook. Somewhat awkwardly he addressed himself to the white and brown bread put before him, along with our own pure honey and coffee of a taste that, he says in his account, he found somewhat out of the ordinary.

~

The dispatch with which Bryant had set off from England meant that he arrived at Mariannhill well before Franz was due back from Europe. I had the porter show him to our guest quarters after my welcome, and met with him briefly again later. I did not have much to tell him other than the expected date of Franz's arrival, but he did ask if there was anyone with whom he could begin his study of the Bantu languages as soon as possible. Franz had arranged with Bishop Jolivet before his departure for one of the Oblate missionaries working north of Durban, Fr Louis Mathieu, to ride over once a week to give our monks lessons in Zulu, and I extended this service to our latest postulant.

I was relieved to have someone new with whom Fr Mathieu could work. Apart from our own failings in learning the language, the Bishop had not, perhaps, been entirely above making a point in sending us this particular Oblate. Fr Mathieu had been sent to St Michael's directly after his ordination in 1880. It was he who had accosted us as we were leaving the Bluff and remonstrated with Franz for not accepting the assignation to St Michael's, and it was he who spent two wretched years there before leaving in utter defeat for reassignment to his new station.

Mr Bryant became by far the most enthusiastic member of the class, apparently relishing Fr Mathieu's tales of missionary hardship as much as his language lessons. On Franz's return, Bryant's offer of himself for the noviciate was immediately accepted. Franz was in full form at the ceremony in which he gave the young man the white habit of a Choir novice, celebrating the response of this David to his call for "the long-legged Englishman, the broad-shouldered Scotsman, the tough Irishman" to join us. Only our new Brother David (eighteen years of age at the time) had accepted Franz's challenge.

Had Franz known that he would become this David's Goliath, would he have been so hasty in taking Alfred Bryant into the noviciate? Strangely, there were times when I think he would have, especially given the areas in which Bryant would come to fame. Franz basked in Brother David's evident admiration and set him to teach us monks English whilst he himself learned Zulu. He also had to learn to ride a horse, city man that he was, and overcame this obstacle with a kind of rough-riding that easily surpassed both my grappling with the English language and my equine pursuits.

Taking a great interest in the zealous young man, Franz soon had him assisting Benjamin in his catechistic efforts. Again, the timing of Providence was immaculate. At the beginning of the year 1884 Bishop Jolivet sent a poor Irish boy to be educated at Mariannhill, and so our first white school child joined us. More of the destitute and the orphaned followed, and the settlers' children also came in increasing numbers as word spread of the new novice and his teaching.

Benjamin's choice of Zulu as the medium of instruction was never a problem for the boys themselves and Franz even had to intervene on occasion to prevent them from speaking Zulu to each other, the white boys' grasp of English often being weaker than their Zulu. Franz was insistent that the children speak English at all other times so that the Native children could improve their English as quickly as possible. Brother David's Zulu, on the other hand, improved so rapidly that within a few months he was able to help us in the use of the grammar and dictionary compiled by the Anglican Bishop Colenso. Continuous daily practice in speaking the language soon enabled him to preach and teach in it, first from texts that he prepared beforehand, but increasingly extempore. He was, meanwhile, the only man in the monastery in complete command of the English language. This was why Franz was able to accept Benjamin's resignation with alacrity. He appointed Brother David "Director" of the school.

More difficult to justify was Franz's appointment of Brother David over Benjamin as missionary in charge of the kraals on our constantly expanding property. Whatever Benjamin's failings in this regard, especially in the hot weather, it seemed odd to replace as missionary a man who was not bound by the observance of silence with a monk who was. The frustration of Benjamin's wish to leave the active apostolate for a contemplative life had at least left him this advantage, and to have even this taken from him must have been especially painful.

Still, as Franz reminded us, a great warlord once said to his Negro servant, *Der Mohr hat seine Schuldigkeit getan, der Mohr kann gehen.* Perhaps, it was time for the Moor to leave, his duty done.

~

We know that the Rule of St Benedict is quite explicit in requiring nothing short of a full year's noviciate, as do the Usages of the Cistercian Order. In his stern desire for rigour de Rancé also specified a two-year probationary period for the Trappist Order, the only alteration possible being the *extension* of this period by six months if the Superior felt it to be necessary. Franz justified the anomaly of shortening Brother David's noviciate on the grounds of necessity, an argument that for the first time made overt the subtle ways in which the demands of our circumstances were eating away at both the letter and the spirit of the Statutes of the Cistercian Order of the Strict Observance. And yet, as was to be the way of things so often for us in Africa, the results of giving in to necessity seemed to confirm the rightness of doing so: in this case, it was the hastily promoted Brother David who in no time found a way of bringing our fumbling efforts at teaching our boys closer to the spirit – if not the letter – of these Statutes.

The essence of our Rule, "prayer and work", was expressed (by virtue of necessity again, rather than conscious decision) in the positioning of our original schoolroom close to our ever more substantial and extensive workshops and Brother David regularly found that his teaching was all but drowned out by the noise of work surrounding him. Out of this frustration was born the organisational miracle that the English monk brought to us.

Some have found it strange, and said as much to me when they have sought me out as some sort of authority on the fate of our Order at Mariannhill, that Brother David is given so small a place in it. I can refer you to book after book that omits him entirely, with my own formal account of the life of Franz setting the precedent for this. Well, it was as A T Bryant, not Brother David, that he was to earn his place in the world's opinion, and so let him be known as such in the annals of temporal things. He was to fade away in the process, becoming only a ghost – and not of the least malevolent kind either – in the records of our work for eternity. His spirit may now haunt only the words we have left behind, but he once strode large through our work when we ourselves were men upon the earth and not spectres to be found in lonely places, the chanting of our prayers lost in the wind that blows through the ruins of our spiritual kingdom.

And never did Brother David loom larger in our mortal lives than when he approached Franz through a haze of hammering that had stopped his lesson for that day and suggested that the learning of the three Rs be confined to mornings in the schoolroom and that the afternoons be used for manual labour in our large assortment of workshops. We had at the time a variety of skilled men – a blacksmith, tinsmith, carpenter, tailor, cobbler, mason, bricklayer, painter, printer and, besides, a large kitchen and our many fields.

Franz was enchanted. So simple an idea, and yet with the potential to realise his whole vision of Trappist teaching! Brother David had barely finished speaking before the idea was Franz's own, and he set about constructing the boys' days along lines very similar to those of a Cistercian monk's:

4.15 a.m.	rise
4.30 a.m.	Mass, wash, and bed-making
5.30 a.m.	first school
8.00 a.m.	breakfast
8.45 a.m.	manual work
11.45 a.m.	break
12.00 noon	dinner and free time
1.30 p.m.	manual work
4.30 p.m.	school
5.30 p.m.	supper and free time
7.00 p.m.	school
7.40 p.m.	night prayers and bed.

It was Franz himself who had introduced earlier the controversial idea of the school becoming a boarding establishment. This was to be enforced for all learners, and although many parents were reluctant at first to entrust their children to us for months on end, most soon came around – even Chief Manzini, who had withdrawn all his children from the school when the new living arrangements were announced. The boys, on the other hand, generally took to the idea very quickly, admiring the hay-beds on which they slept and the uniforms which seemed to glow against their dark skins.

Franz and Brother David soon found they had to divide the boys up into three classes: herd boys, apprentices, and scholars. They all received some religious instruction, but for the herd boys this was where their education began and ended. The aim was to teach the apprentices a craft; the scholars spent more time in the classroom.

And so the confessional character of our boarding school took on its emphasis on manual labour and, even if all the boys were not bound for baptism, they were brought up in an atmosphere of work and prayer. But what work and prayer? Did Franz ever stop to think then, as he was forced to later, what was left behind when he promoted the first of our own to missionary? What lessons were lost in the seventeen months Brother David did not spend as a novice, deep, say, in the Cautions and Counsels of St John of the Cross, or poring over the Psalms? Was this when Brother David, in learning to speak so well in the new languages about him, failed to learn that we ourselves are but words spoken by God, and that a word can never comprehend the voice that speaks it?

~

When we decided, some two years later, to make an attempt at harvesting the fruits of our catechetical efforts, the candidates considered most suitable for baptism were not selected from those who received their spiritual instruction out in the distant kraals. Kantolo, no longer weighed down by his muddy greatcoat, had been chosen; he was about to become Dominic. Shining along with him in white shirt and shorts faced in red were Kaete, Tengiswa and Popomo, three others who would become Bonaventure, Anthony and Augustine respectively, each one brought up carefully in the Faith on our grounds and under a different teacher.

When those four little boys took on the weight of their new names on the Sunday after the Christmas of 1884, Franz went out of his way to demonstrate the trappings of the culture they had adopted. He himself was attired in a gorgeous cope and I was required to accompany him in surplice and stole. We joined a procession that set off from the school and marched

239

towards the church to the strains of Hayden's "Hymn to the Emperor", rendered by a small string and reed band conducted by Brother Othmar. A monk bearing a large crucifix headed the procession, behind him the schoolboys in proper array, flying several banners. Then came the four boys who were to be the beginning of a Catholic community gathered around Mariannhill. An enormous crowd of heathen Zulus brought up the rear.

I caught a glimpse of Benjamin, standing alone between two of our more substantial buildings. His whole frame, which had become somewhat bloated despite all his exercise out amongst the kraals, seemed to droop, and his eyes were blank. Soon after this we heard he had tried to obtain permission to enter a monastery in England, but the English monastery was dubious about the admission of a man who was familiar with neither the climate nor European life in general, and – let us name him more correctly at the last – Benjamin Makhaba, the Mosutho saddler, was not accepted.

He left us quietly one day, saying only that he intended to repair to his native Basutoland. I do not think he went back to Roma. In my mind's eye I see him sometimes, alone there amidst the high, cold, clear mountains that I am told make up much of his homeland. He never walks to their eastern edge where they drop vertiginously to the plains of Natal, which stretch away to the sea.

~

For us, this was a time when everything seemed to be working together for our good, as if the Divine hand was directing accident and design alike. As, for example, when a small girl, clad in an exceedingly odoriferous blanket which had once been white but was now almost black through smoke and fatty bodily unctions, appeared before Brother David and asked if she could attend school. We found ourselves, somewhat to our surprise, equal to the challenge.

It just so happened that there was then a Polish family living on the monastery's farm. They were pious Catholics, but more to the point, perhaps, they were dependent on us, and Franz thus felt himself in a strong position in approaching them with a view to solving our new problem – for the time being at least. The family had a daughter, stocky and as dour as I have in general found most of my national neighbours to be, who was persuaded into becoming the first matron and teacher of our girls' school. Miss Mary Lassak could, of course, speak no English, so the solution was far from perfect. By now, however, such perplexities were second nature to us, foreigners as we were to white and black alike, with as much knowledge of the languages about us as if we had just been expelled from that city on the plain of Shinar where men of one language attempted to build a tower reaching to the heavens.

Franz ordered the erection of a barn-like structure about two-thirds of a mile from our main complex. He announced that this was to be the girls' school. The girls did indeed come in fairly plentiful numbers from the first, and Miss Lassak was able to keep order of a sort. Assisted three times a week by Fr Hyacinth, a colourless man – let me say now what I could not even think then – also from Poland, she was even able to introduce an element of religious instruction, which he would deliver in a very shaky and basic Zulu.

Mostly Miss Lassak taught certain kinds of women's work through example, which suited Franz's educational aims extremely well. As was increasingly the case with the boys, he was convinced that what the girls learned should be thoroughly practical. He made no effort to teach them languages or prepare them for academic examinations. Instead, they were to be trained to be good housewives and mothers; in addition to the catechism, they had mainly to learn how to wash and sew, garden and cook. Within no time at all, it seemed, Franz had a boarding establishment built for the girls – one of the first buildings we began in stone – a twenty-minute walk away from the monastery. It was not, he declared, a place for ladies or a nunnery. It was to be a house where the girls could learn to become good wives.

"A man needs his helpmate even when he is praying," Franz announced at the dedication of this building. "If he prays to Mary, Mother Most Amiable, House of Gold, Star of the Morning, he needs his wife to respond, 'Pray for us.'" He added with what he clearly thought was a twinkle, "And when he sneezes, he needs her to say, 'God bless you!'" Buoyed by the laughter the look on his face provoked (for who is to say how well his humour translated), he sailed towards his conclusion: "Modest and hard-working girls will be real helpmates in their marriage. These two qualities will help their husbands far more than twenty oxen or the mastery of English grammar!"

This attitude won over some of the parents, who were even more reluctant to allow their girls leave of absence from the home than their boys. The girls' school was as popular as Franz could ever have wished, although we were vaguely aware that there were some objections, especially from the fathers, when certain girls continued to come to us against their parents' wishes. Still, for the time being nothing overtly disrupted our success, and we gave many thanks for the manner in which all things seemed to give way before us.

And so, two years after the founding of Mariannhill, began that strangest of things: the missionary work of a contemplative Order. As proof of our failings as much as of our successes, the numbers of converts rose steadily: by 1887 there were no fewer than one hundred and forty-four baptisms, one hundred and twenty-two first communions, and eighteen Catholic marriages. You could not say, even at the time, that this had been achieved by anything improper for the Trappist Order, but soon enough Franz was to run up against one of the firmest rules established by de Rancé. In the process he was to risk as well the good opinion of another Bishop. Or more accurately in the case of our Bishop in Natal, his benign neglect.

I have said that once we were settled somewhere out of the way of Bishop Jolivet's French-accented enterprises, he was content for the most part to leave us to ourselves. His first visit to Mariannhill took place in late 1885, and some way into his tour of our property he was stopped short by the appearance of a number of young ladies dressed in a startling uniform of some sort. When he asked who they were, Franz replied, "These are my mission helpers."

A moment's stillness ensued, during which the Bishop looked hard at the women, and then slowly brought his focus back to Franz. Was the complaint against him – that the zeal for African missions was dying out amongst scholastics preparing for the priesthood because the missionaries were largely being used to look after just a few Europeans in the colony – at the back of his mind? Certainly we were to hear of this later, and gathered that the Bishop sometimes answered this criticism by pointing to the work being done by the Trappists in his vicariate. Still, on the matter of women in religious work he had been quite specific – none but the French. He remained quiet for several heartbeats, during which we stood completely still, the voices of the German-speaking women drifting over to us.

I could almost feel the Bishop's mind working through the problem before him: his directive concerned women in Orders and these were, according to Franz's response, laywomen. They had the appearance, however, of women in some sort of religious society, and even a quick glance at them going about their business confirmed that they were involved in the kinds of activities an Order of Sisters would be engaged in on monastery grounds. Then again, the Trappists had no precedent for a dependent congregation of nuns amidst their communities …

And so his thoughts must have twisted and turned as he came, finally, to the conclusion that he would simply remain silent on this issue. He freed us from our frozen state with a few comments about the problems of missionary work in general and did not refer to the women again.

Qui tacet consentire videtur was Franz's opinion of this incident. He had not been entirely open with the Bishop when, his request for Sisters of his choosing having been turned down, he had on his own initiative dashed off an appeal to the Austrian and German newspapers calling for women, especially teachers, to join us in the work of conversion of Native women. Nor did he feel it necessary to announce the arrival of the first five female missionary volunteers from Europe, who had turned up with Brother Zacharias, our mendicant friar, one rainy day in the September of 1885.

Franz was out overseeing a project when the sodden party, cheerfully chatting about the African superstition that rain was a good sign, was presented to me. I made sure they were served with a substantial meal (schmarren, the egg pie beyond which a Trappist cook may not go as a speciality) and read them a chapter from the *Imitation of Christ* whilst they ate. After this I led them back out into the rain and to their wagon once again, for their quarters lay some distance from the monastery. Once there I showed them to the room designated to them, carefully avoiding notice of their response to the primitive iron bedsteads with straw mattresses and coarse blankets and pillows.

The only other furniture in the draughty room was a rough-hewn wooden board on a cement barrel that was to serve as their table. On this was a kerosene lamp I had found for them, and a small container filled with potash that was the best I could do for soap. I had put a bucket of water for washing on the floor next to the"table". There were no chairs for them, no bedside lockers or even a closet for storing their personal effects. I began to gesture towards the few poor furnishings in a vague attempt at indicating they should make themselves at home but stopped when I saw these items through their eyes. Instead, I retreated into the dull grey drizzle of the evening.

As I walked back to my own austere quarters I wondered how we were to introduce this female element into our activities. Women were meant never to enter our premises and were kept out of our affairs entirely. Needless to say, all our institutions were dedicated to Mary, the greatest of women, and we concluded each day with the Salve Regina, bowing our heads reverently when chanting *O Clemens, O pia, O dulcis Virgo Maria* – the words St Bernard himself addressed to the Blessed Virgin. But we preserved the perfection of this ideal of womanhood precisely by isolating ourselves from women in the world. Indeed, being young as I was then (younger than I can now believe), a flash of the rustling green dark of a public garden in Vienna assailed me as I entered the dormitory. I found it necessary that night to apply the "discipline" to my shoulders, which had grown used to scourging of late, and was forced to be particularly strong in my penance before I put the small whip away.

The next morning Franz welcomed the women with perfect equanimity, making jokes about the rough conditions we shared before going on to discuss the way they should be dressed. His first instruction was that they should make themselves a "nurse's uniform" of some kind – not a religious habit, he stressed, which would have been contrary to the Bishop's instructions. As they talked he developed his own opinion of how this should look. A grey apron, he thought, with a black cape, and a small white cap. And, to top it off, he added in a moment of inspiration, a blood-red coat. He was all for bright colours, he said as the women glanced at each other, slightly bewildered, for he knew the Natives were impressed by anything vivid.

In this last point he was proved correct. On the feast of Our Lady's birthday the women appeared before our community and congregation in their costume for the first time. A group of Native children, who were busy having a catechism class in an open shed with Fr Hyacinth, turned their heads as one and stared in amazement. *Amakhosazana*, they called out. I could not help but wonder what Mina would have thought of the apparel of our "princesses" if she had stood there with us on that bright September morning. The rains had brought the first touch of green to the grass around us and our women looked like a small flock of brilliant birds about to ascend against this backdrop as they fluttered over to the "Girls' Institute" where Miss Lassak stood at the door waiting to greet them.

Soon after the Bishop's visit Franz got the women to elect a leader and an assistant, following long-standing Convent practice. The new "Superior" of the women then asked for a "rule" for their life in community, which Franz was only too happy to draw up himself and even wrote out in his own hand. "I may not be able to import members of a religious society," he said, "but there is no law against my founding my own society." And so he admitted them under private vows to a congregation that fell under his jurisdiction, and even introduced what was in reality a noviciate for the new candidates who arrived almost on a monthly basis from then on. They had all given up marriage, family and money (like nuns everywhere, they had to bring in a dowry, which was put straight away into the monastery's coffers) in Europe to become the lowest of the low in Africa, with no legal status, no right to ownership, dependent for their most basic needs on one of the roughest of men.

And on one thing this sixty-year-old man with his forbidding exterior and unrefined manners was particularly insistent, each new intake of Sisters being reminded of it beyond all possible misunderstanding: "Without you women," Franz would say, "I can do nothing lasting at Mariannhill. Right now, you are worth more to me than many learned Choir monks. My Brothers have to prepare the way for the missionaries of the future, but you are the vanguard of those missionaries. I want you to work side by side with my men, each according to her specific calling." On each of the many, many occasions that he would give this speech he would pause here to give emphasis to his next words – "You are *never* to become Trappistines yourselves! Never! If I wanted nuns, I could import them readymade from Europe."

Importing nuns would never prove necessary. Year after year, new groups of women recruited as "missionary helpers" arrived to hear the same speech from Franz, and each time their fear of this man whose reputation had them in awe well ahead of their arrival would give way to a trusting reverence that nothing could destroy.

In this way the problem of the Sisters was, if not overcome, then circumvented. Seeing that their presence was an established fact, Bishop Jolivet simply gave up and agreed to everything concerning them that the Prior of our monastery put before him. By 1887 Franz had introduced an unambiguous Rule for the religious life of the Missionary Sisters of Mariannhill and a bright red habit. From the following year, the women made their vows in public, and were provisionally recognised as a religious congregation. Much, much later, the Congregation of Propaganda in Rome would give its blessing to the community, and the Congregation of the Missionary Sisters of the Precious Blood would be born.

They would continue to be known as the "Red Sisters" although their red habits were disallowed by the Sacred Congregation for Religious on the grounds that this colour was reserved for Cardinals. A tiny hint of red was allowed to remain in the form of the ribbon from which their pectoral crucifix was suspended and Franz, who had by then experienced not only the heights of his career but his dizzying fall as well, never ceased to take comfort from this shimmer of redness, like a strand of his own youthful hair standing out pugnacious and strong against the white of his old age and disgrace.

~

No hint of the sadness and confusion ahead touched our foundation in the mid-1880s. Everything seemed to be sprouting and growing, as if the Natal earth itself was producing new members for our community and bearing buildings in the same way as it gave birth to our crops. On a more mundane level, it was a new member of our community who was responsible for the sudden surge in bricks and mortar, stone and wood, even iron and machinery. It must be admitted that, some time before his death, Brother Barnabas's contributions to our building operations were already being eclipsed by those of another Brother, similarly qualified although of a decidedly less musical bent. Brother Nivard Streicher, a master joiner by trade, took up the religious life and was professed in 1882. He joined us at Mariannhill in 1883 and, from the very first, became invaluable to Franz.

No construction problem was beyond Brother Nivard, starting with his replacement for our dam, which did not survive the rains of our first season. Having succumbed to the waters of the extremely temperamental Umhlatuzana River, the primitive bank of stones in which we put our trust yielded next to Brother Nivard's masterful masonry wall. Its graceful gradual curve gave it not only strength but a look as fine as any arch in a cathedral. Built about sixteen feet into the banks on either side of the river, the wall was eleven feet high with a seventeen-foot foundation. As for the bye-wash, well, Brother Nivard chose a spot on the river for his wall, which, unlike our original site, had a bye-wash provided by nature. The river at that point divided itself into branches that Brother Nivard had us dig into more definite divisions; this created an island around which the water poured when not needed for the dam, and a channel through which, when it was necessary to relieve pressure on the wall, the water could be diverted by a series of inventive appliances of his own creation.

With no training whatsoever in engineering or architecture, our resident "genius" – so described by one of the many journalists who continued to visit us – produced a series of feats in both areas that earned him glory, if not in the eyes of God (for who is to say what pleases Him, especially in the things we built with our hands and tongues at Mariannhill?), then in the corridors of the Natal Government. If our settler neighbours were to be believed, the Government was by far the harder to please, but as the roads and bridges in which Brother Nivard also excelled spread further and further out from Mariannhill, requests for advice and help came in from far and wide from the colony's officials. The Railways even gave him a free rail pass in recognition of his services. This was just as well, for the extent of the travels he undertook in his work would have been considered extraordinary under any circumstances, let alone those of one vowed to stability of place.

It is all very well to say that many a German architect of the time, including the great Weinbrenner, did not train academically as an architect. Or, for that matter, that there were no trained architects or even masons in the Middle Ages, when the great Romanesque cathedrals were built. It took more than a lack of training to grasp instinctively the lessons of the most rebellious and sophisticated of Weinbrenner's students and to reject outright the famous religious buildings of the past as models for contemporary designs. It was as if Brother Nivard understood from the inside Heinrich Hübsch's *In welchem Style sollen Wir bauen?*, a copy of which he brought with him and was often to be found reading. From this one volume he recreated in Africa much of the philosophy of the architect who had trained first as a philosopher and mathematician at Heidelberg and had, moreover, travelled widely. Hübsch had studied the buildings not just of Germany and Austria and France but of Greece and even Istanbul.

The answer to Hübsch's question "In what style should we build?", Brother Nivard said to me one day in a field he was about to transform into one of his visions, was to be found first in the volume you had to create and next in the material out of which you had to create it. He was a young man then, but already hardly in need of a tonsure as only the lightest fringe of hair circled his broad head. Short of stature and slight of build, his tendency to self-effacement could not diminish the force of his presence, even though it would be some time before the softness of youth would burn from his face and give him the aquiline features of the "Brown Abbot" as he is now commemorated.

I admit to being entirely caught up in the shapes Brother Nivard's voice gave to the emptiness about us as he spoke. The church had decreed the spaces we must enclose, he said, and geography, not history, had given us the material to do it. In some places it was basalt, in others sandstone, and in yet others granite or marble. "What we have here," he went on, "is clay, clay that is perfect for … bricks. And a brick can be held in one hand. Indeed, it is created to be held in one hand, which is why a bricklayer can work all day without becoming exhausted. It is a perfect medium for a small workforce. You do not need a whole stable of workmen carving huge stones, massive blocks that declare their grandeur before they are even put into place. None of our brethren know how to carve, in any event! We must start at the smallest level, with the very bond of the brick itself."

Brother Nivard learned to speak perfectly one of the most important languages of Mariannhill, the language of brick. In mastering the five or six basic building types available to workers in this medium, he created a grammar out of the reddish clay that we pressed into the most mundane of shapes and combined these into an architecture of infinite variety and extraordinary richness. The pride both his vocation and personal modesty forbade him glowed out of his buildings like the warmth of the sun that our bricks absorbed and radiated back.

If it was clear to me that Franz was not above a touch of resentment regarding the extent of the fame of his "faithful helper" (Franz's own term for Brother Nivard), I must also acknowledge that his place in Franz's life and work had the effect of displacing my own. Granted, my contribution to Franz's plans was often only a lack of anything to say that, like Bishop Jolivet's decision to say nothing further about our Sisters, he could read as a steady form of approval. Brother Nivard, for his part, was forever to be found with Franz, the two of them surveying a new site or pacing out some building plan and filling the air with designs created out of gestures and words that soon took on solid shape. They were inseparable and, although Brother Nivard could never become Sub-Prior, not being a Choir monk, he was promoted with almost unseemly haste to the position of Steward – in the terminology of the Rule, our Cellarer. He was in this position "the one responsible for the ordinary administration of the monastery's temporal affairs" as around him our foundation started to take on more of the physical appearance of a monastery.

The first of the brick buildings Brother Nivard designed was our mill down by the river, a building that would ultimately expand to reflect every area of our monastic life. From this he would soon extend himself to the physical expression of that life in all its forms, from workshops to school-rooms to cloisters and churches, cathedrals and towers – towers, yes, bell towers stabbing the sky everywhere as we spilled out over the land. Towers that would be the glory of Mariannhill and her missions, bells pealing out across landscapes of dust and grass and thorn tree, bringing to them the murmuring overflow of our contemplation.

~

But in 1885, as I have said, the showpiece of Franz's "master-architect and confidant", as Fr Adalbert chooses to call Brother Nivard in his history, was the mill. And so, one gritty, gusty day in November, when the heat of the summer air was infused with a grey pall brought in by a front that had blown up the coast, I found myself heading out with Franz and a party of tourists to the developments on the banks of the Umhlatuzana. Curiosity regard-ing the river was always stimulated by our monastery, thanks to Brother Nivard's having outmatched the borough of Durban in its water supply arrangements. Appropriately enough for Cistercians, we had the luxury of taps at every prominent point in our establishment, from which water pumped up from the river could be obtained at any hour, day or night.

Franz chose to lead the tour himself, partially out of his clear enjoyment in displaying our achievements and partly as a result of my most recent humiliation when a group of visitors decided to test my obviously limited command of English by asking me if, on their next visit, I would kick them out of the door. They had noticed my tendency to cover my discomfort at expressing myself in English by replying, "Yes, yes" to everything – as I did, to their great hilarity, in response to this question.

A few days later an ecstatic account by the leader of the touring party was published in the *Natal Mercury*, which Franz read to us with relish. The article extolled not only the wonder of Brother Nivard's two-and-a-half storeyed building (said not to have "its equal for class" in the colony) but the provision it made for a wealth of activities within: the grinding of grain powered by a water turbine and not the time-honoured water wheel; the prospective crushing of monkey nuts for oil; rooms for spinning, weav-ing and dyeing cloth – in short, the base for a completely self-sufficient Trappist lifestyle.

And there it was – turbines and lifts, grinding machines and ventilators, soldering and saws. And there we were, embracers of one of the most ancient lifestyles, no longer lost in the modern world but leading the way with our work. As for our prayer, who was to say? But certainly we no longer had to avert our eyes from a mouldering hunk of metal in the rain, an ancient Order retreating from progress in the shape of the traction engine Bishop Ricards had purchased in his efforts to bring us up to date.

Because of the distance of the mill from the monastery, Franz arranged for those working there to walk down and back via the Stations of the Cross that were carved on his orders along a section of the path bordered with huge rocks. Our rituals for the day were to be observed in a room in the mill set aside for this purpose. Later, the intensity of labour at the mill made it necessary for the monks working there to stay overnight, and so a dormitory was attached and a permanent church built close to it so that the seven hours of the Office required of us could be kept.

Thus, ever so practically, ever so much in the service of the life that the Rule prescribed, the first buildings separate from the monastery came into being – the first of a steady stream of buildings that would tumble from our loose enclosure like beautiful beads on a thread of roads, creating on the maps of Natal a rosary that instead of being enfolded in a praying hand would ultimately enfold the one praying in its ever tightening embrace.

~

I have thought of Brother Nivard and his laughter often of late, especially since the recent news of his nerves giving way. This came just as I had begun writing about his early accomplishments, and I cannot say that I found it entirely unexpected. There was something about the laughter of Brother Nivard that prepared me for such an end, even though I have not seen him now in over fifteen years. As I have had occasion to mention, the Rule of St Benedict tells us *not to love much or boisterous laughter*, but there was in Brother Nivard's laughter a genuine delight in the richness of the follies of the technical things of this world that seemed to free it from the need for censure. Brother Nivard was reckoned one of the most cheerful monks at Mariannhill. It did not take much to make him laugh, and once he began laughing it was truly difficult for him to stop.

I was with him once when he was working on a boiler for a local farmer. Brother Nivard was considered a man of great commonsense, and the locals sought his advice constantly when some piece of machinery needed repairing. On this occasion it became apparent to everyone that the boiler was about to blow. The metal of the tank began to shriek from the torture of the heat and rivets were wobbling in their holes as steam spurted out from every giving seam. The farmer turned and ran screaming into the naked grasslands that stretched away in every direction about us, and this sent Brother Nivard into gales of laughter as he kept on working at the offending valve, letting forth an extra yelp every time his bare hands touched the red-hot cistern.

For myself, I stood frozen to my spot, so much so that I do not believe my posture changed at all when the pressure was released moments before an explosion. All I could do was put my hand on Brother Nivard's back as he fell from the boiler in a fit of coughing brought on by his laughter. So profound was this delight that I sometimes thought it cut too deep, was too close to the thin line between infinity and oblivion that separates mystery from joke, our silence from utter emptiness. I certainly thought this on the day when the heat from the metal of that boiler outdid the African sun and blazed into the face of that laughing Trappist wrestling with eternity for the sake of getting a machine to obey.

And so St Benedict was right to list amongst the "Instruments of Good Works" a proscription against laughter. Forty years of laughing at the unending problems involved in joining and laying, twisting and shaping, supporting and suspending every angle and line necessary for Mariannhill to take its physical form on this earth must have brought Brother Nivard to the realisation that the spirit had evaporated from those shapes and they stood like signs of nothingness posted from Natal to Nomansland.

I would not wish to see him in this way, the man who once, when preparing a plan for inspection in the required imperial measuring system, drew to perfect scale near its metric dimensions a picture of a man's foot with the inscription *Ein Englische fuß*, and then roared with laughter at the ceiling as a be-spectacled and be-suited colonial official muttered his uncomprehending disapproval. Nor do I wish to question the faith of one who put the measure of our faith to its fullest test in the way he constructed its earthly expression.

None of our early buildings were built with foundations. Whether this was a manifestation of our faith or Brother Nivard's engineering skill I am not qualified to judge, but it was Brother Nivard who put whichever this was to its best use when Franz proposed nothing less than a Catholic church and school in the heart of deeply Protestant Pinetown. Franz had bought land in the town surreptitiously, for this was in 1886, by which time word was circulating amongst the settlers that the Catholics of Mariannhill aimed to buy up the whole of the colony. Brother Nivard agreed that building anything on this property would be met with vigorous protest, and so it was that, very early one morning, Pinetown's blacksmith – a Catholic himself but opposed to our monastery because we put spokes into wheels for the Natives at one shilling per spoke compared with his charge of two shillings and sixpence – looked out to see a complete house of wood and iron moving past his forge. The house was deposited on our property just below the railway station.

This manoeuvre was not to be one of Franz's more evident successes, for the withdrawal of the British garrison from Pinetown meant that the Irish soldiers who were most in need of a Catholic institution in the town disappeared just as Franz purchased his five acres there. Still, the name of this, the first of our buildings not dedicated to monastic life, retains something of the man who most gave physical shape to Franz's vision. It can only have been at Brother Nivard's suggestion that the house was called Loretto on account of its similarity to the holy house of Our Lady at Nazareth, which, according to pious belief, was transferred in its entirety from the Holy Land to the town of Loretto in Italy by angels.

Brother Nivard would not have been able to resist this humorous note entering our decision to name all extensions of our monastery after places of pilgrimage in Europe. Even now, as I write from my exile in the one station we did not name in the Cistercian tradition after a famous Marian shrine, I sometimes think I hear his laughter resounding in the hills that hide us from the monuments his genius raised up to the new spirit that began to take over Mariannhill.

~

As problem after problem of construction melted before Brother Nivard, the buildings needed to house our growth materialised, solid and glowing in the African sun. A mere three years after our arrival, our foundation numbered ninety Religious, of whom twenty-two were Choir monks and sixty-eight were Brothers; our Baptismal Register showed two hundred and three Christians, sixty-three of whom had already received the Sacrament of Confirmation; our schools boasted over one hundred African and fifty settler – English and German – pupils; and in most of the workshops the Brothers now had any number of Natives working with them and learning their crafts and trades.

Officially, under wholly unfamiliar circumstances, we lived unflinchingly according to the Rule. The wilderness about us yielded to well-tended fields and pastures, luxuriant plantations, vegetable gardens and orchards. Along with yet more roads and bridges, aqueducts were built, and even more powerful turbines drove our mills. Building never ceased, and the loftier structures we now took on were erected without scaffolding. When not adding brick onto countless brick, we lifted into place stones, sometimes weighing almost a ton, dressed in our habits and on a diet of bread, vegetables and water. No physical challenge seemed beyond us.

One Lenten morning, deafened by cicadas and assaulted by flies I was bound not to swat, I remember looking up from painfully wielding a sledgehammer on a fasting stomach, with wobbling knees and in acrid sweat and a rash of prickly heat. I could see nothing but shining vineyards stretching into the distance beneath the court of the Queen of Heaven. That day I believe I came closest to finding in Mariannhill something of the mysterious state that had earned me my religious name. My arms fell limp before me, my numb hands loosely enclosed around the handle of the heavy hammer that rested now on the ground between my feet. A great bodily comfort stole over me, a satisfaction of soul, and my powers – such as they were – were at rest.

If ever I felt near God it was at this time. I was certain that if I could but draw a little nearer, I would become one with Him. Like a traveller who, within sight of his goal, has stopped to take a breath, I had no desire to move on from this repose; all my faculties wished only to remain always still, for the least motion, it seemed, would trouble this sweet peace. I had no sense of anything, only of fruition, to borrow a word from St Teresa of Avila. In the true orison of quiet there is, she says, only an awareness of fruition, without understanding what that may be the fruition of. It is understood only that the fruition is of certain good, she continues, containing in itself all good together at once.

I use the words of the Saint for this experience because it was for me wonderful beyond anything I could put into words, perhaps a foretaste of a knowledge all the greater for being wordless. Indeed, the wonder of St

Teresa's account is that it attempts to rise beyond a sense of comprehension through language. The senses, she writes, describing perfectly my moment that day in the fields of Mariannhill, *are all occupied in this fruition in such a way that not one of them is at liberty so as to be able to attend to anything else, whether outward or inward. In this state of complete absorption, there is utter rest even of the imagination* ...

I cannot, will not – must not – believe this to be a condition of the senses, or, even worse, the imagination. For I, to whom so few moments of exaltation were given outside the blessing or curse of my illness, have had to learn that sensation, feeling, is no guarantee of grace or the lack of it. So often I have raised my arms to the empty sky and begged in a desperation beyond prayer to *feel* the closeness of God, or even the smallest sense of His being near to me, to be left only with a deep, deep *desire* to believe. And it is at such moments that my imagination wants to take me beyond my lack of faith; but this I have resisted with all my faculties. If, I have told myself so many, many times, the lack of confirmation of my belief by my senses has been granted me precisely to confirm my faith, all other confirmation being withdrawn from me, then this is the nature of God's greatest gift to me.

All too soon I would be required to face that test that is its own solution, but of that day, when I was able – or is it as I write now that I *think* that I was able? – to feel God with me, just as I felt the dirt in my shoes or smelled the rankness of my habit, I can say no more. *He who has had experience of this will understand it in some measure,* says St Teresa, finally giving up on words herself, *for it cannot be more clearly described.*

I must confess that I found much reassurance in this passage when I came upon it, the more so for finding confirmation there of my own experience of coming out of such – dare I say it – ecstasy. The utter absorption lasts only a short while, St Teresa says, and the faculties are "as if in disorder" for some hours afterwards ... And there it was, the sensation I had known since that childhood day on which I first experienced being lost to time, the world and words, and of re-entering these things through a haze of distorted images. I was never again to know at Mariannhill that certainty of ecstasy, exolution, liquefaction, transformation, Christian annihilation, the kiss of the Spouse, gustation of God, ingression into the Divine shadow, call it what you will.

Looking back, it seems that, instead, the rest of our story must be told through the haze of a return to the world. It was in such a haze, a haze shot through with Brother Nivard's laughter, that I and others of our community heard of the official recognition of our stature.

12

On the Friday of Passion Week in the year 1885, a document arrived announcing that Mariannhill had been raised to the status of an abbey, and that it behoved the brethren to choose an Abbot from their number. The promotion was not in itself unexpected, as any canonically erected monastery with no less than twelve Choir monks may qualify for this status. Given the controversies that hovered around the founding of our house, however, such a seal of approval was deeply felt by those who lived, worked and prayed at Mariannhill – not least the one unanimously elected on the Saturday preceding Whitsunday to become the first priest consecrated to the office of Abbot on African soil south of the Sahara Desert.

Fr Franz Pfanner was too sorely aware of the series of humiliations that surrounded his previous promotions to think that his being appointed to one of the oldest ecclesiastical offices in Christendom would have the same meaning for him in South Africa in 1885 as it had in earlier times elsewhere in the world. For him there would not be the life of ease and comfort that would have attended him as Abbot of Mariastern only a few years before. "My life as Abbot of Mariannhill," he said to me just out of the hearing of Bishop Jolivet and his Oblate Fathers who oversaw the electoral process, "will continue to be one of work, worry and vigilance."

The local press, with whom Franz was quick to share the news – hinting at it as he did to guests and reporters alike well before it was confirmed – were determined to make the most of the forthcoming installation ceremony. Well before the event took place it was being referred to in print as "marking an epoch in the history of the colony". And indeed, Pinetown, if not Natal as a whole, was in need of some sort of new era. One could understand then the town's desire to make the most of the event. Here and there, however, amidst the adulation to which we had become accustomed, less happy notes were being struck, especially with regard to trade and our store at the monastery. There had also been some protest at our recent impounding of some cattle.

So confident was Franz by now of our place in the region that, unknown to us, he was at the time composing a letter to the press on a subject more sensitive even than trade and farming. This letter appeared in the newspapers just days before his installation and consecration as Abbot, and the pages and pages devoted to the attendant ceremonies temporarily absorbed its effect. The postponement would prove to be brief, and, if anything, the huge publicity our celebrations attracted were to give added force to the slowly gathering tempest to come.

For the moment, however, even my own concern about Franz's letter to the *Natal Mercury* was buried in the blur of preparations necessary for the formal installation. This was to take place on Saturday 26th December, three years to the day after our arrival in Pinetown, with the consecration ceremony to follow on the Sunday.

The insistent clamour of our brass band's almost continuous rehearsals drowned out the only marginally sweeter sounds of several choirs practising at once, but between them they formed an appropriate backdrop to the host of activities that transformed our contemplative community into a hive of activity. Decorations were being produced in quantity everywhere, both for the various pageants we had planned and our buildings. Horses to be used in the procession accompanying dignitaries from Pinetown station to the monastery were groomed and wagons dressed in full regalia. Flags, streamers, bannerettes, arches and garlands were run up on every available space, and every palm tree over a considerable radius was stripped of its leaves.

A large display of the coat of arms and motto to be conferred on the new Abbot was prepared, and with it a giant mitre. Our miniature mortars, hopefully only ever to be fired in celebration, were oiled and cleaned. Refreshments were prepared for the invited guests, Brother Nivard being in charge of calculating how many ladies and gentlemen could be accommodated in the room designated for them and the issuing of admission tickets. Our store, which would be selling food and drink to the public, was stocked up and several oxen were identified for slaughter so that the Native participants could be suitably fed. To myself fell the duty of preparing our monastery church for the benediction of a mitred Abbot during a solemn high mass. This building was still a somewhat primitive – and, as far as Franz was concerned, temporary – version of the impressive colonial-Romanesque edifice it is today, and there was much work to do.

Two chapels were necessary. The larger one at the high altar had to have six candles arranged around a cross, with a carpet covering the altar steps and the presbytery. This chapel was for the use of the officiating bishop – Rt Rev. Bishop Jolivet, who was to perform the ceremony under a special mandate from his Holiness the Pope in Rome – and I had to have ready in it all the pontifical paramentes of the proper colour and in the proper order: slippers, amice, alb, girdle, pectoral cross, stole, corta, dalmatic, gloves, chasuble, precious mitre, pontifical ring, crosier and maniple.

On the epistle side of the presbytery I put a credence table for the use of the Bishop, covered with a clean cloth and provided with two candles, wash basin and towel, holy water and a sprinkler, shurable and boat, mass cruets with wine and water, chalice and wafer-box. Not having a separate table, I also placed the missal and its desk, along with the pontificale for the Bishop, on the credence table. On the gospel side I positioned a specially prepared armchair for the Bishop, and then instructed a servant how to move this before the beginning of the High Mass to the highest step of the altar on the epistle side, so that the Bishop could place on it the pontifical robes.

Below the credence table I set a cushioned footstool for the Bishop, knowing that he would require this during the seven psalms and the litanies. In the middle of the presbytery and directly below the high altar I set out three simple footstools that would be required by the new Abbot and his assistants; this would save them from having to kneel on the step of the presbytery. On the credence table on the gospel side I had a cushion ready on which the new Abbot could prostrate, and again gave a servant detailed instructions on when to offer it to him, and when to remove it after use.

The smaller chapel, which was to be used by the new Abbot, I prepared as is required on the epistle side of the presbytery. In it I placed an altar set with two candles and a cross, a missal and the pontificale. Upon this altar, too, I arranged the abbatial paramentes, done up in the same colour as those of the Bishop. To these I added three white copes for the Abbot and his assistants. I supervised the erection of a throne on the gospel side for the Bishop, with seats for him and his higher ministers (deacon, sub-deacon and assistants) and for the lower servants. The Bishop's seat was, as it must be, higher than the others.

Near the beginning of the choir I set down a credence table covered with a white linen cloth and placed upon it a washing basin and five towels of fine linen. Candles are not required on this credence table, but two of four pounds each must be placed upon the abbatial credence table for offering, along with the abbatial ring, the mitre, two large loaves on dishes and two small barrels of wine. The bread and wine had to be positioned in such a way as to display the necessary decorations and the new Abbot's coat-of-arms.

I was aware that some of my Brothers were amused at my absorption in these details, and that my reputation as "mother of the house" took on a humorous and perhaps even slightly mocking air in this context. Still, I found deep consolation in this kind of service. No detail was left to my inventiveness or imagination; ancient usage dictated my every move. Every item was set out, laid down, leaving one free from decision, choice, interpretation. My work then was an act of sheer contemplation, physical activity nothing but the spirit's movement through the beautiful order of tradition. Like the ceremony itself, its prescribed form dictated exactly how it would unfold.

And so it transpired, each action flowing from its ancient sanctification, on and on through the pages of ritual that we enacted in perfect obedience. Let me say that here, again, before so much of what shaped and guided us was to vanish, the traditions that we lived were like breath to the body. Far from being rigid and inert, they were the life of the Church, breathed into it by the Holy Spirit. And the ritual and ceremony I put before you now is only the most obvious, the surface representation of this truth. For us monks, every instant of our lives is governed in just such a way and to the same end: the silence of life in God, contemplating nothing but Himself.

In a proper version of the occasion, I would leave out my own sweating hand when transmitting to Franz, at the time the Bishop formally requested it, the Rule of St Benedict; I was uncertain, too, of my grip when, after taking it firmly in both hands for a moment, Franz passed it back to me, as the ritual requires. I was still shaken by having almost forgotten, in the confusion of dressing myself in my unfamiliar ceremonial robes, to have a copy of the Rule about me during the ceremony.

As for the rest of the public festivities, well, these loom up now as out of a distorted dream: I remember the loud snap of banners, the smell of meat, the constant chatter, calls and shouts, the fog of colour, the reverberation of song off our baking walls, the slipperiness of sweat under my habit, the explosion of mortars echoing against the hills, the endless, aching smile I wore for the world as I underwent the penance of a dispensation to speak to visitors for the entire two days of their duration.

I remember Franz turning to the Bishop as the procession was re-forming outside the church and saying, "My lord, now I am an Abbot. But where is my Abbey?" The Bishop looked flustered for a second before he caught the humour in Franz's question: there before us stood the little galvanised hut that still served as residence and sanctum for our Superior (although no longer as printing shop and goods storage), containing only an iron bedstead, a paillasse stuffed with seaweed, a desk, a washbowl and jug, and a bookcase. The inscription above the door, however, had been altered in an attempt to answer Franz's question; instead of "Priory" it now read "Abbey". It was to be the only change in Franz's living conditions for some time.

For the celebrations we had also erected at the corners of the tiny building – "the smallest abbey in the world", as Franz immediately dubbed it – four large Venetian masts, at the top of which a skeleton cupola was formed by branches and poles radiating to a centre. A cross stood on this cupola and the giant mitre hung below it, emblematic of the dignity we could otherwise not afford our Abbot. In front of the building was a display of Franz's new coat-of-arms and the motto he had chosen: *Currite ut comprehendatis*.

"Run that you may win" was a more than apt choice – even as the second day of celebration was drawing to a close Franz was introducing some new members of his "Red Sisterhood" to the Bishop. Showing no sign of his having been out-manoeuvred, Bishop Jolivet bestowed on them the holy kiss and a few cheering words. But as we all – the thousand or so in attendance over that weekend – knelt before the Bishop for his benediction, a twinge of concern must have found its way into the breasts of some as to what Franz would do with his new independence as Abbot. The crook of the crosier he carried in the ceremony was turned inwards, signifying that he had no power beyond his own community, but with his own idea of the tempting prize before him, the course of his running was more difficult to predict than the Rule of St Benedict suggests.

~

And so we come to Franz's letter.

I have already written about my concern regarding the place of teaching in our contemplative life, and of Franz's ingenious ways around this. And of my discomfort that the work of a member of a community dedicated to contemplation should be in the classroom and the land around us, gathering and sharing nothing but words, words, words. Many of my Brothers came increasingly to share this view, and expressed it far more volubly than

I ever cared to. But for now – and is this not the genius of sin? – who could lament the presence of the young amongst us, their voices echoing with such gaiety and innocence at the margins of the solemn Rule that governed us? Could we not, deep in our contemplation, idealise those diminutive roustabouts in a way Brother David could not afford to do, there at the coalface of teaching?

I know this was my failing, but I took quiet joy in the rambunctious learning, working and playing that hovered about our silent life. As I did in the harmonious relations that prevailed between them all, black and white, English and German, in the workshops and gardens or in the refectory, where their bread was cut for them from the same loaf and they ate their meals out of the same dish.

Who then can find fault with Franz choosing to write his letter to the newspaper to share what our experience with the children had to teach us all? "Everybody knows that even cat and dog may be accustomed to live together in peace if they are placed one with the other at an early age," he began. "Why, therefore, should it be impossible to mix white and black boys, and to accustom them to each other?" This would never work, he argued, "if they are always set loose upon each other in the way the South African people instigate their white children against the Natives". Or if they were kept materially unequal.

"The noble Africans too," he wrote, "resist this union of all nations and races as intended by Christ; they say, 'For the white is the feather bed, but let the black be on the ground, below the table.' But we allow the bed for all to sleep on; we give the same blankets to all."

Who could deny Franz in full flight? But who, too, could prevent him from soaring too high and far? On he went, from the loftiness of a redemption beyond race to, of all things … smell.

This, declared Franz, was the "special reason" why the Zulu was not admitted to the society of the white man. "Indeed," he continued, "these people smell so very much that our noses, not at all accustomed to it, have to bear a very hard trial when on Sunday mornings hundreds of them meet in our chapel, and standing shoulder to shoulder in the African heat, and dripping with sweat, diffuse their odours through the wooden grate into our choir …"

Franz's explanation of this phenomenon was related to his abiding interest in diet and its effects. The Zulu, in his view, had in his perspiration the savour of venison and of strong-smelling – "stinking" is the word he uses in his letter – herbs. "Our Brother who has to look after the Native boys at garden-work," he wrote, "once brought me an armful of herbs which the boys spoke of as delicacies; some of them I could not allow to approach my nose unless with great aversion." Franz then produced a veritable treatise on the availability of these herbs, where and in what season, and how they were used in Native cooking.

What was to be done about this? A change of diet, in Franz's opinion was the solution. "Give to your black domestic servants other meals that they be no longer obliged to go for wild food," he wrote. "Then they will acquire your smell. *Probatum est!*"

What is more, all the other evidence of conversion would follow. When our scholars grew accustomed to our food, clothing, beds and buildings, they did not want to go back to their kraals, Franz claimed. He added, "I can give many examples that boys invited by their parents refused in the most resolute manner even to take part in the favourite festivals of the Natives. How is that? Because now they would no longer suffer the disagreeable taste of the Natives' food. They would get sick without clothes and beds; they want work in order to gain proper food and clothing, and without intending it they have accepted civilisation!"

In the eyes of many in the colony, perhaps, Franz had not yet gone too far. As with his letter concerning the distant nuns in Umtata, however, he saved the most damage for the last: "Reading, writing and reckoning alone is not to be called an education. That is a mere breaking-in that will make the Native arrogant and proud, and will never change his heart. With your Bible in your hand, you South African missionaries, you will not even change his smell, much less his manners!"

~

Franz's views on education would certainly serve to fill innumerable pages of newsprint in days to come, but with his final salvo, aimed not just at lady missionaries this time – his target now was nothing short of every Protestant missionary at the southern end of the African continent – Franz announced his involvement in one of the most sensitive areas of colonial religious life. An area, moreover, in which he was forbidden, by the Statutes of our Order, to participate.

Yet now, suddenly, with the installation ceremony of an Abbot of the Cistercian Order of the Strict Observance barely behind us, the editor of one of the local newspapers was comparing our work to what he called the "premier *missionary* body in South Africa", the American missions. Another wrote of "the challenge thrown down by the Abbot of Marianhill" to "the Protestant method of missionary work". All this Franz read out to us quite gleefully, as he did the flurry of print that followed between himself and one Rev. J Taylor, who had set himself up as the spokesperson of Protestant evangelism.

Rev. Taylor began his response by admitting that "in the matter of zeal the Trappists put to shame other religious denominations", but he soon made it plain that much of this zeal was misguided. Without a change first effected by the Holy Spirit, he insisted, "all benevolent efforts are in vain. Following this change, and flowing from it, as streams from a fountain, there springs up in the hearts of hitherto unclad, filthy, and lazy heathens, a desire for clothing, for soap to cleanse it, and for some industrial employment. Then follow neat and comfortable dwellings, school houses, sanctuaries, improved methods of cultivating the soil, and other proofs of the civilising power of the Gospel."

For once, fortunately, Franz's letter in response to Rev. Taylor's eloquence was brief. We were intensely busy with constructing the sort of buildings Rev. Taylor felt should only be a consequence of and not a prelude to our preaching in the fields, and this exchange fizzled out in a few vapid generalisations about centuries of missionary endeavour and some rather silly calculations of numbers of converts on each side.

The whole business of changing lives before hearts or hearts before lives, as far as we were concerned at least, dropped out of public attention for a while before returning with a force we could never have calculated. In this brief lull time we had reason to contemplate another of the effects of Franz's forays into the world of print.

~

We did not know that, just outside the peripheral vision of our preoccupations, every appearance in the press, every report, every rumour, every publication about or from Marianhill preyed on the increasingly fragile and overheated mind of Bishop Ricards. One word about us, I have been told, would keep him from sleep, or wake him in the early hours when the humiliations he believed we had visited upon him would churn over and over in his mind.

The fact that his nerves first gave way at the height of the disagreements that led to our leaving Dunbrody made the Trappists the living embodiment of everything that had blighted Bishop Ricards' career, which was nearing its conclusion. A career that, however shakily it may have begun, had blossomed under official approval and (perhaps more valued by the Bishop in the quiet hours when he allowed himself to reflect upon his accomplishments) public adulation. The hardest blow may have been the effect on his voice, those famous lectures stalling and stuttering, the gleam gone from that display of knowledge, the comic turn dying on his tongue.

Rapt attention and roar of laughter had alike turned into embarrassed coughs and the shuffling of feet as his reputation wilted away into (could it be?) boredom and, most terrifying of all, his own boredom, the failure even of the desire to pull off his old tricks with a crowd, to rise on that strong voice with the benediction intoned above the glory of laughter surging all around at the end of another sparkling performance. Not since that extraordinary beginning to the career of the best public speaker in the colony – when, in the course of his first sermon, he had broken down in the exordium and had to leave the altar – had Bishop Ricards' voice failed him. Indeed, it was that early experience that drove him to conquer the heights of what the voice could do, and made him determined to conjure success out of words: spoken, written, chanted, acted.

But if the Bishop's voice faltered over us, that organ of the public voice, the press, did not, even in the heart of the Bishop's domain. If anything, the newspapers in the area covered by his vicariate took to us much more after we sailed off to our rebirth in Natal than when we had struggled in the dust of Dunbrody. No longer were we epitomised by a traction engine stranded in the rain; the *Port Elizabeth Telegraph* and the *Eastern Star* of Grahamstown surveyed us from a respectful distance as successful sons most unfortunately – and possibly unnecessarily – lost to their soil.

Looking now at these ageing sheets of newsprint I read "Wonderful, most wonderful, are the people called the Trappists" in a copy of the *Telegraph* printed a few years after our departure. "When they landed – we well remember the day – how quaint, meek, quiet, undemonstrative they appeared. Who would have thought them capable of turning no end of waste land into gardens, fields, orchards, and erecting vast buildings equal to Europe in style – all in a few brief years. We read in a Natal newspaper that Fr Franz looks forward to Mariannhill becoming the greatest of all the Trappist houses …"

The report goes on to list the usual physical evidence of our triumphs – mills for flour, oil, wool and sawing, a tannery, an arrowroot factory and, of course, a printing press. How Bishop Ricards must have burned at the thought of the never-used and long-lost crockery set he insisted we have in place of a press, particularly on reading that "the type for the new printing machine has just been imported from Germany, and the machine and plant together cost more than £1 000".

A thousand pounds sterling! Half the amount he had forwarded to Mariastern to ensure that Franz and his party would come to the Eastern Cape! And obtained only by a loan secured through Herr Fraundorfer of Augsburg, a loan still outstanding, along with several others he had entered into. Spent now on a machine no Trappist had any business using, let alone owning.

Bishop Ricards could not have avoided reading the conclusion of the article: a paean of praise to our three hundred Native baptisms. But even this (in a region where Catholic conversions amongst the Natives remained an embarrassment that reached up to the highest levels) could not have hurt as much as the *Eastern Star's* oft-stated regret that "so able a body of missionaries had been lost to the Eastern colony through" – here the sting would have been at its most personal and intense – "the adverse circumstances of the site selected for their first attempts in South Africa".

Franz, I remember, read this article in triumphant tones at our Chapter meeting. "The success of the Trappists *elsewhere* under *great* disadvantages, shows they are *not* – *easily* – *daunted* and that they *do* – *not* – *hurriedly* – *or* – *inconsiderately* – *abandon* – *an* – *enterprise* once entered upon ..."

The implication as to who was responsible for our failure at Dunbrody was abundantly clear, and such reports must have been nothing less than a public mortification for Bishop Ricards. Franz's practice of sending the programmes for each of our festivities to the newspapers of the Eastern Cape (Bishop Ricards had been invited to the abbatial installation but had chosen not to attend) could only have been taken, in the Bishop's frame of mind, as a deliberate provocation. He dashed off letters to the various newspapers condemning their interpretation of the work of the Trappists at Dunbrody and the reasons given for their deserting that place. Set against our subsequent successes, these protestations came across as thin, defensive and carping.

By 1886 the Bishop's spirits were very low. Our sins were now entirely intermingled with his increasingly nervous disposition. "Much depressed in mind lately," he scribbled in the Chronicon Fr Adalbert has put before me. "Doctor says I must go on a sea voyage. Hope to settle the case with the Trappists at least for the £2 000 I loaned them."

Perhaps unwisely combining his need for rest with his desire for justice, he had set off for Europe in the wake of Franz's enormously successful appearance at the Trappist General Chapter of that year. This was held at the monastery of Port du Salute, where the assembled Abbots were gracious enough not to refer to the embarrassing circumstances under which Franz's previous foundation was affiliated to this house. Franz's one visit there previously was barely remembered and certainly not noted; his new foundation, in any event, had no associations at all with Port du Salute.

For Mariannhill the importance of this gathering of the General Chapter lay in Franz's receiving official permission to "send Brothers outside the monastery for the purpose of preaching, catechetical instruction, baptising and similar non-clerical functions". He was authorised, too, "in the cause of evangelisation to erect schools and chapels in remote areas and to assign a priest to them to take care of the spiritual needs of the Sisters and Brothers who work there", which, as Franz saw it, was nothing less than official approval of his entire mission programme. Everywhere Bishop Ricards went, he must have heard nothing but praise for the man he had come to Europe to prosecute – praise that drove him on to sacrifice work and rest alike in pursuit of his claims against Abbot Franz.

This led to his joining up again with Herr Fraundorfer, who worked him up even further, if that was possible, in pursuing this end. Neither the Bishop nor Herr Fraundorfer was able to hurry the arbitration process whilst Franz's successes in Europe continued, for once without taint of controversy, and Franz himself gave barely a thought to the emotional and unsubstantiated provocations of these two nerve-wracked men. Any sensible person with some knowledge of the business would have exposed their false hopes as just that – no reference could be found to Trappists asking for a loan from the Bishop at any time before or after Dunbrody.

On the contrary, the only documents available showed the Bishop to have promised financial assistance to the Trappists in his appeal for them to come to Dunbrody and work there. His whole case depended on words that had vanished into the air in which they were spoken, but so much did he believe in the act of speech, the sacred role of the word once spoken, that he could not accept that the mere thing in itself, objects in the world capable of volition or even simply passive, could withstand the word. Unfortunately for us, we had become the reality that betrayed his faith in the power of words.

Bishop Ricards was forced to leave Europe without his case having gone to arbitration before the Sacred Congregation. He could not have left a better advocate for his sense of grievance than Herr Fraundorfer, but this must have been small comfort when he returned to South Africa to find that not only was the financial state of his vicariate no better but that, as a result of senior members of his congregation having taken over affairs in his absence, the financial crisis was now common knowledge. With the compromising of his good name – the name that, in a way a true Trappist would find hard to understand, stood for everything he was – his mental health appears to have deteriorated further. Only much after the event did I learn that the Bishop himself thought death so near that he asked Rome to appoint a coadjutor to run his affairs. His end would be delayed for some time yet, but from then on he was increasingly reluctant to do or say anything, leaving most matters to the priest in charge.

We did not know of the Bishop's condition at the time and remained confident, meanwhile, that our position was supported by the facts of the case he had brought against us. At all times Franz had described the money as a gift to Mariastern that was meant to leave the monastery free of debt when our party set off for Dunbrody. We had come to Africa at the Bishop's request and the funds for our passage and the bare essentials necessary to start a Trappist house had to be his responsibility. He must have known that our vows of abject poverty would not allow us to repay a loan, or even enter into an agreement for one. Had he not stood before the General Chapter and said he would provide everything necessary?

~

It was from the clearest of skies then – literally, for it was in the August of 1889, just before the onset of the winds that would bring the southern summer rains, the mild Mary-blue of the heavens of Natal hovering over us like a blessing – that a bolt of the Church's power crashed down upon us. Bishop Jolivet arrived, unannounced, at our monastery to inform us that the arbiter appointed by the Congregation of Propaganda had decided the case between Abbot Pfanner and Bishop Ricards in favour of Bishop Ricards.

Abbot Pfanner, he went on, was ordered by Rome to repay the £2 000 to the Bishop, together with the accrued interest. The questions that bubbled to the surface of our initial mute shock burst in the still air to no effect. Bishop Jolivet had no idea how such a decision had been reached, and, indeed, did not seem much interested; all he knew and had been told to tell us was that Bishop Ricards had won his case, and the outcome was final.

Eventually we gleaned, from letters sent by those friendly to Franz, something of the course Herr Fraundorfer had followed to gain the victory that, in truth, was his. At the court of arbitration ordered by the Cardinal Prefect of Propaganda, the proceedings were going smoothly in Franz's favour until Herr Fraundorfer was called up as a witness. Under oath he presented a piece of writing, scarcely legible and in English, said to be a summary made by the Bishop of the discussions in the General Chapter of 1879 that led up to and followed Franz's famous declaration: "If no one will go, I go!"

In this scribbled text Herr Fraundorfer focused on a single word, translated for those assembled as "anleihe". Upon the evidence of this word – "loan" – which no one else present was competent to interpret (or indeed to read at all, from what I have seen of the Bishop's handwriting) the court decided in favour of the Bishop. The full explanation behind this extraordinary decision would elude us for years. Even Herr Fraundorfer had no idea what channels of power he had tapped.

Franz did not take any steps against the judgement. He did not wish to offend his friends in the court of arbitration and all indications were that the Propaganda would give the money to Bishop Ricards. Franz did not for one moment think of repaying the money himself, and in the midst of the explosion of work that was overtaking us at Mariannhill, he soon simply forgot the whole affair.

And what work lay before us! Work of a sort that no Trappist house had ever felt coursing through it along the pulse of its prayers. Dismissing the irritations of the past as he forged on into a new world of his own making, Franz was pulled forward by the same subject that had drawn him so forcefully into the realm of the press. In short, it was not long before Franz would earn the right to debate the merits and methods of missionary work in the newspapers with the confidence of one steeped in its practicalities, both spiritual and material.

MISSIONS

13

T HE SANCTIONED "METHOD" of allowing communities to settle on the estates of our monastery where they could slowly be influenced by witnessing us in the pursuit of a Christian life was barely begun when a chief whose kraal was over a hundred English miles away asked us to establish a school for his people. We rose to the occasion.

I am afraid I must say that there was more convenience than accuracy in this story, repeated in so many documents that it has sedimented into truth. Certainly our school had earned a reputation that spread far and wide, especially as the government of the colony was not doing much at that time to respond to the many requests from chiefs for schools to be established in their areas. The very recently established Council for Education tended to rely on mission schools to meet this need. At the same time – as Franz read to us energetically from a report in the *Natal Mercury* (by now invoked so regularly it had almost become part of our daily Liturgy) – a request for missions from a number of chiefs was turned down by the Government. Care of the souls of its subjects was not thought to be government business.

The situation was too tempting for someone of Franz's nature. The sound of Brother David's children reciting enthusiastically everything from their times table to the Creed was an ever present reminder of how successfully schools were making inroads into the tribes around us. Standing at the doorway of a classroom where the plagues of Egypt were being triumphantly enumerated, Franz fixed me with that glare that I knew would brook no opposition. We must go out into the wilderness beyond our monastery, he declared, and see what could be done for the children of the chiefs the Government had refused.

At that moment I saw Brother David look up from his charges and smile. It was not difficult to guess that he was weary of these offspring of the broken and scattered clans that had gathered in Natal. What he longed for was contact with the great Zulu nation itself, defeated perhaps, but still living life as it was before the white man came to the majestic wilds of

Zululand. His notebooks called out for them as much as his apostolic zeal. When, I wondered, would he understand that his desire to know about customs other than the ones we were meant to be living examples of was a direct contradiction of everything we stood for?

As a Trappist, Brother David was always a mystery to me. He was forever jotting down who knows what when talking, as his dispensation to speak allowed him to do endlessly with his Native charges. And, when words failed him, he turned increasingly to the very thing in which I had once placed such high hopes. It would not be true to say that Brother David alone was responsible for the lens of our camera ceasing to model itself on the downcast eyes and inward focus required of a Trappist monk. When Franz returned from the General Chapter of 1886 he had, amongst the twelve postulants for the monastery and thirteen for the Red Sisters who accompanied him, a couple named Schmidt, who described themselves as artists. Like quite a number of the postulants who made their way to us they found the Trappist Rule too severe for them, but Franz did not dismiss them as he usually did in such cases. Instead, he had a small house built on a remote corner of our property and installed them there.

Soon after their arrival they took over Fr Othmar's studio, leaving him to direct his artistic contributions towards the enthusiastic, if not particularly talented, brass band he had set up amongst the Brothers. From that point on the vagaries of trying to catch a Trappist at work – the changing light, the achingly held postures, the accidents of expression, gesture and composition – gave way to the Schmidts' indoor portraits and tableaux set against large painted backdrops of the scenery which, in its natural state, could not be relied upon to obey the rules of artistic composition. In this form the views around Mariannhill took on, it must be admitted, rather more definition and drama, a stronger sense of the exotic, and a proper aesthetic framing that nature herself had not always been so considerate as to provide.

And so Fr Hyacinth appears with his class: he is seated, leaning back in his clear authority, holding before him an open book, the odd child, despite strict instruction, more captivated by the business of the camera than by his teacher, set in a scene more richly endowed with foliage than anything the rolling hills around us had to offer. And Sr Philippine, her habit reduced to a play of black off the white of her headdress as she leans, eyes uplifted, towards a group of neatly pinafored girls gathered about her knee, transported from the rather primitive *predigtschuppen* into a spiritually uplifted world. One in which a foreground of lissom palm trees and glossy-leaved flora opens out to a vista dominated by a mountain whose angular shape never graced any Natal view I was to see.

These photographs were caught in the dying flare of my interest in the medium. I had learned already that the silence of the photograph was a false silence. All I could see in these new examples as I helped package them for the publications that went out in an ever-increasing stream to our benefactors and patrons was speech itself in a frozen pose. They did not even need an inscription to give them their meaning; they signalled in themselves the hum of action.

Brother David would never have looked to such pictures as the apogee of what the camera had to offer. No, for him it was the new developments in the technology of taking pictures that really set the medium free to serve his purposes. As even Mariannhill obtained lighter cameras dependent on less paraphernalia and simpler chemical processes (I had by then lost all interest in the mechanics of the medium), it was he who first turned the eye of our camera outwards to the unknown subjects surrounding us. From then on it would seek every sign of savagery it could capture before our civilising mission devoured it. I for one understood very quickly why a photographic picture was referred to as a "shot" and how the language of hunting attached itself so immediately to the process of snatching an image out of time and mounting it like a trophy for eternity.

It is all there in the carefully appended inscriptions at the bottom of the photographs: "There is No Place like Home" reads a picture of a young girl in full regalia posed in the low opening of her hut. A series of head and shoulder portraits are reduced to "Zulu Types – Negroid", "Zulu Types – Hamitic", and so on. These pictures are evidence of giving up the search for God within and the beginning of a seeking for Him in what can be done for – or to (and who is to say which is which?) – others. Brother David who was, and A T Bryant who now is, could well continue with his work of pinning the butterfly of the disappearing past ("Other Ancient Customs Now Extinct – First Menstruation Dresses"), for he is at last a missionary of words and pictures, words and pictures alone. But we Trappists?

The camera was, if not a passive follower, then an accomplice in Franz's new vision. By the time he put it to us in Chapter, his plan to reach out to the children neglected by the Government was already clear and, phrased properly, it was impossible to say that it was outside the bounds of our sanctioned work. We could not afford, as our holy forbears had done throughout Europe, to raise large foundations throughout the dark continent of Africa. What we could do was raise branch stations where our presence was requested, with schools attached. These stations would receive their maintenance from the motherhouse, Mariannhill, and fall directly under the jurisdiction of its Abbot. Each would have a resident priest and at least one Brother who, with the help of the Natives in the area, would cultivate sufficient land around the station to provide food for those who lived at the mission and attended the school. Each station, too, would be provided with a small band of Red Sisters to undertake the educational services we would provide.

No Trappist, then, would technically be engaged in *mission* work, but a Trappist station would serve as a base *for* such work in so far as it exposed the heathen to a Christian life. Was this not in line with Bishop Ricards' vision in bringing us to Africa? Strange as it was to hear that name emanating from Franz's lips after his recent stinging engagement with the man, it was difficult to deny that something of this logic lay behind our arrival on that blazing February day almost at the other end of the world from which we had started. Franz had barely been an Abbot for a month when this vision of our work took shape in his mind, but in that month he had already learned, it would seem, just how to exercise his new independence.

~

It began with a brief experiment on the ridge that rose away from us to the south-east. Hidden from the view of the monastery by the fold of hills that surrounded us, the ridge nevertheless dominated the skyline above the mill erected on the banks of the Umhlatuzana River. Almost visible at the far end of the ridge was one of the first "prayer trees", as they came to be known, where Benjamin the Basuto had regularly assembled some of the Shozi people to hear him preach. Franz had a small house built under the tree and set up a Christian convert there with his one wife. They were intended, in true medieval fashion, as the nucleus of the first "farming village" to be established on our extensive properties. As we hoped, other Natives soon gathered around this rather well-supported trial community. When several senior members came to us to ask permission to build a church in the midst of their neat collection of square and windowed houses, Franz felt confident enough to bestow upon the whole enterprise the blessing of the saint in whose name he had been baptised at birth.

And so St Wendelin's Church, the township of St Wendelin and, in the course of things, the long stretch of hillside christened St Wendelin's Ridge came into being – and Franz's given name was etched indelibly into the African landscape.

~

This experiment was not even fully under way when Franz was citing it in support of efforts further afield and on a grander scale. Within a few months an expedition to Zululand was ready to leave. Fr Gerard and Fr Hyacinth were to be accompanied by Fotsholo, who, having been baptised, now rejoiced in the name of Jacob. As the Rule requires for those to be sent on a journey, they were given drawers from the wardrobe (with strict instructions to wash and restore them on their return) and cowls and tunics (also to be returned) that were somewhat better than those we usually wear. The last thing Franz reminded them of as they left our enclosure was never to let the appointed Hours pass by and to say the Office by themselves as well as they could wherever they were.

It would be some weeks before we would hear from our exploratory party. Franz could barely contain himself during this time, mining Brother David all the while for information on the places where our emissaries might be going. Brother David could only share with us long and rambling accounts of great chiefs and their exploits in the past, all hopelessly en-tangled with myth and legend and folklore. Those geographical locations that did emerge from these fabulous stories, told to our teacher by his pupils and their parents and grandparents, were wrapped in the glories of those whose names had become intertwined with theirs. Mountains and rivers and fords and plains rose up before us in an impenetrable mix of saga and metaphor that, to Franz's intense irritation, defied any ques-tions of practicality.

The return of our three emissaries turned out to be less glorious than their adventures suggested, although they were not to know this until their report was completed. This report was given under special sanction in Chapter, for the Rule states clearly that under any other conditions *no one may presume to tell another whatever he may have seen or heard outside of the monastery.* If anyone does so without permission, he must *undergo the punishment of the Rule.*

Taking turns seamlessly in their dispensation to speak, Fr Gerard and Fr Hyacinth told us that they had followed at first the north coast route from Durban across the Umgeni River. There, lush cultivations of sugar cane and maize fields stretched as far as the eye could see. The first houses they came to were, to their surprise, corrugated-iron huts with thatched roofs. These they discovered belonged to the Indians brought to South Africa to work the sugar-cane fields. They had to journey on beyond the Umhloti River before they found the beehive huts and naked Natives they were in search of. These, they told us, were deep in a rolling landscape that made travelling extremely difficult. There were few roads, and in places the Zulu kraals were like ant heaps, thickly covering the uncultivated soil. Eventually they found the homestead of one of the chiefs whose name had been attached to the request for schools.

This was Chief Umkhonto, former headman to Shaka himself, now eighty-five years of age. They had to wait for days for the chief to return to the village, during which time they visited the stations of both the American and Norwegian missions. They met Mr Leisegang of the Norwegian Lutheran Church, who told them that after twenty years of work he had only one hundred and twenty-four Christians on his mission. Zululand, he told them, was in a fearful mess, divided and violent under the system imposed by the British after their invasion.

At the mention of the name of the chief our Brothers were waiting to see, Mr Leisegang threw up his hands and told them that, as a member of the royalist group agitating for the return of the exiled Zulu king, Chief Umkhonto and his people were weak and vulnerable to attack by other Zulu factions. Fr Gerard and Fr Hyacinth had clearly been given a much longer and more detailed account of the situation but returned unperturbed to the homestead that had made them so welcome. After all we were not meant to be interested in such worldly affairs. What mattered surely were the souls of those who called out to us. When they were finally able to meet the old and grizzled chief, he was surrounded by his councillors and was wearing a girdle of goat's hair, a flannel shirt and a red cap. His visitors were seated opposite him on stools formed from the forks of branches. The chief and his councillors had agreed immediately to the proposal of a school, offering land and assistance and promising to send children to the school.

At the end of their presentation, Fr Gerard and Fr Hyacinth, with Jacob standing behind them straight and still as he had throughout, fell quiet themselves, awaiting Franz's approval.

"Zululand," said Franz eventually, "is like Austria – we will find no home there."

Even in their silence our emissaries were clearly surprised, but Franz gave no explanation. I had sensed a slight stiffening in our Superior at the mention of the American missions, and perhaps more interest in Mr Leisegang's analysis of the politics of the Zulu than could be satisfied by the report we had heard, but all Franz would say was that the two Brothers and Jacob should set out again, this time directly inland towards the Drakensberg mountains. He then freed the two travellers to go to the oratory, as brethren must at the end of each canonical hour of the Work of God on the day of their return from a journey. There they were to lie prostrate on the floor, as is prescribed, and beg the prayers of their brethren on account of any faults that may have surprised them on the road through the seeing or hearing of something evil or through idle talk.

Some time later, when it was part of my work at the monastery to sort through the clouds of paper that trailed in the wake of our developments, I found the real reason for Franz's decision. It came in the form of a letter addressed to the "Great Minister Living at Umlazi" and was written in the name of no less a personage than Dinuzulu, King of the Zulu. It must have arrived whilst we were awaiting the return of Fr Gerard and Fr Hyacinth from Zululand.

The letter gave a fair picture of the kind of political trouble we would have found ourselves in if we had taken up the offer it extended: "I send to you, of Rome," it reads,

to ask how it is that we should be allowed to die here. Help Help You of the Chief in heaven. Come and help us. We are dying from the acts of Mr Osborn. I am like one who is in Gaol. The whole Zulu nation has come to grief, through the acts of the Chiefs of Maritzburg. They are people who cause great trouble. The whole country is disturbed without cause. My request is this, come to help us to reconstruct the whole Zulu country with the help of God …

277

It is not right that there should be any division between the Romans and the Zulus. The people are being shot with guns like wild animals. I send greetings to you, my Chiefs. I, Dinuzulu, say do not let any one know you are coming here. Come, and let us see one another and consult together alone because if they heard of it, they would cause great trouble …

To my knowledge Franz did not reply to the letter, the only one we ever received from a potentate. When I questioned him, delicately, about the letter at the time I unearthed it, I discovered just how worldly the leader of an entirely spiritual house is sometimes forced to be.

According to Franz, at the time the letter was written Britain was particularly nervous about Germany's claims to the south-west coast of Africa. Franz himself had met a man ("a maniac", he said), who called himself Dr Augustus Einwald, who had led a "scientific expedition" up to Zululand. Whenever he met with chiefs he told them he represented his country's greatest leader – he even hinted to Sir Henry Bulwer that he was in communication with Bismarck himself.

Einwald and another German named Schiel had come up with some mad document that, in return for a few trinkets and the promise of German protection, gave them rights to a lake on the coast of Zululand that could serve as a harbour. Schiel, it seemed, had borrowed money from Einwald to go to Europe, and then double-crossed him by selling the rights to this lake to a merchant-adventurer named Lüderitz. Such were the times that the British Foreign Office took the matter to the German Chancellery. The British then sent a ship up to Zululand where it raised the British flag, fired a twenty-one gun salute, and handed a written statement to some amazed Natives who happened to be on the beach, reminding them of Britain's long-standing claims to the region.

"I'm afraid the King's offer would have pulled us into all of that, and even I am not clown enough for such nonsense," Franz told me. We were having trouble as it was, he said indignantly, with people in Natal accusing us of extending German influence wherever we went and saying that we – Catholics! – were agents for Bismarck.

And so I carefully filed King Dinuzulu's letter. It remains a moving tribute to the kind of things we could have done had we been of a worldlier mind.

14

The party Franz had directed inland towards the mountains set off again only a day after their return from Zululand, heading up through the jumble of increasingly steep hills directly beyond our monastery into a cleft in the wall of granite that rose up out of the hills. I stood and watched them as they grew fainter and fainter, and could not shake off the feeling when they disappeared that we were losing them in some way. I remember that Franz came up behind me and said, "That path up through the rock could be a road one day, not unlike the road from Lake Constance up to Langen. They would have to blast the rock, of course, and avoid the waterfall up there, but, after all, a waterfall tumbles directly over the road to Langen."

"Yes," he went on as I stood by quietly, not knowing how to respond to this suddenly intimate moment, "when I explored up there and was caught in the rain on the way, I felt at moments as if I were returning from school in Feldkirch and had climbed down from the cart to pass water just off the road. As I stared at the damp rocks covered in moss and lichen and listened to the water dripping off bushes, it struck me that the main difference was that my father was no longer there to hurry me along."

His voice took on an unusual mix of emotions as he continued, but the more he spoke, the more taken aback I was that my awkward reserve should be understood as an encouragement for talk of this kind. Perhaps this was the moment Franz decided I would be the one to entrust with the many, many hours of similar reminiscences that were to come in the years ahead, but what brought about this first unlocking of his past still eludes me. Certainly I supported him in everything he did, but even in his capacity as my confessor I did not feel it right to share such things with him.

Still, he carried on with these unguarded thoughts, almost as if he were speaking to himself: his father had only wanted to hurry him home, he said, to help with the work on the farm, which was how he had to spend every holiday. The other pupils all travelled between terms, but he knew nothing except Langen and Feldkirch, where every young urchin soon got to know that a student with red hair was in town. As soon as Franz appeared on the street, they would gather around and cry out, "Red fellow! Red fellow!" – an unbearable insult. "No wonder I became known for my wrestling and ability at games like Hosenlupfen!" Franz remarked. "Had

I only known then that there was a country like South Africa where red hair is considered beautiful, I would have assuredly desired to be amongst the Kafirs."

He turned away then, ending this strange interlude with the wry comment that even if a road were built through the hills it would pretty soon have a toll put on it – Franz's dislike of tolls and tollgates was widely known by now – and then fall into disrepair anyway.

~

No one was more pleased than Brother David when our exploratory party returned from the northern edges of Natal with another positive response. Chief Sakayedwa's offer to sell his entire location to us seemed by no means as open and sincere an offer as the one from the chief in Zululand, but Franz gave us no opportunity for discussion. Fr Hyacinth reported rather sourly that it was his impression that the chief's request for ten schools and ten teachers was a ploy to prevent his land falling into the hands of white farmers, as was his offer to sell us his land. He was also sure that the chief thought that he could insist that we return the land to him one day. Franz brushed this all aside. His mind was made up – it was towards the mountains that we must go. Only the state of our finances prevented him from packing off some of our monks immediately.

Whatever the settlers may have thought to the contrary, we made little enough from the trade in which we engaged and the donations that came in rapidly disappeared into our everyday running costs. All new projects had to be financed from scratch. In typical Franz fashion, an article appeared within days in our newly titled magazine (Franz had abandoned *Fliegende Blätter* in favour of *A Trappist among the Africans*, and then changed it again to *Vergissmeinnicht*). Set neatly amongst his sermons and talks, this article described his intention of starting Mariannhill's first branch station and asked for donations specifically towards this. By the next issue of *Vergissmeinnicht* – which appeared with a new cover illustration showing a Trappist monk in the posture of a teacher surrounded by eager young Africans – he was able to announce that a brewer's widow had sent not only the amount requested but three times that sum. Through her generosity Franz was able to purchase some land in the district occupied by Chief Sakayedwa.

This was a most attractive site of eleven thousand acres, nestled in a bend of the Polela River. As soon as the transaction was ratified, a party of eight monks under Fr Arsenius was readied to cover the one hundred and twenty miles between Mariannhill and its first real outstation. On the 12th of October, six large ox-wagons were on the road to Polela. That first journey took ten days, with many a steep climb and dizzy drop through the hilly country that built up ever more steeply towards the Drakensberg.

Each wagon weighed nearly two thousand kilograms (left to ourselves, we ignored English measures in those early days) and carried a load of three thousand kilograms, much of which was made up by an entire house that we constructed in pieces at Mariannhill, ready for erection on the station site. The rear wheels of the wagons were nearly two metres high and the axles were of the same length. It took a team of eighteen oxen to pull each one, and when they sank into the muddy roads, as they regularly did, up to sixty-six oxen at a time had to be yoked together to pull them out.

We heard of these difficulties only when a message was sent back to us announcing that our Brothers had reached their destination and pitched their tents in the midst of Sakayedwa's people. Without even seeing the property – although inspired no doubt by Fr Arsenius's account of the river crossing that was the last challenge to be met and mastered before arriving – Franz named our new acquisition Reichenau. As he wrote in our magazine, which by now had a circulation of nearly two and a half thousand, "Here on the Polela, Reichenau shall be to the heathen Africans what Reichenau on the Rhine was to the barbarous Alemans and Bavarians, a haven of culture and Christianisation." After his first visit to his new foundation he was to add, "In this mild, fertile valley, the Polela makes so many serpentine twists and turns that it almost flows back to where it has just come from, forming a number of round and oval peninsulas. Just below the loveliest of these peninsulas is a bewitching waterfall, and it is next to this that we have built our dwelling ..."

I, in turn, was to stand by that rapid scrabble of water (modest in size, perhaps, in European terms, but a fierce rough and tumble nevertheless) and be less struck by its romantic aspect. What did strike me was how foreign our whole way of life seemed in that strange terrain that so easily threw out all our bearings. It was the climate as much as anything else that twisted the Rule out of shape. With each year that passed we were learning how poorly the Rule of St Benedict translated itself into the southern hemisphere, where everything, as they say in Europe, is upside down. The reversal of seasons alone made nonsense of the liturgical year, with Lent, for example, falling in harvest time and monks having to fast in the season of plenty.

~

Those first monks at Reichenau had no time for such meditations. By the time I reached the place it was obvious that Fr Arsenius had set them to work straight away. They built temporary quarters for themselves and a school first, and, a rifle-shot's distance away, a house for the Sisters. Soon after – for the school flourished – a dormitory was built so that the pupils could be kept on the property along the lines established at Mariannhill. The beginnings of a farm proceeded apace at the same time, and a first blessing was that the soil proved far more suitable for the wheat and rye necessary for our bread than the soil of the coastal region. This encouraged Franz's ambitions for the station even further. "In these lovely highlands," he would tell us with gleeful fervour, "we can get wool from the sheep and the soft grass will make our cows give good milk. Reichenau must produce cloth for us, and cheese for all of South Africa!"

But the real blessing came in one of the earliest reports we had from the teachers at Reichenau: to their surprise, the desire of the mountain people for religion was even greater than their desire to "learn the book". During the first year alone, as Fr Arsenius's meticulous records showed, there was an average of a hundred and fifty people at the service every Sunday.

You will know by now that stability is the object of a special vow for Trappists. When we are received into the community, the promises we make are stability, fidelity to monastic life, and obedience, in that order. Stability comes first as the Rule presupposes that a monk takes it upon himself to remain within the same monastery for life, and St Benedict is very strict about any kind of departure from this vow. *Let him be punished who would presume to leave the enclosure of the monastery and go anywhere or do anything, however small, without an order from the Abbot,* he writes.

Even the shortest excursion is strictly regulated: *A Brother who is sent out on some business and is expected to return to the monastery that same day shall not presume to eat while he is out,* states the Rule; the punishment for a monk who eats while he is away from the monastery is nothing less than excommunication. And no matter how far or near, short or long a journey is, a monk must perform the Work of God wherever he is, bending his

282

knees in reverence before God at all the appointed Hours and saying the Office, by himself if necessary.

Travelling to Reichenau, then, which would clearly become something of a regular business, presented real problems not just for our observations but for the keeping of our vows. Franz's solution was to look about for more properties. He soon succeeded in buying a small farm on the old highroad between the towns of Camperdown and Ixopo, the main feature of which was that it was a day's ride from Mariannhill in the direction of Reichenau. He named it Einsiedeln, more for its size than its purpose. Tiny though it was and so remained, it was not intended to serve as a hermitage but as the first sanctified resting place for the teams of oxen and men toiling between the monastery and Polela.

Soon after this Franz bought a farm called Blitzberg, which, with prayers for better luck in electrical storms than its name augured, he renamed Mariathal; this was yet another day's journey closer to our outstation. Although Franz had to be more patient when it came to his next purchase, by early 1888 he had acquired a piece of ground he named Kevelaer after the Marian shrine in northern Germany. This last purchase was yet another day's journey closer to Reichenau. In this way, and with the improvements we made to the roads and our methods of travelling, Franz's ingenious solution to the problems an outstation presented for a Trappist house was in place: we could travel from Mariannhill to Reichenau in four days, stopping each night at our day stations, without ever having to break our vow of stability. As Franz saw it, despite their journeying the monks kept to the rules of enclosure, no monk being ever required to stay overnight off monastic ground.

A Trappist monastery could, in short, have as many outstations as were felt necessary, in whatever direction, as long as these were linked to the motherhouse by day stations that were, as their name implied, never more than one day's ride apart. "Such an arrangement is manifestly good," Franz announced in triumph. "Not only will it mean we keep to our enclosed life, but it will assist in the better direction and maintenance of the stations, and also allow the isolated monks there the possibility of occasionally going to their neighbours for confession."

The chain of stations from Pinetown to the Drakensberg was barely in place when Franz began to reach in other tempting directions. In less than a year, Mariathal became much more than the halfway house between motherhouse and outstation: Franz and Brother Nivard used it as a base from which to move south, exploring the verdant valley of the Hlokozi River. Some way down this valley they established the station of Ötting, and it was then that, for me, the bombshell fell.

~

When Franz was installed as Abbot, I had, in my capacity as Sub-Prior, with a degree of formal correctness rather than well-considered choice, been promoted to Prior. I am not sure if I remembered to mention this. Then again, it is forgotten or barely noted in most of the documents to do with Mariannhill. In any event, with Franz's promotion the position of Prior lost much of its authority. The Rule advises against the appointment of a Prior under an Abbot. *It happens all too often that the constituting of a Prior gives rise to grave scandals in monasteries, we are told, for there are some who become inflated with the evil spirit of pride and consider themselves second Abbots. By usurping power they foster scandals and cause dissensions in the community.* The Rule does allow for the position, but only *if the circumstances of the place require it.* In such a case, the Prior is ordered to *perform respectfully the duties enjoined on him by his Abbot and do nothing against the Abbot's will or direction; for the more he is raised above the rest, the more carefully should he observe the precepts of the Rule.*

I am sure no one was better suited to such a role than myself. I am the first to admit that my record of leadership was not strong, and I was only too happy to reflect in myself my Abbot's authority. And if there was any need for a second in command at the monastery, this role was filled without any doubt by the appropriately dubbed "Brown Abbot". We were all aware that if Brother Nivard – busier than ever giving physical shape to Franz's visions in a swirl of brick dust, wood chips and laughter – had worn the white habit of the Choir, his de facto position would have been confirmed with the rank of Prior that was, in obedience to convention, placed upon me.

There was some convenience in this, too, for those concerned, as my mild ways did not do much to disrupt the manner in which authority in Mariannhill was taking shape. I carried out the most obvious (and largely liturgical) duties required of me with punctiliousness but avoided anything to do with the real exercise of power in the monastery, other than to smile or nod my acquiescence. And when it came to many of the other responsibilities of the Prior – his role in important new decisions regarding the work of the monastery, for example – well, here, too, there were others more than ready to take the lead I left to them.

Most of our decisions involved the stations, an area in which I was particularly ill-equipped to contribute, and in which the talents of others shone far more naturally. If Brother Nivard always went ahead to survey the likely sites and inspect them in terms of their practical requirements (was there sufficient water for drinking, irrigating, and driving a mill? enough timber for firewood and building? suitable arable land, and so on), it was Fr Arsenius who quickly moved in after him to become the force behind the actual setting up of the station. His spirit was a pioneering one, and he loved nothing more than to build in the wilderness for the Lord, creating in the wastelands a place for His house. He was thorough and efficient when it came to carrying out Brother Nivard's plans for construction and farming with Franz, but it was for new souls he chiefly hungered and his pastoral care exuded into the landscape even before there were bodies to blossom under it.

At the monastery itself a new figure was coming to the fore. Barely thirty years old, Theodor Wolpert had slipped seamlessly into our community during the commotion of 1885. An officer in the military when he converted to Catholicism, he came to Mariannhill with the intention of being ordained and was equipped with a natural ability to command. He was professed as Fr Gerard before the next year was out, and was one of the two men to whom Franz had entrusted the abortive excursion into Zululand and then sent out again with more success towards the Drakensberg. Before two more years had passed – even before his ordination – he was promoted to the rank of – yes, it had to come, though come it did before anyone (myself, especially) could have expected it – Prior.

Franz called me in one day early in 1888 to clear the way for this promotion. He was not known for giving explanations for his decisions within our community, no matter how ready he was to put the rationale behind our way of life before the public at large, and it was with his customary bluntness that he informed me that I was no longer to be Prior. And that I was to be transferred to Ötting.

Ötting! The possibility of being sent to one of the stations had never crossed my mind before and I was stunned. As I stood before my Superior bowed in silent obedience, the name of the station sunk in with further numbing effect. Ötting was at this stage barely a day station, more of an exploratory base for possible further stations and a resting place for travellers coming up from the Cape. Indeed, it was never really to become much more, and not only because of my assignment there.

Virtually lost in the overbearing presence of the natural beauty around it, the station was a stretch too far in a direction that Franz did not pursue in his grand design. As such it was to remain as remote as it was when, shaking and exhausted from my discomfort on horseback and the length and roughness of the journey, I dismounted in a sea of singing emerald. The sound of crickets rang in my ears, and my eyes hurt from the intensity of the wild green vegetation, cut through here and there by slashes of red soil. The latter could only have been exposed through some sort of natural calamity, for apart from our tents there was not a sign of human interaction with this remote world. Here, unlike any of our other stations, the Natives lived on remote tribal lands and none were resident on the property we had purchased.

I lacked the skills necessary for my new position – no, I did not even know what skills I lacked, for I had no idea of the duties required of me to carry out my function, as Franz put it to me briefly and bluntly, of occupying the station and seeking out the possibilities it afforded. As far as crops were concerned, it seemed to me the site would support only tropical ones, but I hesitated in reporting to Franz that the best thing to farm at Ötting would be bananas. I spent some weeks there with a particularly stolid Brother, whose greatest virtue was a reluctance to speak that seemed vacuous rather than contemplative.

And then word arrived from the monastery telling me to relocate to Mariathal.

This station was a veritable rush of activity in comparison with Ötting, clearly at the hub of much hushed bustling between stations. Travelling in the days of the ox-wagon was never going to lend itself easily to the observance of silence; the air vibrated constantly with the startlingly loud yelling of commands at the great beasts of burden and the occasional unfortunate servant. Apart from our own vehicles, there was also a steady flow of secular ones, for Mariathal was strategically placed at the junction of the two roads from Natal to the Cape Colony.

If anything I was even more lost at Mariathal, trying to get some hold on the world of distance and travel that crashed through the Office in unregulated and unregulateable ways. I was set mainly to duties that involved the recording of the chaotic activity going on around the station – chaotic for me, that is. I am sure the average settler would have found our life a model of decorum and composure. But I did begin to get a glimpse of what it was to control the business of oxen, wagons, drivers and loads. And there was, or so at least I tried to comfort myself, something suitably monastic about my work of keeping track of the constant movement all around me. You will have gathered from my earlier reference to Fr Luca Bartolomeo Pacioli, the inventor of double-entry bookkeeping, that he was something of a hero to me both in my secular and religious occupations.

On top of this I retained my duty of seeing to the sick. From the first I was taken to be the "doctor" for the stations, treating in my own way not only the Brothers and Fathers but, in severe cases, the Sisters too. The climate on the high ground of the stations stretching up to the Drakensberg was considered far healthier than that at Mariannhill, so some patients were sent up to me from the monastery. On one occasion Sr Paula, whose frail constitution had given way within months of her arrival in Natal, spent over four weeks under my care, after which she was able to return to the convent perfectly able to continue her work. Privately I wondered whether the change of climate did not have more to do with her recovery than my medical attentions, for I was still in the process of adapting the Kneipp cure that Franz favoured for African conditions.

Before I managed to create any sense of stability at Mariathal, I found myself in a lesser version of the same life in Kevelaer for some time, then at the slightly more established and rather incongruously named Einsiedeln. The commotion at this last station was even more pronounced, making it an odd choice to bear the name of that famous shrine in Switzerland dedicated to Our Lady of the Hermitage. Indeed, I have often had good cause to wonder why Franz made St Joseph the patron saint of all the missions (St Joseph the husband of Mary, I am sure you will understand, not for a moment to be confused with that other Joseph, the Gaper, the Dunce). Certainly our Superior claimed to be a great lover of this silent man of the gospels, he who never utters a word and yet plays such an important role in the mission of Christ. He would often acknowledge St Joseph as his helper and his model, although many must have wondered at his associating himself with this example of quiet obedience.

In each of the day stations, it was the sheer proximity of my brethren that was hard to endure. Tiny though their communities were compared to Mariannhill, the smaller space compounded the problems I had begun to experience at the motherhouse. Even in the vast expanse of the monastery, overcrowding was beginning to become a real problem. And to return to the primitive structures of the foundation in its early days on the stations was to experience again how thin a barrier tarpaulin and wood are to the presence of others.

It was not just a matter of numbers: even while we clung to some sort of contemplative regularity at the stations, there was a constant vitality running through these communities that generated a pulsing energy in work and prayer alike. In this, life on the stations was a more concentrated version of what had been worrying me at the motherhouse for some time. Even prayer in the monastery church had come to make me feel stifled, crushed and claustrophobic, overwhelmed as one was by a silent mass of brethren. At least in Kevelaer, and even to some extent Einsiedeln, there were times when I could just step out of the community (enclosure was more a principle than an achieved reality at the day stations) and enter for a while the tranquil experience that should be a monk's life, reciting prayers on a stretch of lonely hillside until one went beyond prayer into a stillness on the other side of words.

It was then that I entertained the guilty fantasy of becoming a hermit, only to have guilt and fantasy alike shatter on my vow of stability in community as I stumbled reluctantly back into the flurry of activity, made more intense by the effort of engaging in it without words. The flurry of hand signals alone was enough to make one long for the Anchorite's solitary combat in the desert.

~

Worse was to come. The rank of the quiet, smiling man jotting down the figures of weights and distances and times was finally remembered. Just over a year after Franz began his pattern of outstations, a new station was founded that in size alone was clearly destined to be more than simply another station. It was named after Lourdes, no less, and word was already circulating of how important it was going to be. Fr Arsenius was dispatched from Reichenau to see what he could make of the vast expanse Brother Nivard and Prior Gerard had won out of Franz's long negotiations with a major landholder in East Griqualand, and I was designated to take the pioneer's place as Superior at our now somewhat eclipsed first outstation.

The road approaching Reichenau curves around a hill and looks down on the busy jumble of buildings, and from here I could see immediately why the word "station" was beginning to be replaced by the word "mission". For there, held in an arm of the Polela River, was an established community that really did echo in miniature, even without the church that was yet to come, its namesake on the island in Lake Constance.

Although our Reichenau was not situated on an island, one still had to endure the trial of crossing the Polela to reach it. The river was, at the time of my arrival, in full flood and the path of stones that formed the usual ford was entirely submerged. There was no other course than to plunge one's horse into the powerful flow of water, trying all the time not to look to the right, where the current swept up to and then over the waterfall Franz had written of in so idyllic a way. His perspective was, as I later discovered, afforded only from the other side of the falls, when one could safely meditate on them from below. Whilst trying to cross the river, all they inspired in me was several minutes of desperate novenas shot through with terror as the water gushed up around the neck of my horse and over my knees.

Not long after my crossing, a Brother was caught up in that steady rush and thrust over the falls to his death at the very spot where Brother Nivard would site a mill some years later that challenged even Mariannhill's in its technological ingenuity. I did not need to know this story at the time to be able to imagine just such a tragic end as I clung to my rearing horse, uncertain as to which to fear more, animal or water.

When I emerged dripping from my baptism of terror it was into a world that it was hard to believe was Trappist. A store and a school were being built of stone quarried about half an hour's distance from the station, and I was told that Brother Nivard visited regularly to oversee this and several other projects – which included, I was relieved to hear, a bridge of stone and iron across the Polela. There was a lot of canvas and corrugated iron to be seen at the moment, but it was not the buildings that threatened my sense of the Strict Observance. There was some intent in their general layout, primitive as it was, to promote a life of enclosure, although I knew very well by now that buildings alone did not ensure this.

The schoolhouse was in any event the most prominent presence, for it had rapidly become a model out here on the western fringes of Natal. Its pupils came from all over the region, and even from beyond the mountains that rose up so dramatically before us, travelling many dangerous miles down the precarious passes that link Basutoland with the colony of Natal. I could not help but think of Benjamin up there, hearing of or even seeing the little ones making their excited way down from his place of exile to the same people amongst whom he had not been accepted. I would stare sometimes up into the mist and say a silent prayer to St Jude for him – ever more often as I began myself to feel the need for the intercession of the Patron of Hopeless Causes. Everywhere one looked there were children who, after tumbling out of their classes, would be working under supervision in the gardens and the kitchens, being taught to help with the animals, or to learn one or another craft or trade with a busy and sometimes, it must be said, irritable Brother or Sister.

Brothers Fridolin, Paulus and Sebastian were stationed at Reichenau, a larger complement than had been originally intended for the outstations, and the scale of the farming they supervised certainly seemed beyond that of a minor foundation. Wattles, oaks, willows and a variety of fruit trees – apples, plums and peaches – were being planted, and plans were underway to import cattle from the Allgäu, no less. Local cattle were already producing an abundance of milk for the community and the Brothers were beginning to experiment with cheeses. Vast acres were put under corn, and vegetable gardens stretched away a considerable distance from the Sisters' dormitory.

Amongst the pioneering Sisters was Mary Lassak – now Sr Clara – who had learned to speak acceptable, if heavily accented English, and Sr Angela Michel, whom I came to know extremely well during the tragedy of the years ahead. Even then Sr Angela venerated our Abbot, a reverence that, along with mine, would be tested in the fire of his final agony. During the time I was at Reichenau, no more was asked of her than that she take command of the hand mill used to prepare flour for our bread and porridge.

For myself, I discovered the responsibility of being the Superior of this busy station to be extraordinarily time-consuming. It was clearly no less than a new foundation, charged with the intention of becoming eventually a large house in its own right. The store veritably buzzed with the business of providing the Christians living on our land with food and the articles of clothing that enabled them to live amongst us.

Fr Ansgar, in the short period he had been at Reichenau, had baptised four individuals. This, it must be said, was with the encouragement of Fr Hyacinth, who was always one for rushing ahead, and who had also been at Reichenau for a while. It was thus deemed necessary to send up Fr Gerard to instruct the neophytes and perform the first solemn baptisms. He was overjoyed to be so charged, for even whilst Prior of Mariannhill he could barely wait to be involved in the work of the outstations. By the time I took over Reichenau eighteen young people were the first fruits of what can only be called missionary work, makeshift though it was. Our small temporary chapel was even being prepared for the first Christian marriages in the region and Brother Nivard, on his regular trips through the outstations, was already talking passionately of where he would site the first church to be built away from the motherhouse.

None of the projects we had underway was easily won, and considerable labour was needed to deal with the effects of frost, snow, locusts, the flooding of the Polela, and severe hailstorms. Dealing with damage to crops and buildings often could not await the sacred rhythm of the Office, which I had, as is prescribed when one is away from the monastery, been reciting on my own in the absence of any other Choir Religious. As for our observance of silence, I was constantly in the position of having to free one distraught Brother or another from a welter of contorted hand-signs in order to find out the latest disaster that had befallen the work he was doing. The Sisters, of course, were not restricted in their speech. Although they were the more practical members of the station community and simply got on with what they had to do, they had a tendency to tell me rather more than I needed to know.

~

Mission life in general kept throwing up bizarre circumstances that defied any attempt at silence or regularity. On the first Eastertide that I was at Reichenau, for example, lightning struck one of our wire fences. It so happened that five of our oxen were leaning against this fence and were killed instantly. The Sisters, whose habitation was nearest to the scene, came running to find me. Their excited voices outside the chapel forced me to give up my solitary attempt at observing the Office, and I emerged to be told of the event and that the Natives would have nothing to do with the carcasses. They would not help the Brothers move them, let alone take any of the meat for eating, which was most unusual, the Sisters stressed, because generally they would do anything to have this rare privilege. From what the Sisters could make out, this was for superstitious reasons only. There was much fine meat on the dead animals, they went on to tell me, and asked my permission to partake of it – if only, they added hastily, to do away with the Natives' superstition on this point.

My smiling agreement and gentle reminder that the Rule for the Sisters allowed them to eat flesh, as they well knew, hid just a hint of irritation that this could not have been decided amongst themselves. They then went off to the unexpected addition to their evening meal and I attempted to go back to my broken worship. Some hours later I was interrupted even more urgently, this time to be told by a young Native that the Sisters who had eaten the meat were vomiting violently. I hurried over to their quarters and spent much of the night prescribing the bathing of foreheads and extremities with cold water.

By dawn most of them had settled into a weak but quiet state, and within a few days they were up and about, although with no appetite for meat for some time to come. Some of the Sisters insisted that they had in some way been poisoned, which I reported to Franz along with the facts as I knew them. He immediately wrote to the *Natal Mercury* giving his views on this incident, although he was forced to conclude his letter, most uncharacteristically, with the admission that "the cause of these strange circumstances I leave to chemists to decide".

This incident was never explained scientifically and, as I write, I am able to see in it a portent of what was to come, a prelude to all those little bodies spelling out in their strange angles the agonising deaths that we were helpless to avert with our water and our prayers. My report on the bemusing occasion of the "poisoning" of the Sisters, I must admit, was mainly intended as an illustration to Franz of the many difficulties I experienced in trying to live within the Rule under the conditions encountered at Reichenau. To my disappointment his only response was to extend to me the dispensation from Choir that he had given to the other Religious travelling between or labouring on the stations.

Nonetheless Franz took seriously the reports of the priests in charge at the stations, especially since some of his more efficient Fathers were now amongst them. Fr Gerard, for example, came up to Centocow, a new site opened on the western bank of the Umzimkulu River that at first fell under my jurisdiction. The land for this had been donated by a Polish princess (its name was a simplified version of the Shrine of Our Lady of Czestochowa) and its position made it a crucial day station between Reichenau and our biggest financial investment in a station, Lourdes.

It soon became obvious that I was not coping with this added responsibility, and so Fr Gerard, freshly ordained and finding his duties as Prior too light and purely liturgical under Franz's hands-on form of leadership – or so I surmised at the time – convinced Franz that he should look into the situation at Centocow personally. He had shown a passionate interest in Brother David's work at Mariannhill and a startlingly quick grasp of Zulu, both of which he was eager to test in the wilds of the interior.

From the moment Fr Gerard was declared resident priest at Centocow it was clear that he had plans to make it far more than a simple day station. Six Sisters were assigned to what had once been the Dronk Vlei area (a suitable name for a property that a Pole would be interested in, my good German-Czech father would have said), but Fr Gerard soon recruited over twenty other members of our community to his station. He gave the old farmhouse to the Sisters, and in no time the horse-stable that he took for his residence was converted into a neat array of mud houses that served as school, dormitory and chapel. If Brother Nivard's plans were anything to go by, the church for this station was to be built sooner and to more impressive proportions than the one he and I were just beginning to discuss for Reichenau.

But Fr Gerard, like myself, was finding it difficult to accommodate the challenges of life on the stations within the Rule. Whereas I found the "missionary" work required of us a threat to our supreme duty of singing and praying the Office in common, it became clear to me that he found the narrow and exact prescriptions of the Rule an obstacle to the work that needed to be done. This he reported in no uncertain terms to our Abbot.

~

A working period of two and a half hours a day was clearly an impossible restriction to those at the missions (how easy it had become to say this word), but the only way these hours could be extended was at the cost of prayer in Choir. We "missionaries" were, accordingly, required to take part only in Night Office, as the Rule prescribed for Lay Brothers. In any event, few of the stations ever had enough monks together at one time to recite the Offices, let alone sing them, and yet there were so many stations by now (Rankweil, an outspan and resting place between Port Natal and Mariannhill, was added just after Lourdes) that the number of Choir Religious without a Choir was growing at an alarming rate.

Along with the relief provided by this dispensation (not the sort of relief I had in mind at all) I received the news that even at the motherhouse work seemed to be overwhelming the monks. Franz invoked the principle of "extraordinary work" so often that it became the norm for all monks, including the Choir Religious, to be freed from singing the minor canonical Hours so that they could work for five hours a day. This is allowed by the Rule when special circumstances pertain, and it is not even the maximum; the Trappist Statutes allow up to six hours of work a day in very exceptional cases. As the Brother giving me this news grumpily put it, the exception had now become the rule, and the Rule the exception.

"Nothing is to be preferred to the Work of God," we read in the Statutes. "Accordingly, the Liturgy of the Hours is to be celebrated by the community which, in union with the Church, fulfils Christ's priestly function offering to God a sacrifice of praise and making intercession for the salvation of the whole world." But the Statutes also say that "in particular cases the Abbot may determine the measure in which an individual monk participates in the Liturgy of the Hours in Choir" and that "in exceptional cases the Abbot may dispense a community from one or two Little Hours".

Franz was technically in the right then, but he claimed even more than technical correctness as he introduced yet more alterations to the Office. Just before his death he said to me, defensively, I thought, as the darkness gathered without and within, "It was the Spirit which guided me when I permitted the recitation of Compline without the long pauses." He went on with what breath was left him, "We spent too much time in the evening with such recitation – I consider that such a Compline at a time when there were four hundred million pagans in China alone, and when the pagans in Africa are not even numbered, a real disgrace!"

Fifteen minutes saved from the last of the liturgical Hours seemed to me far too little to give to so many people in need in a meaningful way, and far too much to take from the night prayer of the Church. I could not murmur against it then, but I must say now that I resented the rush between Paternoster and Confiteor, the gabbling together of the three psalms with their antiphon, the unseemly haste with which one moved to the beautiful hymn *Te lucis ante terminum* and the canticle *Nunc dimittis*.

These were crucial to the examination of one's conscience, and needed the grace and balance afforded them by the silence in between.

You may think me too fastidious – fussy, even – on this point. So would certain of my Brothers if I had put it to them in this way. But not all, by any means; there were some who could easily understand how one of our Order could be prepared to bring down our house over fifteen minutes of silence. Think only of the spirit of Caesarius who, in the last words he pronounced upon his deathbed, summed up his long and fervent life at the Villiers monastery in this way: "I shall chant with those who chant, sing psalms with those who sing psalms. Sing for him who has joined me to himself. There is sweetness in his mouth, and honey, and milk."

Yes, the weight of the history behind our community will tell you that one of its houses could easily have fallen over the matter of eating an apple in Lent. What a test, then, Franz was to present to our house when he carried us far, far beyond the loss of fifteen minutes of silence.

~

Franz at first tried to deal with this clash between prayer and work by handing out an increasingly intricate series of dispensations, the effects of which were difficult to foresee or calculate. It must be remembered that the whole life of a Trappist is one of penance and the acts of mortification prescribed by the Rule come close to the limits of endurance. These are, however, carefully balanced against each other and excess on one side enforces restrictions on another so that the weight of the life should not become unbearable. In adding to the hours of work allowed a monk, for example, Franz had to take into account the direct effect this had on the rule of fasting.

The Rule allows two meals on Sundays, feast days and ordinary week-days: lunch at noon and supper at five in the evening. Days of fasting are prescribed for every Wednesday and Friday the whole year through, for some days of Vigil, and for every day between the 14th of September and the first Sunday of Lent, when supper is replaced by a "collation" in which a hundred grams of bread is the only solid food allowed.

Mine were not the only knees to wobble at labour during Lent, and several monks on the missions fainted from hunger even on our standard diet. Franz therefore gave permission to those Choir Religious doing hard manual labour the whole year through to add a breakfast of soup, bread and coffee, except on days of fasting prescribed by the Church. Religious at the stations were considered automatically to be in the category of those "working hard" and an allowance was made for breakfast for them in the timetable of all the stations. Later Franz added a second breakfast, even during prescribed times of fasting. I noticed that many of the Choir monks did not avail themselves of this mitigation.

Fasting was not the only penance affected by our increased commitment to work: our sleep, too, was altered. Monks at the stations were allowed to rise at three a.m., instead of the two a.m. rising time stipulated at the monastery. As the work required of the missionaries made it impossible to make up for lost sleep during the day in the way that a monk at a regular house could, they did not in effect sleep longer than set down by the Rule. This placated all but the most rigorous of monks. Fr Arsenius, zealous missionary though he was, was heard to complain that although the hours of sleep were the same, those on the missions lost the penance of broken sleep.

Some of Franz's dispensations were less controversial. The concessions regarding hygiene drew the least comment. All the Rule has to say on the taking of baths is that they are *to be afforded the sick as often as may be expedient; but to the healthy, and especially to the young, let them be granted more rarely.* Given our heavy work and the hot climate, no one murmured against Franz's prescription for the taking of a bath once a month at the minimum during summer and at least every second month during winter. General permission was also granted to all who wished to bathe once a week, and only those who wanted to do so daily or several times a week had to get a permission slip from the Abbot. To me this, along with the next dispensation Franz granted, was such a relief that it felt like an indulgence.

For Franz allowed us to change our underwear twice the number of times permitted by the Rule, that is, two times during the week rather than only on Sundays. The effect of this was indescribable, even more in the humidity of Pinetown than up at the stations near the mountains. Whether one was dealing with dried, encrusted sweat whilst at one's prayers after work, or garments constantly sodden under one's arms and between one's legs, this penance did seem to go beyond anything imagined in St Benedict's Rule, created as it was for northern climates.

Perhaps I err now, as I did then, in going along with Franz on this, but it has to be admitted that my skills in healing, such as they were, were required far less for rashes and sores in places of shame after this dispensation was passed. I had begun experimenting with Kneipp's Water Cure in those cases that resisted the aloe juice treatment I had relied upon at first, but even the particularly persistent pustular eruptions on the legs that plagued so many of our brethren became less of a problem when everyone was allowed to keep a second habit in his cell. This dispensation had a marked effect, too, on our external appearance: before this alteration to the Rule one could tell by Sunday exactly what work a Brother had been engaged in during the course of the week from the condition of his habit.

Franz's pragmatism also extended to the introduction of sandals and hats for those working in the fields or on building sites, and he even permitted Brothers going on a journey to wear overcoats. Those travelling by horseback were allowed the unheard of concession of wearing long trousers as well.

But fasting, sleeping, bathing, dressing were nothing in comparison with the challenge the missions placed before the most important characteristic of our Order – it was considerably more difficult for Franz to find a way for his missionaries to bypass silence. The missions clearly demanded exceptions in this regard, but such exceptions cut to the core of our monastic discipline.

~

A Trappist is allowed to speak in case of urgent need but only if a Superior allows it, and even then with the fewest possible words. In order not to embarrass the monks no group is left alone at work without an "official" being appointed who may say the Benedicite – that is, give permission to talk. However, the Mariannhill community was by now so broken up, not only between the motherhouse and the missions but also in the different work projects to which we were committed for long periods in various places, that it was necessary to give many more members of our community this authority than is usual, with the predictable result that some of them were not as rigorous with regard to speech as they should have been.

Here we must be scrupulously fair. Our Abbot tried stringently to fulfil the law on silence. He punished mercilessly any who spoke or wrote without permission, invoking the exact penance laid down in the Rule – lashes in Chapter, followed by fasting on bread and water only. I can bear witness to the number of times we stood by as he ordered one who had been proclaimed for speaking to undress.

The whole community would watch as the one proclaimed sat down on a stool placed on the spot where he had been standing and, as the Regulations prescribe, took off his cowl and set it upon his knees, bringing his arms up through the opened collar of his habit and exposing his body down as far as the belt. Then, sitting still, with his head bowed, and with no words upon his lips except for the constant repetition of *mea culpa, ego me emendabo*, he would submit to the lash. The Brother doing the whipping would not desist until the Abbot so commanded, but when the command came he would immediately go to his Brother's aid, helping him to dress again. The one whipped would then stand, but not move from his place until Franz said, "Go, sit down." Then he would bow and return to his place whilst we were all enjoined not to speak to anyone of the fault committed or to make signs about it.

It is difficult to lay at Franz's door the fault of those who gave permission to speak far more generously than they should have, but it must also be said that whilst Franz remained committed to complete silence at the monastery, and demanded it as far as it was practicable at the stations, a subtle change in so far as silence was concerned began to permeate our daily life. Franz was convinced that the Sisters should never be bound by silence, as some were suggesting might be more proper for what was in effect an Order of nuns. For the Sisters to make dumb signs before the pagans they ministered to was ridiculous, he said, not realising how easily the argument could be extended to his monks on the missions. Many of these were by now in such constant contact with strangers that it would, in practical terms, have made just as much sense for them, too, to be freed entirely from the silence of the Trappists.

~

It was clear that the number of dispensations Franz was handing out needed some sort of regularisation. By late 1888 he announced a set of rules specifically designed for the missions and, concerned as I was by such an unprecedented development in our lives, this provided much-needed respite for those like myself who felt sorely the responsibility of having to administer a constantly changing succession of alterations to our way of life.

Reichenau had by now twenty Brothers and twenty-six Sisters, and somehow the station stumbled forward under the combined weight of their efforts, but I found myself withdrawing more and more into a benign distance when it came to the running of things. I let those coming to me for advice or permission read as much into this as they wished whilst I committed myself as little as possible on any question. It remains quite amazing to me how much good leadership a community can find in this kind of reserve, and I enjoyed the affection and even respect of my Brothers and Sisters despite the fact that on the few occasions when I did make a concrete suggestion it invariably had to be scrapped or corrected. I had become the incarnation of the Proverb: "Even a fool who keeps silent is considered wise; when he closes his lips, he is deemed intelligent."

But, behind the smile that felt ever more like a grimace seared onto my face, problems with the running of Reichenau were mounting, and in the cold clear prose of my written quarterly reports to the Abbot, not to mention the numbers that made up most of their bulk, these were becoming increasingly evident. Crops did not meet expectations, the spread of workers often did not make sense in relation to our projects, responses to natives and neighbours lacked decisiveness and direction, building slowed down, and minor dissatisfactions in the community sometimes became major rather than, as I trusted them to do, running their course. I was honest about all this in my accounts to my Superior, and no matter how much my community held me in their affection, his responses were brutally direct. Translated onto the page, my silence did not bear much scrutiny.

One would have thought that the rearrangement of the responsibilities of leadership Franz now envisaged for the stations would have suited one like myself perfectly; indeed, this section of the new rules seemed designed with someone exactly like me in mind. In my case though, Franz's separation of administrative duties did not so much free me for my real vocation as expose a failing so deep that not even I had fully suspected myself of it.

The Rule of St Benedict was formulated to direct a single, closed unity, protected from the outside world by walls and containing everything necessary for life within this enclosure. Everything within is regulated by the Rule and custom, and it is the chief duty of the Abbot to see that these are observed faithfully. Officials under him have specific tasks defined exactly by the Rule and in no matter of importance may they act independently. The Abbot alone is entirely responsible for any decision where the Rule may be deficient. No unregulated thing may be done without his permission, and permission is mainly needed in connection with work since this is practically the only area in which a monk ordinarily has to make decisions. All other exercises, spiritual and "less spiritual" as we call them, are regulated by the Rule to the smallest detail.

Useful as they were, the rules for the missions affected a double break in the structures of obedience for monastic life. For one thing the work required on the stations demanded a variety of activities for which the Rule was not designed, and for another, the monks at the stations – who were "not permitted to do anything without permission" – lived for days and weeks and even years at a considerable distance from the Abbot.

Now the Rule, being medieval in origin, assumes a situation similar to the circumstances we found in our far-flung colony, but it dealt with matters like travel and the founding of new houses in vastly different ways to those devised by Franz. Under the Rule any subdivision of a religious house must fall under its own Superior. In effect the Rule recognises only an abbey and a priory that is meant to grow into an abbey in the course of time. During this time the titular Prior, like the Abbot, is completely independent in the spiritual and material management of his enclosed community.

But Franz wanted his stations to remain entirely dependent on their motherhouse forever; he himself was to remain the ultimate authority for Mariannhill and all its stations – there were to be no autonomous Superiors taking root in his settlements. He had no intention of giving up any of his powers over the missions; they were, in his view, simply extensions of his monastery, and every individual on them remained directly responsible to him. Those of us appointed as Superiors on the missions were, in effect, Superiors in name only. We had none of the rights of office legally connected with the title and, increasingly, fewer and fewer of the responsibilities.

I have already admitted that I was amongst the first to report the difficulties I had in attempting to be in charge of a station and uphold the Rule at the same time, but few of the other Superiors at the stations shared my liturgical concerns. It would be more honest to admit openly that the complaint of the others was that they did not have enough independent authority. Initially this was put as a need to be freed from the strict observance of the Rule, but, slowly and at first cautiously, as Franz's dispensations removed many of their problems in this regard the point began to be made that it was more independence from the Abbot himself that they wanted.

It was these aspirations towards autonomy that encouraged Franz to announce his Rule for the Stations. The third point of the first paragraph of the new Rule makes this clear: "Since life in the missions may endanger our Trappist spirit," it reads, "members living on the stations may not find it conspicuous that we prescribe the strictest regulations to the missionary priests, Fathers, and Brothers, and you will understand that it must rest in the power of the Abbot alone, depending on persons and places, to make them more severe or withdraw them temporarily, as it also lies entirely in his power (*in suo arbitrio*) to recall without ado individual members of the missions, transfer or change them."

~

Copies of Franz's new Rule, freshly printed, were dropped at my feet by Fr Hyacinth himself, who was fuming with anger. "Our Abbot will not give up his omnipotence," he said, "even where he is clearly not omniscient! He wants the reins in his hands when he does not even know the road!"

The assignment of distributing the Rule for the Stations could not have fallen to a less appropriate monk, but it just so happened that as it came off the press Fr Hyacinth was leaving Mariannhill to return, via Reichenau and the day stations, to Centocow. The attachment he formed to the idea of the missions and to Fr Gerard on their initial exploratory journey into Zululand had led to his entrenching himself at this most Polish of our foundations. Here a passionate spirit emerged out of his former dourness, like a caterpillar of a particularly voracious kind, chewing its way through most of what I held dear.

I held myself back from reminding Fr Hyacinth, when he trumpeted forth on the subject of the Black Madonna, as Our Lady of Czestochowa is called, that several of the most venerated Marian shrines celebrated a Virgin and Child whose faces had darkened over the years by a miracle or simply by the smoke and fumes of centuries of votive candles, who is to say? Not the least of these was Our Lady of the Hermitage in Einsiedeln, whom we had also adopted for our own, even if this shrine was more popular with Germans and Austrians than Poles. Still, it appeared from his opening exclamation that I was not in for another of the hymns to Poland, which he particularly and pointedly felt obliged to aim at me as a Czech. Instead, I was to be subjected to one of his tirades against Franz.

I was disturbed by the personal animosity that pervaded Fr Hyacinth's attitude towards Franz, the reverse of his absolute devotion to the exotic monk from Africa whom he had followed to Mariannhill in 1883. By the time he became a Choir monk he was already thoroughly imbued with the missionary spirit. Never one to take issues lightly or apart from the persons who embodied them, he had turned against the object of his early devotion with the same fervour.

I found myself, as always in his presence, regretting that one of the few marks of distinction left to me as Superior was the freedom to speak – well, to brethren from the other missions if not to their Superiors, for under the new Rule direct communication between the various mission Superiors was forbidden. But I particularly did not wish to know anything about Fr Hyacinth's attitude to the shifts in authority taking place at the stations. My own troubles in this regard aside, the general mood developing at Centocow and, I gathered, at other stations was beginning to show alarming signs of nothing less than disobedience.

I was especially bemused by his outburst because I knew that the modified rules were designed to meet many of the objections raised by the monks on the missions to the strict observance. A firm basis for the loosening up of our liturgical life was exactly what he and others like him sought, after all. Slowly I began to grasp that it was not just Franz's determination to preserve his central authority that was upsetting Fr Hyacinth. What he, on behalf of his Superior, Fr Gerard, resented, and resented as deeply as the other mission Superiors, was a shift in authority on the missions that seriously affected their day-to-day management. This shift (in all probability born of my complaints) involved the introduction of the position of "Manager".

Under the Rule for the Stations, Managers took over from Superiors all control of the material life of the stations. Everything temporal, including the finances of the missions, was assigned to the Managers. To them alone was given the power to dispose of "the craftsmen, day workers, and handymen, as well as the labour power of the Brothers". It was only on their advice, too, that Superiors on the stations had the authority to give any further dispensations that might be necessary. Allowing monks to carry their tools to work in any way that was most convenient, for example, rather than under the arm, as the Rule prescribes, was one dispensation the Managers recommended and we Superiors extended; another was the partial dispensation from the rule of wearing the hood, which we on their advice no longer made obligatory, especially in oppressive heat.

Superiors were left with authority over all things spiritual and educational. The position of Manager was meant to free us for the care of souls alone.

As Franz put it in a letter accompanying the new Rule (the first of many he would have to circulate defending his decisions regarding the stations): "It is best if the Superior does not trouble about any field, any horse, any hoof, not about the kitchen or the cellar. He should busy himself only with souls; he should teach, preach, study, and pray. As soon as he gets mixed up with the farm, the kitchen, and the store, he forgets his prayers, the mission, and the school. Because of his inexperience he often causes much material damage to the station ..."

I confess to hanging my head as Fr Hyacinth spluttered this out, for I recognised in Franz's sketch a clear portrait of myself, clear at least in its depiction of my failings as a manager of material things. Up to this point I had managed to muddle together in a general sense of incompetence that kept from view – even my own – the true source of my reticence. This, in one of a compounding set of ironies that began to beset what was meant to be the least ironic of lives, was revealed to me by one of Franz's more thinly veiled subterfuges.

Fr Hyacinth's anger over the appointment of Managers was driven as much by the rank of the Managers as the division itself. Technically a Manager could be a Choir Religious or a Lay Brother, also referred to as a Convers Brother. The term "Convers" is taken from St Benedict's *conversatio morum* and indicates one who has vowed himself at his solemn profession to the "common life" of monasticism without being professed "for the Choir" – without, that is, the obligation of saying the Divine Office daily in Choir. Whilst the Church does not exalt the life of the Choir Religious over that of the Convers Brother, the life of a Choir monk is considered the highest of the many forms of Christian life. Or so I told my novices when I served as Novice Master, usually to as little effect as the supposed absence of a distinction had on Fr Hyacinth and most of the Superiors on the stations. There the Superiors were invariably Choir Religious and the Managers Lay Brothers.

Franz's reasoning for this – at least his official reasoning, which deceived no one – was that, following the maxim of St Theresa, "confessors of the Sisters may not be their Superiors at the same time; we therefore assign the necessary contact with the Sisters to the Brother Manager, and we appoint a Lay Brother to be the Manager on the stations. It is not that we have less confidence in the priests but because we want the Sisters to be more prudently directed by their confessors and to be more easily governed by their Superior." Franz's own dual role as overall Superior of Mariannhill and confessor to the chief amongst his "Sisters" worked against his own logic here, and soon enough he would remove the term "Superior" from the missions altogether in an attempt to clear up his argument. But his introduction of the title of "Rector" for the Religious in charge of the stations only underscored a general impression amongst the Choir Religious of his preference for Lay Brothers.

It was difficult not to ignore the reality that, for the kind of work he had in mind, Franz needed workers whose hands were not tied by narrow prescriptions. This had been so from the first, no less in his founding of Mariastern and at Maria Dunbrody than at Mariannhill itself, and as a result he had learned the value of competent Lay Brothers early on. Not obliged to follow the Office during the day, they formed a mobile troop that did not need the constant dispensations necessary for a Choir monk to be of use in building new stations. They also tended to be better disposed to manual labour, working harder and for longer periods than the Choir Religious.

It was not lost on us that the Choir Religious formed a smaller proportion of our community than is usual in a Trappist house. Out of the ninety men making up the monastic community of Mariannhill when Franz was made Abbot, only twenty-two stood in Choir. The simple statistical fact of sixty-eight Lay Brothers went against the very foundation of the Order, which rested on the strong basis of the Choir. Yet, with each new intake of novices, Franz skewed the imbalance further. Candidates for the Trappist life are not allowed to choose for themselves whether to enter the ranks of the Choir novices or those of the Brothers. The Abbot alone assigns their future vocation and, at Mariannhill, a few questions regarding the former training of the candidates settled the matter. Postulants with any kind of scholarly background – if, indeed, they had studied anything at all – joined those whom Franz considered not suited or fit for manual labour. They were given the white habit whereas those with any training or aptitude as artisans were put into the brown.

The nature of Franz's propaganda for our monastery, in print and on his tours, ensured that most of those who followed his call came because they had some kind of practical skill they could offer in their enthusiasm for the missions. To me it seemed as if they took upon themselves the strict observance of the Trappists only as the necessary prerequisite for their missionary activity. And this sacrifice was not made too difficult for them; to be blunt, their noviciate was aimed more at preparing them for the missions than to be monks, as was evident when, to my real consternation, Franz started sending them out to the missions well before their noviciate ended.

Now the canonical regulations are absolutely clear in stating that novices are not in any way to be used or employed outside the monastery precincts. In the face of this, Franz used, not for the first or last time, the excuse of necessity. The reality was that the effectiveness of Brother David's lessons in Zulu meant that the noviciates under his schooling gained a working proficiency in that language far more quickly, and to a better degree, than those professed monks out in the field trying here and there to pick up something of the language between their – largely silent – duties. As soon as the novices had this advantage they were sent out to swell the ranks of the Lay Brothers on the missions, giving even more support to the promotion of monks from this category to positions of authority.

Fr Hyacinth and others were having none of this. "The institution of the Lay Brothers," he almost shouted as he thumped his already rather tattered copy of the Rule for the Stations, "was only added much later in the history of our Order, and they have always played a subservient role. Now those who are put above us do not even have to report to their Superiors on the missions. They are obliged to account for their work only to the Abbot! And we Religious have to listen to that Abbot asking if the Pope himself can afford to run to church seven times a day!"

I refrained from mentioning at this point that he was foremost amongst those requesting as much freedom as possible from their liturgical duties whilst at the missions. I simply nodded in my usual way as his tirade continued, not only whilst he was mounting his horse but even as he rode off. I could hear him using words in Polish that I am sure were not worthy of a Trappist as he tried to urge the animal across the jumble of stones that still made up our only crossing of the Polela. I am afraid that no progress had been made with the building of Brother Nivard's bridge, nor was it to be begun until some time after I was ordered to leave Reichenau.

~

My being freed to care for souls alone left me lost and exposed in a new kind of desolation. This was a place where, after years of disciplining myself not to speak, I discovered I had nothing to say. Not to the Sisters, whose confessions I dutifully heard and whom I as dutifully absolved, never enjoining anything other than the most formal penance and utterly unable to find within myself encouraging or admonishing words beyond this. Not to the children, amongst whom I occasionally wandered in the schoolroom, a placid, distant figure bobbing and dipping in agreement with anything the Sisters had to teach. Not to the novices, those energetic and active missionaries with scant knowledge of or real interest in the Rule, over whom Franz had recently made me Novice Master out on the missions. Not even in church, where I let the Liturgy carry the service and, in place of preaching, read sermons and commentaries by the Church Fathers in a quiet voice that hardly carried across the congregation.

And least of all out in the fields of the mission, where I found no lack of inspiration but simply a lack of response to that inspiration as I sometimes wandered perforce through the crumpled foothills of the Drakensberg to various homesteads entrusted to us. We had here, just beyond the rolling greenness that enfolded us in summer, all the majesty of soaring peaks, split with crags and often lost in rolling mist and thundering storm, that one could require to arouse a romantic religious fervour. Was this the naïve monk who, several lifetimes ago it now seems, felt a certain landscape to be an inadequate expression of the presence of God? If ever God could declare Himself through the flare of sunlight against towering cloud and rock, or speak in the crack of lightning in an amphitheatre of stone, it was here. Mountains there were in abundance to which I could lift up my eyes, but they provided no answer to my spiritual emptiness – no, that is too grand a statement; simple numbness is perhaps the best way I can put it.

We had here, again in abundance, the audience we had sought in vain at Dunbrody, before which we could present the spectacle of our silent life. But the ways of those to whom we had come to be an example I found both overwhelming and impenetrable. Usually each homestead was like a large straw hive swarming with a life I stood outside of and could never know – indeed, did not consider it my place to try to know. One day I came to a collection of huts the occupants of which were out, tending to their crops or visiting or whatever it was that would call them all away at once. My Native guide gestured towards one of the wickerwork homes – in shape not unlike an inverted coffee cup – and then opened it for me. I went down on my knees and peered in, like a boy peering into his bird trap to see if he has caught a titmouse. Inside I decried no article of furniture, no utensil, no clothing – absolutely nothing. For a moment I felt as if I was face to face with the same nothingness that God encountered when He was about to create the universe. Then I realised that if I were the one expected to speak the Word here I would not know what words to speak. And if the word became flesh, I wondered, what then did silence become?

Quickly I withdrew from the dark interior and began pulling myself awkwardly into an upright position. In the process I looked up at my muscular guide. If he was not quite the Nubian of the altar in Brünn, he had nevertheless a handsome physique. Suddenly I felt through him the empty yard about me come alive with its absent inhabitants and in the vigour of their babbling presence I understood again – no, perhaps for the very first time – the secret of the silence that was meant to be my vocation.

The silence of the Trappist is born of perfect confidence, the perfect confidence of Christ when he remains mute before Pilate. Words are generated by the lack of certainty, of the desire to explain, to convince. Even by wondering what my silence would become in the language of the inhabitants of that empty but endlessly evocative kraal I betrayed that silence, admitted the loss of the mysterious certainty at its heart, surrendered my vocation. For what else is the vocation of a Trappist but to embody the belief that love is the exercise of prayer, and prayer the exercise of silence.

I confess that I felt that day a deep and almost overwhelming desire not only to speak but to speak in a language not my own. The need to know the language of the Natives who lived in that kraal bubbled up in me with such force I scarcely knew how to resist it – but only when I knew that I would have nothing to say in it. Yes, I hungered after the Zulu language on that day, hungered after it even as I knew the temptation it presented, the trap it would be.

So there I was, finally, no longer able to create out of my bumbling directions orders and dispensations, the illusion that I was, however ineffectually, the Superior of a mission. Instead, I was on my knees in the dirt, a teacher with nothing to teach, a preacher with nothing to preach, a priest with nothing to profess. I stood up, then, and, beginning with the single black man before me, I turned my quiet smile – for the first time knowing truly both its emptiness and purpose – upon the world.

I was disciplined enough not to interpret this realisation as some melodramatic form of alienation in which I, for some inscrutable cosmic reason, had been cast out of the drama of redemption. My condition was not one of great spiritual suffering; it was simply one of deep, dull, leaden bemusement that I recognised as a purely personal emotion and, as such, far beneath an allegory for others. I thus forced myself to be content with reflecting God's silence in my own. *Whoso keepeth his tongue, keepeth his soul* I comforted myself, entrusting my emptiness to the labyrinthine prescriptions of the Rule and Regulations.

I now found myself propounding the Rule to the novices under me with a force born of the desperate knowledge that it was this, and this alone, that stood between me and a fall into a world as confusing and terrifying as anything I experienced when returning from the grip of a seizure. Unable to sense the substance to fill me out as a Superior or even as an ordinary monk, the Rule became my very shape, and the avoidance of speech my way of being in the world. Who more suitable, you would think, to teach our novices the central tenet of our worship: "To Thee silence alone is fitting by way of praise." But I found now that my renewed commitment to this observance was not so much because there is no better means of approaching the infinite than through silence, but because my own finitude, in all its frailty and failure, seemed best hidden in silence.

It was precisely then that Franz decided to recall me to the monastery. You might think that this was most appropriate for me, given my new understanding of myself and my vocation, but it would not be as some humble monk who could spend his days chanting away harmlessly in Choir that he wanted me there. My evident failure on the missions, at Reichenau in particular, was rationale enough for my redeployment to a place where I would be less in the way. But I was certain that, at this time when the desire for seclusion most consumed me, there was something else behind his appointing me to nothing lower than my old position as Prior of Mariannhill.

15

What Franz needed, as I discovered immediately upon my return to Mariannhill, was an additional voice. Or a nod of assent, at least.

"The monastery of Mariannhill itself, as well as the mission stations under the rule of Abbot Franz, arose, we might say, in a storm," I wrote in the official "Life of Abbot Franz Pfanner" produced at the request of the *South*

African Catholic Magazine just after his death. All through that standard hagiography I left the clues that now guide me back to the truth as I knew it behind the mask of sainthood. I find no guarantee of success in reaching this truth, however, as words slip and slide away from me no less in the glare of sunlight reflected off places worn smooth on Franz's rough wooden desk than in the wavering light of the type of candle he perfected.

In a storm, we might say. What else could one call the swirl and noise, the gusts and crashes, the flashes and rolls that thundered in and around and through the place dedicated to silence that I had left? It is a testament to the material strength of each beam raised, each brick laid, that they are still standing, mute before the onslaught in which they came into being. So, let me say "storm" again, and mean it now in its full force, all the while remembering that God reveals Himself neither in the tempest above nor in the earthquake below, nor in the burning fire, but in the thin voice of silence.

~

By the time I approached its gates in late 1889 – balanced on one of our heavy, outsized wagons, my horse having proved intractable for the last few miles of the return journey that I had trusted myself to make in the saddle – Mariannhill was well on its way to becoming the largest abbey of any Order in the world. It had already eclipsed Mariastern, its only Trappist competitor in terms of size, and Franz took a pleasure in outdoing his own early achievements that he could barely conceal.

Not only had buildings gone up at an amazing speed in my absence, they had also taken on much more of the look of a religious institution. A "German" religious institution, people said, although what they really meant was the brick architecture of the northern part of the new German state. This was odd in itself as most of my brethren were, if not from Austria itself, then from the south, where the baroque frothed and foamed in a white profusion of stucco and plaster. Brother Nivard was every inch a Bavarian, as his laughter alone testified, but when it came to designing our buildings in Africa he was thrown back on the one feature that did link us firmly with Germany – the grinding poverty out of which that country sought to raise itself. This threw its architects, no matter how ambitious their visions, back onto the most humble of materials: wood, for the most part, and thatch and, sometimes, brick. Our builder and architect was never more German than when the constraints of his materials drove him to his unusual and distinctive forms.

The availability of stone at Centocow and Reichenau had tempted Brother Nivard into traditional ecclesiastical expectations. Lifted straight out of the European pattern books in Mariannhill's tiny library, the plans I saw whilst I was Rector at Reichenau were for something church-like in the most conventional sense, with spikes and spires everywhere. It is easy for me, I suppose, now that I have been educated by Brother Nivard's genius in its full flight, to smile at his early attempts. I remember that there was a time when I, too, found all that bristly verticality the most satisfying form for a church.

When Brother Nivard moved away from pointed arches, my taste in building moved with him. I learned to love the round arch that he began to favour and made the essence of his best buildings. It was as if he chose to remain true not to the romanesque – as the ever greater experimenting that came with his ever greater confidence demonstrates – but to the graceful arch of the dam at Mariannhill, his first success as a builder, which stands strong to this day. In building after building he raised this faultless form, and made of it a small heaven that enclosed perfectly our world of work and prayer. There is no doubt that brick worked itself more easily into the round than the point, but the subtle variety Brother Nivard summoned out of the simplicity dictated by this material defied its limitations, at least for those who had eyes to see.

To some our blunt and simple brickwork smacked of low-church Protestantism, but did not we Trappists, in our own way, wish to return to the purity of the earliest Christianity, before the corruptions of success and grandeur took over? Was this not the message Brother Nivard sent when, in choosing the language of brick, he refused to allow his arches to be drawn into points? And what did he surrender when, in later years, he taught even humble brick to speak in the voice of the new grandeur that was the spirit not so much of Mariannhill but of some of its missions, rising out of the lost landscapes they came to dominate with their massive forms and, above all, their towers – towers that declared their glory and flung ever louder, ever further, the sound of their bells.

Well, that was still to come, and what I saw on my return were the satisfyingly square and heavy forms in robust brick that lined our roads, dominated our hillside, spelled out our enclosure in no uncertain terms. My lack of inner certainty produced a desperate longing for the proper outward demonstration of my faith, and I was glad to see that the buildings of Mariannhill had a determinedly monastic look and feel. At their heart now was the completed cloister garth, a courtyard surrounded, as is required of a Cistercian house, by church, sacristy, Chapter Room, the novitiate or "Monks' Room", refectory and kitchen. The garth even included its compline, a reading area that ran alongside the wall of the church. Just outside the refectory door a washbasin was set in a beautiful garden the Brothers were still busy laying out in the courtyard. This was truly a place of isolation from the world, with only narrow stairs leading to the dormitory and a small passageway to the rest of the monastery.

Just before I had left Mariannhill one of the many journalists endlessly drawn there mistook the monastery for "a cluster of sheds hastily put up as a shelter for the workmen engaged on building a brick church". Now, just after my return, another wrote: "Even those who have visited the place before were astonished with the change that has come over it in the last few months. In place of the uncomfortable wood and iron church which formerly did duty, a large brick abbey has been erected, and the Abbot has changed the diminutive iron apology for a residence to a brick-built double-storeyed edifice, complete with balconied portico."

Franz's home was indeed a splendid affair, built just beyond the neat complex of workshops to the south-east of our cloisters and overlooking the richest part of our farmland in the valley below. But the real jewel amongst our buildings was the monastery's church, and one of the first things I did on my return was to use an hour of private meditation to soak up this building. Stepping through one of the two lateral arches on the façade, I found myself standing in the open vestibule that fronted the west end of the building. I stood there in awe. Before me stretched a deceptively simple rectangle with the St Anne's chapel, designed for the Sisters, projecting to the left of the altar. Three aisles divided the nave, with steps leading down to the central aisle that housed first the Brothers' choir, and then, below this, the priests' choir.

Our journalist friend may well have called our church an "abbey", but Franz always insisted on referring to it in terms of the model that Brother Nivard both imitated and transcended in building it. Our "basilica" was one hundred and eighty feet long and fifty feet wide, and could hold over two thousand people. Its stone-flagged floors, painstakingly quarried and dressed by our Brothers, covered over ten thousand square feet, and it had a clear height of thirty-six feet. The left aisle was for the accommodation of the locals, Natives and strangers alike; the one to the right contained the children's choir. Set into the left side of the Brothers' choir was an entrance with a portico through which we monks entered the building for the Office.

I remember thinking on the occasion when I first entered the heart of the structure that no one would have dreamed of calling it a brick building. Inside its jacket of brick walls and iron roof it floated free of any sense of such an earthly medium, calling my soul up to God. My eyes followed the dappled light up to the extended ceiling of the central aisle. This rose on slender wooden stilts to allow that light and the air to flow in through its high, open windows.

The side aisles, supported, too, by piers of thin, light, golden wood, were windowless. Clearly Brother Nivard had learned not to ape the European practice of taking the weight off the walls with buttresses and ribs so that they could be made up of as many windows as possible. The sun in Africa was something one courted with care, as the night blindness that afflicted some of our brethren had taught us, and the windows at the very apex of the roof were more than enough to keep our church cool and airy, with just enough light for our candles to burn to some effect. The only stained glass windows (sent to us, of course, by Dr Oidmann from his factory in Linnich) were set above the main altar, and for the most part the light was left to play over the deep glow given off by the stained wood of the high ceilings.

This, then, was no timid and tepid copy of some "Italian" or "German" basilica but a brave translation into brick and wood and iron of a faith nurtured in heavy stone and glass. Here Brother Nivard enabled us to chant the Hours, infused as they are with medieval northern Europe, in a building entirely suitable for Africa. I took quiet delight, too, in the fact that no ostentatious bell tower rose up above our church, and saw in its absence evidence of the peculiarly Trappist atmosphere, plain and unadorned, that our basilica radiated.

More practical structures, as impressive in their own way, had sprung up all over in a tightly organised pattern to accommodate the work that was as much a part of our prayer as the Office. Added to our already established workrooms were quarters for a carpenter and a tinsmith and a dressmaker. We also had a painting studio and a shop, and the bakery and timber yard had been considerably extended. "As I came in sight of the monastery I could hardly believe my eyes," another visitor at this time has commented. "Thirteen months ago it was a lot of iron shanties thrown up higgledy piggledy. Now it looks like a busy little well-built town."

~

My duties had prevented me from coming down for the biggest event that took place at Mariannhill whilst I was away on the missions. Franz's Silver Jubilee, celebrating his twenty-fifth year as a Trappist, was from all reports as big a celebration as his installation as our Abbot four years earlier. It was also, as events proved, the high-tide mark of our monastery as a Trappist house.

Our one constant supporter in the world of print, the *Natal Mercury*, appears to have thrown itself into reporting the Jubilee with its usual mixture of enthusiasm and inaccuracy. It is entertaining to read that our Superiors, at any rate those who could speak English, "placed no bridle upon the tongue when questioned by the hundreds of people from Durban and Maritzburg". According to our verbose friend the *Mercury*, "One rotund, white-flannelled Trappist was as merry as a cricket, and caused roars of laughter as he told some of the lovers of the flesh pots that if the demand kept up at this rate they would be ruined, while he shared the anxiety of other enquirers by telling them that there were too few waiters, and the worst of it was that those who were helping could scarcely speak a blessed word of English."

I had sent down to the celebrations two little girls and three boys from Reichenau, who joined twenty-one other children from the missions. "To the surprise of all the visitors," the report went on, "these five children each in turn addressed the Abbot in the German language, an accomplishment that was warmly applauded." My pride in their accomplishment helped to offset the embarrassment I continued to feel at my poor command of English, not to mention Zulu.

If there was another part of the proceedings that I was sorry I was unable to witness it was the magic lantern display, including "the ghost scenes at the finish" that the reporter said "beat anything of the kind that has been lately seen in the colony". It is not only the reminder of my hopes for the photograph as a silent presentation of our lives that touches me at the thought of this. The reminder that so many of those who joked and laughed for those few days are now only spirits, flickering up fitfully amidst

313

the glories they created out of nothing, makes this old man's throat tighten and his weak eyes damp, and his hand shake on the page.

The magic lantern was followed by a display of fireworks under the superintendence of Brother Nivard. How apt that Mariannhill climaxed in an explosion of light, and that its chief architect was the master of the spectacle, a display in which a pageant of ghosts marched off into the night, white robes taking on the colours of ignited gunpowder, leather gleaming, cowls flickering, faces cadaverous in shadow, our silence scattered to the four winds in detonations and flares.

~

Despite the extent of the new land that had been added in my absence, my main sense of the monastery was still the overcrowding that had begun to bother me before I left for the missions. Forty-six of us arrived in 1882; one hundred and eighty-two monks now filled the halls into which we crammed together to pray, eat, work and sleep at regular hours of the day. For some exercises the novices were separated from the professed, but virtually everywhere we were packed together, shoulder to shoulder. We followed the old system of seniority, so we tended to have the same neighbours almost all day long. Such physical closeness, difficult enough for some of us, had to be endured in absolute silence, a silence in which each quiet clearing of the throat, each modest scratching of an itch, could not be other than a public display.

The monastic hood was some help. It covered most of the head, and although it was obligatory to wear it in this way at Mariannhill only in cooler weather, some of us took to keeping our heads covered on all communal occasions. The hood served as an effective blinker, curbing one's own curiosity and protecting one from the curiosity of others. Franz never expressed his displeasure in this (indeed, he could not, for we were simply following the Regulations), but his own habits of dress carried their unspoken comment. No portrait, from the one executed in oil by Dr Oidmann in the days of Dunbrody to the photographic ones that followed, ever showed Franz in anything but his work clothes, with the hood of his habit thrown far back – an accurate depiction of his preferred daily dress.

The size of the Mariannhill community had begun to impinge on almost every aspect of our practices. The very tempo of our lives was altered, and it was only in such alterations that I began to understand fully the perfection of the Rule in its original form. Under the Rule, the day was punctuated by slight changes of pace and small pauses, barely noticed for they seemed only moments of transition between duties. The slightest deviation from prescribed custom brought out the importance of these interludes, each just long enough for a fresh gathering of one's thoughts yet too short for drowsiness.

When our community was marching in file from one duty to the next, for example, the first to arrive had several minutes to wait in stillness whilst the others came in behind. I always found it blissful to stand unnoticed and lost in the growing gathering, gazing at the crucifix above the Abbot's chair and awakening anew to the mystery of the Body of Christ. With our large numbers, however, this time was now stretched beyond a short period of contemplation into too lengthy a wait, and it became obvious that some of my brethren found that drowsiness was a problem in this extended time of so little outward stimulation. This applied especially, it must be said, to those with their hoods pulled completely over their heads.

The odd snore did not do much to help me in my sense of spiritual abandonment, as I so grandly thought of it at times. Occasionally I saw myself as Abraham, Isaac, Jacob, Joseph himself, those great men of the Bible given over by God to themselves alone, turned inward within the enclosure of their human solitude. This was difficult to maintain as I struggled with each cough and scratch and smell about me. I longed for the Rule to remove my awareness of the shoulder jostling against mine, the breathing so heavy in my ear, so that I could again be absorbed into saying with the Psalmist, "Towards God with silence vibrates my soul."

Franz was not blind to the problems that the rapid growth of Mariannhill occasioned and, in this instance, one of the dispensations that he did have ratified by the General Chapter allowed us to march into the dining hall in columns of two rather than in single file. But the very fact that the practicalities of life required alterations to the Rule in the monastery itself was, even at the height of Mariannhill's successes, a worry for some. What else was this but a sign that the waters of Shiloah which flow in silence, as the Lord describes them to Isaiah, were receding from the swampy ground that had shown us our proper Cistercian place.

~

Franz seemed hardly able to keep the monastery under his control, let alone "the garland of missions" (I borrow the phrase from a very different story of Mariannhill) that he had hung about the colony. Under the veneer of strict exterior discipline, unwholesome cracks and spots were breaking out everywhere. And their cause was nothing other than the one thing that brought us and held us together as an Order: St Benedict's Rule for Monasteries.

Franz's desire for Mariannhill was that it should be, in his own words, "the most regular Trappist Monastery" in the world. Indeed, for those Religious who performed the duty of Choir and served in the various offices and shops of the monastery, strict discipline was observed. Apart from the – by now standard – extended working hours, few exceptions were needed, and few were given. The problem was that over half of the Religious were engaged in active mission work and, no matter how many concessions Franz made for them, they required more.

Already the Rule for the Stations, by which Franz hoped to regulate the dispensations he had granted for mission life, was being relaxed everywhere. This was not, as I tried to explain to him when he questioned me regarding my time on the missions, because of a desire for freedom. The tasks of the apostolate simply left little time for the study and practice of the ceremonies and customs proper to the Order, And where practice is lacking, I told him, in one of the longest speeches I had made in years, the joy in participating in these things is lost. Thus many customs were a burden to the missionaries; the demands of their apostolic life were simply stronger, and for this reason they suppressed many of the exercises of monastic life.

Yes, he said, but many of the so-called "regulars" at the monastery had been condemning even the dispensations allowed for the missions. Some had gone so far as to refuse missionary activity altogether. And most of the Lay Brothers at the monastery were inclining towards them.

This did not surprise me. Even if the effectiveness of Franz's propaganda meant that the majority of those who followed his call did so out of enthusiasm for missionary work, his own selection and designation of them for the missions left Mariannhill with the smaller but equally strong-minded group of Religious and Convers alike who came to us out of a desire to lead a contemplative life. And even if our noviciate trained those who came to us for work on the missions rather than the life of a monk, it was still premised on the fact that the strict observance of the Trappists was a prerequisite for missionary activity. This, too, had an effect, depending to some degree on who was acting as Master of Novices, and helped preserve a good monastic spirit.

Our discussions, carried out with an air of secrecy, revealed that Franz was painfully aware of the split not only between monastery and mission but between the Choir Religious and the Lay Brothers on the missions. By now there was open conflict between "Rector" and "Manager" at almost every station, with the Superiors struggling to swallow the fact that they had no say in material affairs. It had become a source of outrage that Lay Brothers, in deciding what was planted, what was bought, who should work where, and so on, were, in effect, exercising control over Choir Religious. This was not helped by Franz's stringency in censuring and even imposing public penance on the Choir Religious when they were in the wrong, as he often found them to be in disputes with the Managers.

The problem for the Religious on the missions was compounded by their inability to appeal readily in support of their authority to the Rule, that document that expressed the principles by which we live. The very strength of the "regulars" at the motherhouse lay in their ability to refer their complaints back to the Rule whereas the missionaries, for the most part, had to base their arguments on dispensations granted them by the Abbot, usually without these having been put before the General Chapter. Fidelity to the Rule was thus rarely a consolation for the missionaries, even the Religious amongst them, because it could always be used to declare one or another of the concessions made to the missions as unnecessary.

It was at this point in our meeting that Franz put forward his solution to this dissension and the small part I was to play in it. He had in my absence set up a number of Councils which, ostensibly, could provide him with information and guidance about specific areas in the life of our community. Those at the stations never tired of pointing out that Franz did not have much personal experience of mission life, and he hoped that consulting with them would settle matters. Along with the Mission Council, there was a Monastery Council and a Schools Council, each created with the same aim in mind.

The Councils were without precedent in the Trappist Order although Franz was careful to go back to the Rule in support of his move. There, in Chapter Three, which is entitled "On Calling the Brethren for Counsel", St Benedict says: *Whenever any important business has to be done in the monastery, let the Abbot call together the whole community and state the matter to be acted upon.* Our Superior adhered to this quite faithfully, but

St Benedict also says, *If the business to be done in the interests of the monastery be of lesser importance, let the Abbot take counsel with the Elders only.* It was on this basis that Franz created his quite exceptional new ruling bodies.

More extraordinary even than the Councils was the way in which they were constituted. The members of the Monastery Council, for example, were the Prior, Sub-Prior, Novice Master, School Director, and the Manager and Sub-Manager of Mariannhill. This pretty much made up a group of Elders, and so Franz was on safe ground. But, given the status of the missions as administrative extensions of the monastery, he was also required to include all the Rectors – and Managers. Although they were only expected to be at the meetings if they were present at Mariannhill at the time of a particular meeting, it meant that for the first time in Trappist history Lay Brothers were serving on a Council.

Franz announced the Monastery Council to the community first, quieting the low murmur that spread as he did by quoting Ecclesiastes, as does St Benedict in his Rule: *It is written, "Do everything with counsel, and you will not repent when you have done it."* We at the missions had learned of Franz's insistence, again in keeping with the Rule, that he as Abbot *turn the matter over in his own mind and do what he shall judge to be most expedient.* And of the warning he had administered: *Let no one in the monastery follow his own heart's fancy; and let no one presume to contend with his Abbot in an insolent way, even outside of the monastery.*

The "regulars" who, of course, made up the majority of those present at the monastery, might well have given such firmness of purpose their full approval. This was, after all, the authority to which they submitted themselves on entering a monastery, obedience to the Superior being the first principle of monastic life. Up on the missions, however, we heard of the explosive reactions everywhere: "He has bound himself in no way to our approval! He has kept for himself absolute freedom of action! He has reserved all the final decision making for himself!"

When Franz asked me at our meeting how the missionaries had responded to his announcement I reported their complaints as honestly as I could. "Good," he responded. "As long as they understand. I will have no miniature Abbots budding in those remote settlements!" It was at that moment that I caught an inkling of why Franz had made Joseph the Patriarch the patron saint of the missions: what he most demanded of those serving on the stations was unquestioning obedience.

My task in all of this was quite simple and, although never spelled out, quite clear to me. As a result of the strange composition of the Monastery Council, Franz could never be sure of the number of members present, or which members they might be. He needed dependable support at the highest levels possible, something he could not count upon Fr Gerard, in his position as Prior, to give. My history as his "right-hand man", somewhat diminished though it had been of late, made me a natural choice for the position.

In my long association with him and his various achievements, I had never given Franz any cause to suspect that I would ever cast a vote contrary to his desires. I have always found it curious that silence invites such confidence. There seems to be a deep-seated assumption that those who are reticent and restrained are slow, possibly rather limited in intellectual ability; certainly that they are innocents of some sort, safe repositories for secret things and solid supporters of the voluble who claim them as friends, annex them as followers.

~

It turned out that there was another useful role I could play – a relief for Franz, I am sure, as I could not spend my time as Prior waiting only to raise my hand in support of whatever decision the Abbot wanted in Chapter or Council. It was fortunate then that I had, over the years, earned some admiration for what one of my brethren called my "remarkably distinguished handwriting". This went along with what some saw as my meticulous manner and scrupulous accuracy regarding details, and others as yet another expression of my fussy and fastidious nature. Either way, no one was surprised when Franz made my chief duty as Prior that of Secretary to the monastery.

The one thing I had proved myself capable of on the missions, after all, was keeping accurate records of the activities of others. My past life had given me some small talent in this area and taught me, with all the pain of youth and infatuation, to live through scratches on the page when I felt barred from the lived reality around me. It was not that I thought, really, when I examined my deepest beliefs, that the world was more real than the words through which we brought it into order and understanding – just the opposite was often the case, it seemed to me. But my commitment to silence was never stronger than at this time when I learned to fear that without God, as I had once felt would be the case without M, I would have to settle for words.

Who would have thought that a lesson learned so long ago would re-appear in this new shape? And who would have suspected this quiet old man of harbouring memories like those M burned upon me, lingering there beneath the scars they drove me to inflict (thankfully, less and less with age) in the solitude of my cell. Or that the feel of even this poor, rough paper – all we could get out here – would bring to mind, at unguarded moments, the luxurious texture and colour and weight to which I knew this blank medium could aspire.

Well, all that was long gone, and there I was in charge of Mariannhill's makeshift archive, to some degree because of those things I thought were so far behind me. This archive was expanding apace with the records of our growth: bills, receipts, financial accounts of every description, con-tracts, minutes of meetings, communications with the General Chapter and other Church bodies, reports from the missions, letters of all sorts, building plans, land claims, maps, school reports, baptismal records, boxes of the plate glass negatives of our photographs, a rapidly growing pile of newspaper clippings, an incomplete collection of the publications running off our press at a greater and greater rate, and so much more.

All this was haphazardly grouped and stashed into various receptacles and cupboards and was, even when I took over, already beginning to over-flow its allotted corner in the cellar underneath the Brothers' corridor to the church. Books, too, lay scattered about in this random storage room, or were piled in corners. These ranged from the tattered and much-used volumes Franz brought with him from the library at Mariastern to a copy of St Thomas Aquinas's *Summa Theologica*, printed by wood block over three hundred years ago, which I dusted off and placed carefully on the one bookshelf available to me.

My particular corner of the cellar was oddly situated, huddled under the stairs that brought our brethren down from their communal sleeping quarters to the corridor between the dormitory and the church. Given the stipulated layout of a Cistercian monastery, this meant the room was located in the eastern wall of the cloister. Only semi-subterranean, its small, high, barred windows looked out into the courtyard immediately in front of the entrance to the monastery. Indeed, my small section lay directly next to the parlour – I use the word "parlour" here in its original monastic sense of an apartment just inside the main doors to the cloister used for conversing with outsiders; a sort of entrance hall, if you will, or nomansland between speech and silence.

This meant that, hidden away though I was, I was exposed both to the movement of the monks within the cloister and the traffic between the monastery and the world. My new duties made this a particularly apt position as my work with words pulled me into the world despite my every effort to remain cloistered, and meant that I had more insight than I ever wanted into the inner running of the house.

Amongst the records I sorted, those from the Mission and Schools Councils were of the haziest to say the least. These two Councils never gained the strength or the momentum of the Monastery Council. Each of the missions kept its own chronicon, which it tended to guard quite jealously, releasing information only on request, and even the records from the schools were not freely shared with the monastery. Occasionally a few matters from either the Mission or Schools Council came before the Monastery Council and these were properly documented, but even then they tended to get lost in our own careful records of the deep and substantial issues with which the Monastery Council was concerned: building, fund-raising, relations with the Sisters (and the missions), assignment of offices, regularity, abuses, and so on. It seemed that few members of the Mission Council were attracted to its meetings, and not much of importance came out of them. If indeed their minutes were ever taken down, they were lost before they could be sent to my tiny domain in the cellar and an air of futility hung about what little we heard from the missions.

From the Schools Council we heard even less. Their proceedings seemed to be veiled in even deeper privacy, with only those directly involved in the schools and boarding establishments at Mariannhill involved. The presiding figure, Brother David, withdrew into a secretive alliance with the missionaries; it was as if he had pulled his cowl up and over all that went on in what had become very much his personal realm. Even Franz, when he tried to pierce the English monk's increasingly distant attitude, was met with the most banal assurances that everything was proceeding as it should. And Franz was in no position to place trust in such assurances.

In trying to bring some order to my new position, I spent most of my working hours sorting the gathering piles of paper in the cool of my cellar – a pleasant retreat in summer and a minor purgatory in winter. This brought about a rapid improvement in my ability to read in English, even if my ability to speak it remained on what one of my brethren called, in his pungent German, a *kriegsfuß*. Except for those records kept purely for our own use, our place in this most English of colonies was increasingly documented and reported in that language. As the years went by English came to dominate our existence to the degree that even my "not being very talkative" was put down to my "war footing" with the official language of Natal. But by then we were no longer Trappists, and few of us retained any idea of a contemplative vocation. At the time, however, out of a desire to perform my new role at Mariannhill as well as possible, I actually forced myself to read more thoroughly than was necessary those accounts concerning us that were written in English.

~

In my new position I discovered much about our story that had passed me by while I was at Reichenau. For a start, there appeared to be a rising wave of objections from parents to our not allowing pupils to return home when they wished. One document I came across was a formal complaint from the Resident Magistrate of Pinetown in which a clearly irate man from Chief Manzini's tribe challenged our "detention" of his sixteen-year-old daughter. Another was the case of the son of a deceased Christian Native who demanded the return of his mother and sister, who had been admitted into the monastery at the time of his father's death. The son felt he was being deprived of *lobola* cattle, which belonged to him by virtue of his heirship, and laid a charge of desertion from the kraal.

Franz used to argue that in the signing that replaced speech in the cloister lay the basis for what he called a "universal language". It appears that, soon after I left for Reichenau, his views on "the expressive force of a single sign" had been taken up by Brother Leo, a recent recruit who had been promoted to the position of Steward to relieve Brother Nivard of this duty. There in the archives was a legal letter stating that Brother Leo, under his "real" name of Frederick Stearke, was obliged within weeks of his appointment to appear before the long-suffering Resident Magistrate, charged by a Native with assault. The complainant stated that his cattle had been seized for an alleged debt and that he had been assaulted at the monastery by fist and with sticks when he presented a letter of enquiry that he had obtained from the Court. Brother Leo was found guilty and fined 18s or imprisonment or seven days' hard labour.

We had bought the farms that made up Lourdes mission at the time of this incident, and it is no surprise to me that as soon as the transfer was complete, Brother Leo was sent away to stay alone in an old deserted building there for some nine months before anyone else was sent to join him. At the time I was reinstated as Prior at Mariannhill, Fr Arsenius was dispatched to Lourdes with three Brothers, six Sisters and a lay carpenter. They found Brother Leo, so I heard, living in an old hut covered in iron sheets, with a smaller hut on the side which he used as a chapel. Both were so infested with cockroaches and other pests that they had had to be burned down.

Whether Brother Leo's living under such conditions was enough of a penance for his violent act I do not know, but his particular talents were put to good use when our Abbot held to the principle that the first step of mission work was not to preach the gospel but to clothe the naked. Before he sent our Brothers and Sisters to the new station (named after the famous shrine in southern France), he commanded Brother Leo to ride through the huge estate and force all the Natives on it, by use of the sjambok if necessary, to put on a dress or a blanket.

Covering the body turned out also to have some bearing on my rather strange reappointment to the position of Prior. Although I had some idea of Fr Gerard's interest in the missions, I had never understood why one of whom such great things were expected had been sent to so remote a mission as Centocow. Soon after reading the account of the case against Brother Leo, however, I discovered another report in our archive, dated less than a month later. Despite my difficulties with the language, I understood that Fr Gerard had been fined 10s for hitting a Native woman with a stick on the lands of Mariannhill.

This case was not as easily settled as Brother Leo's. Whilst the *Natal Mercury* turned its eyes modestly away after this report, the *Advertiser* chose to unloose the full force of its thinly veiled hostility, reminding us how we had been welcomed in the colony, that we were not a law unto ourselves, that the fines we were given were far too light, and the only mitigation it extended was that perhaps we behaved as we did because of our ignorance of the genius of British liberty and the English principle of justice.

However biased this report may have been, one line from it has remained etched in my memory, I think word for word: "Admitting that the Trappists are on the proselytising warpath in and amongst our natives, we fail to see what propaganda can be aided by assaulting women ..." To this day I am unsure as to whether the now popular assumption that we were fully fledged members of the active apostolate upset me more than the increasing violence with which some of our community seemed to be taking up this role.

Certainly those who came to our support on this matter did not help our case. One local Catholic leapt to our defence in the most unfortunate of ways, claiming that we were to be excused on the grounds that an unconverted Native woman was neither a decent sight, nor did she – and how we had earned this! – smell agreeable. This provoked a flurry of letters, one memorably pointing out that Natal laws do not permit even 'Kafir women' to be assaulted with flails merely because they offended monastic eyesight or smelled disagreeably. On these grounds, as the letter stated, we Trappist brethren would be equally liable to assault for our uncouth appearance and the odour of our habits.

"He who belittles his neighbours lacks sense, but a man of understanding remains silent," I remember thinking as I turned the pages of the newspaper, knowing that it would have taken a far more equable nature than our Abbot's to stand aside from this exchange of words. And yes, there it was: a fiery letter to the *Advertiser* in which Franz would have been hard put to inflame public opinion any more than he did. This has turned up in the material Fr Adalbert has been putting to me, and not just the letter itself. He has a file on the matter, in which he has neatly arranged all the responses I remember reading with increasing horror back then.

Franz openly accused that newspaper of editorial prejudice against us, claimed that the incidents in question had been blown out of all proportion, insisted that we did more for the Natives than all the other missionaries, settlers, farmers, "or even editors", and then proceeded to the passages that really caused offence:

The *Advertiser* speaks of the Trappists as if we had no right in Natal. To this I reply that I am by no means aware that less right is due to us than any others. I am the Superior of a religious community which stands *ex jure*. I am, in fine, a landowner and possess all the rights of a farmer. Should it happen that we do not please the Kafirs whom we find on our land or they do not please me, who can hinder me from expelling them? Is there anyone who will hinder me from doing this?

As for the woman that was struck and her swollen arm, I must just say this much. I was myself conducting a party of eighty native school-girls over our land for a picnic. The Brother-catechist preceded me as he knew the way best. Myself and three Sisters took up the rear. A malicious woman, upon our own ground, took up her position in the middle of the path, placing herself like an ugly obstacle in the way of Brother Gerard and the van of the party, thinking to make us deviate and wade through the long grass alongside. Brother Gerard very naturally shoved her off with his hand in which he carried a small stick. Then she began to cry that she had been struck. Afterwards she cut or scratched her arm somehow and hence it was swollen at the examination in Durban. And were the *Advertiser* to meet me anywhere on my land and place himself in a position to irritate me, I would also shove him aside, even under pain of "deterrent punishment" or imprisonment.

This was quite enough to set off the *Advertiser*. "From such high dignitaries as Abbots, courtesy and charity are commonly expected," fulminated its editors, "but in the present case, in lieu of those traits, we have to content ourselves with defiant egoism and flippant retort." Abbot Franz's attitude was, they went on, "as militant as it was foolish", filled with "sublime egoism", "self-glorification" and "sneers at others". Above all, they objected to his claim to being above the law. "If the self-sufficient tone of the present letter is to be the key-note of Trappist policy," concluded the lengthy rebuttal of Franz's statement, "we know of no place on this side of the Zambezi where elbow room *ex jure* can be found."

The editorial was just the beginning. Letters to the newspaper responding to our Superior eddied about our enclosure like dying leaves in winter (my simile is, it strikes me as I write, perhaps too European in this land of so many evergreens), some objecting to our laxity with the Natives ("Now, Mr. Editor, whoever heard of taking a lot of Kafir girls for a *picnic!*"), others to our misguided generosity ("If the Trappists, instead of making presents of clothes to the 'poor' heathen hero, would instead make them work and pay for their comforts, the cause of Christianity and civilisation would be further advanced"), and yet others to our helping the Natives on our property evade the hut tax by assisting them in the building of square houses with doors and windows. Further letters in our support from "Local Catholic" were refused publication in the press on the grounds of not being written in "good faith" and others who maintained they also had been brutally assaulted by members of our community were advised as to what avenues they could follow for redress.

Worse still, legal interventions into cases where our Abbot was perceived to be acting beyond or outside colonial laws suddenly became all too common. Marriages between Native couples performed by Franz were scrutinised (second or third wives were wives under Natal law but we considered them free to marry); fines were imposed on European parents who, supposedly, had been encouraged by us not to have their children vaccinated against smallpox; and the application of four Natives to be freed from Native law on the grounds that they wished to become Trappists was turned down on the technicality of their being under twenty-one years of age.

~

Even as the newspapers fretted and fumed over the issues the alleged assaults had unleashed, thirty new Trappists had arrived from Europe on the *Tartar*. From the very first they were put to work, mainly with printing. Unskilled as they were, any help was better than none with the murderous work required of the printing press. The *Mariannhiller Missions Kalender* alone was then being printed in runs of one hundred thousand, over and above a constant stream of prayer books, catechetical and biblical books, hymnals, and the grammars and dictionaries necessary for both school-work and evangelising. Brother David had also started the first newspaper in Zulu, *Izwi Labantu* (confident as he was that he spoke in the "People's Voice"), and, when this failed, he moved on to the possibly more aptly titled *Ingelosi yeNkosi*. I say "possibly" because it was becoming clearer by the day that Franz was finding Brother David a less and less suitable representative of "The Angel of the Lord". In any event, the fact that most of the Natives still could not read, and that few journalists knew Zulu, meant that this newspaper also folded in under two years.

Franz's endeavours in print were infinitely more successful – in fact, nothing short of spectacular. He himself wrote most of the *Kalender*, not to mention the *Vergissmeinnicht*, and then embarked on the *Natal Record*, a newspaper aimed at a more secular audience. The result of his output meant that the press ran from six in the morning until ten at night, and virtually the whole Abbey had to help with its work.

"It is more profitable to turn away thine eyes from such things as displease thee than to be a slave to contention," says Thomas à Kempis. It was only a matter of time before the newspapers caught on to the obvious paradox in Franz's apparently endless attacks on others and his defence of our Order. "The Abbot of Mariannhill," begins one editorial in the *Advertiser*, "though a devout Trappist, cannot be said to exemplify the rule of silence imposed upon the brethren of his Order. In the Press, at any rate, he is one of the most communicative of men. He is ready at all times for a joust in the arena of controversy ..."

That "the Abbot of Mariannhill has always made a point of courting publicity" became something of a refrain in articles, editorials and letters concerning us. "He has invited the freest personal scrutiny of his methods and his performances," wrote the *Mercury*. "He has made no secret of the one and has clothed with no mystery the other."

Well, within a matter of less than a year, secrecy as far as the outside world was concerned would be forced back on us, and the mystery – the mystery that I have always believed was our vocation, beyond apology and explanation – would be revived, if only through incomprehension of the failings of men.

~

I cannot trace – it is too painful, and not worthy of this story – each of the controversies within which we became embroiled in the public glare of the newspapers, as I had to do in my post as Secretary. Franz's temper flared at any reproach, whether it was the abnormality of our system or our attempting to convert the Natives into marionettes or our unnatural behaviour. He was almost apoplectic when, again and again, writers warned that the idea of Church above State was being propagated by non native-born subjects of the Government ("Mariannhill is essentially a foreign institution" was a common cry), especially as this was often accompanied by reminders that we would soon, if we continued as we had been doing, take over the entire colony.

Perhaps most painful for Franz was the number of Native views ex-pressed in the letter pages. Just how painful these were may be measured by my finding, not long after his death, that he had kept copies of them, jammed in a jumble of bills, sketches and drafts of articles, notes for what to include in our dictating sessions, and other scraps not considered im-portant enough to be sent on to Mariannhill. "Perhaps your readers, and the Abbot of Mariannhill too may like to know what we Natives think of these ama Roma," begins the first I unfolded, written by one Mxakaza. "We have watched them, not knowing what to think. Now we are told what the Trappists wish to do for the Natives of this colony – to keep them in darkness rather than light."

As for the free clothing, food and education we provided, Mxakaza refers to the poem in his Standard III reading book, "The Spider and the Fly": "Is this, Sir, the reason why they are called Trappists, because they trap people with their kindness? If I am right we must give them a new name instead of 'ama Roma'. We must call them *onoxaka* (traps)!"

The poor humour used here against us is nothing compared to the next passage, however, which brought tears to my eyes. "Many tales are spoken of these people, how they have built large houses in which they shut up their people, and never allow them to speak. Has not God given us tongues to talk with? But this, I suppose, is 'Church rule and Church discipline', and silence the means of submission thereto."

To see our deepest mystery so traduced was almost more than I could bear. Once out in the world, the very key to our separation from it was fair game for all. I remember a "man of business" writing in to one of the newspapers to report, after a visit to Mariannhill, that age had brought vacuity rather than intelligence to our faces and that our deliberately refusing to exercise the faculty of speech had turned – the phrasing has stayed with me – "the grace of human intercourse and exchange of thought into individual isolation and obstinate silence".

But it was, as I say, the deep hostility of the letters from Natives that cut to the quick. S L H Mapumelo writes of the Abbot's policy, "Ignorance is bliss, 'tis folly to be wiser than the Church dictates. But, alas! the Father was born two centuries too late. Neither priest nor people can roll back the wheels of time." More worrying were the words of Saul Nisane: "The Abbot thinks he is more popular amongst blacks than other missionary bodies. I beg to differ, and let the Abbot know what we blacks think of him and his staff. Your religion, Mr Abbot, we think is such that we look at all the Trappists with great suspicion, and we say, these people have only come to spoil our people; and we have begun to watch your movements."

Claiming that the general belief of the "ignorant blacks, i.e., kraal kafirs" was that "these Trappists were very great people in the world, and had come to set their government against that of the English", Nisane accuses us of either implicitly or explicitly planting "the seed of disloyalty". And a certain

Sokaya goes so far as to say, "It will not be a surprise to many colonists to hear of an outbreak in the monastery, or an attack upon it."

And so they went on, letter after letter. Enough is enough, even for my failed attempt at confessing all. The point is driven home by the last of the letters I folded back into the secrets of Franz's desk drawer. It takes as its subject Franz's widely publicised view that it was neither good nor as necessary for girls as for boys in our schools to make extensive study of book subjects. "I am a Native girl myself," begins someone who signs herself as Nolobele, "and have been taught by an Englishman who was our friend as well as our teacher. He taught us on this principle, that 'education was to fit its recipient for life'. This truth should be written in letters of gold on the Abbot's snuff-box, if he has got one. How the Abbot knows which kind of Kafir girls make the best wives," Nolobele concludes, "is a riddle we can't solve. Really his school and all pertaining to it is detested by all classes of Natives."

~

In the heat of this war of words, the Irishman whose lilting call for Trappists Franz had answered in his woefully unbefitting German came amongst us again like a bolt of lightning. On this occasion it was more in keeping with the season, for it was in the summer of 1889 on a day when, typically, electricity played about the dense black clouds of an afternoon thunderstorm that had rolled in after the hazy, hot morning. And again, it was Bishop Jolivet who delivered the bolt. He arrived in our enclosure clearly irritated by the heat, the humidity and the duty he had to perform, which was to deliver to us another missive from the Cardinal Prefect of Propaganda, this time in the form of a severe reprimand for our Abbot. Franz was upbraided for his behaviour towards Bishop Ricards which, we slowly gathered, had to do with his delay in repaying the "loan" advanced to us for our occupation of Dunbrody. With the reprimand came a summons to pay within six months the £2 000, the interest accrued and the compound interest.

Franz responded as if actually struck by lightning. He would never, he exploded, pay this unjust sum, and he went on in this vein for some minutes before his outburst sputtered out in the face of Bishop Jolivet's evident lack of interest. The Bishop had completed the task required of him and, after the briefest of polite platitudes, none of which enabled Franz to question the line taken by Propaganda, he withdrew for some refreshment our

Cellarer had hastily put together. Before he left our gates, Franz was already dictating, faster than my hand could write, a letter to the Vicar General of the Trappist Order declaring his resolution not to pay.

The ink was not dry on that before Franz began a letter to a member of our community, Brother Pankraz, who was in Germany on our business at the time, ordering him to go to Fr Beckert in Würzburg where the records of our time in Europe were kept, and to ask him for the documents corresponding to those used by Herr Fraundorfer to overturn our case. The latter recourse was not only too little too late but, as we were to learn after weeks and weeks of clinging to this faint hope, futile: the documents in question simply could not be found. As for the former, the Vicar General did go so far as to send a declaration supporting us to the Holy Congregation, only to have to report in March 1890 that Rome was abiding by its decision.

In June Franz sent Fr Athanasius to Rome, prepared in every respect to put our case and bring about a revision of the Court's proceedings. All too swiftly he sent news that – unofficially – Propaganda had realised the injustice of its decision and had suggested – privately – to Fr Athanasius that, as a compromise, they were prepared to let Franz pay the amount owed in reasonable instalments. It did not take much knowledge of Franz to know that he would never accept a compromise that compromised only us.

The Monastery Council of Mariannhill then undertook to write a comprehensive memorandum on the whole affair to put before the Congregation of Propaganda, as Fr Athanasius had suggested. This meant that everyone on the Council had their say in drawing up the document. Much of the hurt and dissatisfaction over our entire history up to and including Dunbrody came pouring out in the endless meetings in which we tried to establish the exact circumstances of our arriving at and leaving that place. I can only say that even my quiet role in the manoeuvrings that took place behind the scenes in that stark and painful time came in for a good deal of very vocal criticism.

~

Words, words, words. But the missionaries smelled blood. The attack on Franz from the very source of his authority could not have come at a worse time. After we sent off our memorandum we were to hear nothing more for some time from the powerful bodies to whom we owed full obedience, and this left Franz all the more exposed.

Our Abbot was reeling, with even his one indisputable testimony to the success of his policies – our size – vulnerable to attack. His regular and astonishingly successful appeals for recruits from Europe continued, but the newcomers I watched trooping in through our gates were now invariably expected to learn Zulu and English in the quickest possible time and were then sent marching back out of those gates to one or another of our newly established missions. Franz was tentatively reaching to the north again, having founded a station near the town of Ladysmith (to be named Maria Ratschitz) but also curving with his chain of missions ever further to the south and east, still following the Drakensberg down into East Griqualand.

Not all the arriving volunteers were happy or successful with the work given to them on the missions. With the numbers at his disposal, however, Franz had no hesitation in sending unsuitable individuals away. Some returned to Europe, some found employment in Natal, whilst others applied to Bishop Jolivet for assistance. It was not long before the Bishop Apostolic was requested to report to the Cardinal Prefect on the treatment of these ex-Trappists. In his reply he agreed that they were often put out of the monastery without provision. He intimated, too, that he had frequently urged the Abbot of Mariannhill to be more careful in his selection of recruits, something that I am quite sure Franz was beginning to think about seriously, if belatedly, himself.

It was not one of the more fractious recently arrived novices who became the chief thorn in Franz's flesh, however, but a man of his own making, for whose work he had sacrificed many of the strictest observances of our Order.

16

About the same time as I was sent to the missions, Brother David was sent to Rome to be ordained as a priest. He persuaded Franz to allow the brightest of our Zulu boys to travel with him, with the aim of enrolling him for study towards the priesthood at the Propaganda College in the Holy City. The boy was Kece Mnganga, one of the youngsters from the Shozi Reserve sent to Mariannhill for schooling in the early days of our educational endeavours. Although I was as removed from our teaching as it was possible to be, I was called in to help evaluate the progress Kece (or Eduard as he became known when he was baptised with the name few knew to have been mine) had shown in Latin. I was as much impressed with the quiet confidence with which he negotiated his way through the airy spiritual structures of the new world we built up around him as with any of his parsing or grasp of ecclesiastical turns of phrase.

Kece Mnganga's father, Jamkofi, gave his consent to his choice of vocation, but when it was whispered to him that the father of a future priest should think of becoming a Christian himself Jamkofi quietly slipped away, along with the others who chose to go into exile rather than submit to the demands of the Christian faith.

I can see Kece to this day as I imagined him in Rome, a black speck in the congregation as Father David, for so we must call him from now on in our story, was ordained a priest in San Giovanni in Laterano. To think of that young boy, standing in his own delicate strength in the strong, square immensity of the Church of St John, alone for perhaps the first time since leaving Africa, still moves me deeply. Did he ask himself, I often wondered, as he looked up at the huge figures of the prophets, saints and apostles ranged along the walls, how we, moving about briskly in the open glare of the sun reflected off mud-brick walls and corrugated iron, measured up to them?

As for Fr David, he was ordained by the Latin Patriarch of Constantinople, and thus was privileged to read his first Holy Mass on the High Altar of St Peter's – a sequence of happiness almost unique for a young priest and almost too much to bring back for submission to a rough and ready provincial Abbot with no glories at all of this sort streaming in his wake as he moved through the world. He left young Eduard at his studies in Rome when he returned to us. In deference to his new status, an assistant to Fr David was appointed at Mariannhill, giving him time at last to attend to the literary work that in later life would became his chief calling. He began by translating a small catechism into Zulu which, when it rolled off our tiny hand-operated printing press, was the first book ever printed in the language. None of us looking at its modest sixty pages, wrapped in neat piles for distribution throughout our houses and stations, could have imagined what a powerful seed of division Fr David left to lie dormant for some years amongst us.

His next literary project, *Roman Legions on Libyan Fields* as he called this work in his youthful enthusiasm, took as its subject "the story of the birth and infancy of the Mariannhill Mission" and was nothing less than an appropriation of the story of our contemplative community for the mission faction of the monastery. His two attempts at producing newspapers in the Zulu language followed, and when these collapsed for want of readers, cutting him off from what he considered his true audience, Fr David became an ever more open and antagonistic spokesperson within the monastery for the disgruntled "Superiors" at the stations.

It was Fr David, "the first missionary of Mariannhill" as he liked to be known (or "the enemy within" as those who looked less favourably on our missionary developments took to calling him), who made the most extreme demands on behalf of the missions, maintaining insistently and belligerently that the liberties Franz granted the missionaries were insufficient, and that – being technically of the Choir – the Rectors were not given enough authority over the Managers. He thought nothing of bringing Bishop Jolivet in on his side during these disagreements, and although Franz had stood firm on the matter of dress – the missionaries demanded, for example, that their haircuts and clothing for travelling be adapted to those of secular priests – Fr David succeeded in driving Franz from one of his most fervent principles of education.

From the first Franz had forcefully and proudly refused to make any distinctions on grounds of race in our schools. Fr David came to the opposite conclusion, arguing that the cultural differences between the races, and their varying inherent educative potential, meant that they should be schooled separately. To his other loud and insistent demands was added the call for an end to the common education of our children. Undercut as his authority was by the battering he was taking in the press over our schools, amongst much else, Franz finally gave way before the combined assault of Fr David and Bishop Jolivet and, in 1890, established a separate school for the white boys.

Opposition to Franz was arising from other quarters. Fr Gerard led a more moderate group, which was all the more dangerous for its moderation. Their opposition was always couched within the legalities of the Order and thus was far more difficult to counter. And then there was Fr Adolph, a priest from North America who had joined us and was forever watching the amounts Franz spent on anything other than the missions. The monastery itself is foreign to the work of the missions, he would declare loudly and often, in Chapter or at Council meetings, and the missionaries are being forced to live like hermits because so much money is being spent on the cloistered monks.

This attitude was an indication of the change in our reputation. From the moment he arrived Fr Adolph announced that he was joining us as a missionary and not a Trappist. When Franz insisted he enter the postulancy he refused, saying he had not come to take upon himself the full observance of the Trappist Rule and would rather go and join the Jesuits on the Zambezi if this was to be required of him. Franz, deeply aware of how much we needed an extra priest for our over-extended work, begged him to stay on, promising to assign him to the stations in due course. Fr Adolph finally agreed, but this did not prevent his plaguing me in my role as bookkeeper for the exact sums raised by the ever energetic and successful collecting of Brother Zacharias in Europe and the precise way in which these funds were disbursed.

I did my best, given the impossible position I was in, not to let the numbers with which I was entrusted tell against Franz. I was sure, at the time, that what I did reveal could not harm our Superior, although the clean finesse of my columns felt muddied every time Fr Adolph trapped me at my desk in the corner of the cellar and refused to be satisfied with my smiles and shakes of the head. There were times when my old love for the purity of numbers, the clean, clear innocence of their computation, their inability to spin into paradox and confusion in the way words did, would reassert itself, as if I were still midway in my transformation between employee of the Imperial Lottery and devotee of the Congregation of Mary. But after even the briefest period with Fr Adolph this would be revealed for the thin and cheap nostalgia that it was.

I will admit that Fr Adolph was a factor in Fr Alanus being appointed as the monastery bookkeeper. I had asked Franz to assign an assistant to me in this capacity, on the grounds that I found I could not manage the finances of Mariannhill along with all my other duties as Secretary. I did in my own way attempt to warn Fr Alanus about Fr Adolph, although the earnestness with which I did this was undercut by Franz's refusal to take Fr Adolph seriously. He brushed him aside when he approached with lists of figures in hand, asking for permission to speak. This, it would turn out, was a further mistake on Franz's part, and one to which I may unwittingly have contributed.

In any event, there were a number of other monks taking up Franz's time with their complaints and attacks. Fr Hyacinth, of course, could always be relied upon to take things into the realm of the ridiculous. I was forced to minute in the Protocol Book of the meetings of the Monastery Council the ringing words with which he dared to threaten the Abbot openly: "We missionaries have now grown up," he barked, "and grown-up sons can demand something from their fathers! If you do not give in, we shall make a rebellion!"

I faithfully transcribed this in my neatest script, but no rebellion was to follow. Instead, we were set upon a far more damaging course.

~

All through the dark year of 1890 Fr David approached the Abbot with formal demands from the missionaries. Finally, he stood before Franz and myself, reading out a composite list of these while we listened without comment. Much of it was familiar to us by now, including the immediate separation of the missionaries *a toro at mensa*, that is that the missionaries lay aside the habit and appear on the missions and their journeys like the English – I remember I could not help exchanging a glance with Franz at this point – secular priests, and the request for a specially built mission house outside of the monastery at which missionaries who had to do business in the monastery could stay. In this mission house the food and drink of secular priests would be served ... and so on and so forth, culminating in the demand that the dispensations extended thus far to the missionaries, along with the new dispensations they were now demanding, be made their permanent rights.

To my surprise Franz did not explode when he had waved Fr David from his presence and we were alone. "I recognised in my Rule for the Stations that mission work amongst the pagans was not the task of the Trappists," he said, more pensively than I had ever heard him speak before. Then, picking up the copy of his Rule from his lap, where it had lain throughout Fr David's address, he held it in the air and without reading intoned from it, as if to himself, "Since mission work does not belong to our Order, there is no need for the Abbot to stick to the Rule of St Benedict in the care and administration of the missions. His sole directive must be to guide the affairs of the missions in such a way that the spirit of the Order does not suffer."

Could they not see, he said, hardly loud enough for me to hear, that the Rule of the Strict Observance as it stood made no provision to regulate missionary activities because the Order did not, on principle, do missionary work? And yet there had to be an authority that regulated the life of the monk-missionary, an authority that gave the necessary scope of freedom but also set the limits …

His voice trailed off, but he appeared to realise for the first time that in giving away crucial elements of the Rule, he gave away the basis for his own authority, which was guaranteed only by the Rule. He was in himself, as an Abbot should be, the sole competent authority on the Rule, but without the Rule, or at the least the authorisation of the General Chapter, which was the only body empowered to grant exceptions to the Rule, his authority resided in his person alone.

That person suddenly seemed very small. Hunched over in his chair, he muttered, "I shall have to consult Bishop Jolivet." Then he slowly unwound himself, standing up as if from a position in which he had been frozen for hours.

I had never before known Franz to acknowledge a need for the support of anyone else. As it turned out, he was looking in the wrong direction. A few days later he appeared at the entrance to my corner in the cellar and announced, rather diffidently, that he had met with the Bishop, who had just made one of his infrequent and brief stops at Mariannhill whilst returning to Pietermaritzburg from somewhere else, doubtless of more importance. I had seen the Bishop's entourage arrive from the high, narrow windows in my cellar and heard something of his interchange with Franz in the parlour. It was quite clear that the Bishop supported the missionaries in their efforts to obtain greater freedom from Franz and the Rule.

Franz added nothing to his announcement, standing quietly on the stair. For a moment or two more, he stood staring into nothingness. Then he turned away abruptly. "I shall grant no more dispensations!" he said, his eyes sparking again and his beard quivering as he thrust it forward as of old. "They can make their demands, and I shall listen, but they can get their response directly from the General Chapter. I myself shall go to France and put what they ask before the Vicar General."

~

Franz had been dispensed from attending the annual gathering of the Trappist Chapter because of distances and expense, but was required to appear every fifth year, and that was upon us. Franz was then sixty-six years old, and whilst in good health on dry land he still suffered so terribly from seasickness that we believed this to be a threat to his life.

Perhaps we could have convinced Franz to hold off travel for another year. Certainly the General Chapter would have agreed. During his attendances in 1886, when he appeared as the Superior of Mariannhill for the first time, his report on the monastery and even its fledgling mission activities had been warmly received. No one had raised a single complaint regarding his innovations, perhaps because of Franz's captivating oratory that held at bay any discussion on the legality of his work. The Very Rev. Vicar General had himself written back to the Very Rev. Dom Franz of Natal to express his admiration for the "unheard of *fortuna* of a monastery in South-Africa for the conversion of the pagans".

Unheard of? Yes indeed, our work was unheard of in any other Trappist house, and perhaps when spoken of out loud in the insistent pitch of our Superior's voice or expressed through the furious scrawling of his pen, edited and neatly transcribed in my excellent hand, it was not properly attended to. So much of what we did existed between the lines, as they say, in that realm of the unspoken where a busy murmur of voices continued day and night, just out of earshot.

So Franz, instead of committing himself to the sea, may have trusted in the goodwill of the General Chapter. Nothing of his recent disputes in the local press had seeped through to them, but his past was never far behind him. And, if the speed with which he worked had kept him ahead of it up to this point, it suddenly laid its claim upon him with the force of a nightmare that would not give up its grip on the waking world.

~

Just as Franz was considering throwing himself upon the authority of the General Chapter in order to bring his missionaries into line, a response came to the memorandum in which we had put our fullest possible case for appeal to the Congregation of Propaganda against the results of the arbitration over Dunbrody. This had been delivered to our own Vicar General, and forwarded to us by an extremely stern-faced Bishop Jolivet. It took the form of a simple letter from which I quote: "If Fr Franz does not pay without delay the £2000 to Bishop Ricards, he will not go free of an ecclesiastical punishment and the whole Trappist order will feel the disfavour of the Apostolic See."

Clearly patience in Rome had run to its end, whatever the merits of our case. There was absolutely no question now that Franz would have to attend the General Chapter in person and settle the monetary matter once and for all. Yet, even as we came to this realisation, we did not understand the proportions the Dunbrody episode had assumed. It was now much more than a matter of disagreement over a private arrangement between Franz and Bishop Ricards. Bishop Ricards seemed to have lost no opportunity to inform the Bishops and Cardinals in Rome of what he considered to be the questionable behaviour of the monks at Mariannhill, but his own failing powers of expression (along with the weakening of his position that the Dunbrody case brought about) robbed these interventions of much of their force. However, behind the increasingly ill and withdrawn figure of the Bishop was our true antagonist, Herr Fraundorfer. Not content with the decision against Franz, Herr Fraundorfer was determined to go the extra distance necessary to ensure that it was Franz himself who paid the money.

We had no idea what facts Herr Fraundorfer had presented on Bishop Ricards' behalf, but amongst the flurry of communications we received with regard to our "debt" to the Bishop was one warning us that Herr Fraundorfer had announced that he was quite prepared to report that the money we collected in Europe – more than enough to repay the money "loaned" to him by Bishop Ricards – was secured by devious means. This could only be, we decided, a reference to the South African Mission Association that Franz had formed to make our alms-collecting more efficient. A few benefactors had complained that under such an organisation much of the money raised for Mariannhill could go to other missions, but a more dangerous charge was levelled by others who argued that the stated purposes of the Association excluded the Trappists from receiving any of its funds since, technically, the Trappist Order was not a missionary one.

Franz had responded to both positions with his usual stance that we were a precursor to the real missionaries who would carry on what we began. Herr Fraundorfer had clearly aligned himself with those who did not let what they considered to be a disingenuous hypothesis blind them to the fact that Mariannhill was receiving funds from the Association for direct missionary work. And no sooner had we heard from the Vicar General of our Order that the Propaganda had refused Franz's appeal against payment than another document arrived from Propaganda, this time sent directly to Mariannhill.

The letter came first to me, as Secretary. The stuff of which the envelope was made was a pleasure to hold, to touch, to smell. It slit open with the most excellent resistance to even my best letter opener, the sound it made an expression of gravitas and solemnity, of weighty desks, leather chairs, high ceilings, and heavy drapes keeping out the hum of a metropolis. The seal, too, allowed itself to be moulded open around my blade, not cracking and crumbling like the inferior wax I struggled with every day. But the sumptuous caress of the paper that I extracted so carefully gave way all too quickly to the darkness of the words beautifully inscribed upon it. These I rushed straight to Franz. He tossed the envelope aside, scanned its contents for a matter of moments, and then thrust the heavy paper back at me, saying, "You read this out at the next Monastery Council."

In a voice that I warmed up beforehand, for I wanted no hint of uncertainty in it, I read out at our next meeting the following accusations put by the Prefect of Propaganda and the Vicar General of the Trappist Order:

1. That Abbot Francis had squandered funds that were meant for the missions on erecting useless and luxurious buildings;
2. that by doing so, Abbot Francis deprived the missionaries of their rightful support and neglected their well-being;
3. that Abbot Francis had been remiss in safe-guarding the spiritual and moral life of the community and that the spiritual care of the Sisters was also neglected.

What had Franz expected in reaction to these serious charges? Anything, I am sure, but the intense quiet that held during my reading and continued after I stopped. It swallowed up the faint echo of my voice and filled the Chapter House for agonising minute after minute, stretching past discomfort into excruciation. Nobody said a word. I dared not even risk the scratching of my pen to make a record in the Protocol Book of the charges. Franz, with his eyes as downcast as those of the most carefully trained novice, stood up. With this we were dismissed.

I went to him, of course, after filing out of the Chapter Room in the prescribed manner. I found him standing before the window of his office, and stood quietly in the doorway, waiting. For some time he stared into the space that fell away beneath him and then, without turning towards me, he spoke. He would submit to these accusations without complaint, he said, but from the Council's silence he could conclude only that they were believed to be true. "And this," he said, with a gruffness that betrayed his emotion, "is by far the worst."

I had been thinking furiously but there was nothing to say. Nothing, however, was, I suddenly realised, the point. I put the Protocol Book before him. He looked down at it, glanced quizzically at me, and then looked back to where my finger pointed to the page, which was blank except for the date and a few small preliminary scratches. He nodded, and I left.

Franz excused himself from holding Divine Service on the eve of the next meeting of the Monastery Council, claiming indisposition. At the meeting, however, he looked over those present with a firm eye and asked that the minutes of the previous meeting be read. This took only a few moments and the second I was done Franz spoke, allowing no time for silence to settle.

Why, he asked, was no mention of the accusations made in the minutes? The implication was plain: he wished them to stand for all to see in our records, along with the empty space that would follow in the Protocol Book if the proceedings of the Council at that gathering had been accurately recorded. This silence could only be construed as indicating the agreement of the Council with the allegations.

At this point Brother Nivard leapt to his feet, explaining that the Council had been so dumbfounded that they had been unable to respond. Since then, in sincere meditation and reflection, the members making up the assembled body had resolved to join together and refute the slanderous charges against our beloved leader and clear him of the stigma that had been so unjustly imprinted upon him. Brother Nivard had in his hands a written answer to the Vicar General, which he would attest was written without any participation by Abbot Francis, and which denied the accusations in every detail. This he read out (before he submitted it to me for the formal record), reaching its conclusion in a voice that echoed around the chamber:

In view of the baseness and malice of these slanderous accusations, the Monastery Council of Mariannhill hereby declares its full agreement with and approval of the administrative actions of its leader, the Venerable Father Abbot Francis. It expresses the fullest confidence in him in regard to his mission activities, his leadership ability as Abbot of Mariannhill, and as Superior of the Mission Sisters.

This document was sent off to the Vicar General, and in good time we heard that he had been so impressed with its earnestness and sincerity that he instituted further and more serious investigations into the charges to see if there was any substance to them.

It was clear to us by now that the only way for our Abbot to clear his name and that of our community was by going to the General Chapter and speaking for himself. It was also evident that the divisions within the monastery were no longer only an internal matter. Someone amongst us was promoting our most intimate difficulties to a far higher level, where they were being taken up by someone else well positioned to do us real damage. Who this individual was remained a mystery. We knew only that the complaints put to us by the Vicar General were based upon the accusations sent to Rome by an "unknown plaintiff", the term that passed into our formal records, although speculation regarding the identity of the informer ran wild in the confines of our enclosure.

It was all too easy to assume, as many did at the time and even some of the recent histories of Mariannhill claim, that the well-placed outsider was none other than Bishop Ricards – "a man born for being in conflict with others" as one account puts it – to ensure that the controversy over Dunbrody was kept alive by stirring up other controversies. Some believed that the betrayal came from within, further destroying our rapidly disintegrating sense of community although the charges themselves were cleared up fairly rapidly. The Vicar General commissioned Bishop Jolivet to investigate them and, put out though he was with this extra duty, the Bishop set off immediately on a hasty but extensive tour through all the Trappist establishments in his vicariate.

Bishop Jolivet's report paid tribute to Mariannhill, which he said was the envy of the Protestants and a source of pride to himself and to our Abbot, despite what he called less judicious expenditure that he was convinced, however, would bear fruit sooner or later. "One should encourage the collections of the Trappists," the report stated, "who do a work no one else could do. They give the best lesson of all to the negroes, that of work. They are humble, pious, mortified, and full of affection for their Abbot. Needless to say, there are some who grumble, but a man like the Abbot will always have admirers and enemies. I cannot but admire his fine qualities, though I don't deny certain defects." It ended, "He knows what I have written."

The result of this report was that the charges against Franz were found to be utterly without merit and our Abbot was fully exonerated. How much more it would have helped us to know that the report also stated that Franz had been "the object of a malicious attack by an individual who had been finally discredited", I do not know. The truth now seems very thin in the welter of words that rose up around us, and the actual report I have before me now – courtesy of our historian who wants to know if our suspicions at the time extended to the individual in question – no longer seems of importance. Here, far too late, I see in Bishop Jolivet's own hand his opinion that "Fr Adolph is an *exalté* whose word is not worth much" – how easily we could have confirmed this! – "but the Abbot has treated him too brusquely, according to his bad custom ..."

So there Franz was again, *hinc illae lacrimae*, author of his own troubles. The American Fr Adolph had, after barely a month, stormed out of the novitiate to which Franz had returned him, complaining bitterly about the Abbot and the Trappist Rule. Franz had given him a chance to visit the various stations in the hope that he might see how unfounded his opinions regarding the state of our missions were, but the tour only entrenched his views. He had not even bothered to return to Mariannhill. It was from Durban that he had addressed his letter to the Propaganda detailing his complaints.

Shortly after mailing it, he returned to America, via Rome, and thus was able to press his case directly to the highest mission authority within the church. The betrayers we had suspected both within and outside our community turned out to be one and the same person – Fr Adolph, armed with intimate information about us and in touch directly with Rome. This was why his wild accusations took on the power they did, and I cannot bear to think how much I, in my addled and indecisive way, might have contributed to that force.

His accusations were even more colourful than the formal charges had reflected, as I was to find in Bishop Jolivet's complete report. Fr Adolph's strongest invective had been saved for the character of the Abbot, the source, in his opinion, of all that was wrong with Mariannhill and its missions. He felt obliged to tell Propaganda Fide what an obstacle Abbot Francis was to the proper development of his own foundation. All the grand things he had established at Mariannhill – a "basilica" for a monastery church; many imposing but totally unnecessary buildings; a printing press that rarely served the work of the missions; even an expensive telephone exchange for the monastery – created only to show off to the world what an excellent man the founder was. Abbot Francis, he said, was obsessed with the desire for glamour and fame and this resulted in the luxury at Mariannhill that was made possible only by the primitive conditions at the mission stations.

Although the charges were, point for point, officially discounted, Fr Adolph was merely cautioned by Propaganda Fide. In anonymity, with his status essentially undamaged, he was left to maintain the ill-will towards Franz that he was never to relinquish and others were only too willing to take up.

Knowing nothing of this, Franz allowed himself a moment of deep satisfaction before leaving to address the General Chapter. And just as the Vicar General was expressing his personal happiness at the vindication of our Abbot, Franz made good on his promise to the Oblates and shouldered the task that had first been allocated to us in Natal. I can honestly say that, more than anything else in that last brief flare of public glory, Franz rejoiced in redeeming his word and taking over the reorganisation and development of St Michael's.

I can say honestly, too, that this announcement cast a shadow over my happiness as we prepared our exonerated leader for his journey to Europe in that March of 1891.

~

We were certain that Franz's trip would not only re-establish his authority in his own house but confirm his importance within the rest of the Order. An indication of what we could expect arrived just before Franz's departure: we were informed, through another of those impressive envelopes, that Franz had been made Vice-Vicar of the Trappist Order for South Africa. An unspoken apology for the charges of which Franz had been cleared, this was still an important gesture and a wonderful example of how good could come from evil. Franz, re-invigorated by this news, planned his journey to Europe via Dunbrody, where he hoped to gather fresh facts that would enable him to justify the stand he had taken over that place.

A proposal had been made that if our founder was not in full health when he left he should be prevailed upon to take a priest along as a companion, and that priest should be me. Franz felt well enough to dismiss this possibility as well as the suggestion that a spokesman for the "mission party" accompany him, in order that their case could be put clearly. He decided, instead, that Brother Alexius, one of our more recent intakes, should accompany him, not to attend the Chapter with Franz but to be instructed in hydrotherapy by Fr Sebastian Kneipp in Germany. Perhaps he thought my own work with the Water Cure had strayed too far from its established practices and principles. Be that as it may, I would have looked forward to learning this at the famous pastor's feet for myself, but the wisdom of someone new to help with the sick amongst us surely took precedence over my own desires.

And so it was that Brother Alexius boarded the steamer with Franz in Durban and disembarked a day later with him at East London. The two of them then took the train that now ran right to Dunbrody. Any one of us who lived through those desperate, dry years there would have been as intrigued as Franz was to see what the Jesuits had made of our failure. The last letter we were to receive from him before he returned to South Africa was infused with a sense of being entirely vindicated as far as Dunbrody was concerned.

"I simply didn't know where I was, there had been so many changes made in the layout since ten years ago," Franz wrote, adding, before one could mistake this for a positive assessment, "the Brothers have built a great deal, worked a great deal, and spent a great deal of money, but Heaven has done very little. Everything around is still scorched brown or yellow, and is maimed and dry, just as it was in our day. The blue sky still shines down on Dunbrody but never a drop of rain. Since the Jesuits have worked so hard there and spent so much time and money, I am now convinced that it will always be impossible to exist in Dunbrody. It does not support life now, and never will."

It is to be hoped that these observations comforted him through the long seasickness ahead, for small comfort was to greet him in Rome.

17

Abbot Franz returned to Mariannhill from Europe early in January 1892, accompanied by the Canonical Visitor of the Order, Abbot Francis Strunk of Ölenberg. We had received only an official announcement of when the two were to arrive in Natal – no personal news from Franz at all – and were amazed by this turn of events. We should not have been, of course, as visitation is a part of the normal government of monasteries of the Reformed Cistercians.

We had been spared this annual feature of Trappist life for so long only because of our distance from the governing centre of our Order and had grown used to this extended delay. Certainly we did not expect it to end as a result of this particular journey to Europe undertaken by our Superior. He had, after all, just been cleared – after a thorough investigation, which we had seen as a kind of canonical visitation in itself – of any failures in his leadership, and then been promoted to the second-highest position within the Order. According to at least one European report we had read whilst he was away, Franz was by now "the best known Religious in Europe", a reputation we should have seen for the two-edged sword it was.

Confident in our newly re-established favour, we had the entire community awaiting our Superior and his exalted companion at the station at Pinetown to receive them and form a triumphal procession to the monastery. Initially this seemed exactly the right tone to set, for Franz had in his train no less than thirty-nine new postulants for our monastery and eleven candidates for the Red Sisters. By the time the whole contingent arrived at the gates of Mariannhill evening had fallen, and the Brothers, flaming torches in hand, conducted our Abbot and the Father Visitator to the new dining hall that had been completed in Franz's absence.

It was then that we discovered some of the true nature of what lay ahead. The Father Visitator looked about the hall glimmering in its red brick and polished wood (light also dancing off the decorations done in leaves and flowers, my small contribution), and said his first words in our foundation: "Mariannhill seems all right by torchlight, but let us see what it is like in bright daylight."

The next day, the Feast of the Epiphany, the Abbot of Ölenberg began his canonical visitation. The first step he took was to require our Superior to leave Mariannhill and remove himself to an outstation until the inspection of the monastery was complete. "I will go to Einsiedeln," Franz said to me as he put together a few personal effects for his journey.

~

Only I, in my official capacity as Prior, was allowed to assist Franz in his leaving. This was quite deliberately intended to cut him off from those to whom he could have said his parting words with more effect. As it was,

Franz spent most of his last night in Mariannhill as its Superior trying to let me know, as quickly as possible and with many a glance at the closed door of his room, not only what had transpired at the General Chapter, but some of the story behind it.

They dealt with the matter of the court case between myself and Ricards at the first session, Franz told me, speaking fast and low. There was no question of any new material being put or the judgement being overturned; Propaganda made it plain that they simply expected payment. To this Franz had responded, "Rather pay the sum ten times over than put the blame on the Order; this very day I shall have the money assigned." We were able to do this, Franz hurried on, cutting short the question that came immediately to my mind (if not my lips), because the Vicar General had found a well-known Roman family who were willing to loan the debated sum. This was a relief to me for I knew we did not have anywhere near the amount to hand and I was quite sure Chapter would not again put its trust in one of Franz's ringing phrases. So, Bishop Ricards had his £2 000, which Franz transferred to the account of Herr Fraundorfer. And much good may it do them both, Franz added bitterly.

Two days later, Franz gave his official report on Mariannhill. His exposition on the state of the people and property of our young Abbey seemed at first to fill the Fathers Capitular with joy, he told me, but their faces soon darkened when he began to put before them the issue of dispensations for the missionaries. As he listed to them those that he had conceded, a muttering and shuffling began in the assembly hall. This grew to a "formidable tumult" when he reached the further demands that had been made of him. He was determined, however, to let Chapter know exactly what our missionaries were up to, and so he went on over the noise. Soon there were Abbots jumping up from their chairs to protest. Out of this pandemonium he had gathered that they wanted to know how he could give such dispensations without bringing them to Chapter first. According to Franz, he could not even make himself heard to explain that he did not wish to concede to the more serious dispensations demanded by the missionaries. Clearly, any distinction he had wished to make between these and his much more moderate dispensations was lost in the general uproar. Eventually, Franz said, he had stood on tiptoe, spread his arms as wide as he could, and shouted out, "You would have to be there to judge the whole affair properly."

At this the meeting suddenly quietened down, and before Franz could work out what was happening, a proposal to send a Visitor to Mariannhill was unanimously agreed upon. Franz was not even given a chance to raise the matter of Bishop Jolivet's report. The discussion moved directly to the problem of whom they could get to take on this task. All the Chapter could agree upon at first was that it should be a German-speaking Abbot, but they soon realised that there were only two in the whole Congregation. One of them was Abbot Bonaventura from Mariastern and, given that he had once been Franz's own Sub-Prior and that his house was Franz's own foundation, he was quickly dismissed as a candidate.

"This left only," Franz said, "Abbot Francis Strunk, the Abbot of Ölenberg." He paused then, staring off into space for some moments before continuing in a hushed voice, "Along with his appointment another resolution was passed unanimously. All the concessions to the Rule made at Mariannhill by myself independently of Chapter were suspended until the next General Chapter." Abbot Strunk was specifically ordered to test these and report on them so that the Abbots could pass a final judgement.

"But this gives us something to work with," he then said to me, "and a chance to turn things back our way. Each detail I have told you is vital for this," he added with as much emphasis as the occasion allowed, "and you must let the other members of our community who side with us know them all." He stopped here, went quickly to his door, opened it slightly, looked out, and carefully closed it.

"Now listen," he went on, "this next part is the most important, and you must use what I tell you now only if absolutely necessary, and then only with the greatest discretion." He pulled me towards him, hand tight on my shoulder and held me in this posture as he explained to me something I have already related, but only in its formally sanctioned version – his previous relations with the abbey of Ölenberg. There was much more to his leaving Mariawald and founding Mariastern than I have recorded so far, it turned out.

As his voice was enveloped by the thickening darkness, I could not help but wish that Franz had a more worthy audience for what he had to tell. Almost everything he said to me that night is etched into my memory, inscribed as much by my terror at the responsibility being thrust upon me by his injunction to remember it all in detail. Once before, in those early days in Europe, he had had only one companion, but this had been the wise and able Brother Zacharias and the wide world lay before them. Now, in one of the largest Trappist houses in the world, his own creation and a sign, surely, of the highest spiritual and worldly achievement, he was alone in a room with the least useful of the few senior members of his community he was able to trust. Least useful in terms of action certainly, but he was learning with each passing year just how valuable I was as a custodian of all he had to say.

Was it his confidence in this, my one virtue in his eyes, that betrayed him into revealing things that it would have been far better to leave hidden, or at least kept between God and himself alone? Whatever it was, on that long night he gave me a clue to a secret that could, in the wrong hands, cut the ground from under him and everything he had built. If he was aware of this, he gave no outward sign of it; his urgency was focused on passing on to me what our supporters would need to know if we were to survive this visitation.

Breathing hard, his face inches from mine, he reminded me that Mariawald had been revived as a monastery under the jurisdiction of the abbey of Ölenberg, revived by the same man who was to be made the first German Abbot of Ölenberg. Abbot Ephrem – for yes, it was he who, by virtue of this position, was the Visitator for Mariawald when Franz joined the Trappist Order there – had felt keenly the dissension in the monastery he had brought back to life as a Trappist house. And he did not take kindly to Franz's key role in the removal of its Prior. Even more, he resented the leadership conferred on Franz by the stricter of the factions into which the community split under that completely ineffectual new Prior he, in his capacity as Visitator, had appointed.

I understood the reason for this far better as Franz went on. I heard for the first time that Franz and his "zealots" had complained of various "abuses" in the visitation of 1867 and, when these were not addressed in Abbot Ephrem's report, threatened to report them directly to Rome. This was a very different story to the one in which the Abbot's fear of the schism coming to Rome's attention had nothing to do with Franz's active intentions. Franz had always been happy to leave the impression of the Abbot fearing word getting back to Rome in some sort of vague and general way – never as the result of a direct threat, especially not one emanating from himself – but the exigencies of our present crisis clearly demanded that I know exactly what we were up against.

Brother Zacharias had prevented the fallout at Mariawald from coming to a head by suggesting to the Abbot that, as a compromise, he and Franz be given permission to leave and form a new foundation. I now learned that this was the condition upon which he and Franz agreed not to take the case to Rome. Franz had, he was happy to admit, immediately leaped at the possibility of leading his own community, but he was concerned that I understand now that Abbot Ephrem only agreed to this because he saw in it an appropriate way to divest himself of two troublesome hotheads.

Fate had then played them directly into his hands, for, shortly after Franz and Brother Zacharias set off, Abbot Ephrem was elected Vicar General of the Trappist Order. He lost no time using the new authority granted to him to write the letters Brother Zacharias and Franz received during their retreat to the Sisters of Mercy at Agram, ordering the one to return to Mariawald and the other back into the secular priesthood.

This then was the full context in which Franz had agonised over the exact meaning of the letter he received from Abbot Ephrem so many years before. Whether he was being thrown out of the Order or only advised to leave was never the question – such a question simply avoided the plain fact that, beyond any such niceties, the Abbot did not want him in the Trappist Order.

Now I understood just how humiliating it must have been for the Abbot to have his decision to dismiss Franz from the Order overturned by the Congregation of the Religious in Rome – not only that, but also to have to re-empower him with the authority to found a new Trappist house! He was thereby forced to give his blessing to any foundation Franz made. Not that he gave in to this gracefully: when Franz wrote to him as Vicar General of the Trappist Order thanking him for the permission to found another Mariastern, he had received no reply; nor had any other communication between himself and Abbot Ephrem thereafter ever been acknowledged.

Franz discovered at the General Chapter that when the next Abbot appointed as Vicar General raised Mariastern to the rank of Priory and appointed him as its titular Prior, Abbot Ephrem objected strongly. This was why he had to justify both his foundation and himself at the Chapter of September 1873, Franz told me in a voice all the more intense for being lowered. In this he was entirely successful, and the assembly confirmed its decision. In protest, Abbot Ephrem never attended another General Chapter for the rest of his life, although Franz was now convinced that he had used his influence to frustrate his desire to found Mariannaberg, the house of his dreams.

We should be under no illusion, then, Franz said, almost pulling me right up against him in his conspiratorial passion, as to the estimation in which he was held at the abbey of Ölenberg. The hostile attitude that estranged Ölenberg from any of his foundations had taken an even harder edge because Abbot Ephrem had chosen to keep those within his monastery and at its daughter house, Mariawald, in the dark about the details of the case that Franz took to the Congregation for the Religious when defending his right to remain a Trappist. The Abbot had certainly told no one of Franz's victory over him, and Franz's recourse to Rome was generally held to be an act of public disobedience which – and here, Franz said with great urgency, we come close to the real danger in all of this – rendered Franz's foundation in Bosnia illegal. One recent brochure about Mariastern had actually branded him an "unnatural father".

Many Religious in Europe, he let me know in the black stillness of that night, went so far as to call Franz and those faithful to him apostates. This was something he heard a hundred times a year from our Brothers on collection tours – above all, from Brother Zacharias, who was often thrown out of houses that had close connections with Ölenberg and Mariawald. Some of our Brothers, Franz told me for the first time, had even been attacked. There were clearly good reasons, which he trusted I understood, for not letting this become common knowledge at Mariannhill or on its missions. Even in Europe he chose to keep this matter as quiet as possible, difficult though this was, in order that our collecting for our foundation could continue.

Why, you may ask, did Franz never attempt to clear up the confusion that led to such violent responses to his leadership? I asked him as much that night, and his answer struck me then, as it did over the next months when I would be forced to think through these matters further, as strange, or at least out of character.

~

You will, I think, agree with me that Franz was not one to hide his light under a bushel, or even let his successes simply speak for themselves. And yet he, who was always so ready to speak of, even spell out when necessary, the exact nature of his achievements to any who would listen and even to those who would not, answered me in the words Matthew ascribes to Christ in his Gospel: "By its fruits you shall know the tree," he said, "and half of Europe is competent to make a judgement as to whether we are wayward sons or not, for we have worked for twenty years before the eyes of all in Austria and Germany."

When I raised my eyes to his with only the merest flicker of – what? doubt, confusion, surely not disbelief? – he stared me down with a look that I knew so well. "Up till now," he went on, "I have never wasted a word in self-defence, and when our brothers have wanted to defend themselves, I always quieted them – as I do you now – with the words '*Te saxa loquuntur*'. I always said they can say what they like about Mariastern; about her the stones must and do speak the truth. I say it now as surely of Mariannhill, but do not trust Abbot Strunk to listen to the stones." It was Abbot Strunk, after all, who had taken over from Abbot Ephrem as Abbot of Ölenberg, and had, before this, spent two years as Prior of Mariawald.

Franz had gathered already that the Abbot carried with him what he called "the fatal prejudices of Ölenberg and Mariawald" against him. On the journey to Mariannhill his attitude made it plain that he thought of Franz as quarrelsome and inconsiderate, an agitator and a stirrer. The only thing he said openly to Franz on board ship was, "Since you have come to Africa, the German monasteries no longer receive any alms, no mass stipends and no novices."

"No, we cannot trust this man," Franz burst out, and then suddenly remembered our circumstances and dropped his voice as the Chapter bell rang for Matins. I could not help but wonder as I pulled my cowl over my head why Franz did not try to clear up any of these contentious issues with Abbot Strunk during the long voyage. Then again, a monk is exhorted never to defend his conduct or excuse his actions, especially when charged by a Superior, and perhaps Franz had chosen to demonstrate the obedience required of him (and so often found wanting) in this way. As he led the way down to Choir through the damp summer heat of Natal which pressed in on us even at two in the morning, I tried to turn my mind towards things more proper to the Lauds of Our Lady's Office. I feared what thoughts might come back to me in the half-hour of meditation between the end of this and the beginning of the Night Office.

The next day Franz's actions appeared to support my assumption that he was determined to demonstrate his obedience in every possible way.

Without a further word to myself or anyone else, he did exactly as he was directed by the Visitator. He showed the postulants their places, as he had been asked to do, and then left immediately for Einsiedeln.

~

This was on the 8th of January and Abbot Francis Strunk solemnly opened the visitation on the 11th day of the same month. According to the Rule, a visitation should last three days only, but even on this point Mariannhill became an exception: a full week was necessary for the motherhouse alone, our Visitator declared. I was kept busy during every minute of those seven days finding and bringing to him all manner of documentation concerning our work. Dom Franciscus, as he was to be known on working terms, remained the stern and severe disciplinarian throughout, his large but trim beard, sharp nose and eyes, and high dome of a forehead in themselves forbidding any of the familiarity we granted to our own Dom Franz. Soon the whole community of Mariannhill learned from his unsmiling manner and detailed examination of the records and activities of our house that Abbot Franz's leadership was again considered suspect.

Busy as I was, in between looking for and delivering document after document to Dom Franciscus, I kept searching for a document I had not seen in my time as Secretary to the monastery but was sure must be somewhere in our rapidly developing archive. The original document, or even a record of its contents, had never been called for by anyone, probably because its existence was simply assumed. It was, after all, fundamental to everything that had transpired during the founding of Mariastern, Maria Dunbrody, and most certainly Mariannhill. I found no trace of it, not even an allusion to it, during all of that week when my duties required me to go into the deepest recesses of our records. The document itself, I deduced, must be in our European archives, but the absence of any reference to it struck me as odd.

After Dom Franciscus was satisfied he had seen all that was necessary at Mariannhill, he set off on a journey through our missions and outstations – Einsiedeln excepted – that was to last five weeks. I was much taken up during his time away with trying, as precisely as possible, to pass on to those Brothers Franz deemed trustworthy what he had shared with me the night before he left. But I also kept on searching for any sign of the document that lay, I was becoming increasingly sure, at the heart of a secret that explained some of the puzzle of Franz's behaviour. What I was searching for I still hesitate to put on record. Certainly, at the time, I was prepared to share my fears with no one. All I had was an inadvertent clue from Franz's own lips, and even this depended on an interpretation on my part of an interpretation on his.

It all came down to the letter Franz received from Abbot Ephrem at the lowest point of his wanderings in search of a site for the first of his foundations. No matter how Franz twisted and turned the import of the letter that had found him at the convent in Agram, it could not have been anything but a formal dismissal from the Trappist Order – if, that is (and everything, it suddenly became clear to me, turned on this), he had up to that point made only his *Simple Vows*. No one knew better than myself – one who, in the resounding void that took the place of any felt certainty of salvation or vocation, had come to stake everything on a total and complete submission to every jot and tittle of the Rule and the Usages of the Trappist Order – that a Vicar General had the faculty to dismiss only monks with Simple Vows. Once Solemn Vows had been made, only the Holy See could dispense a monk of them.

A quick and simple calculation on my part, based on what I then knew of Franz's life, made it clear that his Solemn Vows would have been due at exactly the time Abbot Ephrem rejected him in his letter. The letter that Franz had, with ingenious sophistry and a carefully calculated appeal to the highest religious authority, rendered impotent – and invisible. For nowhere in our records was this letter to be found. Once I knew what I was after I found quite quickly the letters of obedience sent after Franz and Brother Zacharias from Mariawald, extending the time they had in which to search for a site; these were, indeed, practically enshrined in our records, set in secure packaging and filed in a manner that would have made them obvious to the least trained archival eye. For me it was only a matter of returning to them for they were amongst the first papers (and I was pretty sure now that I knew why) called for by Dom Franciscus – Dom Franciscus, Visitator to Mariannhill, and, as Abbot of Ölenberg, let us not forget, successor to Abbot Ephrem.

In all Franz's accounts of the letter he received from Abbot Ephrem at Agram, the key issue at stake was the official status of that letter. Firstly, you may remember, Franz weighed up the relative merits of the formal letter from his Prior extending the period granted him to start a new foundation against what he took to be the private nature of the Vicar General's communication, suggesting that he give this up and leave the Order. Then he focused on the contradictions within Abbot Ephrem's letter: on the one hand it "threw him out" of the Order and, on the other, it only "advised" him to leave. Next he questioned the reason given for this, which was that Franz would still be able to do much good in the world as a secular priest, a reason Franz took to be insufficient in terms of canon law. Finally, as far as Franz was concerned, whilst the Abbot may have had the authority to ask him to give up the attempt to found a new monastery, he could then only order him back to his old monastery, Mariawald, where he had taken his vow of stability as a Trappist. He did not have the authority to expel him from the Order.

The fact is that the Abbot *did* have authority in all these respects. He could give every one of these orders to a monk – but only if he were still under Simple Vows. The case, as Rome had settled it, was treated as if Franz had taken his Solemn Vows. Franz, after all, was given a letter of obedience, in Latin, from the Congregation Episcoporum et Regularium through Cardinal von Reisach, for founding an independent monastery, something he often stressed. We belong to the Trappist Order and not the monastery of Mariawald, much less Ölenberg, he would say to any who strayed into this area of our history. We did not fall under either of these monasteries, he would remind us, for he had been declared an independent Superior by Rome, and authorised to found a new monastery.

This could only have been done if Franz had made the final vows necessary for him to be a regular member of an Order. Such an assumption would have been automatic, given that Brother Zacharias, Franz's junior in religious rank, had made his final vows – at Ölenberg. Which was why Abbot Ephrem's letter required him to return there. Franz, on the other hand, was not ordered to return to Mariawald, because he had not made his final vows at that house. And he could not possibly have made them whilst waiting for the outcome of his court case against Abbot Ephrem.

Had he retrieved this deficiency in his monastic life later? In the records accessible to me, I could find no evidence whatsoever that he had taken his final vows, no matter how hard I looked. This in itself was not proof that he had not done so, but it is what I now began to suspect. After all, confirmation that he had made his final vows was all Franz needed to put before those who called Mariastern an unlawful foundation. Proof of this would overturn in an instant the common rumour that this house, and therefore its monks as well, were unlawful and outside the Trappist Order. These were the grounds upon which Brother Zacharias was shown the door on his begging tours with the accusation that he was an illegitimate or excommunicated Religious, and upon which other monks of the houses Franz founded after Mariastern were accorded the same treatment.

As for Dom Franciscus – Abbot Strunk of Ölenberg – why did he not, as Visitator, simply declare Franz and Mariannhill unlawful, and bring the whole issue of the legitimacy of Franz's actions to a head there and then? Well, we must assume he had to proceed cautiously: an extremely public religious career and two prestigious foundations rested on the assumption that Rome had made in 1867 regarding Franz's being a regular of the Trappist Order, and no one was certain that Franz had not since made good the gap in his life as a Religious. He had after all been made a Prior, then Abbot, then Vice-Vicar for South Africa – although nothing much was being said of this last appointment now, and the rank was, soon enough, simply and quietly to drop away from Franz's name. One must assume, too, that Abbot Ephrem, if he knew anything certain regarding Franz having made his Solemn Vows, said nothing to his confreres, leaving them to think the worst if they so chose. This suited his purposes perfectly, if not quite ethically, and it was his own community that was the most vociferous of those to condemn Franz and his foundations. Again, one word either way would have settled the matter, but this was never spoken by either side in the acrimonious confrontation that was all this visitation could ever have been.

Where did this leave me? Without doubt, any open discussion of these matters would have ruined Franz once and for all if he did not have more evidence of his religious status to offer than was available in our store of records. Silence then was the only recourse, and I hugged my doubts to myself throughout the dark days that were now upon us.

~

I needed, urgently, to speak to Franz about my suspicions, although I could not even imagine how I would put the matter to him. When we were told that Dom Franciscus was spending the last five days of his tour in Pietermaritzburg with Bishop Jolivet collecting the final information he needed for his report, I was in an agony of uncertainty. I prayed that there would be some way in which Franz would return to Mariannhill before the Visitator, but as it turned out the Visitator came back to find that he himself would have to wait upon Franz's return.

The Rule determines that, at the end of his investigation, the Visitator will *compose the report on his visitation, of which he will inform the Superior before reading it in Chapter.* Word came from Einsiedeln, however, that Abbot Franz, soon after his arrival at the outstation and whilst still weakened by his recent seasickness, had been laid low by an attack of typhoid fever – so severely that, for two full weeks, the worst was feared. He was eventually confined to bed for forty-three days and after this was still too weak to be disturbed or to travel for some time. We could do nothing but wait patiently.

Not only did this leave me in my uncertainty, it also had a fatal effect on the final report that Dom Franciscus refused to draw up until he had spoken to Franz. The senior missionaries, who had returned with the Visitator to the monastery in expectation of hearing the report, used their proximity with him to their advantage. Events supported them in this: Fr Hyacinth was due to be ordained as a priest and a particular closeness developed between him and our Visitator, who preached the sermon on this happy occasion. This intimacy between the Visitator and those of the missionary party was strengthened further when Fr Notker was ordained and celebrated his first Mass a mere six days later, the Visitator again giving the sermon and clearly enjoying his part in the deepening of the religious life of another monk.

On the very day of Fr Notker's first Mass, another blow fell for the "regulars", as we were increasingly becoming known in the rapidly polarising circumstances of the visitation. Brother Zacharias, he who first opened the doors of Mariawald to Franz, he who had suggested to Franz that he leave that monastery and found his own house, the great beggar before the Lord whose zeal for collecting funds had kept both Mariastern and Mariannhill alive, passed away. Physical weakness had recently brought him back to Mariannhill. I did not know him well – how well did we ever get to know any of our brethren under the strict rule of silence, let alone one whose work kept him away from his house perpetually? But I had admired him from afar ever since joining Mariastern. This was not the only reason I was distraught at his passing; I had hoped that I could find in him some enlightenment on the matter of the apparently missing requirement in Franz's profession.

As it was, when I heard the wooden gong within the cloister struck rapidly four times, I dropped the work I was doing and hurried to the infirmary, saying the Apostle's Creed out loud, as is required. There I found Brother Zacharias, already laid out on his mattress sack of straw under which ashes were spread in the shape of a cross, clearly not long for this world. Even as we were busy with the Litany and the Seven Penitential Psalms, his mouth, moving ceaselessly and soundlessly, fell open and became still. We followed the cantor on into the Subvenite, then the Kyrie and the Oremus with the Tibi, Domine and Commendamus. When these chants ended, it was my duty to organise the taking away of the body, emptied now of its soul, for washing and dressing.

Whilst I was doing this, the cantor went off to fetch the Collectaneum for the Abbot – Abbot Strunk, that is, Franz not being with us – and the sacristan his stole and crosier. The Abbot arrived as this was being done, and the monks lined up as for Choir, with the Lay Brothers gathering in a group apart. He led the community in the rest of the collects and the body was then brought back amongst us, to be sprinkled with holy water and infused with incense. Upset as I was, I could not help but be impressed with how naturally Dom Franciscus moved us through the arrangements for the deceased as set out in our Usages. Each chant came to his lips in the exact order required as we formed into a procession behind the ministers carrying the cross, the light, the thurible and the holy water, and escorted the body into the church. There our Religious too, I thought, performed the Office of the Dead tolerably well, for the most part remembering the correct chants for the time of day and day of the year.

The hour of burial is set in the Usages according to the hour of death, and as Brother Zacharias had died between the bell for Sext and the midday meal, we were required to say the Hour of Sext more rapidly, then say the Funeral Mass more rapidly too, after which we were to go off to the midday meal and then gather for the deceased to be buried after None. No time is lost, as the Usages are sensitive to the possibility of there being "an odour so fetid" that the body cannot be placed in the church for the Mass. On this occasion the procession chanting and carrying the body to its grave arrived at the cemetery before the grave was ready. This possibility, too, the Usages provide for, and so, as is prescribed, the Abbot interrupted the Temeritatis quidem prayer, inserting some of the Collects that follow it until the grave was fully dug.

357

At the appropriate moment the six pallbearers came up and each took hold of one end of the three long straps that had been laced beneath the body. They then took their stand on either side of the grave and, in slow unison, paid out the straps until the body was settled at the bottom, after which they withdrew them. It was then my task, as the nearest thing we had to a doctor, to climb down into the grave, where I was required to stretch the napkin over Brother Zacharias's face, close his hood with pins, and arrange his garments neatly. I always found this to be an exquisite gesture, Mother Church preparing her son to await the Resurrection like a mother tucking her child into bed at night.

I climbed out damp-eyed and the pallbearers each took a shovel and began gently covering the body, starting with the feet. I must say that on this occasion my tears fell as much for the knowledge of Franz's life that we buried that day as for the life that was gone. We had also lost one of Franz's most valuable allies, just when he would have his greatest need of him.

~

Years later, certain brethren who were at Mariannhill at the time would report that it was "with disastrous suddenness that the community was one day informed that their beloved Father, Abbot Francis, had been summarily suspended from office". They may well have remembered it in this way, which was enough for our more popular histories, but the annals of our community record a different story.

Something like the widely held version took place only in the December of 1892, eleven months after the Visitor's arrival at Mariannhill. The Abbot of Ölenberg and Abbot Franz were in each other's company on South African soil only once in the first two and a half months of this year, just before Franz's departure for Einsiedeln. It was towards the end of March that the Visitor decided that our Abbot must now be strong enough to discuss some of the important issues that should be put to him before being included in the final version of the *Visiten-Karte*, as the Visitation Report is formally called. Franz was now convalescing at Mariathal and Dom Franciscus made the journey there to have, as he was in the habit of saying (especially when crucial issues were at stake), "only a few words" before obtaining Franz's official approval. This was required by the Rule, and I am sure he saw it as a mere formality, as he had already completed his report.

Everyone on the mission, as I discovered, soon had cause to remember that the site of Mariathal had once been called Blitzberg. Dom Franciscus met with Franz in his room directly after Holy Mass, and in no time at all the two were locked in a debate that went on for hours without either giving an inch. They fought from morning to evening, their voices exploding into the particularly quiet cloister of the high and remote mission and echoing into the mist-enshrouded landscape around them. After three days of this, Franz – who decided, he told me years later, that the whole situation was becoming rather foolish – tried to avoid the Visitator by escaping into the beautiful gardens of Mariathal immediately after Mass. This only led to the identical scene being enacted amongst the pungent herbs and dew-heavy roses.

Dom Franciscus tried to enforce his opinions by emphasising his authority, which, with a character like Franz, was exactly the wrong strategy. As Visitator, Dom Franciscus may have had the full power of the Order behind him, possessing all the faculties of the Vicar General and the General Chapter, but Franz was entirely unimpressed by any such status. He countered every one of the principles put to him with his own experience and achievements – or, as he put it, simple "good sense". To Dom Franciscus such resistance must have seemed nothing but plain disobedience and insubordination, an affirmation, in short, of all the prejudices held against Franz at Ölenberg.

So it was that the community of Mariathal heard, as they later told anyone who cared to listen, one of the impassioned sessions so foreign to their quiet gardens peak with Dom Franciscus shouting at Franz, "Do you realise that I have the power to depose you!" and Franz hitting back with, "Dismiss me, then!"

The next day, the 3rd of April, Mariathal awoke in a cold blanket of fog, and Dom Franciscus, fumbling in the darkness for the candle on his table, found a slip of paper that read: *Conscientia mihin non permittit, secundum vestra beneplacita procedere, potius debeo dare meam dismissionem.* He stumbled outside in his haste, calling for Franz, but no one knew where our Abbot was. He had simply placed his note on the sleeping Visitator's table and disappeared.

The Visitator must have been at a complete loss. Nothing in the Rule or our Regulations covered events of this sort. He had the power to accept Franz's resignation, but clearly could not decide whether he should.

Neither was Franz's note a legal resignation; this would have required an official form with a signature and those of two witnesses, not just one line from the Abbot stating that his conscience would not allow him to go on in the manner required of him. As it was Franz's scribbled note could be taken only as a threat, and no more.

Dom Franciscus had no choice but to return to Mariannhill, looking rather foolish. After some time we were able to tell him that we had had word that Franz was at Reichenau and would not trouble himself with anything connected with the visitation. After some hesitation, Dom Franciscus called together some of the missionaries to discuss the situation. It was decided to decline Franz's "resignation", and two of the missionaries who imagined that they were closer to our Abbot than the rest were sent up to Reichenau "to move him by kind talk", as the minutes of this meeting record, to take up again the office he had in fact never laid down. They returned to tell the Visitator that Franz would not enter into any discussion with them and, in words that soon spread around the monastery, "showed himself as unapproachable as a Sphinx". I could see that Dom Franciscus did not know how to proceed. His only recourse was to turn to the Vicar General in Rome for advice. This presented a hard test of patience for him, letters taking as they then did three to four weeks each way.

The answer came much sooner than he supposed, in the form of a telegram: ECRIVEZ LA CARTE ET VENEZ. By a whim of fate – or was our postmaster, perhaps, more closely aligned with our Abbot than he chose to declare? – the laconic order to "Write the card and come" fell first into Franz's hands. Who knew what Franz was really up to now? He must have been aware that the Regulations decreed that the contents of the *Visiten-Karte* had first to be shown to the Abbot of the monastery before they could be read in Chapter in order to be legally promulgated. Were his disappearances planned to hold off this moment as long as possible? In any event, access to the Vicar General's telegram let him know that this strategy was now played out.

For his part, Dom Franciscus could only attempt to bring the ruins of his visitation to some sort of closure before obeying the order to return. He drew up his comprehensive report, complete with the reforms it entailed, and had it printed on the same presses at Mariannhill of which Franz was so proud. How these changes were to be implemented by a man who absolutely refused to cooperate in any way is a mystery, but the report did have an air of finality about it. Once printed, the *Visiten-Karte des hochwürdigsten Visitators RRP Franciscus, Abates von Ölenberg*, could in no way be amended. The 25th June was selected as the date for the solemn closing of the visitation.

On the morning of the 24th June, without any warning whatsoever, Franz rode in through the gates of Mariannhill, declaring that he had recovered fairly well from his indisposition. He appeared to be the very spirit of friendliness, acting towards the Abbot of Ölenberg as if nothing untoward between them had ever transpired. For the rest of that day we were all on edge, with only Franz walking amongst us as if this smiling calm was his natural demeanour. On the 25th, the Feast of the Sacred Heart, the monks of Mariannhill assembled in the Chapter Room for the solemn act of closing, set for half-past one. When we were in our places Franz made his appearance and took his accustomed seat. He sat there while the Cantor read the *Visiten-Karte*, listening attentively. The Visitator then made some comments, in which he praised our Abbot and his magnificent works but did not hesitate to announce publicly the resistance he had encountered from him or to spell out his abuses of the Rule.

When he had finished, complete silence fell, a silence as explosive as any I have ever felt. It stretched on to the point of being unbearable, and then, suddenly, the Abbot of Mariannhill rose. He walked slowly to the middle of the Chapter Room and stood directly before the Visitator. With the whole community visibly vibrating in anxiety, he dropped to the ground and, after a heartbeat of a pause, prostrated himself before the Visitator.

Visibly touched, Dom Franciscus raised Franz up, embraced him, and gave him the assurance that what was past was also forgotten. Franz turned to us and announced in a firm, full voice that he would observe and carry out all the instructions in the report, even if his own personal wishes were not thereby realised. The assembled community exhaled as one, and a joyful mood swept through us. When Dom Franciscus offered to us, in the name of the Monastery of Ölenberg, a union of charity with joint communion of spiritual property, Franz affirmed this on behalf of Mariannhill. Some of those present were sobbing with emotion.

Abbot Strunk left us then, confirming as he passed through our gates that he had no doubt that the principles laid down in the report of the visitation were the right ones. At which the now entirely grey-haired Abbot of Mariannhill smiled and waved his good-byes without a word.

18

Oddly enough, the whole matter of the visitation was kept firmly within our walls. One brief article only appeared in the local press, a few lines of which demonstrated just how much could be lost in a simple statement of fact: "The Abbot of Chartreuse Monastery in Alsace-Lorraine," it read, "who came out about Christmas with Abbot Pfanner on his return to Mariannhill, has just sailed back to Europe, after his tour of visitation to the half-a-dozen Trappist mission stations in Natal. This is the first time the General Chapter has found it convenient to send out a Visitator, and his duties, viz., that of examining each member of the Order, hearing complaints and proposals – armed as he was with full authority to enforce discipline and penalty in case of laxity or abuse – have occupied considerable time. We understand the visitation has been wholly satisfactory to all concerned."

And so Franz's extended affair with the secular press ended, in a report that could not have summed things up more inaccurately.

~

The Visitation Report was thirty-one pages long – thirty-one printed pages that line-by-line, point-for-point, systematically undid everything Franz had done to make a house like Mariannhill possible. As was to be expected (and, by some of us, welcomed), the main thrust of the report was the return of Mariannhill to its Trappist character. At the same time it attempted to preserve the monastery's missionary successes. Dom Franciscus saw no contradiction here, no rationale for falling away from any of the Trappist ideals. This was made clear in the report from the first: "Mariannhill is a Trappist mission monastery," he wrote, "a Trappist monastery founded for the purpose of the mission and conversion of the Blacks."

And so one of the highest authorities in the Order formally approved of its monks undertaking mission work, but only by insisting that there was nothing irreconcilable between contemplative and active work. "All the members of Mariannhill's community must be Trappists and monks," the Visitator wrote, "all true Trappists, even those working expressly for the mission, and all true missionaries, be they priests or teachers, simple Choir Religious or working Brothers …" For him, nobody could be a true missionary if he were *not* a true Trappist.

While these ringing phrases could be said to be simply a rhetorical side-stepping of the contradictions Franz had to face every day in trying to achieve a balance between two fundamentally different ways of life, it was clear that for the Visitator being a Trappist came first. "It must always be your principle," read the strongly phrased climax of his admonition, "to remain Trappists as you ought to be, otherwise it would be better that Mariannhill and its missions did not exist."

He did not shrink from dismissing out of hand the calls by the missionaries for ever more extreme dispensations from the Rule and the Regulations; the dispensations Franz had already granted found no grace either, and even those concessions granted by the General Chapter and the Vicar General were annulled. The missionary wing of Mariannhill must have been amazed, given the time they had put into convincing the Visitator of the rightness of their cause, to find that there was scarcely a trace of the concessions they had hoped for in the report.

Prayer in Choir was returned to its proper place of honour; as the Rule prescribed, the Divine Office had to be for the Religious *the highest duty of their sacred service, cui nihil praeponatur*. Dispensations granted too readily were "intolerable". "Anything else," the report stated, "but not Choir. Monks may only miss prayer in Choir when they are ill." Haste during prayer in Choir was also the object of attention; to my deep and heartfelt relief, the long pauses were returned to the recitation of Compline, and it was required that the Office and Mass should be sung in their entirety during the week.

The Visitator also reduced the hours of work for Choir Religious to four hours a day at most, in order to give them time for their own spiritual activity. He had no patience for concessions concerning various works of penance. He lamented the fast days of the Order that had been lost even at the motherhouse, and in the Rule for the Stations he insisted "there was an absolute need to think about what was most necessary, and to give orders accordingly". He did not enter into details, and left Franz free to settle them. Certainly the missionaries must have felt the pinch when the rules for fasting were returned to their proper severity.

Some of the points fought over may seem mere trifles. The Visitator did not find any justification for doing away with the cloaks that, according to the Rule, had to be worn at all times except during hours of work; they should be worn throughout winter, he ordered, and if the days were too hot in summer, then in the morning and evening at least. This was a minor but practical concession that, like many of the others overturned, Franz himself had given. One of the further apparently minor concessions demanded by the missionaries, however, which Franz had rejected outright and which had then become the occasion for one of the worst conflicts, was settled in Franz's favour: the Visitator did not allow missionaries to have the same haircut as the secular clergy (let alone dress like them); they had to keep to the corona, as was customary in the Order.

The Visitator found that the explanation of the Rule was completely neglected, with the result that the majority of the community did not know the Rule at all; it was scarcely even on hand to be read. No wonder then, he said, that he felt little of the spirit of the Rule at Mariannhill. One Choir Religious, under examination, affirmed that he had been at the monastery for four years without knowing that the Rule of St Benedict existed!

This led the Visitator, in his efforts to revive the chief elements of monastic life, to pay special attention to the noviciate. He would not suffer it to become ineffective through numerous dispensations, and insisted that all the required procedures be carefully observed. Scholastics must, he maintained, be thoroughly grounded in the Church's doctrine, especially moral theology, as well as the Scriptures, pastoral theology, and the Liturgy. In order that their studies were not broken, novices must return to the law laid down by the Church that they remain in the noviciate for two full years and, during this time, never leave the monastery for more than two consecutive nights. Because of Franz's flagrant and common practice of using novices in the missions, the Visitator demanded that even the newly professed attend all the exercises of the novitiate for another full year, and be placed again under the charge of the Novice Master. So strongly did he feel about this that he ordered that until they had done so, their canonical vows, although already taken, were not to be recognised.

This was a particularly hard blow for the missionaries as it affected some of their most established leaders. Fr David, with his mere five months in the noviciate, was outraged. The Visitator was barely out of the gates of Mariannhill before the English monk descended on Franz, his face like one of the storms that would suddenly pour down on us on summer afternoons. He would leave Mariannhill rather than submit to the Visitator's reforms, announced this most radical of the missionaries, without even requesting permission to speak. Franz simply nodded as Fr David, looking about the enclosure for as wide an audience as possible, declared that he refused to have his vows rectified. He would become a Familiar instead, he blustered on, and when Franz did not respond in the dramatic pause left after this statement, he added as loudly as he could that he would offer himself in this capacity to Bishop Jolivet. At this Franz, with only the slightest inclination of his head, turned away and walked to his office.

Bishop Jolivet, we heard later, assigned Fr David as a missionary to a group of Bantu from Portuguese East Africa who had settled on the Bluff, the promontory we had sailed around before entering the port at Durban. As usual, none of his Oblates were available for missionary work amongst the Natives, and so we were sure the Bishop was only too glad to pick up one of the earliest victims of the Visitator's report. We were to hear nothing more of Fr David for some years.

There is every chance that Arthur Bryant, as I prefer to think of him, would have left us soon enough in any event, for another of the reforms specified in the report cut to the heart of what was fast becoming his major preoccupation. The Visitator wanted to have all publications emanating from Mariannhill put under strict censure, and the press came in for especially severe criticism. He disapproved of the publication of "trivial" material, such as articles on the history and practices of the Natives, witchcraft, medical matters, diseases, water cures and meat-eating because, "it is not our vocation to instruct the world, still less in the manner in which it has been done". He went on to prohibit the sending of articles to newspapers, on the grounds that Mariannhill had publications of its own.

It is hardly necessary to say that Franz must have felt this keenly, and not only as far as indulging himself on his pet topics was concerned. His policy of publishing Mariannhill and its foundations was an essential part of his fund-raising efforts in Europe. But this was anathema to the Visitator, who dismissed it as embodying "all the exaggeration, self-praise, and the inclination to paint everything in gaudy colours" that characterised the monastery's advertising of itself. Here one of Franz's early fears regarding Abbot Strunk took material form, for the report suggested that it was the ever-increasing circulation of publications such as *Vergissmeinnicht* and the *Mariannhiller Kalender* that had made Mariannhill so popular that the other Trappist houses in Europe were experiencing a decline in donations and even the number of novices.

After the Visitator had left, however, Franz said not a word against any element of the report. He remained, for those who knew him, suspiciously calm and contained. He even kept his peace on what was, perhaps, the most sensitive issue addressed in it: the relationship between the Choir Religious and the Convers Brothers. "Would that every form of envy and distrust between Choir Religious and Brothers disappear," read the report, which then went on to fuel just such tensions by stating, "It seems to have been the intention not to accept able people into the Choir." The basis for this comment Don Franciscus found in Franz's practice of giving "all" responsible positions at the stations to the Brothers. It was clear that when he wrote this he was thinking of the office of Manager, which, as we have seen, Franz invariably gave to a Lay Brother.

And so the hand of the more radical missionaries began to be felt in the report, their months of contact with the Visitator while Franz was absent beginning to show at last. Nearly all of them were Choir Religious, and confined therefore to being "Rectors". They made certain that the split responsibilities in the leadership of the missions was treated in the report as if Franz could find no men suitable for the job of Manager from amongst their ranks, and that only men who were good for nothing else were directed into the Choir.

It is true that some monks were placed in the Choir because they could not, for one reason or another, master any other duty. They were considered good enough only to recite the Psalms, otherwise doing the most menial of tasks. Even some comparatively senior monks (one, say, who had been given the positions of Master of Novices, Sub-Prior and even Prior on various occasions, but had not shown himself to be particularly competent in any of them) fell into this category. But this does not imply that men with real ability were not to be found amongst the Choir Religious. All those who were students, for example, and those who were better at using their heads than their hands were there, and since many of the important offices in the monastery required several years of preparation, postulants with the necessary characteristics for these posts were put into the Choir as well.

None of these monks were suited to be Managers at the stations since they lacked training and experience in or simply the aptitude for practical things – as no one knew better than myself. This was why those Choir Religious sent to the stations as Superiors, or Rectors as Franz would have it, were required to remain *Capellani expositi*, that is, limited to the spiritual direction of the Trappists and the missionary Sisters, the care of neophytes and the conversion of the pagans.

The Visitor, however, had no time for the title of Rector. He saw the role of Superior in its traditional form only, invoking all the faculties connected with this office by canon law. Superiors should govern their stations as direct delegates of their Abbot, which meant that they should have complete control of everything to do with the station, including its property and material goods. In the Visitor's view the Choir monks were, as is conventional in any Cistercian house, the backbone of the monastery and should never be made less important than Lay Brothers in terms of the responsibilities, posts and offices given to them. Nothing was more strongly condemned in the report than Franz's practice of building his missions with the labour and skills of Lay Brothers and under their authority.

The manner in which the governing of the stations was to be corrected represented the real victory of the missionaries over the man who had, in effect, created them. Franz's absence of comment at the time of the reading of the report did not, as I was to discover later, extend to his letter writing, where he made it plain that his authority was under direct fire. "The Visitor wants to change everything, although he is still young and inexperienced," he wrote to Brother Stanislaus, our new collector in Europe. "How things will go, God knows. I resist only where he wants to attack my rights as an Abbot or restrict the welfare of the monastery." As it turned out, the Visitor's reforms struck at the heart of both.

"The Venerable Abbot of Mariannhill will be assisted in the administration of the stations by the Mission Council," the Visitor wrote in his report. "This seems to be absolutely necessary. The Abbot is the Superior with full rights of the mother monastery as well as the stations, but he cannot possibly direct and regulate in person every detail on the outlying stations. Not having been actively engaged in mission work himself, he cannot form as clear a judgement in certain things as the missionaries themselves – he will necessarily depend upon their support." Franz himself could have written this, and it was he, of course, who had instituted the Mission Council. If the Council had no particular significance in the running of the missions this was, he felt, entirely the result of the attitude of the missionaries.

The report went on to ensure that this would not continue to be the case. "It is only fair," wrote the Visitor, as if the missionaries were at his side guiding his pen, "that the missionaries whom the Abbot appoints as his delegates and who are thus his co-operators carrying the whole responsibility of the mission work, should in all confidence be asked their opinion and advice in matters pertaining to the advantage and welfare of the missions."

And there it was. Franz could have lived, perhaps, with every other item in the report but this, a recommendation that flew in the face of the Rule's insistence on the unlimited power of the Abbot. As he put it in his dictations to me years later, it was ironic that the Visitator, who was ever insistent on the Rule, gave up the monastic principle on this one point. Until now, no one in any Trappist community even suspected that a Superior could be tied down by the voice of a Council. Franz may have kept this to himself at the time, but he certainly believed that the Visitator had no power to impose such a limitation on the omnipotence of an Abbot. It lacked, in his opinion, any legal foundation.

When he prostrated himself, then, before the Visitator, he made no admission of guilt on any of the charges brought against him. The Rule requires that *if someone is reproached by the Abbot or any Superior for any, even the smallest, matter, or if he should notice that the mind of the Superior is even the least embittered or excited, he should without delay, in the spirit of penance, prostrate himself at his feet on the floor and remain in this attitude until this excitement has abated again by his blessing.* This Franz obeyed to the letter, but it did not mean that he acknowledged culpability. The requirement applies, after all, if the mind of the Superior is unsettled through a misunderstanding or even an error on his own part.

Error? For all his prostrating, Franz would soon make it clear when and where he believed this to be the case.

~

One of the strongest resolutions in the report had to do with the purchase of land, which was forbidden unless explicit permission was obtained from the Abbot General of the Trappist Order. In effect this made any purchase impossible. Favourable opportunities to buy land, especially by auction, would be long gone before permission could be obtained from Rome. And what of favourable places falling into the hands of other sects if not seized by the Trappists? What of the cost of land, low at the moment, rising in time? What of the potential for influencing the Natives easily and efficiently if they were tenants on Trappist-owned land, with or without the buildings and farms to come?

I could see each of these questions running through Franz's mind as he read and re-read the section of the report that stated: "It must be the first prerogative to make the stations already established into what they ought to be with regard to buildings, productiveness, and mission work. In this there is work for many years to come."

For Franz each new station he opened was a fortress for Christ, raised up within the realm of Satan. The Visitator had probably not even sailed from Durban before Franz was negotiating, through Brother Nivard and unbeknownst to anyone else, the purchase of a new piece of land in East Griqualand, heading off the Methodists. This was just as well, for all applications put to the Vicar General to open new missions would be absolutely refused for years to come. Could this be, Franz must have asked himself, Bosnia and Mariannaberg all over again, after he had worked so hard and come so far?

The Visitator was especially critical of the purchase of the land upon which Lourdes mission had been established. Franz bought this land, amounting to over fifty-four thousand acres, in 1888 and, up to this time, not much of it had been developed. Fr Chysostomus, the monk Franz himself had recently raised up to the position of editor of *Vergissmeinnicht*, had become the chief accuser on this score, and his arguments regarding the large amounts of money spent on gigantic farms that produced only meagre incomes in return had impressed the Visitator. Franz could have given many a valid reason in support of this strategy, but here again the effect of the critical period during which he had remained withdrawn at Einsiedeln was felt. The Visitator had made up his mind on issues of this nature during that time, and he did not expect any alteration or opposition when he finally met with Franz.

What he did not understand, and what Franz could not afford to make entirely clear to him, was the way in which any relaxation of Mariannhill's hold over its missions could bring the whole edifice crumbling down. Even if my duties as Secretary no longer gave me direct access to the finances of the monastery, the essence of the problem was clear to me: Mariannhill was now too large to survive on its own. It was dependent on the produce and income of the missions to survive materially, and if the missions were allowed to become too autonomous, pushing even for independence in their own right as some of the missionaries threatened, this could pull the very ground from under Mariannhill. The continued existence of the motherhouse depended upon its daughter stations remaining extensions of it, directly under its control.

This was crucial when it came to the ever-sensitive issue of how the alms raised by Mariannhill were used. The Visitator was astonished at the "terrific abundance" flowing into Mariannhill, but he was even more concerned that Franz "had only one till" into which all the incoming money went without distinction, all expenditure equally being drawn from it without distinction. It was the opinion of some of the missionaries that alms raised for the missions should be used only for the missions. The Visitator agreed with this and insisted with all severity on Mariannhill "being thrifty and conscientious in the use of alms according to the intentions of the benefactors". Too much money, he said, was being wasted on magnificent plans for new premises, machinery, electrical installations, lithographs, etc.

Reforms of this sort gave real teeth to the Missionary Council, and a means of direct control over not only the way funds were distributed to the missions but the way in which they were used at the motherhouse itself. It was useless for Franz to protest that he, too, had been out begging for these large sums and ought, therefore, to know best for what purpose the benefactors had given them; there was nothing on paper, no record at all, to prove his case, and now no Brother Zacharias to bear him out.

Useless, too, it would have been to shout that it was under the instruction of Pope Pius IX that the Trappists had undertaken missionary work in South Africa; it was over a decade since Leo XIII had succeeded Pius IX as Supreme Pontiff, and Franz had nothing more than Bishop Ricards' word on any such declaration – Bishop Ricards, whose every word Franz had done everything possible to make suspect, whose very ability to remember accurately he had challenged, whose authority on all matters missionary he had flouted.

What was Franz to do then when, upon raising himself up from the floor of the Chapter Room, he had to resume command of his monastery in the face of such evident errors and misunderstanding?

~

Not every issue raised in the report was on such a grand scale. Trappist life would not be what it is if the smaller details were not often felt the most. I hope you will forgive me then for including some matters that touched on my own interests.

Franz's public reserve regularly gave way to more private expressions of frustration – never more private than when vented in my presence. What for did we want meat and beer and English doctors at twenty to thirty pence a visit, he would mutter, and allopathy with expensive and poisonous medicines? In his opinion all we needed was hydropathy with precious water, which was cheaper and better.

My posture, I hoped, indicated agreement, but I must confess that Franz was not being entirely fair to the Visitator. Dom Franciscus did not want to introduce the consumption of meat for the ordinary meals of the community, nor was he entitled to do so. The Rule does state, however, that *those who are seriously ill, or those who are weak, may be given meat and meat broth*, and it was considered one of Franz's personal eccentricities – something like his opposition to vaccination, say – that he considered the eating of meat to be especially harmful for a person who had not taken meat for years and whose body was, furthermore, weakened by disease. When one of our Brothers on a mission died of a severe attack of malaria, Franz publicly accused the Superior in question of killing him by allowing him beer and meat broth; this, he said, had overheated the already feverous patient who should, instead, have been cooled with water.

We were well aware that Franz had become something of a laughing stock in the Order over his belief that water was the only effective medicine. He openly published his views on this and sought to spread his example at every opportunity, as he described so vividly in one of his publications: "I keep influenza away with Kneipp water and weakness of the eyes with 'malefiz' oil which I smear behind my ears when my skin is slightly inflamed. Dropsy I dispel with potter's earth. I sleep very well, but for five hours at most. Then I plunge into water and go back to sleep until three o'clock. For this purpose I have a bath in my bedroom and a hose pipe over the tub." If only those prompted to smiles and laughter at this could have known of the years and years to come when I would have to fill that bath and hold that hose over our disgraced ex-Abbot when sleep would not come, and then help him back to his straw mattress and sit beside him all through the long, long night.

Dom Franciscus had his own reasons for understanding that others thought differently about the healing powers of water, and here I must record that my own efforts cannot be entirely separated from the opinions he formed. Almost immediately upon his arrival his legs had broken out in the sores that invariably plagued newcomers to Natal. I was called in to treat these and so can attest to their particular virility in his case. As usual they began with what seemed like an insect bite, but this quickly developed into a red eruption weeping a thick yellow pus. When one of these wounds eventually healed it left a deep scar, almost a hole in the leg, and with the Visitator, as indeed with most others, the sores immediately flared up elsewhere.

One of the first cures that brought attention to Fr Kneipp's methods was that of a nun with festering sores on her legs that defied the best efforts of the local physician in Wörishofen. Kneipp cured her with cold water compresses and massaging, but this I found had only a slight effect on the Natal version of this affliction. I put this down to the difficulty we had keeping the sores clean while the legs of my brethren, naked under their habits, were constantly exposed to soil, vegetation and building materials during their hours of work. The rubbing against the sores of the rough material of their habits as they laboured, not to mention the hours when the not particularly clean cloth was pressed against the wounds during prayer and sleep, was clearly no help either.

The sores were, I knew, excessively itchy, and the continuously scratching fingernails of the monks (which I had observed furtively in motion during even the most sacred moments of the Office), embedded with dirt and pared only occasionally with rough knives, spread the suppurating lesions despite my every effort with water. Then again, even the far cleaner conditions under which the Visitator lived did not seem to have any preventative power. He rubbed and scratched as much as the least of my brethren, complaining all the while of the oppressive heat and his heavy heart.

My failings with these sores did nothing to encourage the Visitator's confidence in Franz's preferred methods of treatment for illnesses in general. The Visitation Report ordered that if a sick person felt deeply disinclined towards the Water Cure he could not be forced to undergo it. Some medicine, therefore, should be on hand at the monastery and the missions at all times, certainly the most important allopathic remedies.

Whilst I experienced the effect of this requirement in my day-to-day work, which increasingly included the dispensing of medical attention, for Franz it was another blow against his influence and authority. When the report went so far as to make the provision that in serious cases of illness the help of an outside doctor should be called for, he would hear nothing of it. He had never allowed a strange doctor – let alone an English doctor charging his exorbitant prices! – into one of his houses, and there is no evidence, even after the Visitator's Report, that he ever did.

~

Franz's objection to English doctors, like every other objection he had raised with Dom Franciscus during those heated sessions in the garden of one of his most beloved stations, had simply been overruled in the report. On top of this, Franz had sat through the solemn conclusion of the visitation and listened to the censure that came directly from the Visitator's mouth. "God permitted that this visitation became the source of unspeakable suffering and pain for us, in spite of our sincere love for Mariannhill and the best and perfect goodwill on our behalf; and that our stay here had to be much prolonged because of the sad obstacles prepared for us," the Visitator had said, and he did not have to look meaningfully at the Abbot of Mariannhill for us to know exactly whom he meant when he added, "from one side."

Franz's humiliation by then was entirely public and by no means over. The formal publishing of the Visitation Report and its reading in Chapter, by which it gained full legal status, was not the end. In accordance with Regulation number 1446, the report had to be read in Chapter on all the Ember Saturdays of the year to come. Despite our hungering for mortification, it would have been a surprise if the period of false peace was to last. As it was, Franz would not be present, head down and silent, yet still raised up above us in his Abbot's chair, to hear the report read again and again for anything like a year to come.

It was – as it so easily could have been predicted – the Mission Council that would bring into the open the inevitable confrontation between Franz and the Visitator's Report. The report outlined every aspect of this body in such a way as to ensure its new and exceptional significance. It was to consist of the Abbot and three elected missionaries, one of the latter serving as Overseer of the Council. The Visitator ruled that "all the Superiors and the independent missionaries on the stations and the priests active in the missions at Mariannhill were to have active and passive franchise in the election of the councillors, and the appointment of the Overseer". As a precaution Dom Franciscus personally oversaw the election of the first Council before he left Mariannhill. Its members were to be re-elected every three years.

An ordinary session of the Council was prescribed every half year "to deliberate on all questions pertaining to interior and exterior conditions of the missions or the stations". In extraordinary cases that could not be postponed, the Abbot had to ask the opinion of all the Councillors in writing. The Abbot was "obliged to bring before the Council all important matters", but it was in fact the Overseer, not the Abbot, who was to select the items for the meetings of the Council; it was the Overseer, too, who was appointed inspector of the stations, and had to visit each of them at least twice a year.

If a matter had to be put to the vote, the vote of the Abbot counted double. What use was this if the three Councillors all disagreed with him? They could then outvote him, and what then? Was the Abbot obliged to obey? This contradicted the Rule of St Benedict and the Regulations of the Trappist Order. It was precisely to deal with *envy, quarrels, detraction, rivalry, dissensions and disorders* that St Benedict had written in Chapter 65 of his Rule, *It seems expedient for the preservation of peace and charity that the Abbot have in his hands the full administration of his monastery.*

As we prepared for the first meeting of the Mission Council Franz read angrily from the report: "Although the Abbot – according to the Rule – is not bound by the majority vote, yet he will feel obliged in matters concerning the mission to follow the majority vote of his council unless he has important reasons which cause him to act differently."

"What can this mean!" Franz exclaimed. "This sentence is now a law to which we are all meant to submit, but you can stretch it as far as you like." As we made our way to the room in which the meeting was to take place he muttered, "Which has more power, the first or the second part? Of course I would never do anything unless I thought I had 'important reasons'. The whole thing is so vague that anyone can read anything they want into it."

He continued to mutter as we entered the room. "The simple truth is, no law may restrict the power of an Abbot in his own house." And with this, he threw himself down into the seat set up for him.

I withdrew to a corner where a small desk had been placed. On the other side of the table from Franz stood Fr Gerard, Fr Ambrose and Fr Pius. They sat, much more decorously, I must say, than their Abbot, every detail of their posture indicating their awareness of their new responsibility. The Mission Council was after all the greatest and, besides the new powers of the Superiors on the missions, the only palpable success of the missionaries' dedicated endeavours during the visitation. This may have seemed on the surface small consolation for the loss of the former dispensations they had won and the refusal of the new liberties they had hoped to gain, but clearly it was a way to work back towards these. With the decisive vote on any mission issue in their hands, the Council was in effect master of the missions.

"Scarcely the care of the observance of the Rule is left to me," Franz had complained to me – to the world at large, really, but I was the only one to hand that morning before the meeting – "for even this can be reckoned amongst the things that refer to the welfare and progress of the missions."

Much of his attitude could be read in his expression as he faced his "councillors" for the first time. Still, Fr Gerard, who had been elected as Overseer, put the matters for discussion before the meeting with a commendable air of order and calm. He had grown into an impressive-looking figure whilst away on the missions, his girth quite dramatically increased behind the leather belt he had taken to wearing higher than usual, pulled tightly just under his chest. He kept his head closely shaved, but his beard was full and darkly luxuriant and, above this, his sharp eyes glittered behind rimless spectacles that caught the light with each firm movement of his head. For now, those eyes were focused on an impressive array of documents on the table before him, no doubt neatly laid out in the precise order he imagined the meeting would follow.

At the forefront of the issues the Council had to consider were the problems that had arisen of late in the running of Mariannhill's schools. After the departure of Fr David, Franz had appointed Fr Ambrose as Director of Schools. Under his far too kindly administration many abuses had broken out: insubordination, staying away during the night from the boarding house, wasting food, and the like. Previously Franz would have been only too willing to "take the whip and sweep the whole school clean", as he once put it, but now the report declared that "the Director, in agreement with the Abbot, should supervise the school system for the boys and girls".

"Should the Abbot," Fr Gerard read on, "wish to make decisions and changes, be they in the schools of the Sisters or the Fathers, he should not do so without first discussing them with the Director of Schools, who will then carry out his decree." Turning from this reminder of what was stated in the Visitator's Report to the document dealing with the abuses, he added, "Only in this way can the latter preserve his authority and the whole affair be directed uniformly and receive blessing."

Before he could read one more word of the document, however, Franz stopped him. "I hereby," he said, "remove Fr Ambrose as Director of Schools. And I remind you," he added as the members of the Mission Council leaped up in concert to interject, "that according to the Rule of the Order, all offices are assigned by the Abbot, and therefore I remain fully entitled to do this, whatever voting has taken place."

For one frozen moment the mouths of the Fathers hung open like empty Os. Fr Gerard regained his faculties first, but before he could form a single word, Franz stood up and announced that he was not willing to listen to their advice on the school problem, much less follow it, and stalked out of the room. I gathered my papers and pen as quickly as I could and ducked after him, hearing him announce grimly to no one in particular as I caught up, "That's that scarcely hatched cuckoo finished off."

~

Two days later Abbot Franz called the staff and pupils of the schools together and announced new and far stricter rules. The six worst offending pupils were dismissed with immediate effect, and the other boys and girls were given the alternative of accepting the new order or leaving their school. About sixty left straight away, and another hundred or so were to follow over the next few days. About a hundred and forty pupils remained, a number with which Franz declared himself satisfied.

The Mission Council faithfully reported to the Visitator, as they had been asked to do, on the outcome of the procedures he had set in place. What else could they say but that their right to consultation, so hard won, was wiped away in one bold stroke by the Abbot of Mariannhill at the very first meeting of the Council? This complaint reached Rome, as fate would have it, in good enough time to be taken forward to the General Chapter, which had been put off until October so that those concerned could be ready for the particularly important deliberations before it in 1892.

You may remember my mentioning in the postscript I added to the history of the Order given by Franz's Novice Master at Mariawald that there were two separate Trappist congregations at the time. We were about to feel the effect of both the present and the recent past that he, like many other historians and chroniclers alike, felt had no place in a proper account of how things have come to be what they are. The two congregations stemmed from a disagreement between Notre-Dame de l'Eternité, a

Trappist monastery in Westphalia, and the abbey of Val-Sainte, founded in Switzerland whilst the Trappists were in exile from France during the Revolution, but which returned to the original monastery of La Trappe after the fall of Napoleon. Notre-Dame de l'Eternité, along with a number of houses that it had founded, still followed the Regulations of de Rancé. Whilst in exile, the Religious of Val-Sainte resolved to put into practice the exact observance of the Rule of St Benedict. In their fervour they made their Rule even more severe, exceeding, it must be said, discretion. Eventually they had to moderate their observances and in the process introduced some reforms, principally to do with the hour for dinner and the time to be devoted to manual labour.

Nothing less than the union of the different observances of the Rule followed by these two groups was on the agenda at the General Chapter of 1892. All the contradictions entailed in creating a missionary Trappist house in Africa were to come up for scrutiny before an assembly where each and every detail of the contemplative life was to be argued over and fought for. It did not take much imagination to think what the Abbots of two Orders that were prepared to remain separate over the smallest discrepancy in following the Usages would make of the muddle into which Franz and his missionaries had cast the Rule and the Regulations.

And yet Franz seemed oblivious of this. Did he think that the Mission Council would not report his actions? Could he possibly have thought that he was still above their complaints? He made no secret of the fact that he considered this "newly baked council of rulers" an institution created against the prescriptions of the Rule, and one that he had quickly shown "who was Lord of the house". For those of us not blinded by Franz's air of omnipotence, his next step appeared as fatal as walking into one of the new steam threshing machines that adorned his beloved mill.

~

All houses were required to send representation to the General Chapter of 1892 – even Mariannhill, despite Franz's attendance in 1891 and the dispensation that obliged him only to attend every five years. Franz claimed to be too weak to face the troublesome voyage by sea and delegated Fr Amandus Schölzig, our present Novice Master, to attend in his place. As if this were not risky enough, what with this being the first Chapter since our visitation and the one at which the *Visiten-Karte* would be formally presented, Franz

377

also decided to send with Fr Amandus a document, ostensibly prepared by all the Religious of Mariannhill, containing the suggestions that this, the youngest and largest of the Trappist houses, had to make concerning the potential union of the Trappists into a single Order.

What the General Chapter received then, quite unexpectedly, was a document that demonstrated with astonishing frankness everything the Visitator planned to expose in his deeply critical presentation on Mariannhill. Nothing could have revealed the spirit animating the monastery more clearly, and Dom Franciscus could be forgiven for being annoyed at the way his painstaking account was completely overshadowed by this evidence from within the house itself.

In the document Franz declared that "the character and needs of our time" made it advisable that "our Order will endeavour in future more seriously to combine the contemplative with the active life for the greater glory of God and the salvation of souls". He continued as follows: "The world of today is disgusted with such Religious who do not in some way publicly add to and work for the common welfare; the contemplative life does not fill men any more nowadays as it did formerly with admiration, but rather with aversion."

I could imagine the gasps and stunned faces of the Fathers even as I wrote this out for Franz. No tentative suggestion from me could soften his language or modify a single proposal. Franz surged forward on a flood of hubris bereft now of any sense of how he would be heard by his intended audience. "After much deliberation we" – "we" he repeated, thumping the paper on which my pen hesitated – "*we* believe that we ought to give up some of the great strictness prescribed in our Order, and introduce such means as will increase our physical strength for more exterior works of Christian charity. Therefore we wish" – he paused, I remember, in his dictation, before embarking on a list that included a single order of the day for the whole year, so that there would be less disturbance of the monastic life and the novices would find it easier to learn the regular order.

In this new order there would be: breakfast every day, except on days of fasting prescribed by the Church; only the fasts of the Church and no more the fasts of the Order, except the Vigil of St Bernard; seven hours' sleep, without interruption, except on Sermo-Major feasts; and three hours daily assigned to manual work, with those members of the Choir not suited to studies devoting four and more hours per day to manual work.

The shock in the assembly must have been palpable as Fr Amandus read: "To fast daily till Vespers seems to surpass the strength of our weakened generation, and it is wiser to prescribe a rule that is mild and can be obeyed by all rather than one which is so strict that only a few can endure." The very print on the page must have blurred as he heard himself say, "A second period of sleep in the morning is more harmful to health than useful, and is, according to experience, disadvantageous for chastity and purity." By now each detail he uttered would have been dissolving into one thing and one thing only: how negligible had been the effect of the process of the visitation and the report emanating from it on the Abbot of Mariannhill.

All that the General Chapter could do was to thank the Abbot of Ölenberg for "the dedication and circumspection that he had shown in his difficult and important task" and deplore "the difficulties that were placed in his way through the resistance of the Reverend Father". The Visitation Report was then approved "on the whole and in all its parts with their full authority", and the fate of the Abbot of Mariannhill sealed. Abbot Bonaventura of Mariastern proposed the removal of Abbot Franz of Mariannhill from his office for a period during which the decrees of the Report could be carried out, and the commission and plenum of the Chapter agreed. And so Franz's first foundation had its revenge, after all. The suspension was stipulated as lasting for one year, beginning with the publication of the decrees at Mariannhill.

It was impossible for the Abbots of the General Chapter not to take into account Franz's history and character. Many did not believe that he would submit to the suspension, and some expected new opposition from him. To prevent the kind of creative interpretation Franz had brought to previous efforts to remove him, the decree of suspension that was drawn up was as direct as possible. It declared only that he was suspended for reasons of "what had happened before, during, and after the visitation". The Abbots also knew that the larger part of the Mariannhill community sided faithfully with their Superior, and so Franz was ordered either to go to Rome or retreat to one of the mission stations, where, as they well knew, he was less likely to have any supporters. His isolation was taken further with the decision that absolutely any communication, oral or written, be denied to the suspended Abbot. He was also to be informed, several of the Abbots insisted, that any sign of possible rebellion would result in suspension *a divinis*.

A last blow was aimed at yet another of the strategies Franz had used in the past; the Chapter refused, from the outset, to accept his resignation. "Should you submit your resignation because of our decree, it will be declined," the document they prepared for him stated. "You should stay quiet and consider seriously whether you wish to choose another path in directing the monastery and the mission after one year has elapsed; otherwise the General Chapter will remove you from your office altogether." Not even an honourable retreat was to be allowed in this document published under the heading *Roma Locuta*.

"Rome has spoken." With the decree of suspension completed, only the matter of finding a substitute for the Abbot of Mariannhill was left for consideration. The Fathers of the Chapter obviously wanted the writer of the Visitation Report to be entrusted with seeing through its implementation, but Dom Franciscus declined the offer, with thanks. The only other possible candidate stood before them, without the least suspicion of what was about to befall him. Poor Fr Amandus nearly dropped to the ground when he was proposed, as he had occasion to tell me later, but before he could begin to formulate a demurral, the assembled Abbots were upon him: you were chosen by all the Religious of the monastery who had the franchise as their delegate, they said, therefore it can be assumed you have the trust of your confreres, which is the best prerequisite for this difficult office. Fr Amandus simply stood wringing his hands whilst a decree of the Congregation was prepared, conferring upon him all the faculties of Administrator of Mariannhill for one year.

~

Fr Amandus Schölzig returned to Mariannhill on the 12th December, his new rank unknown to us. I had rushed with as much decorum as I could to the monastery doors after seeing his carriage pull up outside my cellar window and ushered him in immediately to the Abbot, who was eagerly awaiting news of how his suggestions had been received. Fr Amandus could only hold out a document, head bowed before the hurt that wrote itself like an opening wound into his Superior's face as he broke the seal and read it. When Franz had finished reading, he fell back heavily into his chair. I stepped in next to him, almost putting my hand on his shoulder. Fr Amandus then said, "Along with the unpleasant task of informing you of this, I am also required to make the" – he could not say "your" –

"suspension known to all at Mariannhill." He turned stiffly and left, and Franz and I remained completely still as we heard the bell tolling, calling the community to Chapter.

And so the monastery heard "with disastrous suddenness", if you will, that Abbot Francis had been summarily suspended from office. I cannot say whether Franz – "astonishingly", as one account has it – decided to submit unconditionally and without contradiction to the decree or whether the Abbots of the General Chapter had succeeded in foreseeing all possible evasive manoeuvres on his part. I can only report that Franz did not speak another word after reading the decree of suspension, and took leave of Mariannhill on the 14th of December 1892.

I saw him only once, and then at a distance, in the next four years. Even when we did meet fairly regularly for a while, it was only under the most strained and formal of circumstances. It would be another thirteen years altogether before we would become, as we were once held to be, "Pfanner and Biegner, one Heart and one Soul" or, on the more mundane level that really governed our relationship, that I would serve again as his "right-hand man", the receiver of his confidence, instrument of its expression – and if nothing else, then at least the holder of his pen, his voice upon the page.

EMMAUS

19

For the second time there was no ceremony to Franz's leaving his foundation. Not a single monk accompanied him as he went through the gates, dressed in the simple brown habit of a Brother and wrapped in silence.

We were told only that he refused to go to Rome, and chose instead as the place for his banishment Lourdes, then the most remote of the stations he had established. Signs and whispers quickly gathered around this simple statement like lost children clutching at a father. A rumour spread that whilst resting at Einsiedeln en route Franz hung his cross around the figure of Our Lady in the chapel and put his ring on her finger. I could imagine the gold glistening on this Black Madonna, the joy of the day we presented these abbatial insignia to Franz absorbed into her darkness. With it went the special place I had in my heart for the gilt-edged blackness of the figure of Africa in the altar dedicated to the missions in the Jesuit church in Brünn. How would that Nubian now earn the grace with which his sculptor had carved and coloured him in an inspired belief in the future?

Fevered, suppressed exchanges hissed through places of work and prayer alike, carrying conflicted breaths of opinion as to whether this act signified our Superior's resignation or not. These were clearly heard by our Superiors, for we were soon reminded in Chapter, firmly and formally, that there could be no question of Abbot Franz resigning as this was expressly refused by the decree that removed him from office. The observance of silence rapidly became only an empty form in Mariannhill and on its missions. The very buildings of the monastery seemed to swirl and spin in the wake of its founder's suspension.

A dark mood took over the majority of the monks, convinced as they were that the humiliation of their Abbot had been brought about by the demands and complaints of a small group of ambitious missionaries. This mood was darkened even further by the furtively spread news that the banished man had at Mariathal, the next stop for outspanning the horses on the journey to Lourdes, prostrated himself before Fr Hyacinth, and asked, through him, for the pardon of all the missionary Brothers and Sisters. The missionaries did not believe this gesture to be genuine. Two monks, we were told, called this act of abasement "sheer comedy" and went so far as to refuse Franz's kiss of peace when it was offered to them in the mission church.

Once at Lourdes Franz, as far as anyone could prove, was calm and resigned, active only in chopping wood, which he seemed to do endlessly. Forbidden all contact with the Fathers, Brothers and Sisters of the mission, he found himself shunned by most of them too. I would find out later just how much he took the reserve of his former subjects as a personal insult, a sign of ingratitude and disrespect. I am sure his gruff manner contributed further to his isolation but one should not forget how humiliated he must have felt. A Trappist Abbot is normally elected for life and Franz must have been keenly aware of living on beyond his office.

Indeed, it was when dictating this period of his life to me that Franz, off the record and very bitterly, told me of the joke he had heard all those long years ago in Mariawald about a Trappist monk asking to be released from the Order and having his resignation accepted all too eagerly by his Superior. Our vows can no more be explained, as I have said, than a joke; when they are subjected to the kind of scrutiny Franz called down upon himself they must seem either laughable or mystifying.

I was not to meet Franz for some time to come, but every mention of him brought him to my mind's eye. I could see him quite clearly at Lourdes whilst I went about my much reduced business at Mariannhill. I knew exactly the angle at which the hood of his brown habit would be thrown back and just how the chips would fly up to catch in his long grey hair. I knew how much he must have felt that he was back in the hills of Mary and Ann, silent and alone outside the walls of St Mary in the Wilds. All this was left to my imagination because Franz kept strictly to the terms of his suspension. Placed under an order of silence, silent Franz remained. Even those articles he had written before his suspension that were due to come out in *Vergissmeinnicht* were signed only with a star. Could he ever have known how painfully appropriate the name he had given our journal would become for him?

It was Franz's silence that fed the fear of revolt permeating Mariannhill and its missions, a fear felt as far away as the very centre of the Order in France. The Abbot General himself wrote directly to our "Brown Abbot", expressing his deep concern that the test sent by God to Mariannhill would be turned by the evil spirit into Mariannhill's destruction. I forwarded the letter to Reichenau, where our master builder was busy with the church I had never been able to bring into being whilst Superior there. It was evident that the Abbot General was placing his faith in the ability of Brother Nivard to use his influence and prestige to heal the divisions that were all too apparent at Mariannhill.

Along with his reply to the Abbot General came the news that Brother Nivard was ill. In preparing his letter for the post I saw that Brother Nivard had understood the concern in Europe that he might lead a crusade for the return of our Abbot. He informed the Abbot General that God had confined him to his sickbed just when the atmosphere had become sullen and the mood tense, giving him the opportunity to think during many sleepless nights about himself and conditions at Mariannhill.

This letter must have created more alarm than reassurance in the Generalate for soon afterwards Fr Amandus was conferred by the Abbot General with the full power of the Order and of the Superior General. Every monk and Sister was ordered to offer complete obedience to him as Administrator. The Administrator was to punish severely those who resisted or agitated, if necessary to the point of excluding them from the Order. Or so I read in the impressive document I opened just days after Fr Amandus left Mariannhill for Rome.

As far as the monastery was concerned, he was on his way to the Eternal City to put the renewed demands of the missionaries before the Generalate. It would not be long before I learned that the real reason for his journey was to appeal for nothing less than the immediate restoration of Franz to his office as Abbot. Less than three months had passed since the publication of Franz's decree of suspension, but everything Fr Amandus had experienced as Administrator in that time convinced him that the attitudes and policies of the Abbot were the only ones possible under the circumstances. Fr Amandus was quite sure that he could not govern the missions in the circumstances that prevailed, nor quieten the stirrings of revolt and restore peace to Mariannhill. As soon as he was relieved of his office he planned to go back to the Augustinian regulars of Klosterneuberg and do penance for deserting them to join Mariannhill.

Fr Amandus was not to know that just as he was embarking at Durban in early February, Franz – who had asked that his abbatial cross and ring be returned to him from Einsiedeln not long after leaving them there – tendered his resignation yet again, this time in a more official manner. Resignation was perhaps not Franz's primary intention when he wrote to the Abbot General demanding either to be deposed or reinstated with every faculty needed to bring about the recovery of Mariannhill, but that was certainly the outcome of his letter.

Franz never even received a reply, and was left free to take the silence of the Order as he pleased. He spent all his time at Lourdes drawing up various plans that would, he believed, save the monastery and its missions from the ruin he saw looming ahead. Meanwhile, the Abbot General post-poned a decision on the matter of Franz's ultimatum until the next General Chapter. This was to meet only in the autumn, but in a letter the Abbot wrote to the Propaganda Fide as early as March 1893, so Fr Adalbert tells me, "Francis's resignation" is already referred to as "accepted".

No wonder then that Fr Amandus let Brother Nivard know from Rome that he felt he was knocking against an impenetrable wall in his attempt to have his Abbot returned to office. Months of muddle and uncertainty followed, months in which Fr Amandus was confirmed as Administrator and then relieved of the position when our ex-Visitator was hastily called to Rome and ordered under obedience to become the next Abbot of Mariannhill. This, it seems, was something Abbot Strunk was so reluctant to do that he was given leave to appeal to the Holy Father, who freed him from the obligation to accept the appointment, leaving Mariannhill without Abbot or Administrator. Fr Amandus saw in this a new opportunity and dispatched a telegram to Franz urging him to come to Rome and make his case to be re-instated.

Unaware that Franz had offered his resignation, Fr Amandus received in reply only a mysterious two-word telegram: VENIRE IMPOSSIBILE. Until his death, it seems, Fr Amandus believed that if Franz had come to Rome, he would have been reappointed as Abbot. As it was, the Generalate decided to reappoint Fr Amandus as Administrator, only to discover through their legal consultant, Fr Llevanera (who was scrutinising the validity of each and every one of the vows taken at Mariannhill in order to establish the position of those who had not completed their noviciate), that Fr Amandus's appointment as Administrator had not been in accordance with canon law in the first place. The irregularity in question was – and you can imagine how I felt when I heard it – that he had taken only his Simple Vows.

It was late June before the whole mess could be worked through to the point where Fr Amandus found himself in exactly the same position in which he had been when he set sail for Rome, Administrator again of a monastery that was tossed about like a lost ship in the billowy hills of Natal.

~

We at Mariannhill knew nothing of these manoeuvrings amongst our Superiors when, from my modest secretarial space, I heard an unexpected knocking at the front door of the monastery. A few minutes later the porter handed me a telegram. It was from Fr Hyacinth, now Superior of Mariathal, warning us that Franz intended to travel from Lourdes to pay a farewell visit to Mariannhill.

Whilst I sat wondering what to do with such a confusing yet clearly hostile intervention, a letter from Franz appeared in the post that arrived that same morning – the first words I had seen from him since he left. He had heard, he wrote, that Fr Amandus was to return as Administrator and had concluded from this that his resignation had been accepted. To Franz this meant that his suspension was no longer in force, and that he was free again to make contact with his sons and daughters, friends and benefactors. He would, therefore, be arriving at Pinetown station at 9.30 p.m. on Saturday 20th May.

I took the letter and telegram together directly up to Prior Pius, who was in consultation with the Sub-Prior, Fr Leonard. None of those who had been close to Franz, including myself, held any position of authority any longer. The whole community had been surprised, however, when Fr Amandus appointed Fr Pius Kohl as Prior. A supporter of the Administrator's strict adherence to the letter of the Rule, Fr Kohl expressed nothing of its spirit. His rigour, like that of many in the extreme pro-Rule faction he led, was directed mainly at bolstering his own importance, which made him extremely unpopular amongst the rest of the brethren.

When I was eventually given permission to enter, I laid the note and telegram on the Prior's desk without a word. I stepped back as he read them and then passed them to Fr Leonard. A few beats of silence ensued, which the Sub-Prior was the first to end by asking uncertainly if the carriage would be made available to fetch the founder from Pinetown. Prior Pius released a small volley of responses. Franz had no business at the monastery! If he decided to come anyway, he would have to get here himself! He would have to stay at the guest house!

I entered the Great Silence that evening trembling. Throughout the night I lay awake and listened for sounds of Franz's arrival but could hear nothing unusual from my place in the dormitory before the bell called us to Choir for Matins and Lauds. The Night Office and Prime proceeded as usual. Then, as we were lining up for solemn High Mass, we were informed by Prior Pius that *Abbot* Francis (the title was emphasised for ironic effect) had been invited to celebrate the Mass and give the homily. We were reminded that this was a very great concession since, for the period of his suspension, the Abbot had been forbidden every form of contact with the monks and the Sisters. Outside the church he was to talk to no one, and no one was to approach him. This order was reinforced by a notice that was fastened to the monastery wall: "Whoever speaks to the Reverend Father is excommunicated."

I do not know what the Prior expected, but what followed was the nearest thing to an uprising I have seen in a monastery. Old Brother Anton tore down the notice and hobbled off to his garden to collect an apron full of his best oranges. The brethren who supported Franz – far outnumbering the Prior's less demonstrative supporters – broke ranks and scattered in several directions, clearly throwing the prospect of excommunication to the winds. It was then discovered that Franz was advancing from the direction of the convent, flanked by the full assembly of the Sisters.

Brother Anton, singing praises and clutching his apron of oranges, led us across the bare ground towards this party, but Prior Pius ran ahead of the old man and cut us off. Fearing a violent commotion, the Prior reached our Abbot first and, somewhat out of breath, offered him the regular monastery Chapter Room to address the monks. Our victory was the Sisters' defeat, however. They were coming with their founder to hear him speak in the monastery's church, but the Chapter Room was, of course, forbidden to them. They had no choice but to obey the order to return to the convent.

We bustled and bumped our way into Chapter in a most unseemly fashion, and when each had more or less found his proper place, Franz stood before us and spoke a few words of reconciliation and paternal advice. He looked drawn and in pain in the full glare of the love about him, and seemed small and insubstantial even as he stood above us. He asked pardon of all and offered pardon to anyone who would accept it, but his eyes were distant and distracted.

For his homily, Franz spoke of St Joseph, he who accepted in silence what the Angel of the Lord revealed to him of Mary's pregnancy and of Herod's threat and had acted accordingly. "If you want to be like Joseph," Franz said to us in a strangely broken fashion, "be as quiet as he was. Should a really heavy cross be placed upon your shoulders, do not, I warn you, ask comfort of the world, but keep still, very still. If you have a guitar or …" – here he appeared to be reaching for words, ideas – "a zither hanging on the wall, or …" – again those eyes wandered across his congregation and one could tell that what his mind was fumbling towards was not really what he was after, or was even appropriate, given the circumstances – "a grand piano standing in your room, begin to sing or play that lovely song, 'Be still, ever so still, that God may do His will …'"

He pulled himself together towards the end, concluding with King Solomon's injunction "not to cut the living child in two". Although he had made no overt mention of anything to do with the current situation at Mariannhill, everyone present understood this to be a reference to the ever-present threat of the "progressives" to break away from the monastery and set up their missions as a separate society.

And then he was gone. No private word was spoken between Franz and myself, and he caught my eye, fleetingly, only once.

It was Sister Luitgardis who, some days later, found a secret moment to fill us in on the circumstances of Franz's arrival. Fr Leonard had informed the Sisters that he would send two Brothers to meet the founder at Pinetown, she said, no doubt suspecting that if he did not the Sisters themselves would organise some kind of a reception. No Brothers were dispatched, however, and Franz had to walk alone in the night to Mariannhill. When he reached the monastery at a quarter to midnight, drenched and spattered with mud, he woke Brother Fridolin, who was on porter duty, only to be told by him that he would have to go the extra distance to the convent. He was received there by Sister Constantia, murmuring her sympathy at his condition. Franz, visibly moved, had responded: "You may well feel sorry for me, for tonight I stumbled about in potholes. Potholes in a road I made with my own hands." He had added wryly, "I came unto my own, but my own did not receive me."

It struck me at the time that this was actually the case. All the property of Mariannhill and its missions had been purchased in Franz's name, and he was officially, as far as anyone knew, still its legal owner. Not that reminding himself of this would have done him any good in the dark of that night. Instead, timing himself with a watch (lest he break the Eucharistic fast starting at midnight), he ate a small and hasty meal and was then led to the convent's guest quarters. At eight o'clock the next morning a note was delivered to the convent from the monastery demanding to know who had given Franz permission to lodge with the Sisters. His calm reply to the Prior that he had come to take leave of his children set in motion the events in which we had all participated.

After he had spoken to us, Franz set off again for Lourdes. Years later he was to sum up for me his visit to Mariannhill: "Tears everywhere as I preached at my own burial."

~

Franz broke his journey to Lourdes at St Michael's, where he lived in complete solitude for several weeks. Here he recognised with certainty what he had seen coming all along: his suspension was punishment for not governing his house by the dictates of the Visitation Report and, although his punishment was temporary in form, it was in fact final – he would never be able to run Mariannhill in the way required of him. In rejecting him, the Generalate had rejected his life's work. He knew that now, and out of this truth he made a supreme effort to regain his peace of mind in an act of total surrender. The future alone could now determine who was right and who was not; surrender was all God asked for. He had still had no formal response to his letter of resignation, but from now on he took to signing his letters "Fr Francis, Abbot – freely resigned".

But who, I have often wondered, really accepted Franz's surrender in those weeks, out there on that rocky spine with only the wind, and the thorns, and the pigs? By then the voices must have been congregating in the gusts that swept up suddenly from the valley below and down from Hlatenkungu Hill; by then Legion must have been gathering his numbers into himself, whole armies of demons released from hell to roam the earth and seduce men. Beginning, it sometimes seemed to me, with the holiest of men, those truly consecrated to God, those who approached Him in what they thought was the sanctity of silence but was in fact a deafness brought on by the swirling noise of evil, the envy, hatred, discord and con-tention that Lucifer's servants work with their whole strength to spread among men.

392

Franz went on to Lourdes in the peace of his "freely resigned", but where is freedom when Satan is abroad, his devils so numerous in the air and on the land that it would be dark if men could see them?

~

One of the first letters we have that Franz signed in this way was written by him at Lourdes to Brother Nivard, the day after it was confirmed that Fr Amandus had been reappointed Administrator of the monastery. "I have never been calmer and more cheerful than today," it begins, but soon gives way to a truer statement of Franz's emotions.

> When yesterday, on the feast of St Athanasius who has been more bitterly persecuted than anyone else, the news arrived, I thought of that hero and was comforted. He was deported from his place and exiled for several years, living in a cistern by his father's burial place. He had to travel to Trier, which is further than Mashonaland from here. Should I then not also be able to die a happy death in a bushman's hut in Damaraland? There, I am sure, the dogs and hyenas will oblige to give me a burial, while my opponents would rather not. St Athanasius, pray for me …

Franz's depression must have been fed by the uncertainty of his position and, above all, having to live without a practical project. The Order condemned him to inactivity at Lourdes, a fate worse than stress or illness for one born to found great houses. In a particularly melancholy moment, Franz later told me, he had considered leaving Mariannhill altogether. Fr Strobino had succeeded Bishop Ricards in the Vicariate of Grahamstown and Franz wrote to him asking for a place there, a place "in which to live in solitude and know nothing henceforth of the world or of the missions and the monastery of Mariannhill". He would like only to prepare for death, he wrote (not for the first time in his life), and if there was no vacancy for him in a small town or village where he might render whatever pastoral services he was still capable of, he humbly begged permission to live somewhere as a private person with just one Lay Brother to accompany him.

To anyone not hardened against Franz this letter would have been truly touching. However, Bishop Ricards, to whom Fr Strobino turned for advice, responded carefully with a letter of his own. He advised Fr Strobino not to have anything to do with Abbot Francis. "I do not wonder that you were touched at the misery of his present position," Ricards wrote – with some private satisfaction, I cannot help but think, despite his next words: "I, too, feel for him very much. At the same time I fear he is not to be trusted and might do harm in our vicariate. Though I feel sorry for him, I cannot help smiling at the picture he set before you of his living a quiet hermit's life. I should always be anxious on his account, and he in return would be unhappy at the restraints that I, in your place, would feel compelled to impose on him."

And so the man who conjured up Franz from the realm of words put in a final word to lay the creature he had created. A bundle of nerves and in ill health, Bishop Ricards wrote of Franz in this way just months before the fit of paralysis that finally put an end to his apparently endless play with words. He suffered a stroke in September 1893 and died the following November. The mouth that breathed us into being and then ate us up was at last still. In the final stage of his illness, I am told, the muscles of his throat were so relaxed as to prevent not just speech but even the act of swallowing.

A flowery account of the Bishop's death soon appeared in the *Catholic Magazine*, a pretty piece, and no doubt deserved. But turn the pages of this volume of the *Catholic Magazine* – Volume IV, 1894 – and the very next lines you read are:

Owing to the amount of discussion perpetually going on about the Social Question, it has become partly known what the world thinks about it; but it may not be uninteresting to show what a Trappist thinks of it, from his solitude ...

And which Trappist in South Africa would have so recovered himself as to be turning out, from his solitude, article after article along the lines of his contribution to the discussion on the Social Question (in this case an "abridged translation of a pamphlet that has been widely read in Germany")?

By early 1894 Franz had found that the idleness into which he was thrust was the perfect state in which to rediscover pen and press. As he saw it, either his resignation had been accepted or he had been deposed; in either case his period of suspension was over and, along with the freedom to make contact again with his Brothers and Sisters, came the right to publish his thoughts wherever he chose.

He took this opportunity by the scruff of its neck and shook out of it every possibility it afforded him – never had he contributed at such length as he did now to a range of publications that is quite dizzying. In the *Natal Advertiser*, news of the Bishop's death is actually flanked by the words of his old antagonist: a description of "the sad and sombre magnificence" of Bishop Ricards' funeral is preceded by "The Native Question: Abbot Franz's Opinions" and followed by "The Native Question: A Missionary's View".

Silent observer at Lourdes though he may have been, Franz began to loom large again in the world – at any rate in the secular world of print, which he bestrode as confidently as ever, stirring up controversy with every ink-inscribed mark he made. In response to an article entitled "The Abbot's Native Policy", we find the irritated response: "Yes, the whole of Fr Franz Abbot's epistle seems to me nothing else but his usual sporting of his name in print, and turning the attention of the rest of the community to his utterances stuffed with some Latin quotations, of which he seems to be a living dictionary." Echoes of this attitude can be detected everywhere in the expanses of newsprint that Franz so effectively colonised.

This revival of the old warrior would not be allowed to last, of course. But as his enemies, both new and old, closed in, Franz was writing all the faster and publishing all the more widely. His now first-hand agricultural experiences were translated into articles for various farming journals, the *Natal Farmers' Magazine* hearing, for example, from "One of the Trappists" on "Wheat Growing in Natal" and "What the Country Wants". As the hand of the Church began to tighten its grasp, Franz took to other less obvious pseudonyms, although the subject, style and tone of "An Old Farmer" writing on "Village Communism" (Franz's latest take on the Native Question) leave hardly any doubt as to the identity of the author.

~

Whilst Franz was beginning to relish and find ways to use his sense of freedom, the vacuum left by his expulsion from office began to draw into itself a new order of authority. On his return to South Africa, Fr Amandus was once again armed as reappointed Administrator with "all the powers of the Abbot General of the Order". During his absence the conflicting parties at Mariannhill had sufficient time to reflect upon their differences and, more to the point, the likely outcome of continued conflict. They were, on all sides, only too happy to have one of their own confirmed in office (merely the suggestion of Abbot Strunk's returning had been enough to achieve this). I watched with some bemusement as they scurried about to set up a secret ballot to test the popularity and strength of the Administrator amongst the Choir monks and then lost no time in writing to Rome that most had voted in favour of Fr Amandus as their next Abbot.

Two months later the General Chapter was held at which Franz's ultimatum to the Generalate was to be decided on. His resignation, as they chose to see it, was simply taken for granted and, with Fr Amandus's appointment as Abbot, had only to be officially ratified. A special dispensation was granted by Propaganda Fide to allow Fr Amandus to anticipate his profession of Solemn Vows by six months so that he could take up his appointment before the five years of preparation for those vows elapsed. However, the new Abbot of Mariannhill, unable to bear the thought of such irregularity, chose to keep his appointment secret for those six months. He used the time to implore the Abbot General repeatedly to spare him this burden. Abbot Sebastian would not relent and so, under the order of holy obedience, Fr Amandus gave up his resistance and agreed to his installation, if not the date on which it would take place.

Thus ended, in the English manner of speaking, the "honeymoon period" of Franz's deposition. From now on he could (and did) use his "Abbot – freely resigned" signature only with those not well informed about his case. Otherwise he signed himself "dismissed Abbot" or, even more bitterly for one still so driven to lead and to work, "Abbot who has served his time".

Some sort of public statement regarding Franz's status had to be made at this time to those who contributed to and supported Mariannhill. Several of us were brought together and finally came up with the following, which was published in our *Forget-Me-Not* magazine under the heading "Thy Will Be Done":

Our readers have probably heard by now that the Chapter General of the Trappist Order, at its meeting on 1st October 1892, ordered the suspension of our Venerable Abbot, Fr Francis.

The reasons for this action were: according to canonical regulations, religious novices are not to be used and employed outside the monastery precincts, and every Superior who does not comply with these regulations is subject to suspension. It is true that our Venerable Father violated this regulation in a technical sense, but he did so out of grave necessity rather than out of disobedience. He was forced to violate the letter of the law since, at the time the Mission was established, it so happened that only those who were novices could speak the Native language, and there were not enough professed monks to take care of all the mission stations.

This condition was discovered at the visitation of the Canonical Visitor. Upon receipt of its report, the Chapter General had no alternative but to suspend Abbot Francis from his office, since there are no exceptions to this strict rule.

The Venerable Father Abbot has humbly submitted to this order of suspension and has retired to the mission station of Lourdes.

We sincerely hope that this statement of the circumstances attending the suspension of our Venerable Father will remove the misunderstandings and suspicions which may have formed in the minds of our friends and benefactors because of so many erroneous and malicious-minded interpretations in the press.

And so it was that the complex web that brought Franz down – the tangle that was his life, his vision of Trappist missionaries that had taken on a life of its own, the personalities who complicated this, the circumstances that frustrated it, most of all the successes that he had won out of every setback – all of this was reduced, officially, to a single issue, a single slip forced upon him by circumstances and, when seen in a certain light, happily yielded to. In one way only was our statement correct. For if anything did cause Franz, and then the rest of us, to fall, it was the need to speak – Zulu, English, German, French, the language does not matter, nor the reasons for speaking; the speaking was quite enough. No matter either that we spoke in order to spread the Word of God, the words themselves undid us.

For once we succeeded in keeping the local press in the dark about our internal problems. The *Mercury*, and even the *Advertiser*, without Franz to drive them on with his steady stream of epistles, had nothing really to work with concerning the monastery and kept modestly to our very few and extremely brief public announcements during this desperately troubled time.

~

Fr Amandus, the "gentle monk" as he was known amongst us – a man, if ever there was one, of study and solitude rather than action – fluttered above all this, trying to fulfil his role as "Administrator" by sticking to the letter of the

Visitator's Report. Previously a Professor of Oriental Languages at a monastery near Vienna, he had come to us in 1888. Franz had made this quiet and sensitive man Father Confessor to the Sisters and he had never once become engaged with the active life of the missionaries. Whenever he was called upon to preach at the High Mass, or give the homily, the topic to which this former lecturer in languages returned again and again was silence.

Staunch protagonist of monastic discipline and the interior life that he was, Fr Amandus did succeed in one of his first duties – to get most of the missionaries (Fr David aside) identified in the report as having to complete their noviciate to return to Mariannhill and, however reluctantly, submit themselves to bells and timetables and Novice Masters. His failures in other areas, however, rapidly eroded his authority.

It had soon become evident, for example, that the monastery could barely feed its own ever-swelling community. The immediate effect of Franz's departure was that our food, always of the plainest sort but never of the smallest quantities, threatened to go under the minimum prescribed by the Rule. Increasingly we faced days on which there had clearly been no oil for the preparation of the food, and others on which the bread itself gave out. It became obvious that to feed itself Mariannhill was now dependent on its missions. And the missionaries brought back amongst us made something of a point of letting us know that there were not enough substitutes for them on the missions to keep the farms running effectively. On top of this, the Visitator's ruling that all positions of management and responsibility on the missions be given to Choir monks meant that in most cases experienced and able Lay Brothers had to sit back in frustration watching their unworldly Superiors muddle about, rapidly wrecking the productive capacity of their stations.

Fr Amandus was no example in such affairs. He was simply not of the managing type. He had never taken any interest in the running of the monastery, and now he was expected to lead us in matters of which he knew nothing. Every inch a contemplative, he did not know how to deal with the most basic of recurring problems in monastic life, let alone the endless complications thrown up by the missions.

The effect on my small cellar was complete disorder. The systems and routines Franz and I had set up to deal with the flood of paperwork even the most enclosed of institutions must generate – and we were by now anything but an enclosed institution – broke down. Tottering piles of paper appeared on my desk in no time. Papers spilled out everywhere, overflowing their proper place in cupboards, drawers and files. I no longer knew what to put where, and feared every minute that something of vital importance would be lost in some stack somewhere, knowing full well that its absence could be felt at the most inopportune moment.

If the Generalate had hoped that Fr Amandus's innate kindness would help ease the monastery through a difficult period, they were wrong. The various factions were simply impatient with his gentle and hesitant manner, and the missionaries saw in it only a weakness they could exploit. The Rectors were more determined than ever to press their increasingly extreme demands and, shortly after the Administrator took over, they gathered at Mariannhill to confer with each other. The result was an ultimatum arising out of the very issues Franz had been unwilling to pronounce upon. If Fr Amandus did not decide in their favour on these, the missionaries resolved they would take action themselves.

When they demanded an audience with him, however, Fr Amandus turned his well-known tendency to procrastination to advantage. Probably having guessed their intentions – I was, you must understand, in no way privy to the intentions of our new Superior – he refused to hear them. "My dear priests," he said at a meeting at which I was present to take the minutes, "write down all your proposals. I shall go back to Rome and submit them to the Father General." With that he gave them his blessing and dismissed them, and me, without a further word.

So, Fr Amandus had learned something from Franz, I concluded privately. He had always been a true and loyal son of the founder, speaking of him with deep respect and protecting his good name even in his darkest hour. Some suspected him of calling on Franz for advice and, whilst I knew of no correspondence of such a nature between Lourdes and Mariannhill, a decision like this was so typical of the kind Franz had fallen back on towards the end that I wondered if there was not some truth in the contention. We were to find out quite soon, however, that Fr Amandus had a strategy of his own to follow, one with far deeper implications than his surface irresolution allowed us to guess at.

~

One of the more obvious ironies of this state of affairs was that Franz, at the time the Trappist Order was trying to wash its hands off him, was at the very peak of his fame in the eyes of the world. Word of his achievements echoed across the globe, and people from all over were talking of "the miracle of Mariannhill". Visitors flooded in from Durban, Pretoria, Cape Town and far further afield.

Amongst the persons who were attracted to Mariannhill at the time was the "Indian champion of freedom", as I have since heard Mr M K Gandhi called (along with a good many other things of which it is better not to speak). It was neither our work nor our prayers that brought him to us but a reference to a "colony of Trappists" in South Africa in Mrs Anna Kingsford's book, *A Perfect Way to Diet*. He had read it whilst in England studying for the law, I was told by this impeccably dressed young man with the neatest of moustaches and the oddest of hairstyles (thick and black, it rose up in a loaf-like shape from the top of his head), when the Brother on porter duty brought him to me.

Yes, I was still Prior in those days, and it thus fell upon me to show him around. Mr Gandhi seemed very taken with the tamarind water and pineapples we served him by way of refreshment, and even more so by the silence into which he and I stepped from the Visitor's Room – a silence broken only by the noise of the instruments in the workrooms and the voices of the Native children in their classrooms. Like many of our visitors, Mr Gandhi felt drawn to comment on our silence, whilst adding a personal note. "After leaving London I went back to India to try and establish myself in the legal profession," he said, "but this proved to be a dismal failure. I opened an office in Bombay, and waited months for my first client to appear. When he did, my nerve failed me so badly that I was unable to utter a word when I rose in court to argue his case. Not surprisingly, my practice rapidly went under!"

Shades of a certain Irish Bishop at the beginning of his career, I could not help but think, although I was not sure at that time that Mr Gandhi would salvage his career quite as successfully as did the Bishop. He had mentioned earlier that he was in South Africa to act in a matter concerning two Indian merchants and was just beginning to discover that there was, as he put it, "a very strong prejudice against the local Indian population". I certainly did not feel it fit to repeat the response given by one of my brethren to a visitor who had been inquiring about our work amongst the Indians: we once had two converts from this community, the Brother had said, but one was killed and the other hanged for murdering him.

Mr Gandhi seemed to consider such prejudice yet another curious and painful result of what he called the "unnatural mode of living" in the colony. It turned out that by this he meant the prevalence of meat-eating. Natal, he explained as we walked on the side of the monastery that overlooked the fields laid out below us like a tapestry, was the Garden Colony of South Africa. The only wonder was that there should be so few vegetarians in such a territory and that the staple articles of food were imported when it was perfectly possible to grow all of them here.

"The Indians," he said, turning from the view over our fields to look at me earnestly, "being like yourselves vegetarians, take to agriculture without any difficulty whatsoever. Naturally, therefore, all over the colony the small farms are owned by Indians, but the keen competition this produces only gives offence to the European population. They would rather leave the vast agricultural resources of the country underdeveloped, than have the Indians develop them."

He said much more in the same vein. When I recall his visit, however, it is another kind of observation altogether that appears to me to characterise him best. After watching a number of our Brothers and Sisters in their day-to-day activities for a while, he announced apropos of nothing, "None of them seem to wear socks." I remember wishing that Franz was there to give his views on both the socks and our vegetarianism. Then again, he would have gone on about the way in which consuming venison, alcohol, animal fats and heavily spiced dishes increases bodily temperature alarmingly for those living in a hot climate. Franz would not have explained to Mr Gandhi that for the Cistercians of the Strict Observance vegetarianism is not a matter of health, economics or even respect for other living beings, but is first and foremost a penance. It was left to our visitor himself to note, after the few comments I made about our diet, "You do not make of vegetarianism a creed, then, but use it simply to crucify the flesh." As I led him to the gates, my smile covered my discomfort in thinking that I could not have said this better myself.

For all my inadequate service as a guide, Mr Gandhi was kind enough to say whilst he stood on our steps rearranging his dapper suit that he considered a visit to our monastery and its farms in itself worth the voyage from London to Natal. "I leave for the Transvaal by train tomorrow," he concluded, "and I shall make a point of telling everyone I meet there that you are a living testimony to the triumph of vegetarianism from a spiritual point of view."

~

One would have to be a particularly devoted Trappist not to know what occurred on that train journey, but it would also be some years before this visitor achieved anything like the fame of the one who arrived at our doors shortly after him. Well, not in the flesh at first: initially I was to take the famous writer known as Mark Twain around our monastery in the shape of his proxy, the man who was meant to deliver us to the author as one of many other items neatly wrapped up in a package of words. Yes, it was the Washington newspaper man Mr J H Riley who knocked at our doors one day in search of Abbot Francis. Disappointed to find the Abbot no longer with us, he proceeded to ask some rather perfunctory questions of me. These dried up quickly and we sat silently in the Visitors Room for some time.

I have had occasion to mention before how silence tends to draw people out, and Mr Riley was no exception. Mr Twain – who did most of his writing in bed, he informed me – had decided that he could make a great fortune out of travel books if he could get someone else to do the travelling for him. The fame of the Kimberly diamond fields made South Africa a natural target for this project. Mr Twain's plan was to pay Mr Riley $100 a month for expenses and to allow his envoy to keep the first $5 000 worth of any diamonds he might come by for himself – anything over that they were to divide. Mr Riley was to keep full diaries, write no newspaper articles, and make sure that none of his private letters was made public.

Once the trip was over Mr Riley was to live with Mr Twain at his house for up to a year, during which time he would receive $50 a month along with board and cigars. For this he would be expected to talk about his adventures for one to two hours daily. Mr Riley's notes, interpolated by his vivid comments, would form the skeleton that Mr Twain's genius would clothe with life. From what I saw of Mr Riley his notes would certainly need some sort of filling out. He did not take down much in his notebook during our interview or the meal that we fed him, telling me more about himself than he got to learn of the history or life of Mariannhill.

A year or so later who else but Mr Mark Twain himself should arrive at our doors. He looked anything but the humorist as he bristled ahead of the monk who ushered him in to me, casting a gloomy eye over everything about him. The comb of a moustache that hung over his mouth never stopped puffing upwards from his constant exhalation of words. Even the fringe of his shock of hair seemed to lift from it, and it was clear from the first instant there was very little I – or anyone else, it seemed – could tell him about anything. As I followed him around the monastery, trying my best not to scurry, the bluster never stopped.

Mr Twain switched topics with a bewildering speed. "Best trees I've seen since Darjeeling" – apparently his travels in the southern hemisphere had now expanded into "following the equator" – "but I've not seen many birds, and those I have seen have no music – like the flowers, which have no smell; everything grows too fast here. Haven't heard anyone call Natal the Garden of South Africa" – I would have liked to have quoted Mr Gandhi on this, but the opportunity did not present itself – "although that is probably what it is."

He continued, "Colenso was Bishop here when he raised such a storm in the religious world, wasn't he? Don't mean *here*, of course" – this was inserted irritably at the smallest of sounds from me – "but the concerns of religion are obviously a vital matter in this part of the world. A vigilant eye kept upon Sunday. Museums and other dangerous resorts not allowed to be open. You may sail the bay, but it is wicked to play cricket."

I was never sure who he was addressing throughout our whirlwind tour, and he seemed quite satisfied that it was over so soon. By the time we were back at our gates our visitor was more than ready to sum us up. "Such a sweeping suppression of human instincts," he announced, and I suddenly realised he was speaking to the invisible audience who travelled with him everywhere, making his words ready for the page the moment they swept past his moustache – "such an extinction of man as an individual."

He then proceeded to draw up a list of all that he said helped to make life worth living that had been carefully ascertained and then placed out of the Trappist's reach: man liked personal distinction – here it was obliterated; delicious food – here he got beans and bread and tea and not enough of it; a comfortable bed – here he lay on a sand mattress, and had a pillow and a blanket, but no sheet; dining in the company of friends – here a monk read a holy book during meals, and nobody spoke or laughed; to lie in bed late – here he rose once or twice in the night; the society of women and girls – here he never had it. "He likes to have his children about him," he added, "and to pet them and play with them" – here we had none.

He paused at this point, but only for a moment. There seemed no end to the steady stream of his composition: "Man likes billiards – here there is no table. He likes outdoor sports and indoor dramatic and musical and social entertainments – there are none here. When a man's temper is up

403

he likes to pour it out on somebody – here this is not allowed. A man likes animals – there are no pets here. He likes to smoke – here he cannot do it. He likes to read the news – no papers or magazines here. A man likes to know how his parents and brothers and sisters are getting along when he is away – here, he is not allowed to know. A man likes a pretty house and pretty furniture and pretty things and pretty colours – here he has nothing but naked aridity and sombre colours. A man likes ... name it yourself."

"Whatever it is, it is absent from this place," he concluded. "And from what I could learn," he said, turning to me, "all that a man gets for this life is merely the saving of his soul."

I wanted to think that this was an example of what I gathered was Mr Twain's famous comic touch, but he seemed quite serious. I would hear some time after he left that he had lost one of his daughters at the time of his visit to us and would lose another soon, as well as the wife who was awaiting him in Durban that day, so the hardness of his tone was to be understood and forgiven. At the time all I saw was a man astray and adrift in the world, one who had lost pleasure in the things he had just listed as making life worthwhile. "This all seems strange, incredible, impossible," he said as he climbed up onto the carriage, "but la Trappe certainly knew the human race. He knew the powerful attraction of unattractiveness; he knew that no life could be imagined, howsoever comfortless and forbidding, but somebody would want to try it."

What could one do but let the confusion of de Rancé with la Trappe go? At the last possible instant I dared to ask him about Mr Riley. Mr Twain looked confused for a moment, as if trying to remember of whom I spoke. "Oh," he said, "yes, he must have been here. I didn't get that far with his notes." Mr Riley, it seemed, had stabbed himself with a fork on the ship on his way home, developed blood poisoning and reached New York barely in time to die. "Couldn't do a thing with the notes alone, so here I am," Mr Twain said, as the carriage pulled away.

Truly, I thought as his words carried back to me, it is as the psalm invoked in the Rule says: "The talkative man is not stable on the earth."

~

"There is still the question of where we are going to send Franz."

These were the words Fr Amandus said to me on an overcast morning in mid-October of that year. He spoke, as usual, deeply into the tangle of beard that seemed all the more abundant because of his almost entirely bald head, and for a moment I had trouble registering what he said. I had gathered that Franz was impatient to know where his permanent residence would be, but I was not amongst the few he was known to be writing to regularly and at length. Why then was the issue of Franz's domicile being put to me?

I did not realise until Fr Amandus's appointment as our Superior how used I had become over the years to Franz's habit of answering his own questions even as he posed them. He would rush in to fill the pauses left hanging after questions almost before one knew them to be such. Fr Amandus on the other hand left great holes in the air that one was pulled irresistibly into filling, whether one felt inclined to answer or not. Indeed, whether one had an answer or not.

The high dome of Fr Amandus's forehead was creased into the inquiring ripple of folds that was now the permanent set of his features, produced no doubt by the counterplay between the ingrained downward cast of the Trappist head and the upward thrust of his eyes that his new position required. One certainly could not assume a question on the basis of this any more than one could from his consistently raised eyebrows – another side effect of the effort required to focus on anything other than the floor when addressing anyone.

I can only assume that my advice was being asked because of popular opinion concerning my closeness to Franz, although it was a letter written to Brother Nivard that Fr Amandus pushed towards me on his desk. I was so hungry for some contact with Franz that I could not refrain from scanning a line or so beyond those on which I was asked to concentrate. Franz was waiting for a decision on where he was to be allocated. His suffering was apparent. "I am truly happy that I am properly despised …" was all I could take in before Fr Amandus quietly leaned over and pulled the letter back.

What to say? There were whispers enough to make it impossible for me not to know that Fr Amandus was afraid of Franz's staying at any of Mariannhill's missions. Rumour had it that Franz might organise a group of his supporters on the outstations and break away from the motherhouse. For myself I was quite sure of the opposite – well, let me put it as Franz did in the memoirs he dictated to me years later: "I was no more thinking of breaking away from Mariannhill than Moses was thinking of laying a railway line across the Red Sea."

"Mariazell," said Fr Amandus. I am not certain this word was given the rising tone that would make of it a question, but it hung in the air long enough for me to feel impelled to treat it as one. I knew that Franz wanted very much to settle on this property, but I also knew how controversial a site it was.

Franz had himself taken the initiative of ordering the purchase of the land for Mariazell, the latest and most remote site of a Mariannhill mission. The area along the southern Drakensberg had been opened up to European settlement just at the time Franz was put under suspension; he had sent Brother Nivard there and told him to acquire whatever he thought suitable at the government auction. In order not to provoke anyone, especially not the French Catholic missionaries already at work in the region, Brother Nivard (dressed in civilian clothes) asked an agent in Matatiele to do the bidding for three farms near Ongeluksnek that he decided we should acquire. Ten minutes after Brother Nivard's secret bid was accepted, a messenger dispatched by the Calvinist minister responsible for the region came running up to the local magistrate with a message: "Any how keep the Romans out." It was too late; the Romans had come, seen and purchased, and the sale could not be cancelled.

Controversy over the site had less to do with the colourful facts of its acquisition than with the Visitator's Report, which forbade the development of new missions but not the buying of new properties. Fr Amandus himself smoothed over the delicate matter of who had ordered the buying of the land by supporting its purchase, although he changed its name from the one given by Franz – "Benjamin" signifying his last and most favoured – to that of a great Marian shrine in Austria. That may have been an oblique tribute to Franz, but the dubious status of its South African namesake made it an unlikely refuge for someone who could still cause Mariannhill a great deal of trouble, as Franz himself seemed to recognise.

"He is prepared to go to Skimpers Nek," Fr Amandus said, consulting the coarse sheet of paper in front of him, dirty already at the folds. "It is a location on the furthest side of the Lourdes estate from Mariannhill. I have had about a hundred acres there separated off for him."

"Perhaps," I ventured, "given the matter of the present ownership of the land belonging to Mariannhill ..."

"Yes," said our Abbot-to-be, "precisely. Please write to the Generalate and say 'Until all legal aspects are taken care of, Fr Amandus will not fix the date of his installation.'" He gave the slightest of nods, indicating that the interview was over even whilst I was still scrabbling for pencil and notepad in the pocket of my habit.

~

Two feasts took place late in the April of 1894. On the 24th, Fr Amandus made his Solemn Vows in the morning and was installed as Abbot in the afternoon. The following day he received his consecration as Abbot from the hands of Bishop Jolivet and a joyful celebration, larger and more elaborate than anything Franz had known back in the more primitive days of his foundation, when he had undergone the same ceremony and filled the monastery with food, light and noise.

At Skimpers Nek there was a feast, too. "The holy and humble Abbot Francis," as his hagiographers would have it, "on that day was wedded to Suffering, the Bride of his soul. He had found a particle of the True Cross that, during the fifteen years of his remaining days, was to draw him ever closer to his God through sacrifice and suffering."

Yes, Franz set out from Lourdes on an ox-wagon loaded with a few necessities the day before his successor's installation and, on the very day that Mariannhill overflowed with ancient ceremony, loving speeches, dignified guests and loud music – the signs of a relieved community celebrating a new beginning or, at least, an end to uncertainty – he spent his first full day at the lonely site of his exile.

For myself, once finished with my duties of assisting with the preparation of the church for the ceremony (for I was no longer the only "mother of the house"), I wandered through the monastery, lost amongst the banners and bands and crowds and feeling as if one of our more garish pageants had taken on a nightmarish life of its own and drawn the whole community into it. Even as my senses were drowning in all of this, my heart reached out to Franz in the wilderness.

20

Two Brothers accompanied Franz on the two-hour ride from Lourdes to what he would call his "grandfather house". They were horror-struck at their desolate and lonely destination when the wagon pulled up at a spot directly beneath a rocky crag. Nothing but stone and grass to be seen, nothing to be heard but the low moan of the wind.

Skimpers Nek lies at an altitude of two thousand two hundred and eighty feet and beneath it stretches the expanse of Nomansland, this "human void" as some early travellers through the region called it. Its high, harsh climate, as I was to learn for myself, gives it a short crop-growing season and prevents year-round grazing, making it an unattractive area even for the Native chiefs that could have been expected to claim it.

For Franz nothing could have been more appropriate than that his place of exile be in no man's land. The name he gave to his new home in the region underscored this. He called his fourth foundation Emaus, a name, like "Mariannhill", whose significance could shift, depending on what one knew about it. When called upon to explain, Franz would say that the word was a play on "e Maus", the common contraction of "E'ine Maus" in the Voralberg dialect. "Like a mouse, poor and lowly, Abbot Franz must now hide away quietly in a place no one else wants," the old Gsi-berger would say.

Emaus, then, with one "m", not two. But, as Franz well knew, it was impossible to suppress the force of the biblical Emmaus in his invented name. The foundation lay on the road between Umzimkulu and Franklin, minor and rough though this was, reinforcing the popular religious sense of the incident "on the road to Emmaus" as related in the Book of Luke. Given the events that had deposited him on this spot, Franz could hardly claim, like Cleopas and his friend, that on this road the risen Christ interpreted the things concerning Himself in all the scriptures.

No, those who made this assumption would have to go back to the meaning for the tribe of Judah of the name of that village seven or eight miles north of Jerusalem. In it lay the biblical allusion Franz really wished to invoke in the wordplay he used to name his last foundation. *A people despised*, they would find the Hebraic meaning of Emmaus to be.

I prefer in my writing to spell the name with two "m"s.

~

The two Brothers did not have much time to bewail their fate at having been ordered to accompany the outcast ex-Abbot. They had to start at once on erecting a tent, the first human habitation ever to be raised at "Emaus". The site Franz selected was overgrown with thick, rank grass; he had made his choice by observing where the free-ranging cattle feeding amongst the

408

rocks found shelter from the wind. Thorns, different in size and shape from those at Dunbrody but reminiscent enough of that failure, protruded everywhere, and had to be uprooted before a place to sleep could be established. In the twilight of his first evening there, Franz prayed, "Lord, stay with me, because it is toward evening, and the day is far spent."

The next morning, the luckier of the Brothers was told to take the ox-wagon that had been lent to Franz for his outward journey and return to Lourdes. Franz then hurriedly said his first Mass at Emmaus and set about raising up his foundation with his own hands. To the amazement of the unlucky Brother Xavier he began by tackling the two hundred foot rocky massif directly behind the tent. Every morning the dismissed sixty-eight-year-old Abbot cut step after step into the almost sheer rock face, hewing out the fourteen Stations of the Cross with only an ordinary field hoe and a small crowbar. The zigzag path linking them cost him six weeks of backbreaking effort. With every blow and chip at the stone, Franz tells us in his memoirs (quickly giving the lie to his "little mouse" story), he reflected on the words Jesus spoke to the disciples at Emmaus: "Did not the Christ have to suffer all this?"

He had completed the Stations before his own house was ready. Brother Xavier had been told to concentrate his efforts on constructing a primitive brick kiln and, once Franz was free to help him, the little brick structure was finally ready for occupancy. From this, the foundation developed rapidly. Emmaus gave Franz the chance to show that he could build from nothing, as he had demanded of his Rectors, and do it without the dispensations they demanded. This became all the more possible when two mission Sisters were sent to him. Sr Angela and Sr Edmunda were two of the most dedicated of the Red Sisters. Sr Angela in particular, simple in manner and slow to speak, was supremely loyal in her attachment to Franz. There was nothing that was asked of her that she would not do. And much would be asked of her, she who became Franz's nurse and support at Emmaus, and in whose arms he was to die.

Franz, his head full of the buildings to come, promptly decided to expand the brick-making process. Brother Xavier had not got beyond the first seventeen or eighteen thousand and had been packed off to Lourdes, which was by now so well established that it had taken on more of the air of a motherhouse than a mission. Franz employed in his place three young Natives who had begun to hang around the mission, overcoming the language barrier with the vigorous deployment of Trappist signs. The men were to be paid by contract, one shilling per cubic yard of bricks. It was soon obvious they were not used to such hard work, however; at first they demanded more money, which Franz refused, and then they refused to continue. Franz promptly dismissed them and from then on, he and the two Sisters did the hard and dirty work themselves.

Visitors were soon reporting a number of striking features at the mission: a gigantic cast-iron crucifix representing the twelfth of the Stations of the Cross surmounted the rock hill that Franz climbed every morning regardless of the weather, meditating on the sufferings of his Divine Master and thereby finding consolation in his own forced retirement. The hill he had taken to calling Calvary, and the cross, presented by two benefactors from Europe, was visible for miles around. It became a noted landmark in Nomansland.

By now Franz generally had two Brothers with him, one busy with building and the other with fencing and fieldwork, but none stayed long. They came and went steadily and Franz and the Sisters soon learned to rely upon themselves. The Sisters made bricks, constructed buildings and drained the marshy land across the road, turning it into a productive field for cereals. Sometimes Franz would, grudgingly, allow them to hire help and they would work side by side with the Natives, always with a view to teaching them how to do the work at hand. This involved them in a considerable amount of training for the Natives, too, never stayed long.

Who were these Natives, and where did they suddenly emerge from? Where, for that matter, did the cattle come from that guided Franz in the positioning of his tent?

Trappists cannot be expected to take much interest in the distant figures moving through the landscape surrounding their cloistered life – until, that is, those figures are attracted to that life by the enigma of its silence. Mariannhill had slipped away from this ideal so gradually that our historians still cannot agree on the exact moment of transition from the apostolate as Franz had practised it in Bosnia – which was, technically at least, entirely compatible with the rules of the Order – to the kind of evangelisation practised at Mariannhill. That transition passed unnoticed by many at Mariannhill itself. Was it with the setting up of the press, or Franz's letters to the newspapers? Was it with the creation of the schools, or the invitation to the "Sisters"? The founding of St Wendelin's, Reichenau, the day stations? The shortening of the Office, the breaking of fasts? I doubt that any one of us within the monastery in those days could have answered this. We only did, we would say, what had to be done in the world in which we found ourselves.

If pressed, Franz would claim that he was still following the "method" of mission work by which the great Benedictine and Cistercian monasteries had once spread the word of Christ and civilisation to the barbarians of ancient Europe. In hiring Native labourers without much thought as to their spiritual needs, for example, he saw himself as acting much as those early monks did when they employed itinerant craftsmen for the more delicate work on their monasteries. But those craftsmen were from Christian countries, such as Italy, and were used when those monks were penetrating Britain or the darkest Germanic lands. From where, I ask again, were these Natives that Franz hired?

Even before he had compromised the mystery of the contemplative apostolate, Franz had discovered that no landscape is truly empty. Finding land for his missions brought him up against this reality over and over again. But none of us knew then just how terrible would be the repercussions here in the very centre of "No-man's-land". Certainly I never imagined it, I who would be thrust most deeply into it, and by nothing less than one of the kind acts of the rapidly fading Abbot of Mariannhill – the truly benevolent Abbot Amandus, whose very benevolence was being twisted out of shape by the pressures of trying to govern a monastery sick now to its core.

The truth is that the site of Emmaus was densely settled. The huts of the Natives may have been hidden from view by the hill Franz called his Calvary, but Chief Sondzaba had been living in this part of the country for twenty-five years and obtained his living from the land, one of the few good grazing spots in the region. In Franz's opinion, however, the land on which he had settled had been part of Mariannhill's property since its purchase in 1888 and he considered it his duty to break up the Native settlement on it. The countryside was still, as far as he could see, a wilderness, not cultivated by the Kafirs except for a few fields hedged in by aloes, and their cattle simply wandered at will.

From the monks at Lourdes we heard that Chief Sondzaba had abandoned the area unwillingly and left the district even more reluctantly. The situation was complicated by the fact that the Wesleyans had set up a mission and a schoolhouse amongst the chief's people and supported his every move to counter us Catholics. Franz appealed to the law, and, although the process took over three months, Chief Sondzaba was finally forced to give way. He moved his people to some ground right up against the fence that contained the Lourdes mission and established a village called Canaan. Lying directly between Emmaus and Lourdes, this effectively cut the two missions off from one other, making Emmaus, geographically now as well as in spirit, entirely independent of Lourdes.

So much said in so few words. What was to come of this would explode the neat summary I have given you now – the summary I was given when, upon the death of Fr Ansgar from typhoid, I was suddenly and unexpectedly posted as Superior to Lourdes.

~

Fr Ansgar had replaced Fr Arsenius as Rector when the old pioneer was sent off from Lourdes to establish new stations. Oh yes, Abbot Amandus, passionate contemplative though he was, gave in to the pressure for expansion that not only the demands of the missionaries but the fact of the missions forced upon him. I have said already that he followed through on Franz's purchase of Mariazell, but once this mission was established, an outstation between it and Lourdes was needed, and so Maria Telgte came into being – and, after that, driven by a similarly irresistible logic, Mariatrost, Maryhelp, Clairvaux, Citeaux, St Bernard, Maria Hardenberg, and Marialinden, in rapid succession.

Fr Ansgar had made an ambitious start to the work of evangelisation before he was cut down and even Abbot Amandus could not think I would pick up where he left off. No, I was sent instead as a gesture of kindness to the exiled founder of Mariannhill. In the Abbot's view, Franz would be deeply appreciative of having not only one of his oldest and most devoted sons near him but also a "doctor" and a priest to whom he could turn for his physical and spiritual needs (since his leaving Lourdes, as Franz pointed out, there had been no one to hear his confession). The Abbot was not entirely impractical, however. I was, he said when informing me of my new duties, to be "assisted" in the mission work of Lourdes by Fr Stephen, who showed much promise in the active apostolate.

I was worried by the change I saw coming over Abbot Amandus in the months before I left Mariannhill. It barely seems worth mentioning that in this time I was made Prior again. Fr Pius's unpopularity became so obvious a hindrance to the governing of the monastery that he had to be replaced, and I can only assume that I was chosen in order to placate those who were still angry over Franz's removal and humiliation. I was also not aligned with any of the factions dividing our community that had sprung up since that event, and so had taken on an air of neutrality. I was, then, a useful sort of cipher, even if I was never to become much more than this.

But I was able to observe directly the change that came over Abbot Amandus. The voice of this man who, by nature as well as conviction, was suave and soft, steadily became more brusque, some said harsh, even whilst he dispensed many kindnesses. How much harsher he must have seemed then when reinforcing the Rule. How does one put down gossip and rumour-mongering quietly, especially when it is as widespread as it was at Mariannhill? For every act of kindness – ruling that a Rector could have his linen washed by a Brother, for example, or that every monk, if he were a missionary, could talk with the Sister Superior or teaching Sister on the stations without asking permission – Abbot Amandus had to instil discipline ten times over. When he ordered that sweets could no longer be distributed to the children at the schools, or that soliciting alms by personal letters had to stop, or that written permission was needed for any Sister or monk to visit another mission, his abrupt manner, a disguise for his real disposition, turned many against him.

I was, it goes without saying, scant help to him in all of this, and so I was not surprised when I was called for and told I was no longer to be Prior. What did surprise me was my new assignment. But whatever the fears it raised in me, I was more than ready to put the unhappiness of the monastery behind me as I departed in Mariannhill's famous two-wheeled carriage, affectionately known as the Spider. In unspoken acknowledgement of my poor horsemanship I was allowed to use this vehicle more than most. Still, I could see that my reputation as a driver had gone before me for Fr Stephen was obviously relieved when I gave him permission to take the reins for the trip to Lourdes.

And so we set off, I with my eyes firmly fixed upon the road between our wheels and the horses' hooves and he with his darting about the countryside. So we remained, each wrapped in our own thoughts, as we covered the many, many miles to Lourdes, staying over at my old postings of Einsiedeln and Mariathal on the way. As we approached Lourdes, I felt obliged to look around as well, to learn something about the place for which I was to be responsible. One of the first things I saw was Chief Sondzaba's village, Canaan, established at the edge of the mission. I remember its inhabitants stared at us mutely and sullenly as we rode by, a mood that I am sure was not helped by the dust from our hooves and wheels settling on them in clouds as we passed.

If this made an impression on my companion, he did not show it. In everything he did, it seemed to me, Fr Stephen led with his chin. He approached the world with that part of his physiognomy extended ahead of any other, which gave him a posture exuding a kind of pugnaciousness. The rest of his body, however, would assume a simpering sort of attitude when called before any one technically his Superior – a Superior he was prepared to recognise as such, which made his overdone obeisance quite different from mine. I, of course, was not extended such recognition, and so was not subjected to the convoluted mix of these attributes as he clambered down from the Spider. We both, however, stood in awe before Lourdes mission as we tried to take it in for the first time.

Mission? Anyone who was not certain that Mariannhill would remain the motherhouse might have been forgiven for thinking that this one of her many daughters would surpass her in importance. Firstly, there was the sheer extent of the station. Fifty thousand acres of fertile soil well provided with water. Two thousand acres of the best timber. Fifteen large farms put together in one compact group. We had gained some sense of its size as we followed the fine post-cart road that ran through the landscape, bringing us comfortably to the mission itself. It was beautifully set on a hilltop, with mountains in the middle distance rising up around it.

Brother Nivard's hand was everywhere in the impressive buildings, and towering over even the two-storeyed red-brick mass of the dormitories and the equally large building that housed the workshops was the most breathtaking of all mission churches. I say "towering" quite seriously. Two square towers, each over sixty feet high and topped with shining metal spires, flanked the imposing façade of the three-nave brick basilica. Over the years I would hear many say that Lourdes had all the makings of a Trappist Abbey, and certainly my first impression of its church was that it was no mere monastery church.

Brother Stephen and I were still trying to take in the wonderful symmetry of the decoratively set round-arch windows that punctuated each level of the towers when, smiling and waving, Brother Nivard himself came out of the porticoed entrance of this most imposing place of worship. "Built with no scaffolding at all," he said, gesturing at the towers. "We inserted boards into the inside of the walls as we built and stood on them to lay the bricks from within. A metre thick, those walls. The designs we did by arranging bricks to point outwards. But come in, come in. Abbot Franz only laid the foundation stone a few months ago, and yet we're almost done."

As he turned towards the impressive doors, I had a moment to register how much our architect had changed along with his designs. The slight fleshiness of his youth had given way to the most distinctly chiselled of faces, although any sense of sharpness that may have been produced by the hawk-like nose and high forehead was offset by the clearest and most sensitive eyes I have ever seen. The thin and straggly beard I remembered had grown into an impressive extension of his chin, exceeding even that imposing nose in length. The overall effect was of a fine and cultivated mind that did not need to take itself too seriously, which was exactly the style of Brother Nivard's manner of speaking. And it was the rush of his words that carried us into the cool gloom of Lourdes' church.

One's first impression on entering was of darkness. Here the Trappist tendency in Africa towards reducing the spaces through which light could enter was taken further than in any of our other churches. The windows were high, and comparatively small when considered against the volume of the nave and its aisles. In addition, they were richly decorated with dense and complex patterns through which light struggled to penetrate. The Rule demands that Cistercian churches be absolutely plain and unadorned, but we broke away from this in our mission churches, which Mariannhill's resident artist, Anton Schmidt, decorated with biblical scenes and illustrations of scriptural stories. This was strictly in the interests of the newly baptised who, like their counterparts in Medieval Europe, were for the most part illiterate. Whilst we struggled with their language and they with ours, they could read our walls and windows in which every detail carried some precise spiritual meaning that we could explain to them.

A flower was never just a flower but the Lily of St Joseph or the Rose of Our Lady. Palms were not local foliage but fronds to be waved for the martyrs. Men and women appeared only in their iconography, St Peter with his cross upside down and the keys of Heaven at his feet, St Clare with her halo and chalice, St Agatha with her severed breasts in a dish (so graphically rendered that they could never be mistaken for loaves of bread, an error of Medieval representation that is commemorated today by the rite of blessing bread on St Agatha's Day). In short, our mission churches were nothing less than giant picture books for those recently converted to the faith; every image in the acres of stencilled adornment had its purpose.

The church at Lourdes was in the midst of being richly decorated, beyond anything appropriate for instruction. On one wall there was a painting of Mary with her Christ Child placed so as to seem to be walking towards the pulpit, and I suppose the ancient symbol of the pelican pecking at its breast to feed its young could be used to make some sense of things for an African congregation. But what of the sumptuous paintings of curtains behind the altar? They had taken on the sacred meaning of the veil of the temple hiding the ark, but this is not how the design began. In the Middle Ages actual curtains were hung along the walls to give warmth to the monks who stood against them in the freezing European winters and, gradually, these curtains were included in the paintings that decorated the great churches. But this blurring of the actual and the spiritual was lost out here in Africa. I am sure I think too much about such things for a monk, but for me it was as if the mystery of what we had come to say was cut off from its proper sphere and floated free as painting for the sake of painting. All the more so, in the case of the church at Lourdes, for the beauty of its execution.

Brother Nivard showed us around the church that first time, explaining in an excited voice that the three ornate marble altars had been ordered from Europe, that the statue of Our Lady of Lourdes – "a work of art" he gushed – was over six feet high and weighed sixteen hundredweight, that the style of the basilica was Roman, cruciform, the nave was a hundred and thirty-five feet in length, fifty-two feet in width and could accommodate over a thousand people … he went on and on. All I wanted to do was escape from the grandeur of yet another basilica – the word came even more immediately to mind here – whilst trying at the same time to accept that this was my new church.

Worse was to come. I joined Brother Nivard and Brother Stephen as they stepped out into the flat glare of Nomansland, only to have Brother Nivard extend an arm towards each of the towers. "The clocks in the belfries have to be worked by electricity," he said, and he had just begun describing the water-powered turbine that ran these and all the other machinery in which the mission gloried when I was treated for the first time to the pealing of the "famous bells of Lourdes", as they rapidly came to be known. All I know is that, on that first occasion of hearing them, their sheer volume took me by surprise, leaving me deafened and dazed. In an instant I found myself washed again in the resonance of the bells of St Procopius, now redoubled by the twin belfries of Lourdes.

I am not sure if my senses gave way then as they had done in my childhood in the apple orchard in Letovice, but the next thing I was aware of was a feeling of coming back to myself, confused and uncertain. As I struggled to re-establish where I was, the landscape around me shimmered and blurred into the bell-drenched vistas of Banjaluka. The vibrations running through the atmosphere around me gradually subsided and I recovered enough to nod at Brother Nivard who was standing before me with a concerned look on his face. The inclination of my head must have been appropriate because he smiled and turned again towards the church, raising his hands to the twin towers.

"The larger bell in each weighs well over half a ton," he said, and went on to tell us of his plans for a monastery up against the north transept of the basilica and a convent against the south. Complete with cloisters and gardens, these would fold the church in their embrace. Turning to look down the broad path leading up to the entrance to the church, he described with his hands another enormous two-storeyed building to the right that would be a mirror image of the existing one to the left. This would house more industrial and training rooms, so that work would flank the way to prayer.

It is a pity that these glorious plans came to nothing. But then again, Lourdes was so different from anything we were meant to achieve, anything allowed even by the troubled alterations to the Rule of our Order that had led us inevitably to this utterly new conception of ourselves. The church at Lourdes stood out from our other work, and not just in its overwhelming proportions. None of the other missions had been privileged to have a place of worship of any kind raised so soon in their development. After Centocow (and my poor Reichenau, which could hardly compete), the other stations had to wait years, in some cases decades, before they were granted churches. But here, in fewer than six years since Brother Leo first stormed through Mariannhill's newly acquired wilderness, whipping its astonished new tenants into clothes, was a basilica worthy of an abbey.

Yes, Franz really was still an Abbot here. I had seen Brother Stephen blink and stick his chin more firmly into the air when Brother Nivard so casually used that title for the exiled old man. But there was something about the scale of Lourdes that exuded the spirit of the founder of Mariastern and Mariannhill, someone far from submissive in his retirement at a place of humble retreat. Physically he may have been six miles away, but at Lourdes my soul, as much as my ears, rang with a sense of his presence.

~

The Natives already referred to Lourdes as "the town" and certainly the mission seethed with more activity than many of the Sleepy Hollows that passed for towns in the region. Or so one of the monks who had been there for some time told me proudly as he led me to my office, I who still found this a strange thing for a Trappist to be proud of. The large room immediately made me long for my small cubbyhole under the stairs at the entrance to Mariannhill. And here work of the most troubling sort awaited me, practical issues of administration in which I was the most perfect assistant but the most useless leader.

I do not remember enough of the routine issues and problems of my day-to-day life as Superior of Lourdes to bore you with them now, but – the Visitator having returned the position of Superior to its strict meaning – it was apparent that all the responsibilities of leadership, both spiritual and material, had fallen again upon my shoulders. I was extremely concerned to find that I was not to be spared the problems being experienced with the Natives although the appointment of an assistant in missionary matters relieved me of some of the burden. So many of the monks at Lourdes were eager to participate in the active apostolate that it was impossible to draw a neat line between the running of the mission itself and its mission work. This Fr Stephen brought home to me constantly, barging in chin-first through my door at all hours and demanding decisions from me.

More often than not these intrusions had to do with the work of one who, technically, fell under his authority. Willibald Wanger, one of Mariannhill's brightest and best, had recently and mysteriously returned early from his theological studies in Rome and was sent on to Lourdes soon after me. He was a fair, good-looking man only twenty-five years of age, and he immediately set about applying his youthful energy and considerable talents to every aspect of working with the Natives. As a linguist and a musician he was without peer, and soon created the best African choir to be found on any of the missions.

No matter that his curt manner and flashes of irascibility often combined to cause offence with Brother and Native alike, Fr Willibald's impenetrable self-confidence generally saw him through, and his projects flourished all around me. Within a year his delayed ordination took place at Lourdes, confirming it as a place where an aptitude for and commitment to missionary work was a sure way to get ahead. I will confess to being concerned about the way in which the young Fr Willibald exemplified this troubling feature of life in the community of which I was the ostensible leader, but my attention was soon absorbed by something far more dramatic.

I took office as Superior of Lourdes just after the mission had been subjected to a series of plagues of almost biblical proportions. A heavy downpour had recently caused the river flowing through our estate to swell by over four metres, the flood sweeping away our barn and two mills. Then swarms of locusts came down on our lands on several occasions, eating up most of our crops and grazing. But neither of these setbacks came close to the destructiveness of the next plague, which struck soon after I arrived.

Rinderpest, a cattle disease that had been ravaging Rhodesia and the Transvaal for about two years, broke out in East Griqualand too. Cattle were the great wealth of the country and to see them wasting to death, the landscape littered with their stinking carcasses, was truly terrible. The Government tried to contain the disease by ordering the official isolation of infected areas, but more and more of these sprang up with each passing week. The Natives, for whom cattle were the only measure of prosperity, felt this affliction most keenly, and when the fearful disease struck amongst their herds on the Lourdes estate, their suffering was impressed on us all – as was the immediate danger that the sickness would spread to the mission's animals. This it did within a matter of days. Just before the Feast of the Assumption of Our Lady we were asked to send two young infected cattle and two old oxen into the segregation camp that had been erected near the Sneezewood store. This was a Government-controlled effort to cultivate the virus for the purposes of inoculation. I would have preferred to follow Franz in his well-known opposition to all forms of vaccination, but our cows were beginning to die at a frightening rate.

At first the camps experimented with inoculating healthy cattle directly with the blood of those stricken by the Rinderpest, but this turned out to be a disaster. The Government then banned inoculation by this method, returning to the slower and more expensive use of serum. It was too late for Lourdes, however. My decision to participate in the scheme resulted in our losing over one hundred head of cattle, as much to the treatment as to the disease. Franz, needless to say, had refused to inoculate any of his cattle at Emmaus, and lost not one cow on his farm, even though he had nine sucking calves. He made much of the fact that at "Emaus" more recourse was made to St Wendelin (who else?), the holy protector of stock, than to medical means.

In my embarrassment I did not visit Franz at Emmaus as soon as I should have, and fresh developments led to further delay. The distress of the Natives grew with every cow that died, their wealth melting away before their eyes. Early in 1897 rumours began to circulate that a rebellion against the authorities was being planned in response to the order that farms must be fenced and a special hut tax paid towards the cost of combating the Rinderpest. The areas of unrest stretched from Natal to Kokstad, which placed Lourdes in the very centre, with hostile tribes surrounding it in every direction.

As it was, open rebellion did not break out, but we were soon to feel the effects of the unhappiness all around us.

~

I had been at Lourdes just over a year, my attempts to keep to the Rule drowning in a sea of bureaucracy and interruption, when Fr Stephen burst into my office, waving a letter at me from under his upturned chin. I have kept it all these years, and give it to you now in full:

Sondzaba's
7th August 1897

D.D. Strachan Esq:
Umzimkulu.

Dear Sir,
I hereby beg to let you know that the Trappists here are not accepted by me. I suspect Mlenzana to have had a secret council with them without my knowledge. I have carefully inquired from him as to what brought them here, but he pretends not to know anything about them, yet all his ways are leading towards helping their cause. I therefore urgently request you to approach the Magistrate about this affair; tell him he must not

sanction anything asked for by the Trappists connected with this place. Am totally against them and besides Mlenzana has not much power of introducing such things in my father's farm without my consent he will have such power after my death. At present, at the strict point of law, am held responsible for this land and the interests therewith connected; therefore nothing can be done contrary to my views. Trappists are a different race to my rulers and as I am under British flag I cannot afford to let unknown people to exercise their wrong influence within my ward and besides

III

I know for a fact they will ruin this State and my large family will be left destitute and reduced to beggary. Should the Trappists call on you on plea that they allowed by Mlenzana please disperse that with all your might. Let them know Mlenzana has no positive right to elect site for them.

I further request you to see the Magistrate to give me a policeman to come and cut down the Trappist's bell. I hate it I won't have it rung within my father's ground. Often have I sent men to go and cut it down but in vain in fear of Mlenzana who has

IV

manifested himself in favour of the troublesome foreign men. I put you in front to fight for me and make all possible ways to have them expelled from my land give me also advice to warn my son Mlenzana who inclines to disregarding me. Relying on your uttermost effort

I beg to remain
Your Obedient Servant
p.p. Dludlushe Sondzaba C.T.P.

Clearly the person to whom the letter was addressed did not wish to bother with it and forwarded it to Lourdes without even attaching a covering note. This was, in his view, a "monastery" problem, and one that the monastery and the monastery alone should handle.

We all knew "D. D. Strachan, Esq:" – it was impossible not to if you lived in Nomansland, or East Griqualand as it was renamed in 1860 after the Griqua people settled there under the illusion that they were to be their own rulers. Mr Strachan, a well-liked and successful trader, had served as the leader of a group of loyal Native volunteers who had made him their chief. He was the only non-Griqua the Griqua ever appointed as a magistrate. The powerful firm of Strachan & Co., as I discovered in the dealings with the law required of me as Superior of Lourdes, included the Secretary to the Government and the Magistrate of Umzimkulu District amongst its partners. Where land issues were concerned, no one stood higher than Strachan; as the most prominent landowner, he could easily afford to add "Esq" to his name.

We ourselves were in East Griqualand because of him. Something of a depression had hit the area in the late 1880s with so much of the land owned by "the Bastards" (as, I was surprised to hear, the Griqua once proudly referred to themselves) for sale that Mr Strachan decided to off-load some of his farms. It was his advertisement in the Durban newspapers that Franz had seen and then sent Brother Nivard and Fr Gerard to investigate. They were shown a block of fifteen farms with a good number of people living on them and had decided the location was good for a mission but the asking price was too high. Discovering (how, only he knew) that Mr Strachan owed money to the Randle Brothers firm in Durban, Franz drove a hard bargain.

Negotiations went on for some time, during which – and this was mentioned to me only in passing as I tried to get to the bottom of our troubles with the Natives at Lourdes – a Wesleyan chief protested against the sale of the farms to the Catholic Church, and asked for the protection of the Wesleyan Methodist Missionary Society. This society was the reason that Brother Nivard had disguised himself as an Englishman when he was bidding for Mariazell. He had in fact snatched the farm from under the noses of the society, who were by far the most active denomination in the border area between the Cape and Natal.

This brings us back to the letter. It was clear to me that Mlenzana was intent on using us to depose his father. Wagging his chin forcefully at the ceiling, Fr Stephen filled me in on his convoluted efforts at winning over Mlenzana to our holy cause. He had, he told me, been in secret negotiation with Mlenzana for some time, and was quite sure that if the father could be undone, the son would be able to bring his whole tribe over to us without even having to wait for his father to die.

And so Fr Joseph found himself, against all his better instincts, competing with the Wesleyans for the souls of those outside the cloister. How could he act otherwise when the evidence before him in the letter shaking ever so slightly in his hand made it plain that in this dispute the Wesleyans and Catholics were at war over the "one thing necessary" for heathen and missionary, Wesleyan and Catholic alike? It was equally clear that Dludlushe, who signed himself "Dludlushe Sondzaba" in an odd mixture of Zulu and Christian naming conventions, had good reason to remain a mortal enemy of the Catholics. Was it not they who had evicted his father from his ancestral land, one of the few good grazing spots for his cattle? Was this not the rationale behind his using his father's name as some sort of surname, to remind Mr Strachan, and through him the Magistrate, that Chief Sondzaba had already lost his land through the imposition of the white man – not just the white man, but the Catholic white man – and been forced to move to this spot right next to the fence of the white man's church, this spot that he, the son of his father, was now in danger of losing to his own son, whom the Catholics were using to take the land again from his people?

We could quite simply have trusted to the fact that it was the very person to whom Dludlushe Sondzaba addressed his letter who had sold us the land we occupied, or on the public support Mr Strachan gave us. He regularly brought visitors of importance to the region to our grand mission, putting me in a position of acute embarrassment that was alleviated by the fact that Franz almost always found an excuse to be at Lourdes when they arrived. But the writer of the letter showed himself to have a subtle grasp of the weaknesses in our position. "Trappists are a different race to my rulers," he had written, "and as I am under British flag I cannot afford to let unknown people to exercise their wrong influence within my ward." This was astute, and not just for playing off British Wesleyans against "German" Catholics: the nearest Catholic missionaries to us were the French missionaries of Queen's Mercy and Franco-German relations, although improved, were still unhappy.

If Mlenzana had aligned himself with the Trappists to strengthen his position, it was my guess that Dludlushe was also exploiting a missionary avenue to power. The clue to this lay in the form itself of the letter. Dludlushe, wily as he was, could not speak English, nor write at all. His appeal to Mr Strachan had been transcribed and translated into English by a proxy, and this made me look even more carefully at the last lines of the letter. "Your Obedient Servant, p.p. Dludlushe Sondzaba c.t.p." No signature as such to indicate who had really composed the letter, which was extremely neatly written in a fine copperplate script. The hand that held the pen was an educated one and not, I assumed from the nature of the letter, one educated in the Lourdes school. This meant, in this region, a Wesleyan education. So who was "c.t.p."?

Active in the Umzimkulu area at this time was one Charles Pamla. I could find no record of his middle name, so the "t" remained a mystery, but in every other way it made sense that Pamla was the one who had written the letter and signed it on Dludlushe's behalf. I had met him at some of the public meetings chaired by Mr Strachan, to which the various sections of the East Griqualand population were required to send a representative. I have to admit that Pamla was, in the flesh, an impressive presence. He stood over six foot tall, was black as jet, and had a deep, resonant, measured voice. Every time I saw him he was well dressed, and his manners were exquisite.

I was told Pamla was a "Mfengu", one of those refugees from the unrest in Zululand who had crossed over to the British. As a "new man", he had become a wealthy and substantial landowner in the Umzimkulu district. He was a "moderniser" and a "Government man" and set himself apart from the more traditional Natives, but he was still commonly used as an intermediary between them and the settlers and colonial authorities. At our meetings he was an undeniably useful source of information on the attitudes and actions of the people in the African locations, and he was an often-quoted informant to the magistrates of the area.

More to the point, Pamla was also a Wesleyan Methodist minister, the very first black Wesleyan Methodist minister, in fact, and I heard him described as a "good interpreter" for the Methodist missionaries. This reputation had been earned as far back as 1866 when William Taylor of the American Methodist Episcopal Church brought a great revival to the Wesleyan Methodist missions of the Eastern Cape. Taylor not only inspired the missionaries but, with the help of Charles Pamla as an interpreter, preached to Native congregations and effected numerous conversions amongst them.

Oh, I was told, over a terrible cup of English tea at the conclusion of one of the Government meetings at which I was required to be present, the effect of the preaching of those two men on the Africans was extraordinary!

Over every one of the mission stations there swept a great tide of new life in God, refreshing and cleansing all the channels of human life until homes and churches alike overflowed with joy. By this point in the disquisition, I realised something of a point was being made about my Catholic status, and, smiling silently all the while, I let the voice drone on about the fire running through the length of the chain of missions stretching from Cape Town to Natal, bringing warmth and light and power …

At another gathering the story was taken up again, over an even worse cup of tea (I allowed myself no sugar, of course, nor even milk). This time I learned that after Mr Taylor's departure the good work continued and the churches rejoiced exceedingly with great joy. Charles Pamla, after completing his special services for Mr Taylor, went quietly to the theological institution at Healdtown, where he sought to make himself more efficient in the service of Christ. Ultimately he was ordained – the voice took on a pointed tone, doubtless with reference to the failure of us Catholics to have produced, as yet, a single black priest in South Africa – and continued to serve the Church – even more emphasis this time, with the teacup rattling in its saucer – *of Christ* as one of its ministers.

I smiled and smiled through all of this, smiled until my clenched jaw hurt, and thought of young black Eduard, still in Rome and negotiating its sacred and historic streets and buildings with, I was sure, as much confidence as he had found his way as a child through the maze of our beliefs and practices. I said nothing of this, of course, but it gave me great comfort to think of him wandering through the Holy City I had never been privileged to visit myself.

I was jolted back to the moment by the harrumphing departure of my interlocutor, and was left alone, the left sleeve of my habit dripping tea, to think about Rev. Charles Pamla. I admit to being in awe of his vocal prowess. On whatever subject he chose, his speech was shaped by a quiet confidence. How clumsy I used to feel in his presence, trying to make the odd point about our mission in my poor English whilst staring at the floor and searching for words. It was fortunate that Franz attended these meetings to put forward the Catholic position, which he did with a brusque firmness that came across as rough and unsophisticated before the smooth and well-turned flow of Mr Pamla's words. Between these contending voices my silence seemed less significant than ever.

It seemed to me that "c.t.p." had as much, perhaps even more, to gain from Dludlushe's success than Dludlushe himself. And as long as Dludlushe remained in control the Wesleyans would have a strong foothold right in the centre of the land we had purchased for our mission. What worried me more, however, was another medium altogether, far less substantial than land and yet as vital to us as Trappists as water is to the Cistercians: it was our invasion of the air itself that had incensed Dludlushe and erased what small distance there was between Lourdes and Canaan.

"I further request you to see the Magistrate to give me a policeman to come and cut down the Trappist's bell ..." Up to that point in his letter Dludlushe seemed happy to ask Mr Strachan to reinforce, through his legal jurisdiction as Magistrate, Dludlushe's authority as father and chief over Mlenzana. But on the issue of the bell Dludlushe called for no less than the intervention of the police. More worryingly still, his letter made it plain that he had even tried to take action against us himself. I wondered whether Fr Stephen realised that it was only his rather shaky relationship with Dludlushe's son that had prevented us, thus far, from suffering a physical attack by the Natives.

The incongruity of Trappists being at risk over their bells was not lost on me. This was altogether a different case from those gentle silvery tinkles that marked time in our cloister, those guides to the precise liturgical pattern of the Night Office and the monastic hours of the day. Where would we be without the rhythm in which no personal indecision could for a single moment of the day disturb the contemplation that was our chief work?

Well, Mariannhill had taught us the answer to that, but even Mariannhill had no campanile attached to its basilica. Large as it was, the great bell that governed life there was mounted on a low wooden structure in the centre of the cloister quadrangle, where it was well placed to summon us to the exercises that could not be controlled by the much, much smaller bells in the dormitory, refectory, Chapter Room and church. When we were told the bell could not be heard properly at some of the more distant fields, Franz had the flag of the monastery, stark in its black cross on a plain white background, run up to signal the more important Offices.

Once the missions of Mariannhill claimed their freedom from their birth within the sternly Trappist spirit, their towers began to claw their way into the air above station after station, throwing the sound of their bells far beyond the ears of their communities for all to hear. And hear them Dludlushe Sondzaba did, as the Pasha had in Bosnia, not only as a nuisance but as a challenge to his right to call his people together when he chose. From my small acquaintance with the writings of Arthur Bryant, lost now somewhere in the wilds of Zululand, I had gathered that this was a serious threat to the chief's power.

As I absent-mindedly refolded the chief's letter, I realised how much the bells of Lourdes had come to represent everything Franz had departed from – disputed, done away with – in our strict Cistercian observances. I could not speak for the souls called by our bells and won over to our missions, for there both my mind and imagination failed. And as a Trappist I was called only to obey, not think through the mystery of our apostolate, the apostolate that called me back ever more strongly as I wandered, disoriented, amongst the buildings and fields of Lourdes.

Yes, the significance of the religious name with which Franz had blessed me came back to me at that place where I became again, within the reverberations of its giant bells driven by electricity in the heights of their towers, Joseph of Cupertino, the Gaper. That first instance of my melting away within their tones as they echoed around the valley of Lourdes was confirmed soon enough and, time and time again, I was to be found, book or rosary dangling from my nerveless fingers, standing confused and bewildered as I came back to myself, eyes blinking, face ticking, mouth open.

As for that sense of impending enlightenment that came upon me just before one of my absences, I leave it to you to decide how much this could be trusted. Was it a distant echo of the saintliness of Joan of Arc or a fool in full force, and not even a holy fool at that?

~

We are told that the monks at the monastery of Vicovaro begged Benedict, then living the life of a solitary at Subiaco, to be their leader. After he had, with great reluctance, accepted, the strictness of his rules proved distasteful to them. One of the monks is said to have poisoned his drink. When Benedict blessed it, as he blessed everything, the jug broke apart. Benedict then returned to his hermitage at Subiaco where disciples, seculars and solitaries gathered around him. He settled the men in twelve wooden monasteries of twelve monks, each with its Prior. They lived under no written rule but by observing Benedict's example. He left Subiaco when a jealous priest, Florentius, poisoned a loaf of his bread, which a raven carried away.

St Benedict is invoked against poison and dying. He is represented, as on the walls of the basilica at Lourdes, holding an open copy of his Rule and a broken chalice. His emblem is a raven with a bun in its beak.

~

The retching of the children started at about seven o'clock on Sunday evening, just as we were beginning the last Hour of the Divine Office. I especially love the night prayer, concerned as it is with sleep and waking and the way this reflects life and death, sin and grace. On this particular evening I had just begun the Paternoster and Confiteor when I could not help but notice that some of the Brothers were hurrying over from their aisle to where the schoolchildren were worshipping with us. The sound of gagging and vomiting bubbled up into the silence of the church. Suddenly the Sisters too were amongst the girl pupils, hushing some and lifting out others, who appeared to be afflicted in much the same way as the boys. The set hymn, "Te lucis ante terminum", helped to mask the disruption, but I admit to rushing towards the Collect and Blessing. All the Religious of our community seemed well, and they, along with those schoolchildren who were still able, left in as orderly a fashion as possible. As soon as was seemly I hurried outside.

There I found the children lying contorted on the ground. They were clutching at their bellies, which seemed to be swelling up prodigiously, and were complaining of pains and prickings in every part of their bodies, but especially in the soles of their feet. Cold sweats gripped them, and many were having trouble breathing. Those who had begun vomiting first were now collapsing into a state more or less of unconsciousness. We carried and shushed and comforted as best we could in the rapidly falling dark, vomit on our habits and hands and shoes. There was even vomit in my beard, I found, after we had got the last child into some kind of a resting place.

By then far too many were ill – seventy at least – to be accommodated in the infirmary. We took the overflow to their dormitory beds (if blankets on the floor can be so described). Once we had them inside I began preparing, as quickly as I could with shaking hands and a shuddering mind, emetics and purgatives. We got those still conscious to drink these, fighting through their spluttering into cups and throwing up again as soon as we had the medicine in them. The sickest of the conscious children were calling out constantly for water, saying that their mouths and throats were burning and that they were terribly thirsty. When we tried to give them water they invariably began vomiting again.

Administering to the unconscious was even worse, the liquid spilling out of their slack mouths as fast as we tried to pour it in and get them to swallow. We worried terribly that they would choke on their own vomit, or even on the medication, and ran about, lifting, pulling, laying down, skidding all the while in pools of sickness and spilled medicine, our prayers and tears mingling in our desperation.

Slowly a silence of sorts began to fall, but it was of the most ominous kind. Child after child ceased heaving and became comatose as we slipped into one of the longest nights I remember. The steely light of dawn found all the children quiet, and some even partially recovered. We moved amongst them throughout the day as they lay weak in their beds, their tummies distended and painful, sores forming around their mouths and fundaments. We cleaned, rearranged, and tried as hard as we could to bring a semblance of orderliness to the chaos of the night. And then, just as darkness began to fall again, the first boy was gone. Scotchman – the name by which we knew him – sat up suddenly and clasped his little belly. He died before we could even register a change in him.

He was one of the youngest and smallest, the youngest and smallest of those little chicks, my doves. I, who never knew how to reach out to a child in all my days, had from a distance breathed in their milkiness, lapped up their young strength, drowned in their smell of life. They exuded every-thing I had put aside, not because I did not want it but because I loved it so much that it seemed the only sacrifice I could make that was worthy of God. And now I stood amongst all of that youngness in the darkness, hearing it suffer and moan in its sleep that was too, too close to the death of which it was meant to be only a symbol, a sign presaging life. I hovered over my sacrifice uselessly, an Abraham it seemed to whom no angel of the Lord had called out.

~

The next day the Resident Magistrate, Captain Whindus, came by. This was purely fortuitous; he was on his way to investigate the death of a Native in a faction fight somewhere in our area. He put himself immediately at our service. We were, after all, the most impressive institution in the area, and he had recently joined his business partner Mr Strachan on the official visit to us of no less a personage than the Prime Minister of the Cape Colony when we were held up as evidence of how much could be achieved in the region. Captain Whindus RM was anxious to clear up this unfortunate business as quickly and quietly as possible.

I took Captain Whindus in some detail through what the children had been given to eat before this affliction had descended on us. With an official frown of concentration fixed on his florid face, and with much twirling of his moustache, he listened to my story of the ox we had slaughtered on the Saturday. The Sisters would have eaten the same meat but it happened that some pigs had been slaughtered too and they preferred the pork. The children had eaten the meat at supper and again on Sunday in the morning and at lunch.

The Captain wanted to know who had prepared the food. The women from the Weibertrost, I told him. Franz had founded the Weibertrost, I explained when he looked blankly at me, to accommodate the wives of converts, who were allowed to keep one wife only. The rest had to be disposed of somehow. On all the larger mission stations there were groups of these Native women who lived in community under certain rules and made themselves useful in house and field work under the supervision of the Sisters. They were generally engaged in cooking the food for the children, I told the Captain, and were expert in its preparation, knowing so well the tastes and wants of the children.

This was a longer and more formal speech than I had intended, but I suddenly found it easier to speak of everyday things to do with the mission than to delve into the horrible guesswork Captain Whindus's investigations required.

"Well, they would have the opportunity," Captain Whindus said. "Is there one or more of them that you suspect could have poisoned the food?"

"These women have their own children at the school and feel quite happy and at home here," I replied.

He grunted, and made more notes. "Is there anyone else you suspect?"

I cannot tell you, even now, the anguish my next action cost me. I leaned over and moved a letter from where it had been placed in neat alignment with the corner of the desk to a spot directly before the Magistrate. He scanned the letter, beginning with the signature appended by proxy. "Dludlushe Sondzaba," he read out. "I know that name, or both those names I should say. Especially old Sondzaba! He's the one who gave your Abbot – ex or late or whatever he is – such a hard time. But Sondzaba's dead now. So I take it Dludlushe is his son. Can't keep up with what's happening with names around here."

He read further, obviously reaching Dludlushe's response to our bells. "Right outside our jurisdiction," he said. "I can tell you no policeman will be coming! I'll have to keep an eye on this Mlenzana character, I can see." His frown lifted at the prospect of some action, something that clearly came more easily to him than this kind of questioning. Promising to look into the matter, he told me, "I've had these old-fashioned types doing things to the children to keep them away from the mission schools before and scaring the parents so they won't allow the children to go there. Going on about kidnapping and that sort of thing, but you'd know about that, wouldn't you? Another one of those cases going on here right now, isn't there?"

I nodded.

"And who does the teaching around here?"

He seemed pleased to hear that our schools, for boys as well as for girls, had been turned over to the Sisters since 1896. "Well, there you are, then," he said. "Whoever did this was trying to get to the school, that's for certain. Pretty much everyone around here knows that you monks don't eat meat, and I'm sure they worked out the nuns did. So it was the children they were after and the nuns" – the repetition of the incorrect word came close to irritating me – "who teach them. Lucky thing that – about the pork, I mean. And, begging your pardon, it's easy enough to believe that one of those leftover wives could've been got to, by her ex-husband, perhaps."

Almost as an afterthought he added, "Not that I want to blame anyone in particular, you understand. I'm sure I can take your word that they're a good bunch on the whole. Could never prove if one of them was rotten, anyway, I'm sure."

Before he left the Captain informed me that he had received a petition from a young Native woman wanting to be relieved from the jurisdiction of Native law. Ulusi, or Humbelina as she was called, had used Biegner as her Christian surname, prompting an attempt at humour on the part of the Captain. "Popular, you must be, with the ladies. Sorry, Father, a joke, just a joke."

Humbelina's parents would, likewise, have signed themselves as uPatla Joseph Pfanner and uKeli Marianne Pfanner. I doubted, however, that

Captain Whindus would have made the same joke to Franz. He gathered his papers and left my office with an odd sort of duck, the kind of uncertain gesture I've seen Protestants make instead of genuflecting when entering a Catholic church. A few moments later the door opened and his face appeared briefly around the doorway. "By the way, Father, you did do everything you could? As a man of medicine, I mean?"

I nodded my assent. I had done all I could, although it had not been enough.

~

And that was that, as far as any investigation went.

During the brief respite of the next morning I sent a message to Franz informing him of what had happened. He was sure it was a case of food poisoning, the beef having been reheated so many times. "No English doctors necessary!" his return message stated.

The first death, recorded as "Native Juvenile, Scotchman", was followed by five deaths the next night. Nothing I could do helped in the least. All had been purged, and some had been douched in cold water. God was – as He had been at Reichenau when these treatments did nothing to help the Sisters sick from the meat of the cow killed by lightning – our only hope. As I arranged the small bodies in the manner prescribed by the Rule even my prayers were exhausted. In the first light of dawn I sent news to Captain Whindus of the further deaths and requested that he send the District Surgeon as soon as possible. Three more died before the District Surgeon arrived, older children this time, two of them girls.

Dr Henry Thomas Platt – for so he introduced himself – appeared to be suffering from a severe head cold and was clearly resentful at being ordered out in this condition. He wandered from bed to bed, sniffing and coughing, taking temperatures and looking at tongues, tut tutting and muttering and shaking his head all the while. He had seen too much, I got the impression, to say much about what he had seen, and he had nothing to say to me about the condition of the children or how they had become so ill. He headed off to our makeshift mortuary, asking us to stay away while he proceeded with a post-mortem examination. I stood numb at the door, listening to the cutting and squelching to which my medicine never extended. Dr Platt came out soon enough, cleaning his bloody hands and announcing that, whilst he would have to send off one of the stomachs for further tests, he was of the opinion that the children had been poisoned. Most probably with arsenic, he said.

I knew that arsenic was cheap and easily available in the trading stores, used as it was for so many farming purposes. "Even if the store kept a poison register," Dr Platt said, pre-empting my unspoken question, "a Native could just say he wanted to kill rats in his kraal. Nothing I know to do about it as things stand now. Odd that there's been no diarrhoea, though."

With these words he spluttered to a close, coughed violently, and climbed into his buggy, one of the stomachs we had fed with our food packed in a bag at his side. He rode off hunched into the light breeze that had come up. We could hear him hacking and blowing his nose as he disappeared down the post road.

Not long after his departure, another of the older children died.

~

Three more of our children died over the next few days, the last one on a Friday, six days after the poisoning. That made thirteen out of the hundred and fifty or so who had eaten the beef on Sunday. The others began slowly to recover and we had no word of further deaths from the parents who had taken their children away. Most of those who were not affected had fled to their homes and by Saturday only sixteen girls and four boys remained at the school. At the end of the week, word came from the District Surgeon confirming that the children had been poisoned with arsenic.

After I received this news I went into the church to pray. As always at Lourdes I felt lost in the cavernous space of the basilica, which was none the warmer for its decorative display. On this day it seemed more cold and empty and dark than ever as I looked up to the aisle where the children usually took their places. Where they raised their voices in the music Fr Willibald wrote in huge letters on immense sheets of cardboard, bound together and placed on a wooden stand before them. It took a boy as small as Scotchman five good strides to turn a page. The voices of the children were somewhat metallic to my ear, but the ease and perfection with which they rendered the melodies, stripped as their scales had to be of the third that set them apart from profane music, never ceased to be part of the wonder for me of mission life.

I could not help but think as I moved from my knees to prostrate myself before the altar on the cold floor whether I should ever have participated in this wonder, consecrated as we were to contemplation, called to give ourselves exclusively and perfectly to the search for God, *recto tramite*. We were set apart from other religious vocations by being dedicated essentially to seeking God rather than seeking souls for God. Was this tragedy visited upon our children not a tragedy of our own invention, a tragedy created by our falling away from our calling, a tragedy born of our – let it be said now, or at least written – sin?

~

At the secular level, news of our tragedy spread only to the most local of our newspapers, at first at least. The *Kokstad Advertiser*, in that special tone they reserved for the spiritual anachronism that had taken root in the region, voiced the suspicion that the children had been dosed with some deadly poison "by the black man".

It was too much to hope that the matter would end there. I understood for the first time physically what is meant by the expression "going cold" when Fr Stephen knocked on my door to tell me, in his most pugilistic mode, that a letter had appeared in the *Natal Witness* making "A Serious Charge against the Trappists in East Griqualand". I stood up at my desk as he rattled on, my mouth dry and my hands only just able to pull closer the offending pages thrust at me.

"Sir," someone signed only as "East Griqualander" wrote to the Editor, "thirty-six dead up to yesterday and a lot more dying as a result of eating diseased meat. We, Europeans and Natives, want to know: is the Government going to make a proper inquiry into this affair? Did the Trappists send for a doctor when the people got ill, or wait until they died? Did the Trappists take any measures to get proper attendance or medicine before at least twenty were dead?"

It is terrible, terrible to say that at this point I began to breathe more easily at the nature of the accusation.

"I have it on the word of a parent who lost two children," our accuser continued, "that nothing was done but praying."

Here we were on safe ground, thanks to our Visitator's distrust of Franz's medical predilections. As was prescribed by the Visitator's Report, we had a respectable array of "the most important allopathic remedies" (or, as Franz would call them until the end, "expensive and poisonous medicines") even if we rarely resorted to them.

As for my real concern, namely who could possibly have poisoned the children in the first place, we could be sure that the actions of all the members of our community would be defended in the highest quarters. Indeed, with the blessing of Mr Strachan I am sure, the Resident Magistrate found it unnecessary to go any further into the matter. "A wicked man who wanted the children away from the school" therefore became the acknowledged, if not identified, villain.

In the one and only letter I have written to the newspapers, I was able to set out the facts of the case in the plainest of plain prose. "By order of Rev. Fr Joseph, one of our doctors, medicine was admitted with good results," I wrote, adding, "It is well known here that a certain Kafir put poison into the food of the children, but we cannot prove it." I ended off with "Yours, &c., The Trappists", which was as close to a flourish as I ever came in my life. Every detail of those nightmarish days still haunts me. I had never appeared so certain and sure of myself in public before, and never less sure that what I was saying was the truth.

To the degree that my skills did approach those of a doctor, I was struck by the District Surgeon's failure to comment on the smell that permeated the air around our sick and dying children. To me this was reminiscent of – of all things – certain of the cakes I indulged in during my decadent days in Vienna. The association was so unexpected and seemed so silly that I tried to dismiss it, but even when I had a few moments to apply my mind more closely the best I could come up with was those confectioneries.

I would not have dreamed of putting something so outlandishly inappropriate to the District Surgeon, who did not, in any event, raise the issue of smell. His physical condition on that day must have limited his abilities to carry out his duties as doctor in this regard, and I did not feel inclined to press him on the point. Certainly he had every confidence that all his faculties were working well enough for him to come to an accurate conclusion. He never even came back to Lourdes to look into any of the other deaths that followed his visit, so tiny Scotchman's stomach remained his only scientific measure of the situation.

Some days after the heartbreaking deaths of the other twelve children, however, Sr Natalia – reaching desperately for some consolation – professed her belief that the bitter sweetness of the air about our stricken children (which reminded her, she said, of cherry laurel leaves) was sure proof that the angels were breathing through them as they died, caring for the agonised little bodies until their resurrection. At that moment, suddenly and unbidden, I recalled the image that had been hovering at the edges of my memory. There it was, the source of that musty but attractive smell so hard to identify – a slice of cake! One of the confections I had tried to dismiss now appeared before me in all its luscious four o'clock splendour, served on a blustery Viennese winter afternoon in a coffee shop. A layered delight, with chocolate and cream dripping over its – marzipan, that was it – its marzipan undercoating, the layer that kept the topping from seeping into the already outrageously rich cake beneath. Yes, the smell was that of marzipan! A substance I had indulged in many a time in those days, but never so memorably as with M, her face inches from mine, wreathed in the steam of the hot drinks before us, flushed with the sweetness of the indulgences we shared.

Again, I could not put forward such a substance, or indeed such an occasion, when Sr Natalia, her face alight for the first time since the deaths, raised her comforting vision of laurel leaves and angels. I kept my memories to myself and left her to cling to her belief, which she announced on any number of occasions for weeks on end. Franz was present at one of these when he joined us at Lourdes for the visit of some journalists from the *Kokstad Advertiser*.

"Cherry laurel," he said, "but musty? You mean like almonds?" Sr Natalia nodded her head vigorously as the smell clicked into correct mental alignment in the catalogue of her senses.

"Almonds?" Franz grunted, "not garlic? There was no garlicky odour on their breath? Then there really was an angel present if they died of arsenic. If I were a policeman who cared enough about this case, I'd check the trading stores for anyone buying cyanide."

At this point the Editor of the *Advertiser*, who – given the prominence of recent events at the mission – had chosen to grace us with his presence, interjected, "Not likely that there would be cyanide in any of Strachan's stores, though." He added, "Can't think what a Kafir would do with it out here. Of course, some of the wealthier newspapers have it at their printing plants. Comes in Monckhoven's Intensifier."

Franz's curiosity was, as always, aroused by any mention of printing, and he asked what the intriguingly German-sounding substance was used for. According to the Editor, it was a standard ingredient for making half-tone plates in the printing of photographs in magazines and newspapers and was kept well guarded. It was very expensive, he explained, but he was clearly more interested in finding out whatever he could about the murders than in the details of newspaper production. He quickly switched back to asking probing questions about the deaths of our children, but between my silence and Franz's brusqueness on the topic discovered no more than the articles already published had made known.

It was with some frustration, I imagine, that he returned to Kokstad able only to write an editorial that stated in admiring tones, as many an editorial had before, that "the Trappists have built schools where thousands of children are trained; they have made bridges, raised edifices, and planted millions of trees. Their church is perhaps one of the largest in South Africa, with its spires and its peal of bells to usher in the morning, and to 'toll the knell of parting day'."

Not the most eloquent praise we had received in the press, despite its aspirations to poetry. But then again the *Advertiser*, consistently friendly to us though it was, did not have the advantages of the newspapers in what passed for metropolitan centres here at the end of Africa, with their superior journalists and half-tone photographs.

~

Arsenic or cyanide? For those who cared this question hung in silence in the air. They were gone now, those innocents around whose deaths it hovered, buried in our cemetery according to our rites, translated by murder into the most perfect of tiny Trappists. They were frozen in death much as they had once been into the shades of silver produced by the lens of our photographer, his studio, as always, amongst our workshops used by shoemaker, saddler, joiner, carpenter and wagon builder. That studio, upon the highest shelf of which there would have been the potassium cyanide that Brother Othmar favoured over the salt of soda for use as a fixative. Contained in a tin canister, the label of which declared it to be highly toxic for inhalation and skin contact, and extremely toxic for ingestion. A canister reachable by a moderately tall man, even one in heavy shoes and hampered by a habit.

For no Native could have approached that building, let alone that shelf. No, it must have been someone who was intimately a part of the mission, someone dressed in a habit, with sleeves full wide enough to conceal a canister. Someone who could wander at will through the mission's buildings

437

and rooms, whose duties allowed him as easily into the photographic studio as the kitchen, or the children's dining hall for that matter.

Or so it would have to be if it was cyanide and not arsenic that was added to the beef.

Unthinkable, surely. It would be difficult, in these days when a detective stalks through the pages of every popular magazine, for even a monk not to know that means and opportunity are not enough in solving a crime. For what of motive? Why would a monk want to murder the children he had made his own, in the only way he could make a child his own? Let us forget for a moment what every priest learns very quickly in the confessional: of all the causes of wrong-doing, motive – "whatever attracts the will" as the Church would have it – is the most difficult to establish. The perfect motive, of course, is the desire to do the will of God, but is not the perfect crime the one for which there is no motive? Your detective may well establish how something was done, and by whom, but what is this worth if he cannot determine why? What even is a conviction if we are left without a reason? Surely this is the most terrible crime of all to contemplate, one for which there *is* no why.

In our case, however, the why and who turned on the how. If we set aside the how, there was no question as to why or who. Who would suspect anyone other than an angry black man dropping the tokens issued by Strachan in place of currency on a counter in a trading store, mumbling about rats. Telling the old men gathered under a tree outside the store loudly in Zulu how he must pay, pay in Madonela's money (that is what they called Mr Strachan) for this poison because he had no child to help him, no child to set traps for him, no child at least who he could own as his. And so now he must lay down poison, all because his children had run back to the school, even after he had been to the white man's court to get them home, he who would never be a Christian but whose eldest son had become a Christian, with one wife only, and his other wives, even the one who his father thought his best wife, the one who treated him more as a father than his own son did. The one his father had been happy to pay many cows for, the one who, even though she had produced no children yet, he still thought a good girl, gone to the Catholics even though she did not want to when his son became one of their Christians, just as so many of his people did because they wanted to, those people who went whenever the bell rang for them …

Yes, if it was arsenic, the who and why were only too clear. Not provable, unfortunately, but all too likely. Obvious, in fact. The Resident Magistrate thought so. The District Surgeon too. Dr Platt was happy to put down arsenic for the record even when he had no sense of smell. And he never came back to hear others speak of cherry laurel leaves and almonds or even marzipan, or to check medical books such as had recently been added to the library at Emmaus. Where a monk from Lourdes, visiting the station to hear an old man's confession, could discover for himself that arsenic and cyanide poisoning have "extremely similar non-specific clinical effects".

Arsenic or cyanide, who could tell? Who could decide between the obvious and the unthinkable? Certainly not a monk who on that Sunday morning came to himself with the air still vibrating about him – no, not so much came to himself as reassembled himself out of a myriad fractured images, pulling himself together as the famous bells of Lourdes finally fell silent. Not a monk who consciously had to close his gaping mouth, wipe the dribble from the corners of his lips, look down to stare in disbelief at what was in his hands …

Not he who, a short while before – who was to say how long? – had stood amidst the tumbling fall of the tones and overtones of the bells, feeling as if the whole universe was about to split open and show its most intimate secrets, as if God Himself had called him, lost as he was between contemplation and action, and told him exactly what he should do. And what it was he might have done to return from being lost, to slip away into the contemplation that was everything to him, to fend off the action that kept pressing in on him and all the others in these cloisters from which the walls had now entirely disappeared. To be replaced by shops and photographic studios and dispensaries and, yes, above all else, schools. What did the Angel of the Lord reveal to His most worthless servant about what he should do to take his small part in the story that made cause and effect redundant? That made ephemeral any action other than the one thing necessary, utterly meaningless anything other than his desire for oneness with God?

No, he could not answer any of this, and no clues came from what he did remember – not from the nursing (but why was there no diarrhoea?), not from the praying (silent words beating like birds against glass, a medium they simply could not comprehend), not from the burying (the breath now gone, and along with it its nagging intimations). But the irritating, insistent fact remained, a fact not dissolvable into words, a fact that not even

Bishop Ricards could have talked away, that the one clue to answering the question no one cared enough to ask lay in deciding between arsenic or cyanide. Cyanide or arsenic?

~

And no one ever did.

The only clear-cut decision made in the wake of these fateful events was that my leadership had failed. People even said – not out loud ever, although the whispers travelled better than any formal proclamation – that Fr Joseph, more through ineptitude than intention, had stirred up the strong feelings around Lourdes that had led to the murders, for which he was then, in a way, responsible. Innocent or not, it was not for me to defend myself against the inquisition to which rumour subjected me. The Regulations require as much. I would have been willing to go even further and confess that my sins may well have extended this far, but I was content to remain silent and submissive.

Nothing was proved against me, and it was not politic to remove me from office immediately. Poor Fr Stephen was the first to be sent away; he was packed off to one of the most remote and least important of our stations, the recently founded Maria Telgte. This was, as I would find out for myself soon enough, merely a halfway house between Lourdes and Mariazell, and even our old pioneer, Fr Arsenius, had not managed to get any pastoral work under way there. Fr Stephen thus fell from Priest in Charge of Mission at Lourdes to a humble builder of fences at Maria Telgte.

As for me, I became ever more invisible at Lourdes, with less and less to do. In my aimlessness, I was drawn often to the cemetery. One evening I found myself standing there, not registering the passing of time until the moon came up, bathing the graves in a silver spectral light. I had ignored the Hours for that day, the only day in my life as a monk. If anyone had missed me, I chose for that day to forsake the living, and let my mind turn to the dead.

Sleep well, my children, I said softly into the night wind just coming up. Pull the ground around you all night long, and dream on until your eternal morning. How many of us from Mariannhill will you find there waking with you in that light, how many? The question stayed with me as I turned to leave and stumbled back to my room in the dark. For myself, I was no longer sure of the answer.

~

440

Before we buried Scotchman, I hung the medal of St Benedict around his neck. Inscribed in Latin on the front of this medal are the words, "May his presence protect us in the hour of death." I had whispered these over and over at his passing. On the reverse side of the medal are the letters CSPB, set around the Cross of the Holy Father Benedict. The letters on the cross signify this message: "May the holy cross be my light; let not the dragon be my guide." In the margin it is written: "Be gone, Satan! Suggest not vain things. The cup you offer me is evil. Drink your own poison."

~

As the months went slowly by, the property of which I was titular head was really run by the new Priest-in-Charge-of-Mission, Fr Theodorich. He was kindness itself, doing everything possible not to make this more obvious than it was and leaving every public formality to Franz, whose eminence even in exile made him the natural representative of the work of Mariannhill in these distant parts.

As for the mission work itself, well, there Fr Theodorich found he had in Fr Willibald a more than eager assistant. It could be said that Fr Theodorich was as free as he was to take over my duties within the enclosure because of Fr Willibald's tendency to assume the leadership of any project in which he was involved. From the moment of Fr Stephen's relocation, the handsome young man with the gold-flecked hair that almost drowned his tonsure had openly begun initiating ways of reaching out into the local communities. The latest of these, to my knowledge, was a magazine of some kind largely authored by himself in Zulu. I did not pay much attention to these developments, but I do remember entertaining the thought that it was unlikely that Fr Theodorich would hold his position for long. My own position would be decided even sooner.

The unfortunate events that had thrown us into such prominence faded rapidly after the children started to return and our schools filled again. It now became my turn to be quietly removed from Lourdes. I was only too happy to go; the sight of the returning children was more than I could bear.

In 1897 I, too, was sent to Maria Telgte, a station far enough away for me to be kept, piously but firmly, in a form of strict seclusion. For a moment, when I was informed of my new appointment, I wondered if the circle of missions we had created was not to become a kind of prison for me, one in which I was condemned to circulate forever, serving a sentence for a crime that no one fully understood. I shivered at the thought of the years stretching ahead of me in these faraway places, but in an instant recovered and prostrated myself at Fr Theodorich's feet.

Only a few hours later Fr Joseph Cupertino climbed into the Spider and was carried off, smiling, to Maria Telgte.

21

What is there of importance to tell you of the years that stretched ahead – years spent away from Franz and the battles he continued to fight that alone seemed to keep the spirit of Mariannhill alive?

Is it of any significance for me to tell you that, officially at least, I was sent to Maria Telgte to assist old Fr Sulpitius Buchauer, who had been transferred there from Mariazell because of his poor health? Or that I found him still the enthusiastic gardener he had been in his prime, trying between the locusts and the hail to lay out an orchard at the mission? Well, for his sake if no one else's, let me tell you that a matter of months after my arrival I came across him lying alongside the pipe he was attempting to run from a nearby spring to the priests' house and, more importantly in his view, the vegetable garden and his new orchard. He was dead, and I was alone.

Abbot Amandus himself had drawn up a master plan for Telgte, as it was popularly known, but it never materialised. Only a small cluster of huts was built, and it did not take me long to realise that it would never become a real mission station. All I was able to do was to maintain it as a place of rest and a night shelter for travellers between Lourdes and Mariazell and, occasionally, between Reichenau and one of those two places.

Visitors were few and I spent most of my days keeping rigorously to the Office, staring out between the Hours across the plain that stretched away from where the huts sought shelter against a low, bare, stony hill. There was no church there then, although I believe the building of one was started in the year in which my story, in effect, came to an end.

~

Only one piece of news sounded a consoling note in the heavy sense of desolation that settled upon me in those first months at Maria Telgte. In the midst of all the worries besetting Abbot Amandus he had the good fortune to be able to welcome back from Rome, in the person of Fr Eduard Mnganga, the first African priest ever. How my heart warmed to hear of the astonishment and joy of the girls, especially, when the Prior of Mariannhill arrived at the monastery school with this grave and accomplished Zulu man by his side. It is difficult to imagine the feelings of the boys at the school the young Kece had himself once attended – awe mingled with envy, perhaps, although this must have paled, I think, before the even more difficult to decipher emotions of the monks at Mariannhill. How did they embrace a child of theirs who returned as a Doctor of Philosophy speaking Latin, English, Italian, German and Greek as fluently as his mother tongue?

The theology, too, that Fr Mnganga had been taught at the Collegium Urbanum would have been far in advance of the basic induction into the priesthood provided by Mariannhill. The College had, after all, been established in 1627 by the Bull *Immortalis Dei* and was under the direct control of the Congregation of Propaganda. Its purpose was to train candidates from all nations for the priesthood who could, if commanded by the Pope, promote and defend the faith anywhere in the world, even at the risk of their lives.

I imagine there was some relief when Bishop Jolivet decided that Eduard would be of most use to the vicariate amongst his own people, and sent him to assist – who else but Fr David Bryant in his work in deepest Zululand. It was only out of interest in my young namesake's career that I had begun to follow the fortunes of Fr David, whom I had thought of as quite appropriately lost in "the wilds of Zululand". He was, it seemed, very comfortably settled on ten acres near Emoyeni, a mission station about which Fr Mathieu used to tell us, regaling us with stories – under the guise of our taking instruction in Zulu – of the great white miscegenator John Dunn who, as he lay dying, begged the Catholic Church to start a school on his land for the hundred or more offspring of his fifty or so Zulu wives.

Much later I came across Bryant's description of the site he had chosen for his first mission amongst the Zulu. I have it before me now, written in his fluent style: "I spent a few months roaming the Zulu country looking for a suitable site for my first Native mission among the Zulu. I at length struck upon one of the loveliest spots in all South Africa, and I immediately named it Ebuhleni. Situated just below the oNghoye all-range, with its great forest, ten miles long by two through, the country was an extensive expanse of hundreds of gentle hills, all of various shapes and heights, and all covered with beautiful woodlands and having numerous crystal brooklets running along the valley. The whole place was furthermore thickly covered with kraals, all heathen, there not being a single 'town native' anywhere around."

A very heaven, indeed, for our ethnographically-minded ex-monk, or perhaps Eden is a better word – an Eden he was not prepared to have spoiled for himself, we would discover, by any taint of knowledge beyond his own. But here I must restrain myself for the moment. A cool head is needed for the rush of darkness so nearly upon us. Suffice it to say that I allowed myself a touch of amusement when I heard that our man of words (who within a few short years of settling in Zululand produced the first Zulu dictionary) had considerable trouble persuading his first house and schoolroom to remain upright. Few knew better than us just how inexperienced he was at building and manual work, and as Trappists we had not in any event set the best example for someone who knew nothing about digging foundations.

But I was both surprised and upset by the news that Eduard – no, Father Eduard, I reminded myself – had been sent as a secular priest to a mission in Zululand. Knowing as I did the young Eduard's love for the monastery (were there never to be any of our converts considered worthy enough to join us as monks?), I prayed for him constantly.

~

As for other news brought to me as part of the baggage of those staying over at the station (rarely if ever for longer than a night), well, wars and rumours of wars did come to my unwilling ears in the desolate silence of Maria Telgte. I had the peace at least of not having to take any particular position, let alone a side, on the British invasion of the Afrikaner republic. The sympathies of my visitors were mainly, if mildly, with the English forces, despite the law in the Orange Free State requiring all teachers to be Protestant and the denial of grants to Catholic schools in the Transvaal. The more liberal wing of the secular priesthood appeared to be strongly against the war. As one of my visitors put it, the fact that Catholics were treated as helots in the Transvaal was a matter for protest not invasion. Another told me that young, predominantly Irish, Catholic soldiers were being buried in our graveyard at Mariannhill and not with Protestants at the British military hospital in Pinetown.

We Trappists did manage one bugle note of glory out there in that world of noise and smoke and blood. The Fathers, Brothers and Sisters at Maria Ratschitz were suffering heavily, cut off as they were from the other missions and from our monastery by the military activity surrounding nearby Ladysmith. A particularly loquacious addition to our Order informed me during his overnight stay at Telgte that Brother Nivard had had the audacity to ride out and enter the camp of General Louis Botha. With his wit and superior knowledge he had awakened in the General a deep respect for Trappists, to such an extent that the General sent a wagon load of foodstuff to our starving mission. "Brother Nivard is a former Bavarian sergeant," the Brother told me proudly, "and he so impressed General Botha with his military knowledge and even more so as an architect and a farmer and an electrician that the General has become respectful of all monks."

I, meanwhile, had been making some progress of my own at Maria Telgte with experiments in electricity. These would not have impressed the Boer General, I am sure, but they were in their own small way intimately tied to the health of our Trappist community. The sickness running through Mariannhill at the time seemed to be erupting even in the bodies of her leaders. In the April of 1899 Franz's brief surges back into some kind of authority at Lourdes were disrupted by a sudden attack of dropsy, or so it was described by monks passing through who had recently been at Emmaus or Lourdes. I concluded from their vague comments that Franz was suffering from what we had come to call "Natalrose".

This was a painful swelling and reddening of the feet and legs, and in his case it was clearly severe. One visitor casually, callously even (unless knowledge of the closeness between Franz and myself had waned so much by now), said he thought that death was slowly closing in on the ex-Abbot. He had not been able to say Mass, I was told, for several weeks. This was disturbing enough in itself, but my distance from the one who despite everything remained my true Superior fed my imaginings more than any description of his symptoms could.

Soon after I received the news that Abbot Amandus been admitted to the sanatorium in Pietermaritzburg. The diagnosis given there was cancer of the stomach. At his own request he was transferred to a local hydropathic establishment. In the intervals between the various cold douches prescribed for him, his attendant monks encouraged him, to no avail, to immerse himself in quiet and tranquillity. Abbot Amandus was only fifty-three years old when he died. It was clear to me that, despite the vigorous expressions of love and reverence for him that filled the air after his death, it was a total lack of appreciation for his extraordinarily sensitive nature that had killed him. I for one will never forget that, when dysentery had broken out at the monastery and a third of the community was confined to bed, he was overheard whispering to a dying monk, "When you depart this life, ask the Good Lord to give me a sign if I am to blame for this epidemic ..."

I could not help but note when I heard of Abbot Amandus's illness that electropathy had been added to his hydropathic treatment. This I knew was coming into vogue. I had read the copy of *Electricity of Heaven and Earth* that Franz owned and I knew that electricity had special properties. It was certainly powerful, as the lightning so common on certain of our stations demonstrated. (Mariathal, for one, continued to live up to its original name, Blitzberg.) Proponents of the use of electricity in medicine propose that the body is like a large magnet, with positive and negative charges. If electricity is applied to the areas where these charges are out of balance, the patient will be cured. It was suggested that electricity was particularly useful in treating nervous diseases, for which there was otherwise no known cure.

There was hardly anything more for me to learn about the Water Cure. I knew as much as I was ever likely to discover in my remote corner of the world about immersion in cold baths, the pouring of water on particular parts of the body, and the drinking or injecting of water to promote internal cleansing. I was even familiar with the "wet sheet treatment". I managed to convince poor old Fr Sulpitius, not long before his end, to submit himself to being wrapped in layers of cold, wet sheets and a woollen blanket, and then to confine himself to his bed until he began to sweat. I must admit that, when I tried to remove his blanket and douse him with cold water, he protested vigorously and would not resort to the Water Cure again, not even the milder version of a loose gown dipped in cold water before it was put on. As for Franz, I suppressed my worries about him as much as I could, not only by continual prayer but also by concentrating hard upon the experiments I had taken up involving zinc and copper, rubber and wire.

Oddly, it was Sr Marie-Gertrude who was much in my mind as I poured the copper sulphate solution I made up from the root killer that I found in Fr Sulpitius's small store of gardening materials into a zinc trough I had devised from the leftovers of his fatal attempt at plumbing. I tried out different ways of creating a non-reactive mounting for the copper insert I fashioned from strips cast off by our wagoner, but I knew that the galvanic cell I was trying to create would not in itself generate a high enough voltage for the electric shocks I needed. There was no possibility of my being able to locate, let alone purchase, so sophisticated a thing as an acid jar battery out here in Nomansland. But I knew from Faraday's experiments – those very experiments at which Sr Marie-Gertrude had been present in London and had made so alive in her accounts of them in Dunbrody – that the humble one and a half volts that my cell produced were quite enough to spin a small electric motor.

I eventually managed to create one of these myself, after many failed attempts at winding a primary wire coil within a many-turned secondary one and then wiring an interrupter's contacts in series between my galvanic cell and the coil. When it finally worked I watched in fascination how the contacts, closed in their resting state, reacted as I applied the power produced by my cell. This activated the coil, producing a magnetic field at its metal core, which pulled the magnetic contact arm towards the core. The interrupter contacts were thus opened, breaking the circuit. As the falling magnetic field then relaxed its hold, the contacts closed, and the entire cycle repeated itself. To my never-ending amazement, the rising and falling magnetic field of the primary coil induced, just as the book said it would, a voltage high enough to give a distinct tingle if one touched it.

Almost as soon as it was discovered that the low voltages produced by a battery could be stepped up to a high enough voltage to give electric shocks, certain "doctors" who were not blinded by a formal training in medicine to alternative treatments began selling these to patients for a wide variety of ills. Now I too could count myself in their ranks. I would watch for hours, transfixed (like the Gaper I was still occasionally called) by the step-up transformer I had created. I soon added to it a method of regulating the intensity of the shocks it generated. This consisted of a metal bar that I could slide into the centre of the coil. The further it was slid into the coil, the greater the magnetic induction and therefore the greater the voltage.

My obsession with things electrical overpowered everything but the discipline of my religious life. So caught up was I in this work that my transfer from Maria Telgte to Mariazell in 1903 made little difference to my life although I had spent, difficult as it is to believe, five years at the station. I was sent to Mariazell as Priest-in-Charge, but Fr Lyssy was appointed to take care of all the mission work at this, the most distant of our stations, and so I was able to maintain both my strict religious observance – even as this all but dissipated in the lives of the Brothers I encountered – and the steady improvement of my electrotherapy machine.

My modest galvanic apparatus was designed, I may add, with only one patient in mind, and only the limited array of illnesses he manifested. It was nothing like Smith's Celebrated Torpedo or Vibrating Electro Magnetic Machine, which I saw advertised in a journal. According to Smith, this could be used with extraordinary success for a host of maladies, ranging from rheumatism, palsy and curvature of the spine to tic-douloureaux, paralysis tubercula of the brain, sick-headache, toothache, St Vitus dance and, of course, epilepsy. However much I improved my apparatus, its only intended patient was even further out of reach where I had been sent, high up in the Maluti region of the Drakensberg. The peace and beauty of this remote mission could not make up for Franz's absence and it had, for me, a strange emptiness.

I knew how dearly Franz had wanted to retire to this place, which I still thought of as his Benjamin, his last child and most darling. There was not much to celebrate on the missionary front here, hemmed in as we were by pagans and Protestants. Fr Lyssy had his hands full, however, with a particularly belligerent missionary monk, a certain Fr Erasmus Hörner, of whom I was to learn again several years later.

In any event, what stays with me from my time at Mariazell are the bursts of agricultural excitement that occasionally found their way through the haze of my struggles with constructing a wooden box for my battery and the instrument it powered. Our Steward, Brother Firmus, carried off eleven first prizes with his Friesland cattle, produce and poultry at the agricultural show in Matatiele – one of the few things I recall from that time. I was preoccupied with perfecting the metal prods – or "Metallic Tractors" as I preferred to call them – that I had attached to my galvanic cell in order to deliver shocks to different parts of the body of my absent patient and it was difficult to get excited by Brother Firmus's much vaunted reputation for producing the largest pumpkins in the region.

~

Much of great moment had been going on at Mariannhill whilst I was lost in the remoteness of Maria Telgte and, for two years, at Mariazell. My last experiences with the higher ranks of leadership at Mariannhill had, I confess, left me only too willing to remove myself from any engagement with those in authority; I could barely find the energy to follow the shifting fortunes of my Superiors. I was kept more or less aware of the broad outlines of what was going on, but this was probably because of their effect on the minutiae of my daily observances, each as precious to me as a tiny jewel of my own that I could polish daily with the full focus of my attention as I learned more and more of its perfection.

I noticed a growing laxity in the observances of those who had occasion to pass through our isolated little house, a laxity that was encouraged by the proclamation of dispensation after dispensation on the stations. These dispensations were a clear expression of the character and inclinations of the man appointed Abbot of Mariannhill in the place of Abbot Amandus – none other than our own Gerard Wolpert.

Abbot Strunk had been brought over to carry out a second visitation and oversee the election of a Superior who would show zeal for the regular order in the monastery and on the stations, one who would ensure that religious life was the foundation of the mission. Fr Gerard, the "archmissionary", was an odd choice for the position. Indeed, when the result was announced, I heard that he wept bitterly and refused to accept the election. I have no doubt his resistance was sincere, but it did not last long. Abbot Strunk took him in hand and made it clear that if he did not accept no other election would be possible. In which case the Generalate would force a stranger upon Mariannhill. More specifically, a certain American stranger.

The name of this stranger had been mentioned several times in the course of the visitation, and it was fear of this prospect more than anything else that unified the community into voting for Fr Gerard and moved him, finally, to accept. Franz was quick to let anyone who cared to know, and a good number who didn't, that he had abstained from voting. This was easy to understand: he would not have wished to support someone who had fought him so hard over the missions, but who else was there? Of course, for those who were firmly of the missionary party Fr Gerard was just the man, and it was impossible to miss the surge of confidence one could feel humming through the mission stations on his appointment as Abbot.

I was more than prepared to remain quiet and watch how things developed. It came as no surprise that Abbot Gerard soon found that it was easier to lead the opposition than the administration. The Visitation Report left behind by Abbot Strunk when he went back to Ölenberg, the report Abbot Gerard was obliged to implement, stressed anew that all the members of Mariannhill were monks and all of them missionaries, and that they could be good missionaries only if they remained good monks. This meant that Abbot Gerard had to make up his mind to be a good monk himself. He delayed this clearly disagreeable duty for as long as possible, travelling to Europe after only five months in office to gain approval for a series of dispensations that, if implemented, would tear the Visitation Report to shreds.

One of Abbot Gerard's first acts in office was to curtail the reading of the Rule. Barely two weeks after the departure of the Visitor, we received a circular decreeing that the full text of the Rule of St Benedict need no longer be read in common. The chapters on the different types of monks and the Abbot and the Monastery Council were to be omitted, as was everything regarding the Office in Choir and the admission of minors, priests, and monks who were strangers. The regulations regarding rank, as well as the prescriptions concerning the Prior and Gatekeeper, were also cut.

Astoundingly, these and every other dispensation put by the "Missionary Abbot" to the Generalate were passed (the only petition refused was the request by Fr Hyacinth that he be allowed to erect a Polish monastery in South Africa, entirely independent of Mariannhill). More surprisingly still, the Visitator himself, Abbot Strunk, used his influence to make sure that they were passed, even those dispensations and liberties he had considered unjustified barely a year before.

Accordingly, monks were now granted a frustulum – breakfast – on fast days, and any kind of food (except meat) could be served during Lent. The motherhouse received dispensation from Office in Choir, which could now be "recited generally". The Choir novices could have recreation daily, and permission was given for them to be sent to the stations during their second year, ostensibly for health reasons. On the stations the daily timetable was relaxed. The hour for rising was put forward yet another hour (to four o'clock), and the Office had to be recited in common only if at least four Choir Religious were present. The Convers Brothers could say Terce and Sext together with Prime in the morning, and their period of work could be extended until …

Well, what does it matter until when? The granting of dispensations was now so common that I, for one, lost in the sanctuary of my distance from the turmoil at the heart of the monastery, simply ignored them all and went back to the strict observance of the Rule. In spite of the joy with which these concessions were received on the stations, I could see that my brother missionaries were not really satisfied, and I suspected that our new Abbot was not either. Dispensations were granted, yes, but dispensations they remained, and dispensations only – exceptions to the Rule that could be taken away by any new Superior in the name of the Rule.

Worse still for Abbot Gerard, he could no longer, on his return to Mariannhill, put off his commitment to being the monk he was supposed to have been from the first. As he must have known, the dispensations he had won could only have been a compromise agreed to by the Generalate to keep him in office, there being no other candidate for Abbot. As a missionary he had never had to concern himself with how the demands of the apostolate could be made to agree with the rules of the Order. But he was now responsible for the monastic observance of over two hundred monks, by no means all of them of a missionary inclination.

To his credit, it was clear that he made a heroic effort at becoming a monk. He also made this resolution officially known throughout the stations and challenged his former companions in arms to follow him in this, just as they had once followed him in the way of disobedience. This not only brought down upon him the anger of the missionaries but also brought home to him just how little acquainted he was with the Trappist way of life. He had come to Africa to work on the missions, had spent his energies working for them and, in truth, loved them alone. He admitted quite frankly that he did not much care for monasticism. This clash between his inclinations and his duty created a conflict in him that informed each of his undertakings, dooming them to failure and spelling disaster for Mariannhill.

It was the custom at Mariannhill that the Abbot join the Office in Choir regularly. Franz, despite his irritation with the hours spent in this way, did this always. Abbot Amandus, of course, embraced it. Fr Gerard, from the days of his noviciate, was seldom required to take part in Choir and actively disliked it. The penance of getting up for the Night Office was simply too much for him and, it appears, he seldom made an appearance before Prime. During the day he regularly found reason for dispensation from Choir because of a slight indisposition or pressing business. He began to stay at the motherhouse as little as possible, leaving for the missions – especially his favourite, Centocow – for the slightest of reasons, and putting off his return for as long as he could.

One could understand why. On the missions the communities were smaller and more loosely organised, making Abbot Gerard's weaknesses less conspicuous. He indulged these to the full, even allowing his sons on the missions to eat meat. Word came that it was Franz himself – active as always and engaged, it would seem, with everything that went on in Mariannhill or any of its stations – who had found this out and reported it. All Abbot Gerard could give as a reason was his health (he suffered from malaria), but even though this was accepted officially no one was convinced. He was very far from setting an example of regularity then, and his admonitions and decrees protecting the regular observance were simply not taken seriously.

No, everyone, not least himself, saw ever more clearly that Abbot Gerard could never make a genuine Trappist. Scarcely four years after assuming office, drained of the dregs of his courage and self-confidence, he left for Europe to ask, even beg, to be suspended from office. Rome was inclined to be sympathetic, but the old problem reasserted itself: if the present Abbot of Mariannhill was allowed to lay down his burden, who should take it on?

The Trappist authorities finally yielded to the persistent urgings of Abbot Gerard, but insisted that he stay in office until a successor could be found. Our failed "Missionary Abbot" could not even succeed in resigning, it would seem, and he returned to a Mariannhill veiled in darkness. The only thing of which anyone at the monastery was now certain was that the stranger would come, the American Fr Gerard had kept at bay only by taking upon himself an impossible burden.

~

I learned of the arrival of Dom Edmund Obrecht, Abbot of the Abbey of Gethsemani in Kentucky, soon after he arrived in 1905, an event that had the most unexpected impact on my life. In no time at all after he had taken office, I received an order reassigning me to ... I was breathless opening the impressively sealed letter: Emmaus.

Yes, I was to hurry to "the aging and ill Abbot Franz, whose strength was fast leaving him". I was told it was Franz himself who had called for me. Nothing else about Dom Edmund could interest me at this point. I packed as quickly as possible – my galvanic apparatus, which I had decided to call "The Helper", needing the most attention – and hurried off to take to Franz the Holy Viaticum. I had barely climbed off the wagon at Emmaus when Franz himself descended upon me. "Only two weeks since I wrote asking for you to come and assist me!" he exclaimed. "The Abbots of Mariannhill usually refuse everything I ask, sometimes before I can think to ask it!" He had an abundance of complaints about my predecessor, Fr Odilo, who, he said, was clumsiness personified and took dictation so poorly that Franz might as well have used his own hands.

I was pleased, if rather taken aback, to find the "dying" Franz so very much alive. Still, he was not his old self. The hands in question were shaking as he spoke and, as he hustled me into his imposing two-storeyed brick house, I was shocked to note how much his eyesight had deteriorated. He was eighty-one years old at the time.

I had visited Franz while I had been stationed at Lourdes and sought his advice on a number of matters. Still I was not prepared for the scale of developments at Emmaus in the eight years or so since I had last been there. The most impressive of his buildings, also a two-storeyed affair, was a hundred by thirty-two feet. Fifty cows could be accommodated on the ground floor, and half of the upper floor was a beautiful dairy. The other half was the source of much amazement – who but Franz would dream of having a piggery upstairs? And under the same roof as a dairy? Yet so perfect were the flushing arrangements (which, like the children's dormitories at Lourdes, had sloping floors) that there was nothing to the least degree offensive about this veritable drawing-room for pigs. Certainly the animals looked as happy as they were sleek.

"This was built according to a system invented by myself," Franz announced, "although most of the building was done by Brother Melchior and Sr Laurentia and Sr Pacifica. Two Kafir boys helped them, but soon after we laid the iron slabs on the floor they ran away, like all the rest!"

Stalls for horses had been put up at the end of the barn, a three-storey warehouse erected to the east of the combined cowshed and pigsty, and a massive building for the Natives constructed directly in front of it. The thousands of bricks used in these constructions were explained by a brick factory, which was worked entirely by the Sisters. Yet more bricks had been used to construct the very latest building, a church. The good Sisters Laurentia and Pacifica served as both bricklayers and plasterers in this enterprise, with Brother Melchior acting as stonemason and carpenter.

The church had been blessed by Franz, assisted by four priests, in

December of the previous year and dedicated to St Francis Xavier. That the sermon was preached in the native tongue, as Franz put it, compounded the irony of a Trappist church bearing the name of a saint with a legendary disdain for learning the languages of the countries to which he took the Word. The preacher was the newly ordained Fr Aloysius Mncadi, the second of our Native converts to return from Rome trained as a priest – a secular priest again, however, and still an assistant priest at that.

And yes, it was Eduard who sprang to my mind when I was told this. Whether Franz sensed my response or not I do not know, but I felt his eyes on me when he added that Fr Aloysius had some interesting news of my young namesake. Well, namesake of sorts it would appear, for not only had he come to be known as "Edward" in Zululand, that place of English aspirations, but he had also taken to calling himself "Fr Edward Müller" – umlaut and all, as Franz put it. "He acquired this name in Germany," Franz explained. "He used to go there on holiday when he was studying in Rome. They couldn't pronounce 'Mnganga' and so 'Müller' he became."

The small matter of a name cast only a tiny shadow upon that bright day when I stood next to Franz again. Looking at his church, I noticed with quiet satisfaction that it stood free of a bell tower, a matter of grave concern to me. Not long after I moved to Mariazell, an excited passer-through had informed me of the completion of Mariannhill's "Campanile", which, he enthused, "seems to have stepped out of the twelfth century from Italy to visit South Africa". As he spoke, I silently wondered what architectural visions possessed Brother Nivard's imagination now, and trembled at the thought of the monastery trying to outdo its missions in breaking this rule of Trappist architecture.

Franz had jerked me back to Emmaus and the present with a eulogy to the steam engine he had set up on concrete foundations at the back of the pigsty, and I was relieved to see, bearing in mind the surprise in my luggage, that his love for engines and engineering was by no means diminished. His latest labour-saving device, shown off with a pride barely concealed by much self-deprecating humour, was a narrow-gauge track running through the stables that transported the heavy milk cans to the door when they were filled.

I had no time on that first day to unpack, let alone show off "The Helper". Franz was as full of his own ideas as ever, and the pressure of these, when they could not be written directly onto the world around him, could only be relieved through the tip of a pen. By the end of that very day I was again dispatching letters for our ageing but unquestionably vital founder.

~

Franz was, however, noticeably weaker. He managed his dictation well enough, but his voice was thin and raspy and, at its most querulous, broke or gave out on him entirely. I was not surprised when he told me, in between letters, that of late he had had to omit preaching and even exhortations in the confessional. He was able to say Mass but only with assistance, and my new duties, he informed me in that brusque tone that he adopted when concealing a weakness, would include that assistance.

I noticed that Franz's failing eyes prevented him from reading as well as writing. And I soon found that he had not been exaggerating his need for assistance. It was relatively easy, then, for me to introduce my electromagnetic apparatus. As I had hoped, Franz's naturally progressive tendencies predisposed him towards my machine and, amidst a flood of questions on every aspect of electrotherapy, he was only too happy to submit to it. I set up my galvanic cell to charge and tried to respond to some of his questions. Good health, I informed him, was the result of the equilibrium of magnetic and electrical charges, and magnets and electrical devices applied correctly to the ailing body restored this balance.

Franz jumped when I pressed the metallic tractors against his skin and administered the first shocks. Moving these "electrodes" to a different set of joints, I directed the electric current there to increase the blood circulation and accelerate the process of repair. To encourage Franz I told him that the treatment was good not only for problems with the circulation of the blood and the heart's action but also infections, high blood pressure, headaches, constipation, dyspepsia and insomnia. It worked well, too, for nervousness and melancholia …

With this I had said too much. Franz jerked up and barked, "I am simply unaware that I have nerves. And I have never, as you well know, had so much as a headache in all my life as a Trappist, let alone a pain in my belly or my stomach! If I cannot sleep I simply plunge into the bath of ice-cold water I keep in my room."

Franz could afford to be as dismissive as he was of nervous disorders, but a significant number of Brothers at Mariannhill had shown signs of mental disturbance. In the past I had prescribed a change of air for those so afflicted, moving them to the higher stations whenever possible, but this rarely had the desired effect. It was one of my most fervent – and secret – hopes that magneto-electric treatment could help the men I saw weeping for hours for no apparent reason, or falling into staring silences so deep that they were noticeable even in a Trappist.

Electrotherapy is a slow and time-consuming process, but Franz, somewhat to my surprise, was quite patient with me. Later I extended our sessions to include time in a galvanic bath, which I myself set up. This I would use locally or generally, at times asking Franz to keep a particular limb in the electrified water to treat its rheumatic joints and, at other times, requiring him to immerse himself fully to get the necessary electrical factor effect on his circulation irregularities. I have met those who are sceptical of the treatments I embraced for Franz's sake, but let me say that I never went on to experiment with the magnetic belts and countless other items of therapeutic magnetic apparel announced in the newspapers and journals I read to improve my ability to heal. I was not concerned as they were with restoring "vital power" missing from middle-aged men (of course), nor did I aspire to the virtues of the "Volcanic Belt", which could, besides improving health and posture, comb the hair, press clothes, and promote a luxuriant moustache in thirty days.

Yes, I have lived long enough now to smile at these excesses of the time, and even at most of my own hopes for "The Helper". I still believe, however, that it was by progressively slowing down the process of calcification in Franz's blood that I kept him alive for the next three years. And it was not so long ago that I dragged my old machine out again, this time for use upon myself. I remembered that one of the more convincing claims made for electrotherapy was its effectiveness in treating writer's cramp.

~

Hard as Franz worked me as his amanuensis, the taking down of his dictated letters, articles and memoirs alone would not have brought on the painful turning in of my right wrist that has made work on the latter part of this story so painful physically as well as spiritually. Isolated as he was, there were others who were only too happy to serve our founder in any way they could. Favourite amongst the devoted Sisters who gathered around him was Sr Euphrosina – Sister Frohsin, as Franz dubbed this intensely cheerful woman – who visited Emmaus regularly, riding over from Lourdes on horseback whenever she could. Franz particularly liked her to take down his dictation, often saving his more intimate and sensitive thoughts, it seemed to me, for her hand. His letters on a range of topics were flying out of Emmaus as furiously as ever, meanwhile, and there was more than enough for me to jot down on the page in the course of the usual working day.

I learned from Franz's letters that our new Superior, Dom Edmund, appointed not as Abbot but as Administrator, had not been pleased to leave his peaceful and beautiful abbey in Kentucky to become captain of a ship tossing about in a storm. He had agreed to come only in a temporary capacity, insisting that he keep his own abbey and be able to visit it once a year. As Administrator his task was to investigate conditions in the monastery and on the missions and improve them to the point where a new Abbot could be chosen. For this he had demanded that the General Chapter and Propaganda grant him (the words were transmitted to us directly) "great powers of authority". These had been given, on the understanding that he restore peace to Mariannhill by dealing with the situation "energetically" and by "enforcing again strict monastic discipline".

Dom Edmund was swept to us on the crest of a new spirit within the General Chapter or, more precisely, a revived one – revived in no small part by the troubles of Mariannhill. Out of the discussion of our problems a resolution was formulated that read: "Our Order, which is dedicated to the contemplative life, shall not accept any mission or exterior activity in the actual sense of the word. But if circumstances demand this partly, these shall only be undertaken with the reservation that life in the community in a monastery is observed regularly."

It was strange hearing these words, even as one read them out for the benefit of a Superior with failing eyes at a well-established mission station that formed part of a well-established chain of mission stations. How my soul stretched towards them, those words that guaranteed silence and the one form appropriate to a body and soul as adrift as mine. I feared now that I was forever lost to them, for if anything they underscored the anomaly Mariannhill represented within the Order of the Cistercians of the Strict Observance. They were a clear signal that no new undertakings would be allowed to get out of hand in the way Mariannhill had, but held no promise for those who knew just how far Mariannhill had drifted from them.

Despite the great powers granted Dom Edmund, he had little latitude for manoeuvring. Whatever doubts some of us harboured, as far as the Order was concerned Mariannhill was a Trappist monastery and should return to being one. Above all else, Dom Edmund was to ensure that the Cistercian spirit came into its own again.

~

On paper at least, Dom Edmund was just the man for the job. When he took over Gethsemani Abbey in Kentucky, founded by the Trappists of Melleray in the 1800s, it too had been lost in darkness, a darkness deepened by a series of very public attacks and calumnies. Determined to blast out its spiritual dust and polish its public image he began, typically, with the latter. The buildings of Gethsemani, much like those of Mariannhill, had bare and austere brick walls. Dom Edmund saw to it that these were coated with a material that looked like warm, mellow stone. So much for the outside; he also had the church remodelled and redecorated, and even embellished it with stained-glass windows. These were, of course, contrary to the Cistercian tradition: in the twelfth century, Abbots who put in stained glass did a considerable amount of fasting on bread and water under penance from the General Chapter. But, as he argued (convincingly, it would appear, for he escaped censure), stained glass was a better way for the monks to counter the ferocious Kentucky sun than to daub the windows, as they had been doing, with white paint at the beginning of each summer season.

But Dom Edmund had also reintroduced the strictest of Trappist discipline at Gethsemani and, in no time at all, improved the reputation of the monastery in the eyes of the surrounding populace. We were unable to learn much about his methods of achieving this. All we knew was that, in the twenty-three years he had been a Cistercian before he took over Gethsemani, he had acquired a wide practical knowledge of everything a prelate needed to know. He had begun his religious life at La Grande Trappe itself, no less, and had, therefore, been formed as a monk at the centre of the Order. He had served in administrative posts at other Abbeys, one of them being, Franz was intrigued to discover, Cellerarius at the very Tre Fontane that Franz had resurrected from the swamps around Rome.

To top it all, Dom Edmund went on to spend many years in the Roman headquarters of the Trappists, where he gained an intimate working knowledge of the way things were done in our Order. He won his appointment to the troubled Kentucky Abbey by earning a reputation for dealing with problems throughout the Order quickly and efficiently.

Why Dom Edmund's deployment now to the southern tip of Africa? We learned that Gethsemani had offered refuge to a group of seventeen men who had arrived one day in 1903 at New York City, where Dom Edmund was awaiting them at the French line docks. Newspapermen swarmed around the Abbot of Gethsemani, inundating him with questions about these singular immigrants. Dom Edmund knew exactly when to remain enigmatic, and so word got out that the seventeen were Boer generals who had escaped from an English concentration camp in the Transvaal, and who were now being offered refuge amongst the monks of Our Lady of Gethsemani. The men were, in fact, refugees from the Abbey of Fontgombault, which the government in France had persecuted to the point of its closing down. Facts were rarely the means by which Dom Edmund got his way. He did not bother to clear up the misunderstanding that gave him an apparent South African connection as he made his way towards Mariannhill tasked with returning it to the proper Cistercian spirit.

Such a directive did not guarantee him a warm welcome. His reception at the monastery, we heard, was cold and sad, and his first act as Administrator did nothing to change this atmosphere. He began by calling a halt to all building projects on the missions and forbidding any other programmes aimed at their consolidation or expansion. This confirmed the widespread opinion that it was his intention to liquidate the missions as soon as he could, an impression reinforced by the changes he began making to the motherhouse almost immediately.

Many of Mariannhill's buildings were still quite primitive and provisional; the monastery was still – as Franz had always seen it – a temporary arrangement, the product of my accident with the first of the wagons carrying us to the site that our founder had in mind. The foundation stone for Mariannhill proper had not yet been laid and the hill was still unoccupied, the monastery buildings and the schools and shops and workrooms crowding together at its foot. It must be admitted that by now the temporary structures had grown to such an extent that it was difficult to even think of moving them.

Dom Edmund began his work by creating a proper and effective enclosure. The size of Mariannhill militated against a wall, and so he ordered that the property be fenced in with strong wire. It would take several years and no less than fifty tons of wire for this to be completed. By early 1907 the fence was one and a half miles long, and a sign to the world of Mariannhill's monastic isolation.

The sense of enclosure was reinforced by the building of an imposing gatehouse over the main road into the monastery. Visitors now had to enter through the elaborate archway of an entrance porch that took its architectural inspiration from the entrance to Tre Fontane, more, it must be said, in honour of Dom Edmund's time at this monastery than Franz's hand in bringing it back to life. This had inscribed upon it the symbols of the Orders out of which Mariannhill sprang and images related to key moments in its development. The Cistercians are there, I am told, in their coat of arms of three black lines on a white ground; the Benedictines too, with their black TAU Cross on a white shield; and the shields at the far ends bear the names Tre Fontane and Dunbrody respectively. Mariastern is inscribed below the central panel.

The Abbots of Mariannhill are there too: Abbot Amandus is represented by his coat of arms of a golden anchor on a blue background, Abbot Gerard by a crosier entwined with a Bantu spear. And Franz? Well, his shield is there, with its golden lions on a black background and the most literal of allusions to his name – a pan, to represent the "pan-maker". His motto is there as well, although at the time it must have been seen more as an indict-ment than something to be emulated: "So run that you obtain the prize."

Dom Edmund did not tire of announcing on every possible occasion that he knew only one Gospel, and that was the Holy Rule. He condemned, loudly and roundly, any person who preached another. All dispensations were wounds on the body of the Rule, he said, and he began issuing decree after decree setting aside each and every regulation that had been altered to suit the life of Mariannhill. He abolished the second breakfast altogether, and the breakfast for the days of fasting during Lent. The beginning of his administration coincided with the beginning of Lent as it happened, which provided him with many other opportunities to make his point. He forbade the taking of dessert during Lent, for example, despite the fact that dessert at Mariannhill consisted only of fruit or fruit preserves without sugar, and that it had been granted during Lent because in our inverted climate this was the season when fruit ripened.

Even I, won over to the Administrator as I could not help but be by my reassignment, would gaze mournfully at the groaning boughs of our apple trees. However, I allowed myself some hope in our new Superior when he returned prayer in Choir to the forefront of our lives. Vespers and Compline had to be sung every day in the monastery again, and Dom Edmund stressed that everywhere, in the motherhouse and on the stations, the Office was to be said precisely as set out in the daily timetable of the Regulations. No times were to be shifted, as they had been, to allow for the pressures of work, and prayers to be said in common were reintroduced on the stations.

Manual work was to replace the hours of study allowed to the Choir Fathers, monks had to wear their cloaks in daytime again and not only for the Night Office. Deep bows, going down on one's knuckles, had to replace genuflections and prostrations were reintroduced even on the stations, where they raised much confusion amongst our new Christians. The time of rising was moved back from four o'clock to three, and the observance of silence was enforced again in its full strictness.

~

My presence at Emmaus was enough, in its humble way, to make Franz one of the few on the missions to receive our zealous Administrator cordially. He could scarcely wait, in fact, for his visit to "Emaus". Franz was prepared to take this in the formal sense, for what else was the Administrator but a Visitator with no limit set to his visitation? When it was announced that he would be touring the stations, and that he would be with us just after Easter, we were more than ready, with everything done that could possibly be done to show off our work to its best advantage. As it turned out, his carriage was already receding into the emptiness of Nomansland before we had quite registered its arrival.

"At Emaus he wanted to see absolutely nothing," Franz fumed in a letter to Rome that ran to thirty-two pages. It was only by force, he claimed, that he had got the Visitator into the new cow stables. Despite the favour our new Superior had shown me, I was not called before this stocky man, his beard and hair trimmed to exactly the same close nap all round his head, his cheeks already beginning to hang over his tight, constantly pursed mouth, the aquiline cut of his nose just saving his face from fleshiness. I watched him from a suitable distance whilst he did his quick turn around our station, his brow knitted over his eyes in a permanently knowing expression, as if

461

he never saw anything in the world but what he expected to find there, little of it to the good. He called no else forward either, and in this it seemed we received the same treatment he meted out everywhere he went.

At no site had he allowed any member of the community who so wished, as was the usual practice, to approach him for an audience. And those he chose to interview found it to be a very one-sided affair. They were given no chance to say anything, and what was said to them, at great length, was invariably negative. It was not out of the ordinary for them to find themselves addressed as "scoundrels" and "good-for-nothings". From the moment he dismounted at a station, Dom Edmund would begin issuing orders; if any missionary dared to question these with a suggestion, he would be cut short with "You can't tell me anything! I know all about you already". And Franz's outrage was not as well founded as he believed – he was a full cow stable ahead of most of the other missions, where Dom Edmund had barely looked into a single workshop or at a building of any kind.

Our Administrator seemed to make it a principle not to get any information from the person or place he visited, relying instead on his study of documents and third-person reports. "He appears amongst us as the all-knowing and almighty, this … this … *Omnipotens*," fumed Franz, heavily stressing the French rather than the German or even Latin form of the word. For not only was our new Superior a stranger coming from America but, to add insult to injury, he was – certainly as far as Franz was concerned – "a Frenchman through and through". Franz refused to be fooled for a second by the German name of Dom Edmund's hometown; everyone knew that Stotzheim was in the pro-French part of Alsace. And for all the renewed stress on silence that Dom Edmund brought, the nickname Franz had given him spread rapidly through the stations.

Dom Edmund had clearly decided that the solution to the tension between the missions and the motherhouse was to centralise the governance of Mariannhill, concentrating it in himself. The Monastery Council continued to meet, but scarcely any place was made under his chairmanship for the exchange of views. Those votes that were taken were a farce. Any decision or action not originating from the Administrator was deemed "agitation", and Dom Edmund saw agitation everywhere.

No doubt to suppress resistance to his plans, he decreed that the exchange of letters would be permitted only "for important and necessary local affairs of the mission or station". There was to be no exchange of thought about general conditions at the mission, no criticism about our present situation, or any comment about Propaganda. To enforce this, all letters had to pass the censure of the Administrator himself. Censorship is in accordance with the customs of the Order, but it had never been applied to letters between the higher Superiors as was the case now, even when the letters were sealed.

As with Dom Edmund's nickname, I had never known rumours, facts and opinions to fly about the motherhouse and the missions as fast as they now did. It was not only that monks are endlessly inventive in finding ways to circumvent the observance of silence, for who else is more practised in it, and therefore in ways to bypass it? A major part of the problem was the contrast between the restrictions the Administrator imposed and the obvious pleasure he took in talking. He himself was the chief carrier of news within the motherhouse and between the stations, although I doubt that he realised this.

Whilst travelling, for example, Dom Edmund could not refrain from holding forth on anything and everything that had caught his attention at the places he visited. No matter that his only audience on these occasions was a lowly coach driver, the Administrator could keep nothing to himself. And the coach driver, quiet and humble as he was in the presence of authority, was a man who could not wait to spread what he heard once amongst those of his own rank. The coach driver's accounts of the Administrator's thoughts and anecdotes appeared in different versions in every corner of Mariannhill.

The Religious at Mariannhill had soon discovered this unfortunate aspect of Dom Edmund's character. Unlike those of us on the missions, they had been granted individual audiences with the Reverend Father, and they had opened up to him with the simple confidence encouraged, even demanded, by this practice. They were to regret their sincerity, for Dom Edmund thought nothing of betraying the confidentiality of his office. "What they tell you in secret, shout out from the rooftops," the Scriptures tell us, and never was this applied more inappropriately. Our Administrator would casually and carelessly reveal the most private information shared with him by Fathers, Brothers and Sisters who had trusted in the discretion their formal relationship with him was meant to guarantee. He would also happily reveal information from classified documents he had been given access to whilst he was at the Generalate, something that brought many of the past secrets of our troubled relations with our Order alive again in the most vicious way.

It was as if every demon we had tried to defeat was unleashed again, and many of them, once released into the air, made their way to the isolation of Emmaus and gathered in a chattering swarm around the head of our founder.

~

None of Dom Edmund's strange mix of arbitrariness, rigour and indiscretion ever seemed to harm his rapid rise through the religious ranks. We learned far too late that he made his way not only by understanding all there was to know about chant, ceremony, liturgy, canon law, but also by being a linguist, a cosmopolitan, a diplomat, a connoisseur of books and manuscripts – and more. He had put Gethsemani firmly on the map of American Catholicism by becoming the intimate friend of not just several of the most high-ranking prelates but of politicians too, like the successive Governors of Kentucky, and countless influential businessmen. He soon let them know that his connoisseurship extended to cigars and whisky, and he became widely known for his skill at poker, especially when travelling, as he often did, by train. It was not unusual for railroad executives to run a special train to convey him or his honoured guests to and from Louisville to the Abbey – until it occurred to them, not without a gentle suggestion or two perhaps, to make him the gift of a motor car instead.

Dom Edmund threw his monastery open to men who would never have dreamed of coming there before. He had a popular book published about the place, and soon word spread that Gethsemani was anything but a penitentiary for censured clerics. He built up one of the finest monastic libraries in America, over forty thousand volumes that included Migne's Greek and Latin Fathers, sets of St Bernard, St Thomas, Duns Scotus, many incunabula and even manuscripts of St Bernard. Numerous ancient Cistercian liturgical manuscripts were gathered up, most of them antiphoners, one from the twelfth century. I could not help the pricks of envy when I read of this, especially since, soon after my arrival, Franz decided to give away his library. He sent all his books as a gift to Mariathal, hoping that others would follow his example and that a missionary library could thus be formed on this relatively neutral site.

What with his own eyesight fading, and his irritation at my too slow and too quiet reading, I suppose Franz had reason enough for this action. But it certainly left a hollow space in the life of a monk who had stolen many moments from the time set aside in the Rule for private meditation to read about the secrets of lightning and thunder, the healing power of water, the poisonous effects of certain chemicals

As for our globe-trotting, poker-playing, whisky-drinking Administrator, in everything he did he proved just how deafening silence can be. Surely no one can be harder of hearing than one who imposes silence on everyone else and then reserves for himself the freest of speech. And yet, I have sometimes awoken in the middle of the Great Silence and asked myself, is this not, ultimately, the attitude we as an Order had brought to Africa? Was not our observance of silence, filled with its prescribed sounds – the chants, the prayers, the psalms, the hymns – the very thing that sealed off our ears? Were not our lowered eyes a refusal to see any sign or signing out of Africa itself, an imposition of our blindness too on a world we could not – *would* not – hear? And were not the missionaries the loudest of all, hearing and seeing and speaking only with a view to converting what they heard and saw into the echo of their own voices?

Be that as it may, there was no doubt that Dom Edmund's startlingly simple view of the religious life, rendered simplistic by its total absence of the questions that had the best of our Superiors awake and sweating in the dark, and made dangerous by its unawareness of dire inner contradictions, had nothing to offer to those of us who were drowning between true silence and the all too real temptation to speak out on the missions. No, Dom Edmund's sophisticated ways left him without the ability or inclination to look into the logic of the way we coped in our primitive conditions; instead, he absorbed it all into his permanent air of outrage.

And unbeknown to us, something he noticed during his visit to Emmaus had shocked his sensibilities more than anything else had succeeded in doing thus far in his time in Africa.

~

Franz never failed to show off his Red Sisters as the reason for his success at Emmaus. To him, they were a living lesson in self-reliance, a topic to which he had given much thought. "Properly understood, such work does not interfere with contemplation," he dictated to me for one of his journal articles. "On the contrary, it leaves the soul free to turn to God, while the fresh air takes away the sickly colour caused by continuously working in-doors, and thoroughly restores the Sisters' health. Moreover, their example of manual labour, willingly done and with dignity, is a powerful incentive to our African people to follow suit – not to mention that it saves the mis-sionary treasury much expense, suffering as it always does from chronic consumption."

On the occasion of the Administrator's visit, Franz had not even been able to make his point about work as contemplation, let alone dignity. Usually his complaints about Dom Edmund centred on his abuse of the power of speech – "He cannot listen to anyone!" he would announce to those who passed through the mission. "He is a powerful boaster who just shouts everyone else down with his loud voice!" But this time the Administrator had restricted himself to one withering look at the Sisters: at their rolled-up sleeves, their work-stained clothing, the sweat dripping from under their headgear as they mixed mud and fed the roaring fire and lifted unsteady piles of bricks onto their shoulders on wooden supports, all the while silently obeying Franz's commands that this or that be done more swiftly, more accurately, more efficiently. "No, like this, not like *that*," Franz remonstrated even as Dom Edmund looked on, and in the middle of the Administrator's pointed silence he grabbed a trowel to show how it was to be used, every inch again in his old age the son of a farmer building roads outside Mariawald whilst hopelessly untrained monks bumbled about.

Dom Edmund looked, and Dom Edmund stayed silent – ominously so. Without another word to Franz, he climbed into his coach. And then, as he drove away, the first words of a veritable tirade whipped back to us in the dust that plumed out behind him. We could not make them out, but it was obvious that his coachman would have much of interest to relate when they arrived at the next stop on Dom Edmund's tour, and that, soon enough, we would be hearing more on what had already become the vexed question of the Sisters. Franz had stared after the carriage, and then muttered through the ugly curl of lip that had become a constant feature of his expression of late, "He does not even wish to quarrel with me. He and his collaborators have decided to wait until I am dead, so that they may have a free hand to do what they will with all I have built – even my Red Sisters."

It was Abbot Amandus who first set in motion the idea that the Red Sisters should be absorbed into the Trappist Order. Franz had fought him on this, using every inch of his influence amongst the Sisters to resist their being given over to contemplation. Many of them remained kindled by their founder's fiery spirit, seeing themselves in Africa with one purpose and one purpose alone: to be missionaries. But for some, the image of a Cistercian nun doing a limited amount of work between bells calling them to Choir seven times a day had become attractive. Abbot Amandus moved them ever further in this direction. Under his rule the Sisters sang their first Mass in Latin, the Marian Office was recited everywhere, and the Trappist ceremonies of public correction and prostration were observed in Choir and Chapter. Privately, in their cubicles, many Sisters took on the old monastic discipline of flagellation one morning a week.

All this drove Franz to paroxysms of anger and protest. For years he had told each intake of his beloved "Light Infantry" that the Brothers were there to prepare the way for the missionaries of the future and the Sisters were the vanguard of those missionaries. "Above all," he would say, "you are never to become Trappistines yourselves! Never!" The fact is, however, that the community of women Franz had created by sleight of hand against the wishes of his Bishop and his Order had no formal existence within the Church. As such they were exposed to every shift in the winds of authority gusting out of Mariannhill.

Abbot Gerard attempted to formalise their situation in a very different way from that pursued by Abbot Amandus. Like many of the missionaries, he did not think highly of the Sisters as a community. He certainly did not wish to make them the equal of his Trappists on the missions by affiliating them to the Order. Practical issues, especially economic ones, led him to decide that some sort of association of the Sisters with the Trappists was, nevertheless, necessary.

His idea was to keep the Sisters, in effect, as a cheap labour force on the missions, where their industry and skill at economising would save not only the missions but Mariannhill itself from collapsing. Even he had to admit that the Rectors on the missions had developed expensive habits over the years, and he was open in his demands that they reduce the subsidy they received from the motherhouse. But no one, least of all Abbot Gerard, was prepared to be open about his other need for the Red Sisters: their presence helped stop the gap within the ranks of the Lay Brothers formed by the shortfall in religious vocations in Europe. This was aggravated in the case of Mariannhill by the sudden dwindling in the number of novices after Franz's deposition.

467

And yet Abbot Gerard's sense of what the Red Sisters were good for was radically different from Franz's. Under the "Missionary Abbot", they were forbidden to hold religion classes, to enter any homestead or visit the sick or baptise anyone. In short, all missionary work was taken from them, as was most manual labour. Ploughing was forbidden, and building – except on Emmaus, where even Abbot Gerard knew better than to come between Franz's Sisters and their making of bricks. Everywhere else the Sisters were placed entirely under the jurisdiction of the Rectors, and virtually the only activity left them, beyond seeing to the needs of the Brothers, was secular teaching.

Franz raged. His life's work had now come down to preserving the Sisters in the form he had created for them. This could be achieved in one way only: total separation from the Trappists. He dedicated his last years towards this goal – and thus ensured his persecution to the end.

With Dom Edmund the wind turned again to Abbot Amandus's quarter. Dom Edmund let it be known that he was not against the Sisters being involved in work, even heavy work, provided the common standards of personal conduct, propriety and decency were observed. Domestic work and gardening were acceptable, perhaps even some painting or light indoor trades; hat-making would prove a great success. But Sisters standing on top of scaffolds, mixing cement and making thousands of bricks! He had no respect, he said, for missionary Sisters who strained themselves physically, neglected their personal grooming and appearance, and showed scant regard for tidiness and common order. Given the state of dress of certain Sisters he himself had seen, how could a monk conscientiously observe the rule of modesty of the senses, especially the eyes!

From now on, a Sister was, in effect, to be cloistered. No Sister was to be permitted to go out at any time, except when she visited a critically ill person – and then only if escorted by a schoolgirl. If a Sister was sick, I for one was informed in no uncertain terms, she was to be treated by another Sister, and not by a monk. On the subject of weekly confessions, the Administrator claimed to speak for all the priests when he said they were "much relieved" when the Sisters troubled them with confessions as little as possible. According to Dom Edmund, the priests agreed that hearing the Sisters' confessions was for them the most unpleasant chore of the week.

As for the remainder of the Sisters' personal sanctity, Dom Edmund, like Abbot Amandus, measured this by their silence, by which he meant the perpetual silence of the Trappists. When the Sisters tried to engage with him on this (or any other) point, he responded with a challenge: "How is it," he asked, "that so many of you are upset about keeping monastic silence? Does your excitement not prove that you have neglected silence all along? Faithfully acquit yourselves of even the most insignificant chores, and abandon yourselves to a childlike trust in Divine Providence, not talk and conjecture ..."

Franz retorted angrily that by Divine Providence Dom Edmund meant nothing more than himself, the "All-Powerful One". But what did the Sisters themselves think of all this? I have learned with age how dangerous it is – impossible, as well – to speak for others, especially those of another sex. And did St Theresa of Avila not say, "It takes a long time to know us women"?

Well, a lifetime has not been long enough for me, and I must tell you, instead, of a man who entered our midst and, on behalf of our Sisters, completed Franz's ruin.

~

On a late February evening a year or so earlier, I had looked up from the neat transcriptions I was making of Franz's memoirs to see a man appearing around the bend of the road leading from Umzimkulu to Emmaus. It was an evening that crackled with dry electric heat, the clouds on the horizon lit from within by pulses of silent light. Not a good day for walking, although it was doubtful whether the distant bluster would actually break upon us. It struck me then how strange it was to see a white man walking out here, so far from any possible point of departure. The man stopped at the gate to Franz's house and looked at me, lit up as I was in the window of the front room that served as Franz's study. Then he turned and made his way up to the white latticework edging the veranda and the portico over the front door.

Something prevented me from getting up to open the door. The change in atmospheric pressure brought about by these African thunderstorms always gives me headaches, especially when they hover, as this one did, for hours without breaking. There was nothing I could do about the pain, and it made it even more difficult than usual for me to think clearly. Perhaps it was the dull throb in my head that kept me pressed to my chair, frozen for the moment in that room in Franz's strong, neat house. It is difficult not to think that it was something more, knowing as I do now who was out there.

When the knock came, I eased myself up, stiff from writing and my aching head. As I opened the door, the figure before me was backlit by the display of soundless illumination in the cumulus nimbus looming over the empty expanse of land that was the view from Emmaus. Just as I was thinking that this was far too melodramatic an arrival to be taken seriously, the first wind from the storm breathed on my face, and thunder like the offstage waving of a metal sheet clattered towards me.

Now, the man at our door was not some stage devil wreathed in flames, nor did he wink a glowing coal of an eye at me from a blackened face. But something about him made me recall that the Regulations for guests tell us that "we receive only those whom charity and piety bid us receive, and whom we have reason to think have been directed to us by Divine Providence". The storm was reason enough for my charity, I suppose, but nothing in the smooth-faced man standing on the step suggested the hand of Divine Providence, neatly dressed though he was in a well-made suit that was a little dusty.

To my surprise, he offered me a letter of obedience, signed by the Abbot of a monastery I was not acquainted with. The letter directed Wolfgang Bens, a Choir Religious, to join the Trappist missionaries in South Africa. For some reason his appearance made me feel uncomfortable although I cannot imagine why I would hold a man's manner of dressing against him. And then it suddenly struck me – I had never seen a Religious who looked so at home in secular clothing.

It must seem that I exaggerate my sense of something unwholesome, even evil, in this new arrival. Let me remind you that the Rule of St Benedict is full of warnings against the Devil. It talks most sternly of the "temptations of the malicious Devil", of how we must learn "with the help of our many brethren to fight against the Devil", of our "not giving any occasion to the Devil" or "ever listening to the persuasions of the Devil". And, in the chapter on the reception of guests, the Regulations tell us that the one receiving the guest should pray together with the guest first, before exchanging the kiss of peace with him – "for the kiss of peace should not be offered until after the prayers have been said, on account of the Devil's deceptions".

Although neatly folded, Brother Wolfgang's letter of obedience was worn and much used. It led me to suspect that he was a modern version of what St Benedict calls a Gyrovague, that "fourth kind of monk", those who "spend their whole lives tramping from province to province, staying as guests in different monasteries". He says that they are "always on the move, with no stability, they indulge their own wills and succumb to the allurements of gluttony", concluding that they are "in every way worse than the Sarabaites, and of the miserable conduct of all such it is better to be silent than to speak".

It is only if a guest arrives during the Office that he is not announced to the Superior. Technically this was the case at the time of Brother Wolfgang's arrival, but I knew that Franz had, as usual, shortened his observance to the minimum and was busy with the Sisters outside. I saw him size up our guest with a disapproving air, eyeing his fleshy neatness before he turned back to Sr Angela and weighed in his hand the fresh brick she had just passed him. It was left to me to take Brother Wolfgang to the church and give him the prescribed holy water and stand behind him whilst he made his prayer. I showed him to the guest room, and then arranged a meal for him from the standard fare of the refectory, with the addition of eggs and butter which are the sole addition allowed for a guest's meal.

Brother Wolfgang met with Franz that evening. By the next morning the two were on surprisingly good terms and Brother Wolfgang, clearly no longer a guest, was already clothed in a habit and a member of our small community. A member I might say who was not often to be found amongst us, either in work or prayer. He was away for days at a time, and when he was at Emmaus he and Franz were forever in a huddle, talking in spirited but suppressed whispers, Franz looking around all the time. Although I was still called in for my regular hours of dictation, this had to do solely with Franz's memoirs. I could not help but notice that either Sr Angela or Sr Edmunda was called in to take down Franz's correspondence, and that Brother Wolfgang was often present at these sessions.

Before Brother Wolfgang's arrival I used to assist Franz in circumventing Dom Edmund's censorship through an alternative postal system, with the assistance of a few faithful Natives on our small estate. Franz no longer seemed to need my services in this respect although his letter writing continued apace. I was still in charge of our official post, but few of his letters came to me to be sent on their way, unsealed as was required. For whatever reason, perhaps a lack of faith in my abilities, I appeared to have been cut out of Franz's inner circle.

I was thinking rather ruefully one day of the time when Franz seemed to have more need of me, when a heavily sealed letter from Mariannhill, weighed down by its wax, dropped out of that morning's post. I recall to this day, quite clearly, the racing of my heart as I bent down to pick it up and saw that it was addressed to "Fr Joseph, Rector of Emaus, Physician and Confessor to Abbot Francis, Dismissed." Before I had registered through my amazement the implications of the rank bestowed upon me by the address, I found myself reading a terse instruction from Dom Edmund that henceforth I must intercept all letters between Franz and the Sisters, and pass them on to him.

I sat down, stunned. In the same post there were letters to Franz, no doubt informing him that he had been deposed as Superior of Emmaus. There was also a legal document removing all monies, from whatever sources, out of his control. I stood up, the letters to Franz scattered before me, and at that moment Franz entered the room. His hair, all grey now, and much receded although longer than ever, was plastered down over his skull, and his yellow-white beard was straggly and tangled. Visible through the hair, his lips were curled back, as if set in a permanent snarl. His eyes were piercing under the sharp cleft of his brow and the skin wrinkled up beneath them in furrows. Three lines were slashed across the ridge of his nose by the never-ending fury of his concentration.

It was as if I were seeing Franz for the first time, unadorned by the history his vigour and drive had created. My eyes fell away from that face and I walked past him through the door with the briefest slump of my body in place of a bow, leaving the letters addressed to him on the desk.

Oh Franz, I thought, what have you done now? I heard nothing from inside the room as I walked blindly down the stairs, but it was now clear to me that I had been kept in the dark about what was really going on at "Emaus". Even before Franz had ceased to use me as the scribe of his letters, he had taken to appending notes to those letters in his own crabbed hand. Something begun in those furtive additions had grown into dangerous maturity in the shadow Brother Wolfgang had cast over my Superior's doings.

My Superior? No longer. My new rank meant that Franz was again effectively deposed. His authority, such as it was, was thrust on me. And this left me directly responsible to Dom Edmund. It was to him now that I owed my unmediated obedience, that obedience which, according to the Rule of St Benedict, *is the virtue of those who hold nothing dearer to them* than Christ; who, because of the holy service they have professed, and the fear of hell, and the glory of life everlasting, as soon as anything has been ordered by the Superior, receive it as a Divine command and cannot suffer any delay in executing it.

It was with desperate relief that I gave thanks for not having been included in the writing or receiving of the letters that must have raced secretly across Nomansland from Franz to this Sister, from that Sister to Franz.

But Franz did not need me to be his Judas. It would be by his own hand that his destruction would be made complete. We arose for prayer one morning to find Wolfgang Bens gone, his habit tossed on his bed, his suit taken from storage. Franz was wild-eyed, raging about money and farms and the Sisters. Slowly I worked out from his ranting that he had been in the process of buying three new farms, in direct contradiction of both the order forbidding any further expansion of Mariannhill's missions and the personal restrictions the Administrator had placed upon him. This he was doing in the hope of winning the entire congregation of the Sisters away from Mariannhill and settling them on land adjoining Emmaus, thus flouting Dom Edmund's specific instruction that he stay out of the "Sisters question".

Worse was to come. Bens had been his middleman in these clandestine and illegal purchases. In the course of the transactions, our new Choir Religious had embezzled all the money – money that Franz had raised from two of his longest-standing friends and supporters in Germany, the Josten brothers. He – no, they – had been swindled out of thirty thousand Deutschmarks. But more damaging still, for Franz, was the exposure that ensued. Nothing could be done now to save the tatters of Franz's reputation, or make of his many hard-won achievements at Emmaus proof of the correctness of his ideas, especially regarding the Sisters. He could barely keep his anguish to himself, and was often to be found wandering about the grounds, hair awry, habit at odd angles, his mouth moving silently as he endlessly wrung his hands.

~

Brother Nivard arrived within days, charged with smoothing over and settling the whole sad affair. It was comforting to see an old and trusted face although Brother Nivard's attempts at friendliness could not hide the distance that had grown up between us in the years of our isolation. I say "us", referring to the few who had known the "Brown Abbot" of old, but I

473

mean Franz and, to a much lesser degree, myself. I hovered as close to him as I could, trying to draw comfort from this monk for whom no task had proved impossible in our brief hour of greatness.

Brother Nivard did sort out the financial mess to a reasonable degree in his usual business-like and competent way. There was, however, an air of sadness about him that could not be explained simply in terms of the unsavoury conditions that led to our being reunited. It was as if something had gone out of the spirit that once burst from him in creations of brick and stone, filling out Franz's visions with mills and workshops and dormitories and churches, yes, and schools too, and, ultimately, towers from which bells could scatter our calling across the hills of Natal and Nomansland.

Something of this sadness was captured in what he wrote of Franz in one of the letters left for me to post: "Our old friend Rev. Fr Francis cannot say Mass at all now. His arms and hands are almost completely paralysed, and he has to be dressed and undressed by others …"

Others? I asked myself – one other, perhaps.

"I was very touched," he had written, "to see how the Sister who nurses him has to feed him like a child. Anyone who has known as I have the agility and drive of this man and felt his iron will, would be struck now with awe at the sight of him." He added that he did not think that "Abbot Francis", as he still insisted on calling his old friend, "could safely be asked to sign a legal document any more, or take an oath on it. His memory, which used to be absolutely reliable, has deteriorated to such an extent that, while he remembers certain things very accurately, he often does not recall other more significant ones at all …"

Well, so much for any further business arrangements, I thought, as I tucked the letter into one of our rough brown envelopes, not bothering, as had been the case for some time with our official post, to use the seal.

~

It was true that Franz often could not remember what he had agreed to the day before regarding some simple arrangement. Nevertheless, he insisted on continuing with his memoirs, which he had started dictating to me soon after I arrived at Emmaus. He had chosen to begin, pretty randomly it seemed to me, with his studies in Italy from 1845 to 1846, perhaps because his hatred of "dismal, sad, and dirty Padua" chimed with his present circumstances, although it was in this city that his vocation was settled. "I came to Padua undecided what I should be," he intoned. "In one month, however, I had already decided that I would turn to the priesthood. After I had observed the detestable life and behaviour of the Italian students and got to know the corruption of city life in general, no other profession or way of life other than the celibate life of a priest had any attraction for me …"

And so we went on, awkwardly enough at first, and I must admit that my attention was held not so much by these broad strokes by which Franz tried to define his life as by the fleeting images rising up out of the darkness of a past he had rarely revisited at the peak of his strength. Anecdotes of minor incidents would now and again break the main thread of his narrative: for example, a visit to a "strange villa" just outside of Milan during an end of term tour, where a never-ending echo could be heard. "Every cry, blow or shot comes back twenty-fold," he murmured, "one sound of laughter makes a long continuous laugh. The *ciceroni* illustrated this echo for a tip. She fired a pistol that set off a whole platoon-fire …"

He continued, "Often in my life, I remembered this episode in Milan, while nowadays I don't remember on Tuesday what I did on Sunday. That tells me already how full of holes my mind is, and it reminds me that it is nearly evening and the day is almost over …"

Yes, it was this fear of his own forgetfulness in the face of the coming darkness that made him sit me down at my tiny desk whilst he poured out as much as he could of his life. More and more the meaning crept away and hid in the images that flared up and burned away his sense of a storyline in his life. It was in these, then, that I began to listen for the truth of what had happened to us in the wake of Franz's turbulent career. I would learn to hear in Franz's memory of a courtyard echo in a villa outside of Milan Brother Nivard's laughter, the laughter that was just a distant echo when he came to try and save his old friend at Emmaus from his own failings.

I was never to see Brother Nivard again after that last sad occasion, but years later I would hear how that laughter returned twenty-fold and claimed him completely.

~

Franz's dictating sessions were now taken up solely with his memoirs. It goes without saying Dom Edmund forbade him any letter writing; not content with having removed him as Rector of Emmaus, he also took all his freedom of movement and expression, personal and postal. He had by now, in any event, used his influence in the highest levels of our Order to ensure that nothing Franz said or wrote was given a serious hearing. Amongst the last letters I ever took down from Franz was one to a friend in our offices in the Holy City, and it said everything that needed to be said of the end of his days of corresponding:

"I must presume from your absolute silence," Franz dictated in a voice so thin one could barely hear its breaking, "that in Rome I have lost all my chances, even with you. I hope nevertheless that you will not throw this letter into a wastebasket unread ..." He paused here, swallowing and looking up to the ceiling with red-rimmed eyes, and then went on: "Just as all my hope that our situation will improve is gone, so my life will soon come to an end. Really, such a life cannot mean much any more. I hope that God will not treat me as cruelly as Abbot Obrecht has treated me ..."

And so silence fell upon us. But it was not a silence freely adopted, an observance that allowed us to come closer to God. This was a silence imposed from without, not called up from within. Silence was once for us the most eloquent form of revelation, just as it was the most eloquent means of adoration; now silence became our meanest form of survival. We huddled, each within ourselves, cut off from God and man, quiet in our isolation and mistrust. Where once we spoke of love as the exercise of prayer and prayer the exercise of silence, now it was frustration that made us forget our prayers and fear that coerced us into silence.

It was characteristic of Dom Edmund that he did not know the difference. For him, Franz was his last and greatest victory. With Franz's voice stilled, as far as Dom Edmund was concerned, peace fell over Mariannhill and her missions. He wrote confidently in one of his many circulars: "With a heart filled with consolation we are urged to tell you without hesitation of the joy we feel that our words, admonitions and decrees have been generally received with childlike submission. My dearly beloved sons, the ear of your hearts is inclined to the words of your father."

It is difficult to believe exactly how far Dom Edmund misread the situation. What he called "childlike submission" was not, in fact, brought about by insight and a change of heart; on the missions it was the result, rather, of cool calculation. Whilst those in the monastery remained submissive out of fear of the Administrator's draconian measures, the apparent submissiveness of the missionaries merely reflected their understanding that this was not a time to voice their opinions freely.

476

The Administrator was watched constantly. Every word he spoke and everything he did was noted: how often he appeared in Choir and how often in the refectory. Nobody resisted him on the Councils or in the conferences, but reports were sent secretly to the higher authorities, secular and religious, of anything that might cause trouble for him. And occasionally the real mood would surface, as when Dom Edmund returned to Mariannhill from a trip to Rome – a trip in which he announced to the General Chapter that "Mariannhill might yet become the glory of the Order, thanks be to God". A written order was needed before anyone was prepared to decorate the driveway, and it was not by accident that some of the banners had holes in them that disfigured their inscriptions, or that the triumphal arch collapsed just as the carriage bearing Dom Edmund passed through.

That so much destructive energy would gather strength and boil over was only to be expected. And so it did exactly where one would expect it to. Where else, but in that centre of the evil that haunted us, that dogged our greatest achievements, mocked our triumphs, flaunted our failures, revelled in our defeats. Where else, I say, but at St Michael's.

22

POSITIVE FACTS OF MYSTERIOUS OCCURRENCES OF DEMONIACAL POSSESSION

The writer of this treatise in English is Fr Erasmus Hörner RMM, Eye and EAR Witness, Port Shepstone, Natal, October 1920.

During the years 1906–7 very strange and wonderful things happened at St Michael's, a Mission Station situated halfway between Umzinto and Ixopo (Stuartstown), Natal. I – the writer – worked there as a missionary from 1906–1920. My missionary career began when in November 1891 I left my home in Rhine-Palatinate Germany. I arrived at Mariannhill in 1892.

After two years noviciate – I learned the Zulu language during that time – I was sent to Mariazell at the foot of the Drakensberg. There I stayed until 1906. In April of that year, I was recalled by Abbot Edmund Obrecht, Administrator of Mariannhill at the time. I was sent to St Michael's. I was quite a stranger there and did not know anybody.

Now for some of the facts …

So begins a document dropped on my desk by our young historian a matter of weeks after its composition. I read on steadily, continuously, not looking up once from the handwritten manuscript. Here, at last, I had before me a full first-hand account, written some thirteen years after the dramatic incidents at St Michael's that had filtered through to us in whispered rumours, broken anecdotes, even the odd salacious newspaper article.

Busy as always with his history of Mariannhill, Fr Adalbert discovered in our records that Fr Erasmus Hörner and I had worked together at Mariazell, and he wanted to know my opinion of him. My response was that the period in which our duties intersected was brief. In any event, Fr Erasmus was very much of the fervent missionary party and I was not trusted by those of that persuasion. I did not think I needed to add that I was so caught up in developing my electrical machine that I paid very little attention to the colleagues assigned to me at that station. A vague recollection of a ferrety face, a pointed nose and large ears emphasising its thinness, came to mind. As to his character, what I read certainly accorded in attitude and tone with what I remembered of Fr Erasmus. When it came to the accuracy of what he had recorded, well, I became certain that the document was informed by a truth of sorts, but only when I had looked further into it.

I was working through my material on Dom Edmund when Fr Erasmus's account was put before me. This meant that I was in a position to make some suggestions regarding the events as they were recorded, perhaps even explain some of them. Explain? To Fr Adalbert? He was a good enough historian to manage the more material issues hovering beneath the surface of the "mysterious occurrences" at St Michael's. But if there is one thing I learned from those occurrences, it is that phenomena may retain their mystery even after their apparent causes have been uncovered. To explain an event is not to undo any of the power of that event. To explain, in short, does not mean to explain away.

The Oblates had returned to St Michael's when Franz made it plain that he had other plans, but the station was never worked as a farm and, as in all the other broken periods of occupation by the Oblates, no converts were made. A few children attended the school reluctantly and irregularly, but a sullen, brooding spirit pervaded classroom and chapel alike. Perched on its bony spur of rock that descended sharply into the hostile reserve spread out below it, St Michael's remained exposed to the still and baking heat or the winds, alternately dry and hot and then dry and cold, that whipped through and around it. The only things that flourished over the years were the pigs, though they were not much good to anyone, thin and mean and ugly as they were.

Fr Barthélemy, the priest who replaced Fr Mathieu (he who had confronted us over our refusal to go to St Michael's, and then become our first teacher of Zulu at Mariannhill), surrendered his faith whilst at the mission, leaving both the Order and the Church amidst rumours that he had been a secret sympathiser with freemasonry. But freemasonry was not enough to explain or do away with the strange reputation that continued to hover about the station. By all accounts as mild mannered a man as one could hope for in a priest, Fr Barthélemy rapidly gained a reputation at St Michael's for being quick-tempered, especially in his relations with the fractious chiefs in the area. There were three of them, each as hostile to the others as they were to the mission. One in particular, however, a certain Chief Maboon, had not only challenged Fr Barthélemy as to the limits of the mission's lands but had raised this to the level of a formal legal dispute – and won.

It was not just the behaviour of the chiefs that was cause for concern. The youngsters showed no desire for education, which meant there was no daily school on the mission, and the people settled on the mission lands refused to pay rent. According to Fr Barthélemy, they refused to acknowledge the mission or its missionary in any way.

Fearing the loss of another priest he could ill afford, Bishop Jolivet sent a layman to act as missionary at the station, one Baron de Pavel, a recent convert to the Catholic faith. Baron de Pavel was equally unsuccessful in his efforts. The tribesmen still refused to pay rent, squatters invaded the mission land, there was an almost complete absence of labour, faction fights broke out continuously, and Chief Mabuni, as we came more correctly to know him, took possession of yet another portion of the mission's glebe land. When de Pavel complained to the Resident Magistrate, he was told that nothing could be done because the original beacons did not clearly show the boundaries of the glebe.

After he received no less than three letters in one week from an entirely undeterred de Pavel, the Resident Magistrate complained that the missions were beginning to be a source of trouble in the colony, owing, as he put it, "to the wish of the missionaries to be chiefs in them". This was more than enough for Bishop Jolivet to re-open negotiations with Franz, and Franz, shortly before he left for the General Chapter in 1889, had felt more than ready to honour the promise he had once made to Fr Mathieu.

Reports from the four Sisters who were sent to open a convent at St Michael's the following year bore out my sense of the spirit of the place and the reputation it had earned over the years. Sr Humbelina, who took over the school that de Pavel had endeavoured to set up, found that not one of the twenty or so children was baptised, and there was a marked animosity on their part. Not even at first meeting did they exhibit the shy reverence towards someone in the service of the Church characteristic of Native children in our experience elsewhere. They were, on the contrary, persistently disobedient and stubborn, and their elders kept a cautious distance from everything to do with the mission. One of the earliest of the convent's chronicles states: "Many sacrifices will be required before these souls are freed from Satan's snares."

Franz, of course, would recognise nothing of this. A soul as prosaic as his seemed immune to what deterred and destroyed others of a more sensitive nature. The monks he sent to St Michael's were of the fervent missionary party and even more plain than Franz about their objectives. They swept through the place in a blast that neutralised the winds that haunted it, initiating our by now tried and tested missionary methods with a grim force that overwhelmed material and spiritual resistance alike.

By 1895, after five years of Trappist administration, there were sixty Christians on the property, twenty-six boys and seventy-three girls attended the school on a regular basis, and a church was being built. Eight monks and nine nuns lived in the glebe, working with a rigour and determination that soon earned them access to what was, after all, a well-populated mission reserve. A year later, Bishop Jolivet visited St Michael's to find the church complete, and seventy Natives from the mission presenting themselves for confirmation. By 1906, when Fr Erasmus arrived at St Michael's, eight hundred and sixty-two baptisms had been recorded and there were forty catechumens – just enough spiritual victory, it seems, to allow the evil there to come to its full head.

~

Fr Erasmus begins his account of the events at St Michael's by noting that although it was a "hard Mission field" it was a very good one – good in the sense that "hard fighting brings glorious victory and triumph". He

480

then writes briefly of his predecessor, Fr Mansuet Poll, a pious and zealous priest who had been at St Michael's for only nine or ten months. "He did his work with energy and zeal," Fr Erasmus reports, "but he also spent hours in the church before the altar, and sitting in his little room weeping. He told me what he considered I ought to know, and left for Himmelberg Mission, ten miles from St Michael's, blessing God for his release."

With these few introductory remarks, Fr Erasmus launches into what he insists – again and again – are the "Positive Facts" of the "Mysterious Occurrences" he witnessed.

"Strange things," he writes, "happened to Klara Germana Cele, a Native girl of 16–17 years." She was a pupil at the school at St Michael's, "tolerably gifted, her character merry and gay, full of tricks", as he puts it. Soon after taking her First Communion, however, she became morose and sad. Whilst remaining obedient and honest, she became more and more passive. On the 5th of July 1906 Germana handed over to Fr Erasmus – as her Confessor – a piece of paper that was nothing less than "A written promise selling herself to the Devil".

From this point on, the evidence of "Demoniacal Possession" that makes up the bulk of Fr Erasmus's document escalates steadily. Germana's possession begins with furious rages and the tearing of her clothing, along with the gnashing of teeth and animal-like growling, barking, and grunting. She disputes furiously with "One Invisible", and speaks in a number of "Voices" that deny being Germana. They demand the removal of holy images, complain of the Blessed Stole pressing on them and Holy Water burning them.

Germana was particularly disruptive at Mass on the 26th of August, although she was guarded by Sisters and the strongest of her fellow pupils. "She cried loudly, shrieking and yelling with all her might, clapping her hands and gnashing her teeth, foaming, affronting, insulting, raging," writes Fr Erasmus. She refused to sit or kneel, ordering her peers to refuse to confess or to lie in confession, insulted God "and then, during the Offertory, before the eyes of us all," Fr Erasmus records, "she was raised up about four or five feet in the air. She floated towards the Presbytery and descended laughing behind the servers. Then she turned her back to the Altar and said, *Ungikuleku mina* – adore me." The Mass ended with Germana uttering blasphemies that could not be recorded.

All of this continued and intensified in the days that followed: at one point Germana burst into flame, and complained of suffering from burn wounds although all that was found was "a big hole burnt through her skirt". Even the environs of St Michael's were affected: "dark, large frogs with staring eyes like live coals appeared outside", Fr Erasmus tells us, and a large vessel filled with frogs refilled when emptied. Diabolical laughter was heard in the distance and a mysterious mighty power banged on doors and slammed windows at night (which Fr Erasmus and another priest attempted to track down with shotguns, to Germana's great amusement and mockery even though they were certain she could not have known anything of their attempts).

Again, Germana levitated ten feet high, this time before her fellow pupils, and in Fr Erasmus's words, "frightful things happened when her severest paroxysms came on. Her face would swell, then her chest, then her stomach, as if inflated. Her neck would become as long as a swan's neck, her eyes glowing like fire. She growled and gnashed, grunted, barked, made a low but loud continuous snarling, rolling noise, bellowing like a wild beast in the wilderness. Often all the noises were heard together, a diabolical concert of hell.

"Sometimes, something like a swollen vein appeared under her skin. It went over her whole body. You could see it start on the hand; running up the arm until it appeared on the neck, it went up the cheek, across the forehead and down the other cheek, then down the leg and foot, torturing every limb it went through."

Fr Erasmus tells us that the priests and Sisters at St Michael's eventually decided to write detailed reports to the Bishop of Durban on these extra-ordinary occurrences. Since the Bishop was away in Europe, the Episcopal Ordinary sent a letter giving Fr Erasmus full power for an open Solemn Exorcism. Priests from other stations came to assist, and the Exorcism was set for Wednesday, 12th September. It was held publicly, with all the priests, Brothers and Sisters from the station present, as well as "other Christians from outside" and some schoolchildren.

The rituals and procedures followed are those of *Titulus x* of the *Rituale Romanum*, the first edition of which was published under the papacy of Paul v in 1619. Germana's possession displayed all three of the main indications of possession set out in the section of the *Rituale* "Concerning the Exorcizing of Possessing Demons". These are use of an unknown tongue; knowledge of hidden things; and physical power much above the expected.

Examples of the first abound in Fr Erasmus's account. Just before the Exorcism, for example, he reports: "All of a sudden Germana began singing a jocose German song, *Ach wennesnur immer so bliebe hier unter dem wechselndem Mond* ... After the first verse she added two more of her own composition, full of wit and humour – in perfect German." Apparently she only knew a few words of German that she had picked up from the Sisters and Brothers, and throughout all that followed she understood other languages that she had never learned, including Polish. Later, Fr Erasmus adds, "It was obvious that she understood all the Latin prayers and Exorcism in the Roman Ritual. She answered correctly in Zulu all the questions put to her in Latin; she corrected defective pronunciation in Latin and other faults; she recited whole sentences in Latin, saying, I know all that you are reading in your book, I don't need any book."

Equally extraordinary is Germana's "knowledge of hidden things". Before the fact she was able to state that "the Bishop Vicar General is sitting at his table in Durban writing a letter for the Baba of St Michael's giving permission and full power for the Exorcisms". And when, during the Exorcism, one of the priests was called away, she not only confirmed that this was to nurse a sick child – something Fr Erasmus himself did not know – but was able to name the boy and his kraal.

"Germana said many things she could not have known," Fr Erasmus tells us, adding that "the Devil in her was very indiscreet. He revealed what happened secretly, at different places, at different times, things Germana could not have known. He especially revealed sins not confessed, or concealed in confession. He told all these things in the presence of those concerned, to their horror. They then went to confession as soon as possible. Once the sins were confessed he did not refer to them again."

As for her exceptional physical powers, once the first Exorcism was under way, these were demonstrated again and again. From the first, Fr Erasmus reports, "Germana became more and more excited. She tried to run away. The Sisters and big Zulu girls seized her, put their arms around her shoulders, loins, and legs and forced her down on a chair. It was very difficult to keep her down. Handcuffs were put on, but they were of no use; nor was binding her arms and legs with ropes. She rose up again and again off the chair to stand free and upright."

This was only the beginning. As the Exorcism continued over the two full days, we learn of how Germana's powers grew. On the afternoon of the first day, "she tried to stand up and the Sisters pressed her down. A fierce struggle began. Three Sisters and six grown up girls were holding her arms and legs, and then all were raised up with the chair, their feet about one to one and a half feet above the ground. Germana's body would lift in whatever position she happened to be in, seated, lying, or standing, with the others hanging on as best they could.

"Germana foamed with rage," Fr Erasmus continues; "she cursed, her face disfigured terribly, full of hatred and wrath. The priest went on with the Exorcism, In the name of the Most Blessed Trinity, in the name of Jesus Christ Crucified, Holy Mary, Mother of God Immaculate pray for us, St Michael pray for us. Germana raged furiously, and again and again, all were raised upwards, Sisters, girls, chair and all, now to a height of about two yards.

"Germana's head and body were swollen, her eyes glowing with diabolical fire, and that deep low continuous snarling rolling noise began again, and then that howling voice of desperation, Woe, woe, woe. The children were sent away towards evening when things became unspeakable, a picture of Hell."

Roarings, risings, disfigurements and much else continued for the rest of the Exorcism. "Everything seemed to be in motion," writes Fr Erasmus, "and there was a tremendous uproar everywhere, in the presbytery and church and outside, on the roof and above the roof too, as if armies were fighting in the air."

As I read on, I could not help but notice that throughout Fr Erasmus's account of all this noise, there is a curious silence. By this I mean that more is hinted at than is disclosed. There is a kind of teasing, deferred references to revelations, hints at secrets at the very heart of the events that will not be spelled out. Whenever they threaten to surface, one side or the other in this supernatural struggle cuts them short.

In the course of the Exorcism the priest, writes Fr Erasmus (referring to himself, as always, in the third person), "often had to demand silence, commanding with his priestly power and authority, whereafter the Devil said, 'I am bound by the priest; if I were not, then I would tell you terrible things.'" Germana's possession seems to have become a struggle in which speech and silence were used as weapons by priest and demon alike. "When the priest commanded her," we are told, "she ceased and was silent. When questioned, the answers came out of her reluctantly, as if forced, by starts and jerks, full of rage." But when Germana "asked again and again for the prayers of all that she might be delivered from the Evil One, the Unseen One interrupted her each time, saying, 'Be silent Germana, you belong to me. Be silent – keep your peace. Otherwise you shall see, *Uzaubona*, you shall see'."

Fr Erasmus and his assistant priests persisted. Late on the second day Germana, "foaming with rage, her face horribly deformed, her body hugely swollen, with roaring and howling that were unspeakably terrible, was raised and lifted up into the air together with all those who held her, three Sisters and five strong girls". And then suddenly, she sunk down. "Those holding her left her," says Fr Erasmus, "and, like a dying person she lay on the floor before the Altar steps. It was all over. The terrible noise was gone, all was calm and quiet."

Soon after Germana returned to her "bright and innocent" self and, he reports, "All was quiet and peaceful everywhere in the Mission Station; the Evil One was gone, and a new and better spirit had entered. Thanks to God, the Mother of God, and St Michael Archangel, the powerful protector of St Michael's."

~

Fr Erasmus closes his account of the events of July to September 1906 with the words: "Germana behaved herself very well afterwards. She was obedient and obliging, praying and frequenting the Holy Sacraments. So she went on for months. She needed a rest, of course, as did also the good Sisters in charge. I myself felt very tired. All for God. May He protect us. The Holy will of God be done now and forever more."

I turned the page after that hopeful attempt at a conclusion to find written on the next, still in Fr Erasmus's poor hand:

PART TWO, THE SECOND DIABOLICAL POSSESSION
AND SECOND EXORCISM 1907.

This opens with the words: "I – the writer, am afraid to write the second part. Anyhow in God's name I will try to give a true account."

The truth of the account of the Second Exorcism is of a different order from that of the first. Fr Erasmus was not, in the phrase he repeats so often out of a delight in his own cleverness, an "Eye and EAR Witness" of these events, having decided in January 1907 to go himself to Rome to see and speak with the Superiors of the Order. He told no one of his plans and managed to make his way to Rome without passport or Ecclesiastical letters to Rome. At Durban harbour he narrowly missed bumping into Dom Edmund who had just returned from Europe.

Fr Erasmus's knowledge of the second diabolical possession depends on the accounts of witnesses and on a letter that he received from Natal telling him what had happened at St Michael's after his departure. The letter included "a description of the most horrible occurrences and phenomena and a series of terrible sayings and revelations". Fr Erasmus was clearly put out that it was handed to him unopened by "the higher Authorities of the Order", contrary to the standard procedures of church censorship. He felt so strongly about this that he returned it to them for perusal, "asking them what they thought about these things, especially the oft-repeated revelation, made openly and repeatedly by Germana before hundreds of people".

The response was not a satisfactory one: "They hesitated and said, Satan is a liar." To which he replied, "That's all very well, but are the revelations true or not?" He goes on to say that he "received no answer" but "was treated very kindly".

I am sorry to say that, insofar as his time in Rome is concerned, this is simply not true. Word had made its way at the time, even to those of us isolated at Emmaus, that on his arrival in Rome Fr Erasmus was immediately confined to the Trappist Monastery Ad Catacombas. He was denied all contact with the Roman Congregation, and, as Father Definitor Symphorian assured Abbot Obrecht (in a letter scrutinised by one of the many pairs of eyes at Mariannhill checking on everything to do with the Administrator), "any correspondence of the prisoner was watched over very carefully".

Fr Erasmus must have been sure this would be the case. After all, just before leaving South Africa he had written a letter – one sure to be subjected to censorship – in which he stated, "I shall uncover to the last detail the deceit and cheat of the visitation and reformation of Mariannhill." This had prompted Dom Edmund to address a circular to us all in which he forbad most severely any correspondence with Fr Erasmus, since he had become an apostate, *ipso facto*, with his flight.

It is highly unlikely then that the letter to Fr Erasmus from Natal had been handed over to him unopened. It is far more likely that the "higher authorities" of the Order simply did not wish to become involved in its contents. The Definitorium, one may be sure, would have liked to send their unwelcome guest back to South Africa as soon as possible, although it is equally sure (and Fr Adalbert's investigations confirm this) that Abbot Obrecht wanted nothing to do with him either.

It appears that Fr Erasmus's objective was none other than to present to the Sacred Congregation of Propaganda a Memorandum that had been printed secretly in a workshop outside of Mariannhill and smuggled from station to station for the signatures of those monks who agreed with it. Needless to say, it aimed at resurrecting the old idea of a separate Rule for the missions. In this, the prime mover ("chief conspirator" as Dom Edmund would call him later) was Fr Willibald Wanger who had succeeded Fr Theodorich as Rector after my departure from Lourdes. He was subsequently to join Fr Erasmus in Rome.

Why was Fr Erasmus, a determined opponent of the kind of censorship Dom Edmund had introduced at Mariannhill, so exasperated that the official censors in Rome had not opened the letter from Natal? This could only be because it was vital that the Administrator of Mariannhill and his powerful friends be disqualified from intervening before the Memorandum was seen by the highest authorities concerned with the active apostolate. The contents of the Memorandum were couched as general problems to do with Trappist missionary work; they could only be read as a critique of Dom Edmund's manner and method of re-imposing full Cistercian observance at Mariannhill if they were associated with the revelations in the letter.

What then was it in this account of the events at St Michael's that Fr Erasmus believed would compromise Dom Edmund so thoroughly that he would be unable to oppose the Memorandum? The letter itself appears to have disappeared, but clues as to what it contained were scattered throughout the account of the exorcisms that Fr Adalbert placed on my desk.

~

Fr Erasmus stresses that his account of the Second Exorcism is based on "Original Notes" ("I got and still possess these," he writes), although he does not say who made them. "I had the unique opportunity," he tells us, "for 12 years more till 1920, to see and speak with hundreds and hundreds of eye and ear witnesses, Priests, Brothers, Sisters, Children, Adults, and

Christians from outside etc." But it is not the "positive facts" that are at stake in his account of the outbreak of the second diabolical possession so much as the force driving them. The "mysterious occurrences" in themselves are, after all, similar in nature to those he himself witnessed during the first possession. They differ mainly in intensity, an intensity created, one is left to suspect, by whatever was lurking behind those strange silences in the first exorcism – imposed by priest, or demon, or Fr Erasmus himself in his account.

The second possession involved Germana and her close friend Monika Mdhledshe. It is Monika who gives us our first clue as to the distinctly worldly matters informing the even grander spectrum of the Second Possession. Nineteen to twenty years of age, Monika, we learn, was "strongly built, industrious and obedient, but very reserved". In the few days before Fr Erasmus left the mission, she had hardly spoken a word. Then, "all of a sudden dumb Monika began to laugh loudly, and said in Zulu, *O nina zilima* – oh you simpletons, you think the Baba went over to Himmelberg and will come back tomorrow. He will not come back for a long time; tomorrow he will go to Umzinto and Durban, then he goes on board ship and the next day he will leave sailing overseas going to Rome".

With Monika "howling and growling so horribly that she could be heard from a great distance", Germana in turn became more specific in the "hidden things" she revealed. "She became very excited," Fr Erasmus writes, "and ran around with frightful glowing eyes. She also began to speak about terrible things done by different people, but this time people in high positions; she told names of places, even a house in America and one in Rome – she gave towns, roads and streets, and the number of a certain house in a town in America. She revealed terrible things in German 'aussagen' daily for weeks and weeks, 2-3-4 times a day sometimes. She made these declarations openly before all the people. When commanded to be silent she cried indignantly, This is my time, and I must be allowed to say these things!"

What strikes me in Fr Erasmus's account is that as the demons become more detailed in their accusations, a strange alliance begins to form between himself and the demons. "Out of the blue," he reports his informants as saying, "Monika said, Just now the Baba – Fr Erasmus – arrived in Rome. She named a street he was walking down, and the number of a house he turned into. She gave other particulars too," he writes, "all of which I can verify as true. Then she said, Another one will join him there, and they are doing good work. Then Germana, speaking in a loud voice like a preacher, began to repeat the Terrible Sayings – first she spoke about many things concerning St Michael's Mission, and of other places far away. She called persons by name, Natives and Europeans, and used the names of other places, saying the devils were working there also, but the priests did not know.

"Then came again the long Litany of the most frightful sayings already mentioned. Of a certain person, giving his name, Germana also said, He is in Rome telling lies before the Holy Father and the Cardinals about Mariannhill Monastery and the Missions …"

The coyness with which Fr Erasmus introduces that name is soon dropped. Within a few paragraphs he tells us that "Germana raged furiously about the Rt Rev. Abbot Edmund Obrecht, the Administrator Apostolic, calling him angrily and sarcastically, *Edmundi lo, this Edmund. Let him come here this Edmundi lo, I have to tell him many things.*"

And so the figure behind the possessions at St Michael's is pulled into the foreground. "The Bishop Edmundi lo, this Edmund, why doesn't he come?" Fr Erasmus reports Germana as saying. "I want him. It is not Germana who speaks and does these things, it is me, Satan! *Siyozana* – we know one another. I know him from America, ha, ha, ha, ha. I have to tell him things openly. Now is our time, I am permitted by God – whom I hate – to publish these things."

With the Abbot's name out in the open and the charges against him coming out of the mouths of the demons ever more explicitly, it is not surprising that the Church decided to send a delegation led by Bishop Dr Delalle, who had recently replaced Bishop Jolivet in the Natal diocese, to St Michael's to carry out the second exorcism. Bishop Delalle has written his own account of the mysterious occurrences. First published in the magazine *Rome*, Fr Adalbert tells me it was later translated into German in the booklet *Are there still Devils even in our Day?*

By his own admission, Bishop Delalle was very much annoyed by the letters he was receiving from St Michael's and was himself inclined to think that this was a case of hysterics rather than possession. He retains his cautious attitude throughout his report: he testifies to no chorus of hellish sounds, no diabolical physical transformations, no flights to the ceiling. Germana is only able to tell ordinary water from Holy, understand and speak some Latin, and expound with ease upon the fall of Lucifer, the creation of his demons, and the nature of Hell. She has some surprising knowledge of a few minor occurrences at St Michael's, and is noisy and disruptive throughout, but little more.

More importantly, his account includes nothing of the "terrible sayings", the "Litany of Frightful Publications" so central to Fr Erasmus's version of the second Exorcism. In the Bishop's brief report the exorcism quickly builds to a furious climax, after which Germana "fell to the floor. It was the end evidently, but the struggle was terrible. She moaned with awful pains, and her face swelled suddenly so that she could not even open her eyes, and tears came down her cheeks. But the Sign of the Cross brought the face instantly back to the natural size. Then followed a kind of convulsion, and she remained motionless as if dead; *locus vero foetore redolebat*. After about ten minutes, she opened her eyes, and knelt down to thank God."

Bishop Delalle concludes, "If anyone can explain the signs, the symptoms, the words, and the cure otherwise than by possession, he will be more clever than I am. I have in my possession a letter sent me by Germana afterwards, in which she begs that I will pray for her death. She has seen too much and is afraid of life."

~

The poignancy of those last words has not left me since I first read them. In his version Fr Erasmus informs us that it was more than fear of life that haunted Germana to the end. "She had much to suffer on account of these terrible sayings," he reports, "of which she did not know anything afterwards, but she was humble again and asked for pardon and forgiveness, and was given permission to stay at St Michael's. When I arrived at the Mission in April 1909, I found Germana there still. How she rejoiced to see me. She behaved herself well, prayed and received the Sacraments regularly; she was obedient, honest, industrious, and thankful. In 1913 she caught a bad cold, and galloping consumption set in. On September 13th she passed away. RIP."

And Monika? Apart from some howling and a few revelations, her possession made itself known through a deep despair. Several times she tried to drown herself in the Indonyana River and even to hang herself. Like Germana, she had written a promise to sell herself to the Devil, but then destroyed it. When the Sisters insisted that she write it again so that the Bishop could see it, she inscribed neatly in the copperplate they had taught her, "Satan, if you give me a new song for my mouth, then I will do

490

anything you ask of me." When the Sisters told her the letter was not complete, she answered, "Only the song is still missing. The new song sounds out, Lucifer, if you can teach me all the languages of the world, then I shall be thine, body and soul."

Bishop Delalle's reluctance to carry out Monika's exorcism was based mainly on a letter to do with the mastering of languages (something we of Mariannhill would learn, within a few short years, could have much to do with the selling of one's soul), but once begun it was as dramatic and terrible as Germana's. At last the evil spirit was induced to leave. Fr Erasmus tells us that "Satan's going out of Monika was visible: the eyes were broken, as with Germana, but all could see the opening of her mouth, the ugly distortion of her face, and the putting out of her tongue. Finally, it cracked loudly in her chest and neck, eight times. And then Monika was lying on the ground like a dead person. After a while she opened her eyes and asked for a cup of water. It was well past midnight when the Second Magnificat was intoned, when Monika was liberated from the Devil."

The exorcisms successfully performed, His Grace the Bishop returned the following morning to Durban after a thanksgiving Mass. A few weeks later Monika went to Lourdes. She was obedient and frequented the Holy Sacrament, Fr Erasmus tells us. She did not wish to marry or to become a Religious Sister. She liked to help the Sisters in the Sanatorium, where she found a home.

As for St Michael's, well, Fr Erasmus concludes his reminiscences of the Exorcisms thus: "From the time the Exorcisms were over, Satan was gone. A new life began in the Mission of St Michael's. Many came for Instructions, Conversions of the Heathen and Baptisms were many every year. 7 000 Baptisms have been recorded in the Baptism Register, and 8–10 Mission Outstations with Schools have sprung up and are prospering. There is wheat and weed together, light and shadow as everywhere in the world. But Satan worked against himself at St Michael's. *Mysterium iniquitatis* – Mystery of Iniquity. St Michael the Archangel overcame Lucifer again. Honour, glory, thanks, and adoration to the True God!"

~

Fr Adalbert has, in the course of his historical research, obviously scanned every syllable of the *South African Catholic Magazine* for any mention of Mariannhill and her missions. For Vol. xvii (1907) he records: No Entries.

For myself, I remember mainly the words of the Devil on leaving Monika, *I will not go to Hell! I will enter another one.* I have heard it reported that of late when the Christian Natives at St Michael's show anyone around the Mission, they always take them to Germana's room, the one where the poor girl famously and mysteriously caught fire. They point to the roof beams, which are apparently still charred in places. And they say that the spirits that flew out of her streamed out through the roof, burning the wood on their way, and in an arc like a rainbow of fire, poured across Nomansland to the towers of Lourdes.

Perhaps they are thinking of Germana accompanying Monika to Lourdes, but soon after the girls left St Michael's there was evil enough abroad in all the missions of Mariannhill for any one of them to be seen as the destination of the expelled spirits. We at Emmaus could be the first to claim this.

23

One day in late 1907, Franz was again climbing slowly with insecure steps the Way of the Cross which he had cut into the hill rising up behind his Mission. By now 177 steps had been scored into the rock, but even this did not make his painful daily exercise much easier. He had just reached the Tenth Station and prayed, "We adore Thee, O Christ, and we bless Thee, for by Thy Holy Cross Thou hast redeemed the world", when a great weakness overcame him, and he had to sit down on the rocky steps to rest.

Then a tremor shook the mountain, and Franz turned around just in time to avoid being hit by a giant stone that had been shaken loose out of its resting place. This boulder bounced just past his right shoulder and tumbled down the rest of the precipice with tremendous force, leaping this way and that before heading directly towards the mission church, with Franz's house just behind it.

"*In manus tuas, Domine,*" mumbled the old man in terror. And the rock stopped abruptly, "as if held by a miraculous hand", metres before the altar end of the recently completed church. Trembling, Franz continued up the Stations of the Cross until he knelt before the iron crucifix on the summit of his Calvary. Here he commended his whole work to God's protecting providence, and then slowly, achingly, descended the many steps back to the mission.

The path wound down behind the church, where he found the Sisters standing around the rock that had so nearly destroyed the church. They were all talking at once. "Venerable Father, did you see this big rock leaping down the mountain?" "It could have crushed our work." "It stopped so suddenly."

"No rock is big enough to crush our work," replied Franz. "Our work is in the hands of God, and He will guard it against rocks, earthquakes, and all evils."

His answer was rapidly worked into myth. It appeared in book after book written about him after his death. Was it only I who heard, coming around the church (too late, as always, for the event itself), the note of cynicism wound into the exhausted tone of his reply?

However this may be, Franz's health deteriorated rapidly soon after this event. He was no longer able to walk about, even with assistance, and before long he was forced to lie in bed for days on end.

~

It was at this dark time that we learned how Fr Erasmus's spirits at last had their victory. I have only come to see the events that unfolded in 1907 in this way as I tried to make some sense of the accounts of poor Monika and Germana's suffering put before me so recently.

What troubled me about Fr Erasmus's report of the possessions was that for all the detail he goes into, it was strangely empty. By the Second Exorcism, certainly, it is plain that the Terrible Sayings, the Litany of Frightful Publications, the Awful Revelations, are at the centre of the Mysterious Occurrences. But nowhere in his report does he set out what these were, even though everything in the whole diabolical display is directed towards them.

Fr Erasmus's report was written many years after the events in question, in itself a suggestion that his documentation of them could not be risked earlier. And we monks are used to those gaps in manuscripts where some part has been lost or obliterated. When we come upon them, we are taught not to ask for more, not to search further for that which Providence or more earthly authority (and who am I to separate the two?) does not wish us to know. We are meant to copy on, using just what is before us. The travails of Germana and her friend Monika, however, have demanded more of me.

Using what I have learned over the years, I have become convinced that when Fr Erasmus's attempts to get Rome to read the letter conveying the Terrible Facts revealed by the possessed girls were frustrated, the enterprise lost much of its force. Enough, anyway, for it to no longer be necessary, nearly a decade and a half later, to risk bringing down the authority of *Edmundi lo* again upon Mariannhill. The Church has, after all, allowed Abbot Obrecht to wear the zuchetta, and extended to him the privilege of using the cappa magna, which ordinarily is granted only to Bishops solemnly officiating in their dioceses. Left unprovoked, however, his power is unlikely to be directed at Mariannhill again. This is because the voices of St Michael's were never really silenced by the exorcisms; Fr Erasmus and Fr Willibald found another route for making public the revelations of the demons, a modern one that Franz himself could have recommended without reserve. Indeed, it is hard not to think of Franz as the inspiration for what the two Mariannhill monks, adrift in Europe and restricted as they were at the same time, got up to next.

When Dom Edmund returned to Mariannhill after squashing the Memorandum, which he took as a direct attack upon himself, he lost no time in beginning a canonical process against the priest he saw as the embodiment of the resistance against his administration.

Willibald Wanger had entered Mariannhill at the beginning of the year 1892. Initially he showed great promise, especially of the intellectual kind. This "Bavarian genius", as some called him in his earliest days in the monastery, was the first member of our community to be sent to Rome to pursue his higher studies. Whilst there, however, the true nature of his character made itself felt. He was sent back to Mariannhill before the completion of his studies, the Abbot General declaring him "unworthy of becoming a priest". The saintly Abbot Amandus either could not or would not believe this of such a talented son, and allowed him to be ordained. Some said this was purely because the Abbot had too few missionaries (he never had Franz's gift for attracting postulants), but in due course Fr Gerard, too, saw much to recommend in Fr Willibald.

It was Fr Gerard who, when he became Abbot, sent Fr Willibald to Lourdes during the time I was Rector there, and whilst I had appreciated deeply Fr Willibald's abilities as a musician – it is still the chiming voices of his choir that hover over my worst memories of the poisoning – I was under no illusion as regards his ambition. He was already well versed in Zulu and a brilliant writer, and used these talents to start a pastoral

494

magazine, *Pastor Bonus*. This was chiefly a bulletin of information concerned with questions and suggestions concerning missionary life, and therefore not something to which I gave much active support. It played a large part, however, in Fr Willibald's being appointed Rector of Lourdes.

All this, Fr Adalbert informs me, turned about rapidly upon Dom Edmund's becoming Apostolic Administrator of Mariannhill. One of the Administrator's first acts was the suspension of *Pastor Bonus*. He gave no reasons – as Superior he was not required to give reasons for any of his actions – but soon after his arrival he had seen an article written by Fr Willibald for the next edition and decided that it was directed specifically against his administration. It was this article that really set off Dom Edmund's fear of "agitation" and all those connected with the publication immediately fell under suspicion.

No official act of the Administrator's ever went without a deeply felt sense of personal affront, and it was no surprise to hear that Fr Willibald was one of the three or four Religious whom, on his first trip back to Europe after taking up his position at Mariannhill, Dom Edmund had tried to have dismissed from the Order. He failed in this only because the Religious in question were protected by their vow of stability. No Superior could force a monk to change house or leave the Order. As Franz's Superiors had discovered all those years ago, the only means a Superior had in this regard was the power of persuasion. And Fr Willibald, like Franz in the past, was having none of this.

Fr Willibald's rectorship of Lourdes had been so freely in the missionary style that there were lapses aplenty in his implementation of the Rule on his station, each of which could be treated as a calculated affront to the Administrator and to the Regulations he was determined to enforce. The outcome of the process was swift and harsh: Fr Willibald was given the choice of transferring to another Trappist monastery (it was this case that led the Order to declare, in the General Chapter of the autumn of 1906, that the vow of obedience took precedence over that of stability), or of spending a year at Mariannhill performing a penance, or secularisation.

Not surprisingly, he chose the last, and he was given a year in the world to find a Bishop who would accept him back as a Religious. Willibald Wanger, as we must now call him, left immediately for Rome to begin a process of appeal against the judgement. I have heard that he may have shared his friend Fr Erasmus's "protective custody" for a while, but Dom

Edmund would find in him the wilier antagonist, one well versed in the labyrinth of the ways of the Holy City.

He was in Rome when newsprint did what all the evil spirits out of hell could not. An article appeared on the 17th of August 1907, first in the *Bayerischer Kurier*, the newspaper of Germany's centre party, then in the *Augsberger Postzeitung*, and then in newspaper after newspaper throughout Germany, each of which copied it verbatim. With its publication all the attempts made by those friendly to Dom Edmund to keep an air of ordered and silent sanctity about everything to do with Mariannhill vanished.

Here at last in the cold lead of type, the black ink of print, were those Terrible Things that could not be spoken outright by the missionaries or even put plainly in the mouths of the possessed in Fr Erasmus's account of the Exorcisms. In reality now a Litany of Frightful Publications, the article barely paused to inform its readers that "since April 1905 Edmund Obrecht, Abbot of Gethsemani in America, has been appointed as Apostolic Administrator of the Missionary Monastery of Mariannhill" before proceeding with a list of all he was doing to bring the monastery "down in ruins".

The whole of the letter, which continues as follows, is worth recording:

Let alone that the Administrator, by birth an Alsatian but by education and culture a Frenchman, was not a suitable reformer for a monastery made up exclusively of Germans, especially given his contempt, even downright hatred of Germans and Germanness, this man has no clue as to the duties of a Superior of a Monastery. Instead he allows his ego and moods to rule. He dictates draconian regulations to his subordinates, whom he addresses only as '*diese Kerls*' even if they have sacrificed themselves over decades for the service of the mission, whilst he himself disregards everything.

He lets the Lay Brothers starve. They have to work on just two ounces of bread under the burning African sun from two in the morning until midday, while he consumes six eggs for breakfast and drinks wine and whisky and three secretaries have to do the work for which he is employed.

If he knows he can hurt one of his subordinates deeply, you can be sure this will be done, even without a reason. There are examples at our disposal. If a member of the Order happened to make a mistake many years ago, this will be made public over and over again in the most merciless manner. He wants to break the moral spine of each of his fellows completely in order that they become slaves creeping in front of this egocentric Superior.

For non-obedience of the Rules of the Order, even if there is a sensible explanation for it, this man imposes punishments so exorbitant that those affected by them are pushed into suicide and apostasy. Facts with names and dates are at our disposal, and are only not published out of respect for the families of the poor victims.

If somebody tries to make him aware that things cannot go on like this, he says 'I have all the authority, I can do whatever I want.' At the same time, in complete ignorance of the practical life of the missions, he proceeds in such a way as to make sure the missions suffer the greatest damage possible. Experienced missionaries cry tears at his orders.

The Administrator also wastes the property of the monastery and the alms of the missions. During his many journeys to Europe and America he behaves like a lord and a millionaire. He travels in luxury cabins, he tips up to ten German Marks when twenty Pfennig would be sufficient, and he has not handed in several thousand Marks which were given to him for the missions. Nobody knows how much he has appropriated for himself from the collection points in Europe, because nobody is allowed to look into the matter.

It is easy to guess what we should think of the character of this man after these hints, which are just a few grains of sand from the mountain of material against him. He is the embodiment of egotism. His ego is his God and should be one of his Superiors. And woe betide anyone who does not worship before this Idol!

Thus it is that under his leadership sixty to seventy percent of our priests have resigned, and of those who remain yet more would retire if they were not bound by material considerations, especially the loss of subsistence in this desperate situation. This is made most clear by the words of the Founder of Mariannhill, Abbot Franz Pfanner, who is still living in Africa: "This Frenchman has turned our life in the Order into a prison!"

Finally, his phenomenal love of gossiping must be mentioned, which must be unsurpassed anywhere in the world. Each Father and Brother and Sister learns from him everything about everybody else. In the same way he pulls the monastery down into the dirt before strangers.

And this is the man who was meant to reform Mariannhill! Even more ironically, there was not that much at Mariannhill to reform! The few human frailties that have surfaced amongst over six hundred Trappists and Sisters together could easily have been improved by a little Christian charity and an intelligent Superior. The current Administrator lacks both these qualities entirely. Where there are some real problems and fundamental difficulties, such as the relationship between the Trappist Order and missionary work, the 'reformer' does not even touch them with his small finger!

Before we end for now, we must touch on his abuse of the Mariannhill missionary magazine, *Vergissmeinnicht*, which he uses solely to mislead public opinion in his favour. He tells the Prior of Mariannhill (currently his nephew!) which topics should be elaborated upon, and how they should be treated. It is not uncommon that passages have to be changed five to eight times a day until the glory of the Administrator is laid on thick enough.

Therefore we conclude that this man, when in danger of being exposed, will not draw back from any means of covering himself. He especially loves to terrorise his inferiors, and therefore Rome itself will have to investigate him before we can learn the whole truth from the intimidated people under his heel.

From what has been said, it should be clear what value one should attribute to any attempt at defence from his side. We stand for what is written down here not only with our word of honour, but also with our oath.

The letter was not signed.

~

Lost on the edges of Africa, we heard echoes of the noise this article unleashed in Europe, but I have not come across a single monk here who would admit to knowing anything of the particulars behind it. To this day, in all the piles and piles of paper Mariannhill has generated, it is impossible to find a writer who does not side-step the unhappy affair. It was left to Fr Adalbert to follow up on the commotion in the German press of a decade and a half ago and to write to the publications in question, several of which are still thriving newspapers. The only one to respond was the *Augsberger Postzeitung*, which was kind enough to include not only the initial letter but some of the follow-up correspondence as well. Our historian has put these items before me in recent days in the hope that I could provide some clue as to the identities of the authors of the article.

This I could not do. One of the two chief suspects, Willibald Wanger, wrote to the newspapers denying authorship (but adding that "the truth forbade him to contradict the facts described therein"). Fr Erasmus went so far as to say, in a letter to the newspaper in question, that he had "tried with all his power to prevent those articles from being published". Both denied knowing who had written the original or its various versions.

As I sorted through Fr Adalbert's clippings, it became clear to me that whoever wrote the article must have been based in Europe at the time. Bishop Delalle had sent a telegram from Natal defending the Administrator and, when this was published, barely a week passed before an anonymous response appeared in all the major German newspapers dismissing it point for point. Who else besides our suspects could have had the necessary knowledge or been so conveniently placed to do this? Still, I am loath to accuse two members of our community of outright lying. I took it that Fr Adalbert could easily draw his own conclusions from the material he had put before me, and passed his pieces of newsprint back to him with a shake of my head.

This matter must seem to you in the world a very modest scandal to emerge out of so much drama and upheaval, but it must be understood how much the silence of our lives amplifies the least noise, and just how large the smallest of deviations can become in a life dedicated to perfect order. The specifics of Dom Edmund's irregularities promised to blow up very quickly into an Order-wide debacle, as the letters written in his defence make plain even to my unsubtle eye. His defenders were only too pleased to point out that the regulations he followed were "absolutely in accord-ance with the Rules of the Order", the dispensations he granted "approved by the highest authorities of the Order", and the penalties he prescribed "determined by the customs of the Order". It was precisely such arguments that moved the scandal from the scale of a few personal indiscretions to a questioning of the practices of the Order as a whole.

It was not hard, then, to see why this unfortunate affair is played down in written material within our Order. Even Fr Adalbert seems to have given up on the whole matter too easily, content to leave its substance for its effects. These would prove dramatic enough in any case. All attempts at the time to clear up the matter made matters worse by fuelling the rapidly grow-ing public interest that was turning Mariannhill and the whole Cistercian Order into a religious sideshow. In their embarrassment the Superiors of the Order were only too happy to look for the quickest and easiest way out. Dom Edmund, who was already en route to South Africa again, was encouraged to resign as soon as the opportunity presented itself.

Well, no suitable opportunity did. He returned to a Mariannhill where it was now impossible to apply any further disciplinary action. The Memorandum made it apparent that at least twenty-three priests had sided against him, enough for him to feel that his authority was thoroughly undermined. Pausing just long enough to appoint Fr Leyendecker as Prior and temporary Administrator, Dom Edmund returned almost immediately to Europe. As soon as he arrived in Rome he tendered his resignation both as Visitator and Administrator of Mariannhill and then, no doubt much comforted by the cigars he allowed himself when travelling, headed back to his most austere of monasteries in Kentucky, where smoking was never countenanced.

~

Did the demoniacal violence tearing through the bodies and mouths of two young Native girls thus come down to a little arrogance, a touch of extravagance, some whisky perhaps, and some wine, and a few eggs? Only Trappists could understand the scale of such things within their community. But let us allow poor leadership too, and poor communication between a Superior and his community – and, yes, excessive garrulousness, chief of Trappist faults, but even then, what do you have? A couple of textbook exorcisms, bearing out every detail in the *Rituale Romanum*?

This we had, but was it necessary, I ask myself, for the gates of Hell to be opened in order that an unpopular Superior be unseated? And should it have been left to someone like me – bearing as I do the name of a saint who would, you may remember, rise from the ground and move about in the air – to ask what all this business of young Native girls rising into the air was really about? Yes, the smallest thing would suffice to make Joseph of Cupertino levitate: a word of praise for the Creator and His creatures, the beauty of the sky or of the trees on the roadside, the sound of a bell or of church music. What was it then that raised poor Germana above the ground? If my saint was lifted up by his holiness, what lifted Germana into the air?

Joseph of Cupertino has recently been made the patron saint of aviators and air travellers but should we not add to St Joseph's patronage all those who are lifted up, who find themselves adrift in the air, even if this is not always – as poor Germana was to find – a result of their saintliness? Well, spiritual mysteries, as I have had occasion to note, must always exceed our ability to know them. But I have wondered since, many times, if the evil sensed by others and myself at St Michael's was a physical expression of spiritual malevolence or whether it was a sign of some kind, a figure for our failings as Trappists, or missionaries, or both.

I do not know. I know only that by the time the demons crashed into Franz's Calvary, the founder of the greatest Trappist House in the world was ready at last to proclaim, "If I were to be born again, I would no more become a Trappist!" He burst out with this suddenly, violently, from his bed, his weak voice strained already by the day's worth of memories I had taken down.

Never before had I seen Franz doubt for an instant that the Order was right for him, and he for the Order. Now, with red eyes brimming, he tried to raise his thin limbs and to look out of the window, my arm behind his back. Eyes darting around him, he said, "Truly, truly, many times the thought has occurred to me as I lie here, would that I had never seen this Africa and laid the foundation of so many sins and scandals!"

He fell back, and, as I endeavoured to extricate my arm as gently as I could, muttered, "Now I, the founder of all this, must watch its destruction." Even now, trapped in the prison of his bed, he found it hard to grasp that his days were numbered. His iron will still reached out, he clutched at every hope of life to the very end.

Soon after, a stranger from Rhodesia, a tailor he called himself, appeared. When introduced to Franz, he claimed to be familiar with certain medical treatments and quickly gained the full confidence of our patient. Certainly his measures had a marvellous effect and, within hours, our tailor friend was promising Franz another ten years of life. The "Helper" was set aside during this time, of course, but even I could not begrudge this as I watched Franz hobble around his room without needing to lean upon my left shoulder for support.

What did concern me was how this newfound energy was directed. It is hard to believe, but as soon as he was up Franz called me to him and started dictating rapidly, even violently, a new set of Constitutions – one that was, it soon became quite clear, suited to a modern missionary congregation. The only thing it took from the Trappists of Mariannhill was their missionary methods. Here then was the basis for a complete break with the Order, a separation as solid and final as the most fervent missionary could ever have wanted.

But oh the perversity of man, and of monk too! In everything I have told you, I have found myself, again and again, tripping over the one figure of speech that Trappist life cannot entertain, the one trait of words that most drives us to avoid them – that split between meaning and expression that undercuts the most powerful prayer, the most serious of vows, the most desperate attempts at the truth. Is it not this figure, lying at the heart of speech, that makes us so fervently embrace silence? And yet, even the silence left to us was to become true silence no more, only the silence of the unsaid, the silence of the Nomansland of speech, the silence of that space between the stated and the implied that is – what else, but irony? A silence no longer born of a desire to approach God in the purest way possible but one created only by the noise of the world cancelling itself out.

You would think, would you not, after all we had been through, that the missionaries amongst us would be overjoyed to find that Franz now embraced their cause entirely, to the total exclusion of the Rule that so limited their work. That their founder, the one who gave birth to them out of a vision of Trappist missionaries that not only bridged the divide between apostolic and contemplative ideals but did away with it, the one who had insisted that only a good Trappist could be a good missionary, had now so revised his position as to state – briefly, succinctly, and brutally to the point – "Trappist and missionary in one is incompatible."

No single statement could be more devastating for Mariannhill. I can only pray that Franz in his age and infirmity did not quite understand this – although the prayer must rate high amongst the most fruitless.

Here then was Dom Edmund's real legacy, worthy of the sufferings of a Germana and a Monika. For it was not until he brought with him the true Trappist spirit – or, more accurately, the exact letter of the Trappist Regulations, although the two are separable only in the life of a Trappist like Dom Edmund – that Franz realised just how mistaken he had been. And so he had me sit down and write as he stood, hands clenched on the back of his chair, beard jutting in and out with each word:

"If one wishes to be a real missionary, at least three quarters of the Trappist Rule must be cancelled. And this means the chief points, such as silence, fasting, and withdrawal from the world, as well as the control of all correspondence, abstinence from meat consumption and smoking, and so on. If I were to start again, I would enter a missionary society where there is no need to fight between Mission and Rule each step of the way …"

I was appalled, and barely heard the rest of what I took down. When Franz's dictation stopped, I came to, as it were, to hear him telling me to address this letter to the Abbot General of the Trappist Order and the Propaganda Congregation.

~

Even I had no idea at the time just how great was the irony of what was written on the pages I folded and tried, with shaking hands, to insert into one of our envelopes. All I knew was that a commission of five leading members of the Mariannhill community had just been called at Centocow. Abbot Gerard, in the chair, put two options before them: that Mariannhill stay within the Trappist Order and be content with mission statutes that have the binding force of Constitutions for its members; or that Mariannhill form a separate Congregation, affiliated to the Trappist Order. And the decision? It was agreed that "the first mode is preferred in so far as it does not lead to a formal separation from the mother Order".

Why this preference? The answer was simple to those of us who wept with relief to hear it, but it was also never far below the surface of even the most strident of the missionary revolts. As the commission stated in setting out its decision: "The second mode would cut the Gordian knot with one stroke, for the relaxing of the observance of the Rule would no longer be a problem. But it would mean the loss of Exemption, and of Solemn Vows."

Monasteries united with other monasteries under canon law, like those of the Trappist Order, are complete and independent organisations. They retain their autonomy in all that pertains to their internal administration, and their Superiors have no one above them except the Pope himself. The Solemn Vows by which the monks of these communities freely commit themselves to the religious life make them exempt from the authority of the local Ordinary, usually the Bishop of the Diocese. We fell under Bishop Delalle, as we had once under Bishop Jolivet (and before that, so disastrously, Bishop Ricards), but only in matters affecting secular relations in our parish. Our missionary activities were considered parochial work, and as such were open to being regulated by the Bishop, but within our enclosure we were subject to our own Superior alone.

Whatever difficulties this entailed, none of the monks of Mariannhill, of whatever party, had any desire to become members of a separate Congregation, independent of our Order and bound to the religious life by only Simple Vows. The loss of Exemption would open us up to a new range of authorities, and each of us knew all too well by now the effect of insensitive interventions into the rules that governed every detail of our daily lives.

The General Chapter of the Trappist Order could be forgiven, however, for not attending to such niceties. What they had seen over the years was a house a large number of whose members displayed a hostile and disrespectful attitude to the Order, along with an indifference, no, an antipathy towards religious observance that often took the form of an outright refusal to participate in it. Regular observance was made to look ridiculous, and the regulars along with it. Even the Rule for the Stations these missionaries found too "Trappist-like"; the incompatibility of mission and Order was repeated in every statement they made. One Religious had made so bold as to affirm that "Our greatest enemy is the Order", whilst the founder himself had dared to write that the recent attempts at reform under Dom Edmund made a "prison" out of Mariannhill. In short, the behaviour of the monks of Mariannhill had showed in every way an inconstancy in their vocation, disrespect for the religious life, and a disregard for the vow of obedience.

As far as the General Chapter was concerned, the Memorandum drawn up earlier by the mission party was nothing other than proof of the desire – the intention, even – to separate from the Order. It had to be so for everything else in it was nonsense, given that the legal formulation it demanded was in existence already, as far as the General Chapter was concerned, in the form of the Visitation Report compiled by Abbot Obrecht in the summer of 1905 and approved by the Chapter in the autumn of that year.

The irony of ironies, then, in our increasingly ironic existence as Trappists, was that by the time my colleagues – who dared to call each other Brother in these days? – were debating the nature of our status in the humming heat of Centocow that January, with insects buzzing loudly in the Chapter Room as they sought out the sweat that dripped in rivulets down heavy habits, the General Chapter had already decided to separate Mariannhill from the Order. They were quite simply fed up with the endless difficulties raised by the "rebels" in South Africa; to cast them out must have seemed the neatest and safest of solutions.

Having made a firm resolution, the Order faced the disagreeable problem of finding a way to inform their child that it was cut off. The answer was to keep this resolution secret and let Mariannhill come to the same conclusion itself. In their Memorandum the missionaries had requested permission to hold a plenary conference at Mariannhill to discuss their fate. What else could the Chapter do but agree to such a conference, the outcome of which must inevitably be the wish to be released from the fetters of the Order?

Hearing that the document he had brought to Rome was being exhumed from its burial place in the depths of the deepest Church bureaucracy, Fr Erasmus had written excitedly to the missionaries of Mariannhill: "Everything shall be organised on the basis of the Memorandum!" By this he meant all the intricate details of a missionary life with a base in the Trappist Order. Not for one second did he, or any of the other signatories of the document, consider it the basis for an order of separation.

But for the General Chapter, this was all it was. They wanted us to have nothing in common with them any longer, not even the name of Trappist. All that was needed for a conference to be convened at Mariannhill was the appointment of a reliable person to head it.

~

And so it was, in the May of 1908, that Mariannhill was given its "death sentence", as even our own Bishop Delalle would call it. This was delivered by a pale and rather sharp-faced Irishman, Monsignor Miller, first Vicar Apostolic of the Transvaal. I have since found in Fr Adalbert's pile of papers a strictly confidential letter (no longer so, needless to say) from the General Chapter to Monsignor Miller: "It is our wish that the Religious of Mariannhill express the wish for separation of their own accord. The help which we expect from your Lordship is either, as we expect, that you accept the spontaneous confession of a desire for separation from the Religious of Mariannhill, or, by directing their minds in such a way, that they come to wish and accept it."

Franz had not been invited to the conference, of course (to say nothing of myself), and no one seems even to have noted the oddity of his being in agreement for once with the General Chapter. But then, his views had not been taken seriously – except as an irritation – for a long time.

It was Fr Baldwin, I heard, who finally forced Monsignor Miller to confess that "in reading between the lines" he believed the General Chapter tended towards the course of separation. When pushed further Monsignor Miller gave up all pretence and declared that the only choice before the

"Mariannhillers" was, as he put it, "Trappist monastery without mission or separation from the Trappist Order". We know now that not even this bald statement corresponded with the truth, for the Order had left us no choice at all. With or without missions, we were to be expelled.

Had I known then that one thing that I most needed to know of all things I have ever needed to know, how much might have been spared me. Nothing else I ever came to know would make up for it, or erase what I did through not knowing it.

As the red bricks of the monastery glowed in the warmth of the early autumn sun and the green of the farm twinkled below, Mariannhill discussed the only question left to be discussed: what form of affiliation the monastery could maintain with the Trappists once it became a separate congregation. And here Monsignor Miller stuck fast in his own logic. Left to his own devices in allaying the fears of the Mariannhillers, the smooth-talking Irishman made up promises of his own, right, left and centre. If we changed our constitution as little as possible, Rome could not object to our remaining in the Order. Oh no, no reason to be afraid concerning Solemn Vows – we all had them and no one would ask for dispensation from them. Spiritual community of property with other Trappists could be kept and through this the same privileges as the rest of the Order. So he went on, fabricating a congregation in the air, one for which there was no precedent or possibility.

As I said, I did not hear any of this for myself. Versions of what happened at the conference reached us at Emmaus and have become woven with my own imaginings and the reports I have read since. Brother Nivard, it seems, had worked as hard as he could to get a hearing for the Lay Brothers whose views, as usual, had been pushed to the periphery. He had complained bitterly about the infidelity of the monks of Mariannhill, who now suddenly seemed so ready to tear themselves, together with the flourishing mission stations, from the stem of the Order. The Convers Brothers, he pointed out, had far fewer difficulties with the Rule; they had needed, and asked for, fewer dispensations than those demanded by the Choir Religious. They, therefore, had much less difficulty with the Strict Observance, and were extremely suspicious of any break with it.

The Convers Brothers also had no vow of stability and hence no obligation to remain at Mariannhill, a point of real concern for Monsignor Miller. Mariannhill and its missions would be nothing without its chief labour force, and he rose to inspired oratorical heights as he worked at allaying their fears. Monsignor Miller's responses to the Mariannhillers' concerns were effusively convincing. Deeply pertinent issues were taken up into his words and there dissolved, melted away – at least for the time he was speaking. For a cold eye would have seen that once his voice stopped, the issues remained as problematic as they had been before. At one point in this exercise, we heard, Brother Nivard could no longer help himself, and let out a resonant guffaw. I hear in that outburst the end of Brother Nivard's real laughter. What passed for laughter after this was the noise of a breaking heart, a breaking heart that went along with the tearing of nerves and the collapse of reason.

We heard later that Monsignor Miller had tried in Rome to present Mariannhill's position: that separation from the Trappist Order was acceptable only if we retained our Solemn Vows. "It is impossible," he is supposed to have said, "that a community of nearly three hundred persons have, against their will, the obligations of their Solemn Vows dissolved." This was met by the blank presumption, a presumption that nothing could shake, that what he was presenting was a new constitution for a congregation with Simple Vows, completely separated from the Trappists. Any notion of some other sort of affiliation was dismissed in the light of the recent unification of the Trappists into one Order "in which there shall be no difference and in which we live in one and the same love, after one and the same Rule and according to the same customs".

Nothing else was even thinkable for a Trappist house and on the 18th of January 1909 the Consultor advised the secretariat of the Congregation for the Religious that Mariannhill be separated from the Order of the Trappists. On the 2nd of February, Pope Pius x signed a decree declaring "the total separation of the Missionaries of Mariannhill from the parent body of the Trappists and their separate existence under their own rules as a religious institute".

24

Even after Dom Edmund's proscriptions fell away, few of our confreres saw much point in communicating with Franz. Often he said to me that he felt this silence more painfully than he would any news, no matter how contrary to his ideas, which they could share with him. "It is as if I am a leper, everyone seems to shy away from me," he would say, over and over, as I helped him into his bath, or lifted him to his chair.

This may well have been the case as far as Mariannhill and her missions went, but the fact is, as I knew better than anyone else, the "Abbot freely resigned" continued to report directly to Rome in great detail on issues crucial to the monastery. And his ideas, dismissed completely as they had been over almost the whole of the last decade, suddenly took on an altogether new significance. Some have even said that, whilst they may not have initiated the idea of separation, his remarks may well have nourished it. Having the founder of the vast enterprise that was Mariannhill on their side must have been of great use not only to the General Chapter but to the Congregation for the Religious itself.

No one went very far out of their way to assure Franz of this or give him a renewed sense of his importance, but it was obvious to me that were he not so compromised and so old he may well have found his position rapidly re-evaluated. A clear sign of this – and the one great joy that lightened the sorrow and suffering of his last years – was the canonical approval finally granted by the Holy See for his "Missionary Sisters of the Precious Blood". At the lowest point in his hard-fought battle to save his Sisters from becoming Trappists, when Dom Edmund had not only removed Franz from being Superior of Emmaus but sent away Sr Angela, Franz's devoted companion and Superior of the Sisters at Emmaus, I wrote at Franz's dictation: "It seems as if all the devils of South Africa, America and Rome are conspiring against the Red Sisters."

And yet there they were now, a community in their own right, with the devils defeated and Sr Angela back at Emmaus. I had rarely seen Franz as happy as he was on the day that we received the news that the Trappist Chapter had ratified the Red Sisters as a separate congregation, and that this had been endorsed by Propaganda Fide. I was never to see him so jubilant again and, even as I wondered if this separation of the Sisters was a precursor of things to come at Mariannhill, I watched in despair as Franz's latest return of health thanks to the Rhodesian tailor waned. Soon enough I was firing up "The Helper" again twice a day, but this time it seemed that even electricity could not stimulate Franz's apparently inexhaustible ability to regenerate himself.

Nothing I did could bring back a semblance of his old strength. I wept on the last morning Franz tried to climb the Way of the Cross. A passing priest from another Order had compared Franz's daily toiling up the almost perpendicular face of the krantz to one of the most picturesque scenes from the Ages of Faith. Well, no more. I managed on that final attempt to get Franz as far as the Third Station. There his body gave out entirely, and he slumped back onto the rocks overhanging the zigzag path. He was mentally alert enough, however, to call out, "Jesus falls the first time under the cross: my fall is similar, loss of the office of Abbot, and my second fall my removal from the Rectorship of Emaus."

By the time I got him back to his house and then into his bed he was a bundle of misery and suffering. I stayed with Franz day and night from then on, for he was utterly helpless on his bed of pain. Much of the time his tongue was so paralysed he could scarcely open his mouth. At most I could give him only a third part of a host in Communion.

What then could bring me to do what I did next? What indeed could bring me to kill a speechless, dying man?

~

Word came at this time that Bishop Delalle had decided that the ordination of two young black men who had been sent to Rome to become priests – Julius Mbhele and Andreas Ngidi – should be postponed. He had written to the Cardinal Prefect of Propaganda requesting that they be sent back to Natal where he would ordain them himself at a later date. Behind this turnabout, it seemed, lay his fear (based on a report from the Benedictines at Inkamana) that African priests would foment unrest among the tribal Zulus. It was claimed that Fr Aloysius Mncadi, the second of our black priests, was already doing so.

I had not yet shared this news with Franz when Fr Aloysius himself visited us at Emmaus. One of our Lay Brothers had signed at the door of Franz's room that someone wished to see me. I gave him dispensation to speak and was told it was Fr Aloysius, but the man who was hovering just behind Brother Leo's shoulder called out, "Majonga, it is Father Majonga."

I asked Brother Leo to show Fr Aloysius to the office, and then quietly raised myself from next to Franz's sleeping form and followed them. I signalled Brother Leo to leave, and greeted our visitor in the prescribed form, waiting in silence for him to speak. He was clearly quite agitated, but once in my presence seemed reluctant to speak, or at least unsure of how to begin. Out of kindness I said, "Majonga, why Majonga? And why not Mncadi, if not Aloysius?"

"Majonga," he said, "that is a Zulu custom. All the Mncadis are called Majonga, the Majongas being their forefathers. So sometimes the Zulus use that. We call it *Izithakazelo*. I do not simply call myself Majonga, I *am* Majonga."

This sort of thing was all very well for someone like Franz (although his ethnographic interests had faded quite quickly in the swathe A T Bryant cut through us) or Fr Willibald Wanger, who was now acting as if he knew Zulu better than the Zulus themselves. My own struggle with the temptation of finding out about those in whose midst we were cloistered was well and truly over. This was the one bit of wisdom I felt coming upon me with my advancing years. When it came to those who gathered evidence on Zulu customs and made a name for themselves publishing the results, I now went firmly along with St Paul: A good Christian should know nothing and speak nothing of what was happening in a pagan community, still less have it printed on paper for everybody to read.

Instead of responding to Fr Aloysius's declaration, I said, too bluntly perhaps, that I had heard that he was at the centre of the unrest. "Have you heard too," he replied, "that I wish to become Bishop after killing you all?"

I remained silent.

"Well," he continued, "I have heard of many priests who would like to become Bishops. I have even known missionaries who buy purple socks because they want to become Bishops. But have you heard yet – seriously, now – of a black priest who can even hope to become a Bishop? Are we not destined for perpetual subservience to the white priests, assistant this, assistant that. Not even allowed to perform marriages. Drinking our coffee in the passageways of the white priest's house, from tin cups with wire handles. Treated like children forever, back paddler curates to the end."

He stopped, and contained himself. "I have not come here to defend myself," he said, "or to explain things that come out of circumstances that I know are of no concern to you. I have come here to tell you something that I believe is close to your heart. Something to do with your name, not mine."

I waited in silence. After a long pause, he said, "It concerns Kece, the one

510

who calls himself Müller." I stayed quiet, my expression unchanged. He could not see my hands tightening under the sleeves of my habit.

"Have you heard that he is in a hospital?" he asked. In response I moved my head the smallest degree to the left and then to the right and waited for him to continue.

"Well, not a hospital," said Fr Aloysius, "rather, an asylum – the Government Asylum in Pietermaritzburg."

I, who am known for my stillness, have never held myself so still in all my life. And so I remained while he spoke of my Eduard, now not even as Father Edward.

"You know he was never invited to share the priest's house at Ebhuhleni when he went to assist Fr Bryant? Well, there was a boarding house there, very poorly built. Fr Mnganga was given this to stay in and made a tutor in the catechism school. He was given the care of all the outstations, as far as Nongoma, forty miles away. He had to visit these on horseback. Often he was away for two or three weeks."

Fr Mnganga was prosperous in his work, he told me. He attracted many students, apparently much to the dislike of Fr Bryant, the parish priest. Each time he returned from the outstations, he would find that several of his best students had been expelled by Fr Bryant. Fr Mnganga took exception to this. He explained to Fr Bryant that if there had been any misbehaviour amongst his students, he felt responsible for this. He expected his Superior to wait until his return and report the cases to him. The two of them could then discuss what had occurred and decide on the steps to be taken.

The next time he came back to Ebhuhleni from the outstations, he found that all his very best students had been turned away from the school. He went up to Fr Bryant and demanded to know why. Fr Bryant simply turned away from him, refusing to give any reason at all. Some people said Fr Bryant had burned and buried Fr Mnganga's vestments whilst he was away, and others that when Fr Mnganga came back he found Fr Bryant pointing to the private parts of a naked Native woman as part of his studies into Zulu ethnography. But Fr Aloysius believed that Fr Bryant's turning away was in itself enough for Fr Mnganga's temper to flare.

"You knew him as a boy," he said, "but he has grown to be a big, tall man. We are told that he attempted to assault Fr Bryant physically. One of my friends tells me that Fr Bryant ran away, sneaking through the back door of his house whilst Fr Mnganga was raging. He drove in his carriage to

Umtunzini and demanded that the police come and arrest Fr Mnganga who he said was mad, breaking windows and doors and threatening to hit him. Of course, if a white man says such a thing about a black man, it is taken as the gospel truth."

After much humiliation and assault at Umtunzini, Fr Mnganga was transferred to the asylum in Pietermaritzburg as a madman. I could well believe, as Fr Aloysius told me, that the officials at the asylum recognised quite soon that Fr Mnganga did not suffer from a psychological sickness. They referred the matter back to the diocese and requested that he be collected and taken back. What I did not expect was what Fr Aloysius told me next. Fr Mnganga, he said, wanted those who had committed him to the mental institution to come and collect him themselves. He wanted Bryant and the Bishop to declare that he was sane.

"They would not do it," Fr Aloysius said, standing up and leaning towards me over the desk. "But he has refused to leave the Natal Government Asylum until they come for him. He has been there over two years now, still waiting for them."

Fr Aloysius stopped speaking. It seemed to me, however, that his voice went on in the silence that fell, that its reverberations continued in the air all about me. He had a good, strong voice, not unlike that of Rev. Charles Pamla, a voice that rang out in its measured confidence at the level of normal speech. I could feel it enveloping me, and unaccountably my nose filled with the scent of apples, over-ripe apples dropping from trees, apples crushed beneath my feet. And in the after tones of Fr Aloysius's voice I sensed an immanent revelation, something vital to him, myself, all of us. Something I could feel, as surely as I have ever felt anything in my life, but not quite grasp.

And yet it was no less real, no less certain for my not being able to take hold of it, translate it into the terms of my comprehension. Everything in me wanted to fall into it, embrace it, let it take over the emptiness of my life – but I dared not move. I felt that if I released so much as the smallest muscle, every part of my body would burst into uncoordinated and chaotic activity, and I would collapse to the floor, unravelling completely. So still did I remain that I could only hope my jaw had not dropped, that I was not gaping at this smart, neat, well-turned-out young man.

Fr Aloysius was getting ready to leave. "You Mariannhillers will never believe that an African can be a priest," he said. "You send us overseas just because we cannot be accommodated anywhere here. When we come back, you do not know what to do with us."

At one level I understood what he was saying perfectly, but my faculties kept reaching after those insistent tones somewhere beyond the sounds he was making. "Do you know that I was not sent to Rome alone?" he was asking. "Charles Mbengane from Mariathal was sent with me. He took ill while we were at the College, and was sent to Würzburg to recover. But he died there, and is buried there, in Austria, in Würzburg. I think it would be easier for you if this were the fate of all of us you send away, that we die in the places where you come from. In any event, do not expect more black priests from Mariannhill."

Abruptly he turned and went out the door. I can tell you now that his parting words were correct: no more black men from Mariannhill have been ordained in the decade and a half since I heard my door being closed gently but firmly by the departing Fr Aloysius.

And, yes, for that decade and a half, on top of the two years he had spent there already, Fr Kece Edward Mnganga Müller has been in the Natal Government Asylum in Pietermaritzburg, waiting.

~

I sat immobile, immersed in silence after Fr Aloysius left, but all the while I was trying furiously, desperately, to take hold of what had floated around his words, of the meaning not in them but somehow of them. At first my attempts were hampered by a dense haze that seemed to have settled over my faculties, a haze that was not so much a blur of sameness as a dappled interplay of soft light and shadow, cool and green. I was certain, absolutely certain, that whatever it was that hung just beyond that haze was exactly what I had to do – the secret of how, precisely, I should respond to what I had just heard.

Slowly this certainty gave way to a blacker state, all the more dark for the glimpse of promised illumination. I refused to give in, however, as the hope of revelation that had flared up dimmed, sputtered and then died; the memory of young Eduard would not let me. The thought of him in that foul place drove my mind, aching and weary as it was from straining after the ineffable, towards, well, a plan. Slowly, clumsily, I started working my way out of the confusion that had come over me once the intimations of certainty ghosting through Fr Aloysius's voice had waned, and began to put together, piece by piece, in no logical order at first, what seemed like the only appropriate way to respond to what I had been told.

Evening was falling when I rose, for the first time since Fr Aloysius had left. I looked at my hands, thinking of the things they had done, left undone, may have done; then I lifted them, one by one, flexing my fingers. Slowly I unfurled myself from my frozen position in the chair, every joint and muscle resisting the effort in a way they never did even after I had spent hours immobile on my knees at prayer. Finally I was upright, holding at bay as best I could the vertiginous feeling that threatened my every step.

I left the office and picked my way back to Franz's house through the flat greyness that passed for twilight at Emmaus at this time of year. There I found him with his eyes open, staring blankly at the stretch of Nomansland beyond his window as it was swallowed up into the gathering darkness. Sr Angela moved from her post at his bed when I entered and quietly left as I took her place. I took Franz's flaccid hand in mine, and then I spoke into the silence of the room as the few objects in it – the cupboard, the bath with its hose, the hard chair, the table at which he used to kneel for his prayers – lost their shape and merged with the gloom that enveloped my voice, took it over, made it part of itself.

"*Loquamur de Ordine nostro*," I intoned into the darkness now upon us. Technically, although I had never invoked the status thrust on me after the Wolfgang Bens affair, I was the Superior on this station, and thus able to use the words prescribed for instituting a Chapter of Faults: *Let us speak of our observance.*

"*Quid dicitis?*" I continued, in the full knowledge that Franz would not be able to respond as is required, *Culpas meas.* This Chapter, I knew, would not be one in which he would examine his conscience and open his fault before the assembly (such as it was on this occasion) so that by common prayer it could be healed. No, today it was required of me to step forward and say out loud, as the formula states, *I proclaim Father Francis.*

"I must tell them," I said instead, speaking to myself as much as to Franz. "I must proclaim your secret fault. The one thing that will undo all you have done." I paused and looked at him. His eyes were still open, still filled with the emptiness at which he stared. "The one thing," I went on in a voice hardly above a whisper, "that could destroy the special place prepared for us by God in the wilderness, where we were meant to hide our faces in the mystery of Divine silence."

514

Franz's hand lay absolutely still in mine, flat and lifeless. His eyes did not blink. Was this in obedience to the Rule, the fourth degree of humility that commands a monk *to hold fast to patience with a silent mind when he meets with any kind of injustice?* I said, "Have we not learned by now that a zeal for souls amongst those for whom such a zeal is forbidden distorts that zeal, twists it, disfigures it, until it does not know itself? That it then turns not just on itself but on those for whom it burns, and burns them with the fires of Hell, not devotion."

Was the boy Kece in the furthest shadows of that room? Was that the face of Father Eduard in the murky glass of the window, Father Mnganga calling out faintly in the wilderness beyond?

"In Hell," I said, "they will sink to the bottom of a burning lake, joining all those others who, in that terrible phrase, God forgets." And now I was gripped by an urgency that few would ever have recognised in me. "We have a last chance now for the Order to save them from this. To call us back under obedience to live hidden in the secret of God's face. To live in sanctuaries of silence filled with the fragrance of prayer. If this cannot be done, if we are to be cut off, root and branch, from the Order of the Cistercians of the Strict Observance, then it is better that all you have created be done away with."

I could see Franz's stare narrow. It seemed even to take on a focus of sorts, but not on anything in the room. I kept on speaking. "A few words will be enough to do this. A few words proclaiming that the founder of Mariannhill has not taken his final vows, his Solemn Vows. You know that everything you have built is illegal under canon law, unlawful in the eyes of the Church. Mariannhill and its missions will be swept away in an instant, erased as if they had never been, when those who should know, know what you know and I know."

Franz's head turned slightly, and an agitated expression took over his face as he brought himself, with tremendous effort, to look at me. His hand started to grasp at mine, its weakness purely physical as I felt through it a frantic spirit trying to express itself.

"To be silent when we can rebuke is to consent. I can no longer consent."

The smell of his old man's body came up to me from beneath his habit. I would not look at him, but I could not avoid his desperation. I almost believed that his mouth, working away soundlessly in the hole of his beard, would speak. But his infirmity held and nothing came out of those lips, wet though they were with the spittle of effort.

"I have trusted in your intention for too long. I must now, as the Regulations require, expose the fault as it appears."

And so I stood up, and walked out of Franz's room, and out of his house.

~

Sr Angela, Franz's faithful nurse and housekeeper for the last fifteen years, was taken aback to see me leaving Franz's side so soon. She dropped whatever it was that she was doing and bustled in to be with him as I walked out into the early dark. Behind me I could sense rather than see Calvary looming, the great iron crucifix on its summit awaiting the one who had mounted it there, and would never make his way to its foot again.

I had now to act upon the decision I had taken and announced to Franz. Given the censorship of Trappist correspondence, a letter would not do. I had to ensure that such explosive information was delivered to no one but the Abbot General himself. Either I, like Fr Erasmus, would have to make my secret and illegal way to Rome, or I would have to find someone to whom I could entrust this duty.

I feared myself far too weak and clumsy and impractical to manage any sort of travel, clandestine or not. Many years had passed since my one other covert action, that attempt at a secret trip to Grahamstown from Dunbrody to telegraph Franz about the possibility of our moving to Natal. Even then, everyone from a neighbouring farmer to Bishop Ricards had known of my movements, if not exactly what I was up to. As for finding another to serve me in this, who else would have the necessary blend of sympathies to understand what was being done and why? My isolation over the past years meant that I would have to look as far as Lourdes at least – Mariannhill, more likely, considering the attitude towards the missions such a person would have to harbour in order to go along with what I had in mind.

It was too late that evening to travel to Lourdes, a place I had not been back to since I was first sent there. But did I have time to wait? I had no idea what decisions had been made regarding the future of our monastery or the correct way to intervene in these. And if there were the remotest chance that we would be kept within the arms of the Order – as I in my ignorance of what had been going on at the conference at Mariannhill, let

516

alone in Rome, still believed was a possibility – did I wish to risk upsetting this by denouncing Franz to the legitimate authorities? Would I not rather hug my sin in silence to myself, risking even the hardening of my soul to the inspirations of grace and repentance?

I am not sure that these words, increasingly formulaic as they sounded in my own head, meant that much to me then. Instead I stumbled amidst the practicalities I would have to master before I could do anything at all. I had not left Emmaus in so long, certainly not to go any distance away, any further, that is, than required by the duties of baptism and doctoring amongst the Natives. Ordering a wagon to be set up for a journey without an excellent explanation would throw our small community into complete confusion. And given the legendary nature of my poor riding skills, any attempt to saddle up a horse and ride off alone would attract even more attention.

I carried out my Offices and retired that night with all of this spinning in my head. How I longed for those hints of certainty that had hovered beyond the sound of Fr Aloysius's voice, that sense of revelation that even his words could not dispel. Once gone, however, as I had come to know from my periods of absence, there was no way to recall their initial warm suffusion, their glow of promise. I was left alone in the cold, dark wreckage of the present, with only the rags of my memories – not comforting in themselves, but mine, at least – to pull around me. So it was that the little peace I attempted to preserve through faithful attention to the details of Trappist observances was torn to shreds by the questions I returned to obsessively all through the Great Silence.

~

The next morning I was no clearer in my mind, nor the next two days. I did go in to see Franz and sit with him, although not for the length of time I usually devoted to him. "He is only quiet when you are there," both Sr Angela and Sr Edmunda told me. It was true that whenever I made to leave, Franz's hands would begin to scrabble at the bedclothes and his eyes would stare wildly. His mouth, too, would work uselessly, chewing at the paralysed tongue that filled it. But what could I say? What had to be done had to be done, if I could find a way to do it.

And then the news came that I knew must push me past my own incompetence. A letter to Mariannhill from the Abbot General of the Trappist

Order, Abbot Augustinus, was circulated throughout the missions. It was a farewell letter to a daughter that had come of age and been thrown out of the house by her mother. In it we were reminded that we had left the Order of our own free will, and it admonished us to live from now in harmony and love. No mention was made of the decree of separation.

Franz lay inert and impassive as we gathered around his bed to read these words to him. Only his eyes flickered, and Sr Edmunda asked me afterwards if I had seen how desperately he looked for me. I made a non-committal gesture as we left him in the isolation imposed upon him by his illness. We each went about our business, attempting in our separate ways to come to terms with what, after all, was a perplexing message. Separation of some sort was in the air, but there was no formal declaration that we were no longer Trappists or, if not, how we were to be reconstituted as a community.

Did this mean there was no point now to my plan? I did not know. The only thing of which I was sure was that the Mariannhill I loved so dearly as a house of contemplation and which, until so recently, I had hoped to save from itself, was gone. The missions had destroyed it, and now they needed to be destroyed in turn, through the destruction of their founder. I made up my mind to leave Emmaus by foot the next morning, walking to Lourdes and then, if necessary, to seek some way to get myself to Mariannhill. When morning came, however, it was evident that Franz had taken a turn for the worse, and that his end was not far off.

I went to Franz and read to him the prayer of Pius x for resignation to the will of God. I then administered Holy Communion as it is given to those in danger of death. "Receive, brother," I said, "the Viaticum of our Lord Jesus Christ, that he may preserve thee from the malignant enemy and bring thee to everlasting life." His tongue was so twisted and swollen in his mouth that he could barely take the crumbs of the host. I then gave him Extreme Unction and the Last Blessing.

Later that day – Sunday – it was clear that his agony had begun. He still had much to suffer, and we looked on helplessly as hour after hour he wrestled with death. I sat with him in his room and recited the Litany for the Dying with the seven penitential psalms and, finally, with tears streaming down my face, gave him General Absolution.

After this he was quiet. As Sr Angelina would say, he was patient and wrapped up in God, and no one heard him utter a word of complaint. Of course, no one had heard him speak for some time, and so there is not much evidence for what Fr Adalbert has written in the drafts he has put before me: "Abbot Francis found his greatest consolation and strength during his last suffering in the constant and devoted presence of his beloved companion of forty years, Fr Joseph. The good Father attended to him, encouraged him, prayed for him, and did everything to make him as comfortable as possible."

Perhaps I did these things, and it is not for me to say what the others passing through Franz's room in those hours made of the fact that every time I moved out of Franz's limited range of vision he grew agitated. The reasons for Franz wanting me to stay close to him are hidden now with God, and have been for these many years across which my mind must make its slow, tired way to write of them. So many writers – historians, hagiographers, chroniclers, tale tellers – have, despite this, come to the same conclusion as Fr Adalbert that there is almost no point in my telling you differently.

In the late afternoon of that Sunday word came that a Native far down in the valley was dying. There was no one to answer the sick call but myself. It was an agonising decision to make, but Fr Joseph, as it was said then and has been said many times since, felt the call of his duty to be greater than his attachment to his beloved Superior. Fr Joseph had to tear himself away from the dying Abbot's bedside, assuring everyone that he would return as soon as he possibly could.

During Fr Joseph's absence, the Abbot's suffering was at its height. Again and again he turned his closing eyes towards the door, seeking his beloved friend. But Fr Joseph did not return. Even on his deathbed, God asked of his faithful servant a last great sacrifice. Abbot Francis, obedient and humble as always, willingly made the sacrifice and submitted himself to the Will of God; his friend of forty years was, by the dedication of his calling, to be denied him in the dying moments of his life. "This, too, I will suffer," he was heard to say very softly. Sometime after midnight, he called out "Light". This was the last word he spoke. His noble soul finally took leave of his broken body at twenty-five minutes to two o'clock in the morning of the 24th May 1909. He died, a candle in his hand, on the day the Church celebrates the Feast of Mary Help of Christians.

~

Events themselves are easily agreed upon, but not what lies behind them. Am I thus going counter to St Bernard who, as I had occasion to note in the very first of these many pages I have written, maintained that an act cannot be judged by the intention of the doer? I trust not. I am beyond all matters of judgement, and must leave these to you.

The distance I had to travel that night to the dying Native – a child, I was told as I set out, who had been badly scalded – was greater than I realised. To make matters worse, I lost my way back through the mountains of Skimpers Nek and went round in circles for hours. It is a matter of record that I did not return to Emmaus until four o'clock in the morning. The worried and frantic Fr Joseph broke down with grief, they say, when he returned exhausted and covered with mud, only to be told that he was too late.

Well, perhaps so. No one mentions that my destination lay at a sufficient distance for our Lay Brother to insist that I go by horseback. And no one could know that I saw in my task an opportunity to get to Lourdes, which was why I agreed to mount up. Nor that, riven with indecision, I tried, once out of sight, to turn that obstinate horse's head away from the grass track I had set out upon and attempted to cut across the hillside towards the road to Lourdes. No one was there to see me alone on that hillside, a cold wind blowing through the tall grass that seemed to grasp at my horse's reluctant hooves, totally uncertain as to what to do. A dying Native on the one hand, the destruction of everything Mariannhill had become on the other. The darkness, thick and green, drawing itself together around me, a low mist rising up to my feet, wet and slippery from the grass and unsure in the stirrups. No Fotsholo to guide me as he had the first time I had set out into the hills around Mariannhill to save, in body or spirit, a dying old man.

No Rule either, this time, to guide me, no God even. There was no one to bear witness to how many times I shifted my course this way and that, and then this way again. Or how, finally, my face as wet from tears of furious indecision and frustration as from the dank night air, I more or less stumbled upon that humble hut, that gathering of sticks pulled together for protection against the black universe pressing down upon it, and found there that tiny, empty bundle of bones and flesh smelling of smoke and vomit and urine, whatever passed for spirit now gone. The eyes of those who had awaited me were not really interested in an old man tripping over his long dress as he dismounted awkwardly from his horse, able only to mutter, in words long since stripped of their magic, an incantation to call up a name for that little dead thing. A Christian name, a name meant to serve as a defence against being lost on a night as dark as that one, against vanishing into the air like a squall of night vapour before a breath of wind.

Yes, I was lost again in my efforts to get home, back to the bedside of my dying betrayer, but never as lost as on my way out, when I did not even know my destination. By the time I staggered into Emmaus, dragged now by the horse I had given up trying to control from the saddle, I was so drained of anything approaching sense or emotion that I remember only being surprised that Franz had not made another of his extraordinary recoveries and was no longer alive.

Then again, it was just like Franz to be right to the very end. Some months before, he had concluded the last of his letters with the words: "Now, let me hand over to Sister Superior. My health is more or less unchanged except for these attacks of late when every other day or so this calcification presses for my heart. It will kill me when it reaches my heart. I say with the Psalmist, My heart is ready, O God, my heart is ready."

Sr Angelina had added a note: "Here, the Founder cries so much, he can hardly finish the dictation." Since reading this I have often wondered whether Franz was as ready for death as he said. Well, if his soul was not, his body was. As the one in charge of his physical health I was able to establish that the immediate cause of his passing was a ruptured artery. Whether or not his last months were "a martyrdom", as has been written, one thing can be said of him that cannot be said of me: in the words of Sr Angela, to whom went the honour of closing our dying founder's eyes, "He was a Trappist, and remained one to the end."

Yes, Franz lived and died a Trappist whilst I, to whom the Order was sweeter than life itself, will die as a "Religious Missionary" or under some such name. There is no end to irony, it seems. Sometimes, in the long and empty days that I have endured since Franz's death I think that this is all that eternity guarantees us – a gaping hole between intention and expression into which we slip and disappear.

~

More immediately, Franz's death did not undo the validity of my plan; the scandal of what I had to say would be as great, if not greater, in the light of his passing. But it did make the form of my plan and the best way in which to execute it even more elusive. Not just during the fraught and busy days of the burial of Franz's body but in the empty months ahead. The sheer scope and complexity of what I intended to do continued to hover beyond any hope of my turning it into action as one month, and then two, slipped by for me in a haze of uncertainty. And then, all of a sudden, my plan was robbed of whatever logic it may have had.

On the 29th of July 1909, just two months after Franz's death, Pope Pius x's decree was promulgated at Mariannhill. The monastery became a separate mission institute of papal right – "The Religious Missionaries of Mariannhill". More devastating than this, at least as far as my grand scheme was concerned, was the announcement that the members of this mission institute were to be, as the decree stated, "of two categories, professed Priests and Lay Brothers, bound to the institute by" – and there it was, all of the good Irish Monsignor's assurances aside – "*Simple Vows*".

What else were we now but the children of Franz – the dying, disillusioned Franz – in every respect? Now we were publicly reduced to what Franz had been in secret all along, men without final vows, monks outside of an Order. It was at that point that I gave up any idea of trying to go through with my muddled and hopelessly over-ambitious plan. There was nothing now to be won, nothing even to be destroyed.

I think I had understood this from the moment we were told Franz was to be buried at Mariannhill, in the monastery cemetery. I knew that only as a corpse would he be allowed back into the house he had founded and built. And if death was enough to erase the enmity that would not have countenanced the living man's return, it also made nonsense of trying to bring down a house that no longer held within its walls any semblance of the meaning behind its creation. Let the dead bury the dead, indeed.

Franz's coffin was made at Lourdes out of wood and lead. It was soldered closed when his body was placed in it, and then bought to the church at Emmaus. There I imparted the two solemn blessings over it, my mind throughout focused on the peak of the hill high up behind us where a small pile of stones huddled just below the foot of the great iron cross.

Were the ancients correct in assuming that the heart is the abode of the soul? If so, there was some sense in my following the baroque custom of burying the heart separately at a place especially dear to the deceased. The Austria of the Habsburg dynasty that I knew from those far-off days in Vienna had countless heart shrines scattered all over it. And then, just for an instant, the thought flashed into my mind that if my heart were to be buried anywhere other than in the hard, poor earth of Nomansland, perhaps it should be buried in one of those Viennese parks newly laid out in the days of my youth, those parks in which M and I became one flesh in that brief time of fullness before I had become merely words. No, even less, a vehicle for words in which I believed all the more desperately for not feeling their meaning as a physical presence. I shook off that thought with another: there was nowhere now for my heart than beside Franz's, if anyone would think to do me that service when the time came.

From Emmaus the coffin was conveyed by wagon to the church at Lourdes, where Fr Augustine blessed it for the third time whilst I sat in that overly vast space with its decorations that burned my eyes and echoes that humbled even Fr Augustine's fine voice. Throughout the service, as was reported in *Vergissmeinnicht*, "the bells of Lourdes pealed forth in funereal tones".

The wagon then rumbled on to the railway station at Riverside, "accompanied by the faithful Fr Joseph as conductor". I remained overnight in the waiting room with the coffin, alone in the Great Silence, forgetting even to think of the Hours as the earth rolled us through eternity towards dawn. It was during the deepest darkness, the darkness just before the first greying of the day, that a single line formed itself in my mind. *I have learned at last to measure grace by silence.* I had no sense of its meaning, of anything before it or to come. It rose up out of a jumble of images that flickered and flared as fantastically as any of Mariannhill's magic lantern shows or Brother Nivard's fireworks displays, a still point amidst their coming and going, their whirling and twisting.

These died away in the thin sunlight of morning. My mind was silent and blank when I stepped out to do the brief business required of me as the coffin was put on the train for Pinetown via Pietermaritzburg. I am not sure what I felt as I stood on the platform watching the engine squeal and clank and rattle its way out of the station under a huge plume of black smoke. Whatever combination of relief and emptiness may have haunted my numbness, I knew only that nothing was up to me anymore. It would be Bishop Delalle who would join the train at Pietermaritzburg with two other priests, and at Pinetown Brother Nivard would be ready at the railway station with a carriage and horses to bear the remains of his spiritual father the last few kilometres to the cemetery at Mariannhill.

What happened next I report to you as it was told to me. Just as the cortège reached the peak of the last rise before the monastery, one of the horses took fright at the crowds of people gathered there and set off a panic amongst the others. They broke into a mad gallop, running away with the carriage down the slope towards Mariannhill. A matter of metres before the main buildings, they ran into a lilac tree and came to a halt. Brother Nivard, thrown by the sudden stop after pulling back on the reins as hard as he could, fell under the carriage. He was not badly hurt apart from a severe swelling of his left arm. He made light of this and did not let it prevent him from being amongst the bearers as the body was carried to its grave the next day.

The coffin was blessed before burial by Bishop Delalle, assisted by Abbot Gerard, Prior Isembard, and Sub-Prior Dominic. All four dignitaries gave the Solemn Absolution four times. The Governor of Natal was unable to be present; he sent as his representative an Irish Catholic military officer.

Franz was laid to his last rest beneath a spreading fig tree, right next to his successor, Abbot Amandus Schölzig, who had died nine years before him. His coffin was placed in a grave lined with bricks and a substantial monument has, I am told, been raised over it. So much, then, for being buried coffinless, with just a plain wooden cross stuck in the earth, not even bearing a name, which is all a Trappist may expect at his earthly end. No one seemed to remember, either, that it was this custom that first gave our strange ways some sense for the Zulu.

~

It was this thought, obliquely, illogically even, given the changes that had come over us, that gave rise to the compulsion – for I remember no rational, reasoned path to a decision as such – to begin writing what you have before you in my words, not Franz's. I cannot say, for example, that I saw this as the last way available to me to execute the plan to expose Franz that eluded me in every practical dimension, to use words where my ability to act failed me. I did not think of it as a way in which to reveal, explain or, least of all, confess. Perhaps my hands were so conditioned to write every day, and desired, of their own volition, it seems, to carry on, even when the voice that once directed them was still – I do not know. I know only that the sentence that came to me during the long, dark night I spent next to Franz's coffin at Riverside Station – the last night I would ever sit and watch over the man who had not so much been closest to me in life as my very life itself – refused to go away.

And then suddenly, unexpectedly, in one of the days of unearthly quiet at Emmaus after Franz was gone, I was seized with the need to write down those words, *I have learned at last to measure grace by silence.* The moment this sentence was committed to paper, it was followed by another, one that brought into the light for the first time the sins – actual, intended, possible – that I had committed for the sake of silence. Unspeakable, each of them, written down now in an act of penance that flowed from that first sentence into the next. And then another …

MARIANNHILL AND ITS STATIONS, 1907

Afterword

FOR A MONK, nothing is as it is, everything stands for something else. Meaning is everywhere, the whole world a book read intensely for signs of God's invisible presence. It was so tempting, for example, to see in the flat red disc of the sun that hung against the leaden sky of the autumnal month in which Franz died a blood-charged host, the wafer in the mouth just as it is saturated with the wine.

The dull and dreary setting of East Griqualand in that month worked against this perception, as did each of the hard, cold months to follow. The hills were burned by black frost into a dun sameness, altered here and there only by the smoke of a grass fire hanging motionless in the frozen air, or pools of fog caught in the gullies abandoned by the rivulets of summer. Hills of ice and fire indeed, but not, as St Augustine puts it, pregnant with the causes of things that are born, like mothers pregnant with young; not charged with God's grandeur, proclaiming His glory, showing forth His handiwork. The flat and empty sky of that land with no horizons remained frozen, locked. Monk enough as I still was then, I remember being torn between seeing this as a symbol of desolation or else as a simple refusal – perhaps even the inability – of the universe to communicate.

With Franz's passing we became what in reality we always were, an outstation of Lourdes with no independent status. Brother Melchior and I wandered through the mission like phantoms, as if it were we who had died rather than our founder, an impression the empty bustle of the Sisters could not erase. Our duties were hardly enough to absorb us during our hours of work now that we were not being pushed to expand our every operation or start new ones even before Franz's latest interest was established.

I spent much of my time trying to maintain the cheese-making enterprise that Franz had set up just months before his end, although the books he had the Sisters in Europe send him on the subject were not always as explicit as one could have wished – I could never get the right amount of rennet from the milk of the evening before into the fresh milk to begin its curdling, and I invariably put in either too much or too little salt to check the action of the germs after the whey had been drained off. Brother Melchior and the Sisters were more successful with the hay-reaping instrument Franz had purchased and the steam-powered threshing machine of which he was so proud.

As for "mission work", someone was soon sent to help us in an area in which our lack of progress was visible to all. Fr Innocence Buchner had come to South Africa as a boy and had grown up playing amongst Zulu boys. He spoke their language with the most subtle of its inflections, and I sometimes saw old Native men rub the skin on his arm to see if it would come off and reveal the black man beneath. He joined the monastery at an early age, and rejoiced in the role of *advocatus diaboli*, defending the customs of the Natives and the usefulness of Zulu traditions, even elements known vulgarly, as he would say, as superstition and witchcraft.

I could see that he soon became irritated with this bumbling old man who, when he was not spending hour after hour inside writing, kept his eyes on the ground and his rosary in his hands, only going out amongst the Natives when the call came that one or another of them was dying. He was surprised at how limited our apostolic work had been: the Baptism register, kept since the founding of the mission, stood at No. 837, most of these won to the Lord whilst Franz was still alive and many since lapsed. Driven by an endless source of energy, Fr Innocence hurried around our little collection of buildings, heavy shoes stamping up the dust under his black habit as he tried to turn this state of affairs around. Near collisions with the one Brother and six Sisters left to me were a common event as he came barrelling around corners, for they too had settled into the somnolence into which I had fallen.

Barely a year after his arrival Fr Innocence was replaced by Fr Marcellin Bruno, who made of Emmaus a far more promising field for souls by ignoring me most of the time and teaming up with Fr Emanuel Hanisch, the missionary from Lourdes. My reputation for insisting on visiting the sick remained unaltered, however, even if it cost me hours of riding. My horsemanship being what it was, good Brother Melchior argued that there was nothing for it but that we should come up with a safer means of transport. He devised a kind of two-wheeled cart that could be attached to a horse and would carry me in relative comfort out into the hills. I have to admit that the comfort is relative and my new form of locomotion is dusty, bone-shuddering, and often extremely precarious.

Still, given the character of the horses available to us at Emmaus, almost anything is preferable to mounting up into a saddle. In the main they come from stock commonly known as "Boerperd". Stamina, hardiness and endurance they certainly have, but I find them fiery and proud, with their high, long gait covering too much ground at a stride. I try to ignore the amused expressions of Native and settler alike as I pass them on the roads, tracks and cattle paths of Nomansland, perched on my little seat between the bouncing wheels of Brother Melchior's chariot.

~

It has been some years now since Abbot Gerard began replacing what he termed our "rough and amateurish medical care" with professional clinics and (oh, dear Franz!) dispensaries. A few years ago he started arguing for a full hospital, and a provisional one was in place just in time for the influenza epidemic of 1918. The dedication of the Sisters and Brothers at this time won over many of the Natives from their medicine men and witch doctors. It must be said, however, that there remained much confidence in the Native herbalists, a confidence that is not always unjustified, as far as I can see. Some of their diagnoses and treatments are not far from those put forward by Fr Sebastian Kneipp – not his Water Cure, of course, but certainly his belief in the healing power of plants, roots, bark, stem, leaves and flowers.

Whatever bemusement I felt at the new developments overtaking yet another of Franz's most strongly held convictions was thoroughly erased during those terrible days of the epidemic. Given the special gift I am thought to have for ministering not only to the sick but the dying, I was called out into the Native community again and again as people died in hundreds and thousands throughout the country. They died in their huts and their fields, in the bushes alongside our roads. Entire families were suddenly overcome by the epidemic. The people had no food reserves in their huts, they had no fuel to burn as the air turned to broken glass in their throats when winter swept in over our low, black hills. They had no one to fetch water from the icy trickles in the drying rivers of this strange world in which summer was the time of rain. There was no one to cook, no one to tend to the sick or to see to the wailing of babies that seemed endless, but for baby after baby ended too soon.

The Natives attached to our mission were stunned and terror-stricken and I wandered amongst them mumbling incantations and wringing my hands. I heard the rumours that this new disease was a device of the Europeans to finish off the Bantu races of South Africa, that those who survived would be killed by poison at the order of the white man. The pills that I in desperation handed out were thrown back at me. I watched the efforts of the Native medicine men fail too, saw huts fill with the pungent smoke of their burnt medicines to no effect, saw the disastrous results of their emetics and incisions that only hastened death. I saw some mothers performing the ceremony of *ukulahlwa kwezingane*, burying their children up to the neck in the white sand of the rivers. And then I heard the heart-breaking wailing that set in to convince somebody or something that their children were dead and that there was no further point to striving after their lives. Yes, I saw each mother take her child out of the sand and go home to die together with the tiny dead scrap of humanity.

~

When the epidemic had spent its force, those who were still alive seemed dazed and disheartened in the flat vastness under the washed-out sky of Nomansland. I count myself amongst them; something in me had broken and left an emptiness beyond any consolation the world could offer. Not that the world did offer much by way of consolation: the Great War that had broken out in Europe raged on, although sometimes it seemed merely a distant backdrop to the in-fighting that continued at Mariannhill.

That we were not interned during the war was thanks to Bishop Delalle, a Lorrainer and a naturalised British subject who pledged himself as warranty for our good behaviour. Little interrupted the silence of our remote station, but we heard of the rage that flared up after a German U-boat sank an English ship and of the property of Germans being plundered in the larger cities of South Africa. Mariannhill itself was infected with spy fever – German aeroplanes, it was said, had taken off and landed in the vicinity of the monastery and we were supposed to have hidden caches of weapons underneath the altars of our churches. A mob actually set out from Durban to burn down the monastery, "an evil deed", as our records have it, "which Providence in some mysterious way prevented from being carried out". The stillness of Nomansland absorbed it all, swallowing it as if it had never been and leaving us to carry on with our barren routines at Emmaus.

The Rule tells us never to despair of the mercy of God, and I struggle against the wilful rejection of hope. I have never fallen into the mortal sin of distrusting God's goodness and fidelity, but I have been – I confess to you, my Father Confessor, buried now in a double coffin of zinc and prime wood – immersed in the venial sins of melancholy and fear of my own weakness. And never more so than when I began to see that the problem of trying to tell this story of silence was not that it was taking so many words; it was, rather, that every figure in which one thought one had caught the inner meaning of silence insisted on transmuting itself into the all too literal, the straightforward, stubborn facts of the pedantically prosaic.

Mariannhill, having chosen words over silence, has drowned in words. This is merely an accurate description of the events following on Franz's death, events that I was left on this earth to watch with a kind of disinterested horror. What I put before you could not be further from any kind of figurative play; I give you no simile, or metaphor or symbol, or any other attempt to wrestle significance out of what, quite simply, happened.

We came to the place we called Mariannhill without any knowledge of the Native tongues, as I have told you, or even of the language spoken by the majority of the settlers. For contemplatives this could have been a blessing, a wall of silence made of language itself. But once we became missionaries, this rather fanciful metaphor quickly gave way. Quite literally, to teach the Christian religion it was necessary to describe it in the language of those to be converted.

We received our first lessons in Zulu from old Fr Mathieu, as I must call him now, the one Frenchman with whom Franz got along. But it was the young Englishman, Arthur T Bryant, who truly laid the foundation for the tower of Babel we went on to build. It was his flair for languages that enabled us to begin using the Zulu grammar and dictionary compiled by the Anglican Bishop Colenso, and it was he who gave us the confidence to use our printing press to disseminate the words we at first so clumsily put together in that language. Zulu prayer books, extracts from the Gospels, hymnaries, short histories of the Church, all rolled off that clanking, smelly, oil- and ink-ridden machine along with, most important of all for us Catholics, a variety of catechisms.

Yes, it was Brother David, as he was then, who translated the first small catechism into Zulu. Printed and bound, his *Katekisima lobufundiso Bwamakristo* was the very first book in that language – and the fuse for a charge laid in the foundations of our enclosure, waiting for the right spark to bring down our towers, and what was left of our walls, completely and irrevocably. Not that this appeared so at the time. With a Zulu catechism in hand, missionary priest and Native catechist alike were no longer dependent on their shaky grasp of theology or language. They had, as one of our historians put it, "a sound form of words by which to teach the Christian revelation". Or, as this same historian was forced to add with the hindsight that is the peril of his profession, "thought they had".

~

Franz had not been dead a year when, with the encouragement of Abbot Gerard Wolpert, Fr Willibald Wanger set to work revising the six different versions of the catechism that had been generated in makeshift fashion out of Brother David's original translation.

Yes, the "Bavarian genius" was back amongst us after his expulsion from Mariannhill by Dom Edmund. To the best of our knowledge he could find no house that would accept him as a Religious following the period of secularisation he chose over spending a year at the monastery performing a penance. We had only heard of him fleetingly in his time away, mainly as a name connected in some shadowy way with the whole business of the exorcisms and the removal of Dom Edmund – although I have had good cause since to put that before you in more detail. None of this was known, of course, when Abbot Gerard, for reasons that could only be guessed at the time, decided to admit Fr Willibald back into the community.

Somewhat thicker of frame and fuller of beard than the clean-cut young man of his early years, Fr Willibald was determined to pick up the literary endeavours that were cut short when his *Pastor Bonus* mission bulletin was suspended by Dom Edmund. He was convinced that our – or, more precisely, his – "exact knowledge of the Bantu languages", as he put it, could and should be put to use in teaching the Faith.

Most of our missionaries at the time were quite content with whatever version of the catechism they happened to be using. The direct renderings into Zulu they employed appeared to be understood, and it had scarcely occurred to them that – as Fr Willibald would repeatedly announce, fuming all the while – "the concepts of Christian revelation were no more likely to find ready-made expression in Zulu than in the Greek of the early centuries of the Christian era".

"Zulu is a highly developed and subtle language," he would fulminate, "the matter of tone in itself is a subject for serious *scientific* inquiry! Father Bryant" – he was always reverential about the English monk – "has already produced a dictionary of over 20 000 words, and here we are still using words like *igrasiya*! What place have these bastards of Latin and even *English* derivation in the expression of some of the most intricate mysteries of our religion! We missionaries are bound to explain what we mean by the Latinisms we throw about. And we must do this with proper Zulu words!"

I have before me an article he wrote recently in which he argues that the Bantu languages, of which Zulu is one, are a southern branch of the Ugrian or Uralian family of languages, the northern branch of which includes Sumerian, Samojedian, Finnish, Lappish, Esthonian, Permian, and Votish. He makes it plain that he follows Professor J F van Oordt (BA) of the university at Cape Town in this, and goes on to demonstrate, entirely to his own satisfaction, that uNkulunkulu – one of the eighteen words for God in Southern Bantu – is without the slightest doubt of Sumerian and Assyrian origin.

I would have been more than happy to leave Fr Willibald in his self-made purgatory of words. If it is provable from the Sumarian that the meaning of uNkulunkulu is "the all-great uN", that is "the All-Great God of (or in) Heaven", and that – their language being ultimately European – the Zulu are capable of being Christianised, so be it. For myself, every word for God has in the end betrayed our ability to know God. And who would know this better than one who has put before you so many words in place of God, one who has sat up through long days and even longer nights to tell you such a long tale about God, or the loss of God, instead of simply, as Gregory the Great put it, resting in God?

Fr Willibald's aggressive arrogance, every bit as fierce as it had been at the time of his expulsion as a student from the Generalate in Rome so many years ago, had earned him the enmity of the majority of our brethren at the monastery. It was also becoming clearer why Abbot Gerard was reluctant to have done with this most troublesome of monks. Fr Willibald rapidly made the printing press to which the Abbot assigned him his domain. The press had barely been used since Abbot Strunk prohibited the printing of any books or pamphlets without the permission of the General Chapter during his visitation of 1892. Now, from dawn until deep into the Great

Silence, Fr Willibald would be translating in the small office attached to the workroom or tinkering with the press itself, oiling and adjusting it back into full working order, sorting muddled type, experimenting with ink.

When he emerged from these preoccupations it was to hold forth on the proper way to teach the Faith, advancing from forthright attacks on the terminology used by the missionaries to the violently expressed conviction that the missionaries were going about their work of conversion in the wrong manner. You must first eradicate superstition from the hearts of the pagans, he declared, before you can implant Christianity in them. No longer content with mere terminological substitutions, he began to add to the catechism a detailed enumeration of the superstitious ideas and actions of the indigenous people that he felt the Church should identify as sinful. The list is extensive: initiation exercises for boys and girls, in which ceremonies and material with alleged magical properties were employed; sexual practices forbidden by Christian law; the eating of human fat, at least a pretence of it; charms and herbs and, worse still, the attribution of illness or misfortune to the malpractices of others by witch doctors, who then induced mass hysteria to ensure their accusations were believed and, in some cases, caused the murder and mutilation of the victim to provide ritual magic.

Fr Willibald insisted at every opportunity that these practices must be described in detail in the catechism, and in accurate Zulu terminology, and that the reasons for their condemnation by Christian law should be clearly stated. Catholics would then knowingly reject them and would be less likely to revert to or tolerate them. The missionaries tended to take the opposite view: most Catholic Zulu children grew up ignorant of these customs and detailed catechetical instruction would only have the unfortunate effect of awakening their curiosity. It was sufficient, they thought, that adult penitents who accused themselves of the relevant sins were forbidden these practices by a confessor. As the number of converts increased, the forbidden practices would die a natural death.

But if you make no specific mention of the pagan customs and ceremonies unique to the native races of South Africa, Fr Willibald would thunder from the heights of his unassailable authority, this could be construed as permitting them to continue, on the principle that silence implies consent! And how can you allow missionaries – not to speak of Native catechists – to denounce and forbid these evils on their own? Without an authorised form of words, accurate theologically and linguistically, they would have to frame a Christian judgement in their own words, basing it on what we could all see was their extremely slender knowledge of the technical intricacies of the Church's teachings.

There was something in this last point: in true Trappist fashion (if for very different reasons) there had been little training in philosophy and religious studies at Mariannhill under Franz. The curriculum for novitiates was restricted to devotion, obedience and manual work, and not necessarily in that order. Still, it was rather a long stretch from this to Fr Willibald's oft-repeated assertion that his opponents were ignorant people with whom one could not even argue, a point he returned to incessantly in defending the changes he wished to make.

Although no one could deny that there were some worthwhile improvements in the new translation, Fr Willibald insisted on the acceptance of all of his changes or none whatsoever. No compromise was to be entertained and hence every individual example chosen for debate stood for the whole. Moreover, Abbot Gerard's clear support for and protection of his friend meant that even the slightest hint of dissatisfaction with Fr Willibald's catechism could not be taken other than as a criticism of the whole work and of the Abbot and the Definitorium as well.

Very soon Mariannhill was again awash with words, this time in any number of languages as missionaries rose to defend whatever version of the catechism they had been using, catechist and priest set against each other by the authority of the text they once shared. Congregations mouthed words that were no longer felt to be pre-ordained, the perfect and eternal manifestation of the beliefs they embodied. It did not help that Bishop Delalle decided to treat the whole affair as a matter of discipline. This resulted in the dispute returning us to the worst days of division in the monastery, threatening even to outdo them.

Before the last of the five hundred and fifty pages of Fr Willibald's first catechisms sputtered out of his hot, oily machine in the broiling February of 1912, I could hear the voices of outrage spreading over the hills of Natal into Nomansland. Even the quiet of Emmaus, a place now commonly associated with the absence of the boisterous spirit that had once filled it, caught the furious echoes of "the catechism controversy". Ten thousand copies had already tumbled off the press when a telegram from Rome ordered production to be halted until a commission of Fathers had revised the censure. A limited number were sent out for comment by the commission. I still have mine, virtually untouched, a beautiful thing to feel and hold after all these years. I was particularly impressed by the fine Indian paper that was used, and I remember thinking, through the odd circuits by which my tired old memory made its connections, that M would have approved.

I knew from the first that it was into the dense pattern of the letters of the Zulu words on the page that the demons had made their escape from St Michael's. I understood now their facility with languages, their ability to translate themselves into any tongue and speak it to their advantage, which is our confusion. Lucifer, it is clearer than ever, is first and foremost the sovereign of language, all languages – German, Latin, Zulu, English, Polish, it is of no matter. A joking German song, the Latin of the *Rituale Romanum*, a newspaper article in English, a catechism in Zulu, all are one before him, entrance ways to the soul, to keep out the true work of God.

~

Examples abound of the dissension a single word can generate. One that caught the attention more than most was the word *wamithwa* for *conceptus est* in the Creed – what could be more amusing to the world than a set of monks tearing their community to pieces over the linguistic details of pregnancy, in whatever language?

Fr Willibald insisted that *ukumitha* was the only suitable Zulu word for "conception" and that it was the most becoming word. Most of the rest of Mariannhill insisted that both assertions were wrong. First of all, Fr Notker Vorspel informed us, *ukumitha* does not mean "conception" but "pregnancy" – Latin: *praegnantem esse, gestare, gestatio.* In the case of women, *ukumitha* lasts nine months, in the case of sheep, four and a half months. This fact alone shows that *ukumitha* means pregnancy and not conception because, as he testified before a commission arranged in full seriousness, conception does not last for nine and four and a half months respectively.

It did not help that Fr Vorspel was widely known to dislike Fr Wanger (he could not bring himself to use the more familiar form of Willibald). Nor did it help that it was public knowledge that Fr Vorspel had been disappointed in his hopes of becoming Provost of the new independent congregation instead of Abbot Wolpert. Was it jealousy of Wolpert and suspicion of Wanger or a genuine concern about the new translation that drove him on to make the point that not all Zulu verbs change their meaning in the same way in the different moods and tenses?

Fr Wanger had defended his choice by comparing *Ubanibani ulambile* ("So and So has become and is hungry") with *Ubanibani umithi* ("So and So has become and is pregnant"). So far so good, said Fr Vorspel, but Fr Wanger had then stated that in the present tense *Ubanibani uyalamba* meant "So and So has become hungry" and *Ubanibani uyamitha* meant "So and So has become pregnant" (at the present moment, i.e. "conceives"). By this example Fr Wanger wanted to prove that, although *umithi* in the static perfect meant "she is pregnant", *uyamitha* in the present tense meant "she conceives". "But *uyalamba* in the present tense does not mean 'So and So begins to feel hungry' at the present moment!" Fr Vorspel said slowly and carefully to the assembled Fathers. "It does not," he stressed, turning about and looking, in turn, at each Father on the commission, and emphasising each word, "denote an act but a condition – meaning that 'So and So is starving, has no food.'"

In the same way, he stressed for what by now must have been some glazing minds, *uyamitha* in the present tense did not denote an act but a condition; it did not mean "So and So at the present moment begins to be pregnant"; it meant "So and So bears children, is not barren". And even if it did mean "becomes pregnant", he concluded – for the moment at least – "it would not for that reason mean conception, because 'becoming pregnant' is the consequence of conception not conception itself!"

High theology indeed, I thought as, occasionally, I allowed myself to follow each desperately fought for twist and turn in a controversy that unravelled more messily with each attempt to have the last word. When grammar pronounced itself conclusive, one could be sure some overlooked cultural convention would overturn it. Christian Bantu women, for example, said that they did not object to the word *mitha* in itself but did not use it before men out of reverence for human fruitfulness. *Tabu*, as Abbot Gerard pointed out with an array of illustrations, was not directed against indecent words amongst the Bantu but usually indicated respect, just as a wife covered her breasts before her husband but not before other men.

The degree of shuffling amongst the assembled commission of Fathers when Abbot Gerard made this point might have given him some forewarning that they would rule out the use of *mitha* on grounds of propriety. And the devastation that this word alone occasioned was enough to shake the foundations of any possible future for Mariannhill.

~

Out of all of this I must confess that the one issue that did concern me is that no Zulu word has yet been found to denote "grace". The word *igrasiya* has been well assimilated now but is understood only after you read the explanation in the catechism. Fr Wanger insisted on the word *ixosho* in its place, and claimed that we had rejected it only because we could not pronounce the "x" click. As with so many of his arguments, this was rather petulant. After all, *ixosho* is derived, I am told, from the word *xosha* – "chase away" – and usually means a gift bestowed by a chief in recognition of services rendered. What we so badly needed then was just what we least deserved, the charity of silence, grace alive in the world.

~

In November 1916, Bishop Delalle received what he called "a filthy, criminal letter", which had been printed on the Mariannhill press. It was addressed to the Holy Father, ostensibly by two Native catechists, Mathias Maphalala and Vitus Khati, and a Native girl, Maria Zulu. These three had been the chief advisors to Fr Willibald when he developed his catechism and they defended his terminology vigorously. The "letter", a pamphlet printed in Zulu and Italian, was addressed to "Baba Ocwebileyo" and "Santo Padre". The Bishop blustered that the translation had been done by a Zulu priest and abounded in sophisms and gratuitous assumptions.

Final responsibility for what was printed on the press lay with Abbot Gerard, but he could throw no light on the matter. The Bishop was convinced that the author was not one of the signatories to the pamphlet and set in process a full formal investigation. In the meantime he directed his fury at the translator, who turned out to be none other than Fr Julius. The Bishop had finally, with great misgivings, ordained Julius Mbhele and Andreas Ngidi after recalling them from their studies in Rome in the light of the misbehaviour, as he saw it, of the first two Africans who had returned from the Holy City as priests. Now one of them dared not only to aid and abet a secret assault on authority but to engage directly in the controversy. For Fr Julius, not content with his translating activities, had written to Rome in his own right to defend the use of the word – here it was again – *mitha*, saying it was only from white missionaries that Natives learned to think it indecent.

The Bishop had barely begun to think about how he could deal with such insubordination when he discovered that another letter was on its way to Rome, this time from Fr Aloysius Mncadi (although I am sure it was signed Fr Majonga), who wrote to insist that Europeans should not correct Zulus in the use of their own language. Bishop Delalle responded promptly, ordering amendments and revisions to all the controversial points in Fr Willibald's translation, uniformly in line with the old terminology. He then allowed it to go to Rome for the Vicar Apostolic's *imprimatur* – on condition that it was to be used *pro solis sacerdotibus*.

For the rest of the faithful a straightforward translation of the short catechism of Pius x was made, with the addition of just a few passing references to Bantu customs. This was the only catechism authorised for missionary work in the vicariate, suspension being imposed *ipso facto* on all priests who did not employ the official form of prayers. The Bishop excluded the signatories to the pamphlet from the sacrament of Communion for three months, and pressed forward vigorously with his investigations into the identity of its ghostly author.

Abbot Gerard, who initially "declined" to undertake the printing of the amended version of Fr Willibald's translation on the Mariannhill press, eventually broke down and confessed that Fr Willibald had indeed been the author of the pamphlet attacking the alterations to his catechism. The "Bavarian Genius" was then sent off to Lennoxton in northern Natal, where he caused so much trouble that the Commissioner of Enemy Subjects ordered him to leave the area. He would have been left to wander the earth forever without a home had he not been offered asylum at – of course, it could only be – St Michael's.

And so the evil within Mariannhill began to gather again at the site from which it had so furiously burst forth. No need for spirits and demons now, with their glimpses of hell. Words, Christian words even, have proved quite enough to tear the heart out of our community. Fr Willibald continued to storm on unceasingly over his translation, and to this day the controversy over the catechism rages on.

~

After its expulsion from the Order of the Cistercians of the Strict Observance, Mariannhill existed in a state of paralysing insecurity. Our best minds had been applied to the terms of the decree of separation, but no one really knew what attitude to adopt towards it. Some felt that the only way forward was to establish a union with some other Order, and so an approach was made to the Cistercians of the Moderate Observance. At the very moment this was initiated the controversy over the catechism grew loud enough to be heard beyond Mariannhill and her missions. The Cistercians, briefly intrigued by Abbot Gerard's request that we join them, suddenly announced that the union was impossible on principle. The Cistercians were committed to fostering only the contemplative life.

It was the same old story and Abbot Gerard decided that, if Mariannhill was to be saved in anything like its present form, it would have to steer clear of a union of any kind. Not all the members of our community agreed, by any means, but the decree of the Congregation for Religious confirming that Mariannhill would be administered in a manner similar to other institutions bound by Simple Vows was written on 24th June 1914. With this went the last hopes of maintaining our ancient alliances and Solemn Vows.

The outbreak of the Great War barely two weeks later made it impossible to carry out any of the formalities necessary for the reformation of the Mariannhill community. Abbot Gerard simply remained in office and carried on business, as far as possible, in the old style. "Abbot, Titular", I should have said, as our once proud Abbey had by now been formally degraded, in line with our new status, to the rank of the dwelling of a Provost. It was small comfort that in the person of Gerard Wolpert our first Provost was still an Abbot; an Abbot is an Abbot for life, but in our case this was in name only. Abbot Gerard's title derived from what was, in effect, an extinct Abbey.

The world's return to peace brought an end to our living on as the ghostly remnants of an Order to which we no longer belonged. In March 1920 our white habit and black scapular were done away with and the Religious were put into the new uniform of a black cassock with a red cincture although a white cassock was permitted during extremely hot weather. And in June of that year the Mariannhill Mission Congregation was submitted in all its concerns, including religious discipline, to the Congregation of Propaganda. Now we were truly devoted exclusively to the work of the missions. I take little comfort from the fact that people – even the Religious of other Orders – still refer to us as "the Trappists of Mariannhill".

In February 1921 the application put forward by our Superior for dispensation from prayer in Choir was agreed to with remarkable promptness by Rome. At the monastery this had already been the case, as the Choir had too few members and was therefore forced to be silent. I suspect, even as

I write, that when the new Constitutions for Mariannhill that are being prepared are approved, the Rule of St Benedict will also recede into the background. At present our vows are still made according to the Rule – the Rule for which I was prepared to give up, if not my own life (for there would have been little use in such a poor sacrifice), then Franz's. It has not been required for years that the Rule be read aloud in the community.

~

I wrote earlier of my young Eduard in the Natal Government Asylum, waiting. I heard today that Fr Edward Müller has finally been released. Fr Jerome, one of the new priests at Mariannhill, effected this, how I do not know.

Seventeen years. Seventeen years that he spent in the place to which Fr Bryant had him committed. He has agreed to return to the Mariannhill diocese, from which the others have now gone: Fathers Aloysius Mncadi, Andreas Ngidi, Julius Mbhele are all determined to live and die as priests but no longer with Mariannhill. They have gone over to the Zululand diocese, leaving us just the boy who came to us as Kece Mnganga and showed such early promise in Latin.

They tell me Fr Edward was sent first to Centocow, the hub of the missionaries' power, where I cannot imagine he would have been happy. He was soon transferred – as an assistant priest – to Mariathal. I must now think of him there, on that Hill of Lightning as it was known before we renamed it, wandering amongst the shelves that hold the gift of Franz's books. Other books may have found their way there too, as Franz had hoped. If not on the scale of the missionary library of which Franz dreamed, Mariathal has nevertheless become the Seminary of the Mariannhill Mission Congregation. With the present catastrophic inflation in Germany, the candidates for priesthood who once trained in Reimlingen and Würzburg are being sent out to South Africa. And what better place to train for the missions than at a mission where they can learn Zulu at the same time and, untroubled by the history of silence, go straight out to the mission fields when their studies are completed?

And Eduard? Well, they tell me that he has started a catechetical school at Mariathal and that he is writing books and articles now. His main interest, they say, lies in fostering black vocations.

~

I have come of late to think that this has never been our story. *Let Ethiopia hasten to stretch out her hands to God*, I have intoned many, many times in my life as a Religious, but recently Psalm 68 seems to blur into everything else about me as it, too, settles into the literal. We may well have blamed the Protestants and their emphasis on Bible-reading for the breaking away of black Christians from the established churches, but almost everywhere one looks Natives are setting up sects of their own. Black ministers are resigning from the Methodists and Presbyterians and Congregationalists and starting their own "Ethiopian Churches" at a rate it is difficult even for us Catholics to ignore. Our adherence to the catechism and our training of converts for only the lower levels of service has made us relatively immune to breakaways, but who knows how many of the Natives have been lost to the Faith by taking up cries like "Nations go to sleep that Zulu may be audible before the *uMsindisi*"?

Our own local magistrate came to us complaining of a "scurrilous fanatic" who had set up a ministry just south of us on the coast. He wanted every missionary church in the region to endorse a letter he had drafted to the Chief Native Commissioner that left us in no doubt as to the views of the secular officials on this phenomenon. "I consider that we should deal with this mischievous growth swiftly," his letter read, "and destroy the trouble in its inception root and branch. I ask your authority to forbid this man right of entry into my district. I earnestly hope you will give all the assistance you can in ridding those concerned of this canker in your midst."

Withdrawing into my quiet smile and well-known lack of ability with the English language, I passed his draft back to him with a few murmurs and nods that could have meant any number of things, and watched as he rode off on his proud horse, the peak of his cap glinting and his leather straps gleaming. I was disturbed and uncertain about the whole business and I was glad Fr Marcellin was at Lourdes that day for that was where the magistrate was headed. He would no doubt get a more definite statement of support from the missionaries there.

As for myself, well, I spend my days disciplining my stiff and aching body to stay at Franz's desk as I set down, day after day after day, this story of our failures, which seem quite enough for one old man to deal with. When I am called to the kraals to say the Prayer for the Dying and close unseeing eyes, I sometimes hear of this man Shembe, Isaiah Shembe no less, this prophet who, as the magistrate complains continually, "is under no European authority". He appears to be having much success in southern Natal and over into Pondoland; certainly he had better luck driving out troublesome spirits at Mzimkhulu, from what I am told, than we had at St Michael's.

The catechism war may still wage furiously over the ways in which "witchcraft and even ritual murder and mutilation" have been given new vigour in Bantu sects like Shembe's by their incorporation into imitations of Christian words and ceremonies and doctrines – all because, some of our missionaries insist, there is no "explicit attack" on these notions in our catechetical teaching. Just the other day I could not help but overhear a Native holding forth about the Gospel he saw approaching, carried by royal leaders "of our own", he said, adorned with the feathers of the red-winged Gwalagwala bird.

Fr Innocence, in one of his many unsuccessful attempts to teach us something of the world around us, had told us of this bird – also called Bloukuifloerie or Purple-Crested Gurgler. He tried to point one out to me, initially with no luck (my knowledge of local fauna still being as bad as was my grasp of local flora when we arrived in the Eastern Cape), but eventually I spotted the furtive dark-coloured bird. At first I thought its crest was black, my old eyes being what they are and the light not of the best, but as it leaped from one tree to another I saw the iridescent purple of its head and the flash of red under its wings. *Ko-ko-ko* it went, and then, more slowly, *krr-krr-krr-krr*. When it saw us silently staring it flapped into the sky, calling to its partner with a wild, explosive *kok kok, kok kok*.

I turned to Fr Innocence. "Zulu custom holds that only poets are allowed to sport a feather of the *iGwalagwala*," he said. Well, there has been little enough room in this tale for that medium which Franz so despised from his schooldays. I can remember the vehemence with which he related his difficulties with Latin prosody whilst at university at Innsbruck. He could not, even in his old age, get over the fact that his Jesuit professors gave the highest ranking to those most proficient in Latin verse; his annoyance that his marks went so low on account of "stupid poetry" vibrated through his dictation some sixty years later. But there are days when I regret that our silence could have been worn like bright feathers when we approached the graceful Nubians I had once dreamed of at the altar to the missions in the Jesuit church in Brünn, their upheld, welcoming hands a poetic filigree, their glistening blackness giving back our true reflection.

~

543

I write now from my bed. I am not afraid to say that I am in pain, and that I believe the pain to be fatal.

I was called out again two days ago, to a sick Native – a dying Native I am sure, as I am almost never called out unless all hope is gone. I prepared, as always, to set forth, but when I pulled my "chariot" from the barn I found that one of the central stays supporting its seat had become dangerously loose. Brother Melchior was out in our cabbage fields, some distance from the mission itself and, after fumbling with his tools for some time without success, I realised that it was in any event growing too late for repairs. I called our farrier, Paulus, and asked him for a horse I could ride. This faithful Native has been with us for some years now (our hired help stays with us longer since Franz has been gone) and I hardly needed to add that he should bring me one of the milder animals.

The Boerperd Paulus chose had an alert and aristocratic look. Its slightly curled mane and tail were typical of the breed, as was the flat, broad forehead between its prominent eyes. For some reason I remember noting that its ears were particularly sharp-pointed, and close together. As Paulus brought the horse towards me, I heard him address the horse by name amidst his usual chucking and clicking. "Come, Danger," he urged, "come on, the master is waiting, he is in a hurry, Danger, come, come."

"Is this the most agreeable horse available?" I asked him. He replied, "Yes, the others are being dipped, there are too many ticks. But don't worry, Father. Danger was given this name when he was a young horse, he is old and gentle now." Like you, I almost thought I heard him add, but he just gave the ghost of a smile as he helped me up into my unsteady seat on the animal's back.

We rode out from Emmaus in no unbecoming form. Danger lived up to Paulus's assurances as we took the path that curved up and around the base of Calvary, moving along easily through the grass that was already gathering the evening dew. We were soon wrapped in a soft, wet mist, typical of mid-summer in this high country of cool, even cold, nights, and, sure enough, after a while I lost all sense of direction. I kept pressing on at a moderate rate, not knowing what else to do, my legs slipping on the wet flanks of the horse, my arms almost around its hot neck at times. The last of the sunset was flaring through the white haze about us when a wind came up from nowhere, tearing the mist to shreds that twisted and boiled as they were whipped away. From being almost blind, I was in an instant able to see for miles and miles over a landscape that looked impregnable in every direction.

More directly, however, right before us, was a rivulet trickling through stones amidst the long grass. I lowered my eyes in proper Trappist fashion an instant too late. Modest as was our pace, when Danger jerked to a halt and thrust his head down to the water I went slowly but inexorably over his neck and into the marshy ground and onto the rocks.

Perhaps I was unconscious for some time; of this I am not sure. Gradually I became aware that I was wet and cold, and in immense pain. I was just able to move my neck, and so discovered that in my meanderings I had not wandered far from the ground rising up to Calvary. I was still in the slight depression between its northern shoulder and the next hill, and I could even see, as the darkness drew in, the lights of Emmaus coming on one by one below me. Occasionally a voice made its way up to me, but I knew it would be of no purpose to attempt to raise mine, thin and querulous as it is now through age and lack of use.

I watched the lights go out one by one as the Great Silence took Emmaus into itself. I could not see Franz's cast-iron crucifix from where I was but, even in the dark, I imagined its shadow over me as I lay helpless and shivering, too cold to be grateful that this was not a winter night. If it were I would have frozen to death in an hour.

I attempted to pray, but my mind would not hold the words in place. I drifted in and out of prayers and imaginings. At times the set phrases of our worship scrolled past me, clear but meaningless, at other times random images flared up, amongst them Bishop Ricards' face, slack and fallen in on itself as it must have been towards the end; the breath on little Scotchman's lips; the possessed Monika's song bursting out of her when she was dumb and suicidal; Danger galloping on through some endless night (although another part of me was aware of him snuffling and stamping around me in the dark); the tower at Mariannhill which I have never seen but which has always haunted my imagination. What is the point now of this sad rehearsal? Enough to say that wreathed amidst it all was Franz, talking and stamping and shouting, although oddly enough this image of him blurred quickly, almost before taking shape.

At one point I jerked awake from a sensation of slithering and slipping as if on a slope covered in a rotting substance, consciousness robbing me of a fall into some other world. My hands flailed about, setting off stabs of fire throughout my wrecked old body, but they only confirmed what my mind told me as I came achingly back to reality: I still lay broken amongst the stones, pinned fast to the earth by injuries too extensive for me to specify. In that moment the familiar early signs of one of my seizures teased at me, but the faint intimations of that always frustrated, always false sense of pending revelation only hovered around the edges of an awareness of who and where I was, etched in pain.

I lay in this state until a small party from Emmaus, alarmed at my not returning by the early hours of the morning, made its way out, lanterns flaring and stuttering in the dank gloom. They found me just before the bruise of dawn. I did surrender then, not to revelation but to total blankness.

~

They tell me that I had no sooner come round than I was asking for writing materials. All I have been able to get onto paper since then are these last few pages. As a conclusion, if this indeed is what it turns out to be, it has little to recommend it, but I do not think I can set down much more. Or should dare to – Christ's words in Matthew's gospel have been in my head all day: "But I say unto you, That every idle word that men shall speak, they shall give account thereof in the day of judgement. For by thy words thou shalt be justified, and by thy words thou shalt be condemned."

Sr Angelina has come in, and wishes to take the paper and pen from me. I am ordered to rest, and this hand – this hand that has never given up the voice that once was its life – must now obey.

Author's Note

THERE WAS LITTLE ENOUGH REASON to head inland once you had crossed over the uMzimkulu River, even in the days when something of a town still flourished around this bridge on the then main route between the colonies of Natal and the Cape. Today, someone with a reason would be hard put to identify the dirt track to the north, but if you turn right after the hotel (now little more than a bottle store huddled in the remains of one of the three buildings of any substance still making up the town) the road does wind in an unpromising sort of way up a rise. It becomes steeper, rockier, and still less promising as it meanders further up and across bare hills that are powdery dry from the baking heat of part of the year and the freezing cold of the rest.

This road does not appear on most maps, and asking for directions from the few locals you may come across is not likely to produce results – the only two places that could have given you a reason to strike off in this direction are not towns or even farms. Some twenty or so "Englische Meilen" further, as indicated on the 1907 map (which is of more use than any current one), you will see on your left a surprisingly neat and well-maintained double-storey house with a few well-built barn-like outbuildings. There is every chance you will go straight past this in search of something that looks more like the place you have imagined.

Nothing you have in mind will prepare you for what you see, rising up out of a landscape as flat, unimposing and underdeveloped as any other in this barren part of the country, in fewer than five of those English miles – a cathedral? a basilica? Certainly "church" will not do as the massive twin bell towers flank an imposing entrance to a two-tiered nave of immense proportions.

You try to take in the glow of the red brick and glint of the steel roof that tells you that this is no ordinary European vision of a sacred building and see to the left a complex that must have been the living quarters and working area of an extremely large religious community. Larger than Mariannhill itself, you guess, at least in intention, even if what you are seeing, Lourdes Mission, is now but a ghost of its motherhouse. Where the modern Mariannhill has at its centre a busy hospital and its surrounding hills are covered with rapidly proliferating low-cost housing, here the hills in the near distance still serve to mark the monastic house's enclosure. Where the tarred, busy, multi-laned M1 cuts its brutal way between the industrial parks that have sprung up around Mariannhill to the predominantly black locations created during the apartheid years, here the single sandy track almost peters out.

In the eerie silence of Lourdes, four black nuns – seemingly the only inhabitants in this vast ruin (and closer inspection of the buildings reveals they are, indeed, close to ruin) – invite you in for Fanta Orange and Marie biscuits, apologising for the non-appearance of the Polish priest who, they let you know in the most circumspect of ways, is drunk (one gathers, as usual) and therefore not available.

The conversation is friendly and far more illuminating than you have any way of knowing on your first visit – why, for example, do they ask if you want to see the graves of the children, thirteen children in particular? As it is, your ignorance leaves you under the impression that the most important thing you have learned is that the place you were really after is the huddle of buildings five miles back. It was there, at Emmaus – yes, two m's – as it is known, that the person died who was the driving force behind Mariannhill and the phantasmagoric collection of buildings you now drive away from.

You may choose to climb the steps cut into the hill rising behind the double-storey house at Emmaus. At the large cast-iron crucifix on its summit, you look out over a land perhaps still most aptly named Nomansland. However much you think you can see, the story you are after is hidden by more than the haze from veld fires and the exhalations of the land. It will be a long time before you discover that the thirteen children in those graves – that you could, possibly, see with binoculars from this promontory – were murdered. And even longer before it occurs to you that there is a possible alternative to the commonly accepted, although never proved, assumption as to who the murderer was.

In retrospect you will learn, too, why the Sisters at St Michael's, another of Mariannhill's missions en route to Emmaus and Lourdes, insist on showing you the burn marks on the beams of a room that is still a dormitory for the girls who attend their school. On this first visit what can you know of demons streaming through the air to settle, some say, in those well-ordered buildings shimmering in the haze of the middle distance before you?

548

Does that cairn of stones at the foot of the cross mark the grave of Franz Pfanner's heart, as one of the black workers on the property tells you? Or is his heart – unlike his body in its stately mausoleum at Mariannhill – buried just across the road that runs in front of the property below, as a small metal sign claims?

That is just one of the many, many questions that came to be my real work for nearly a decade and resulted in *For the Sake of Silence*. Finding the answers was so central to the writing that the book could, I suppose, be called a work of "creative non-fiction" or the "literature of fact" – if I actually believed in the distinctions upon which such categories depend. Certainly the record, as I discovered when researching what I thought would be merely the background to a quick follow-up to my verse novel *Sinking* (published in 1997), proved at almost every turn stranger and more interesting than my own invention. I have departed from it in only a very few instances: as, for example, in altering the date of Chief Sondzaba's letter (actually written on 17 April 1908) so as to conflate his protest with the murders of the children in 1897. On the whole, however, such fictional devices proved largely unnecessary as the facts that may be ascertained of the story of Mariannhill and its missions simply took on a life of their own.

But beyond such facts stands the one figure who, even in the material details of his history, compels this to be, above all, a work of fiction. For all its fidelity to the research that informs it, it is ultimately the imagined perspective of the narrator of this work that envelops the story and draws the historical record into whatever credibility you are willing to grant the imagination.

The figure of Fr Joseph Biegner is based upon a tantalisingly obscure monk of that name who appears in the records of Mariannhill in much the way he represents himself in the fictional narrative: present at every major event, but always on the margins; regularly a figure of authority, but never for long in one position; Pfanner's "right-hand man", at the centre of the battle over the observance of silence, yet always silent. The only known picture of him (other than as a face difficult to detect in group photographs of the Mariannhillers) hangs to this day, small and to the side, in the common room of the monastery. And in all the writing about Mariannhill, only four and a half pages, in German, are dedicated to him in *Sie waren Boten der Liebe: Mariannhiller Porträts* by Adalbert Ludwig Balling, a regular producer of books on Mariannhill who is the model for the 'young historian' framing and punctuating the novel. I have taken the liberty of giving him a different surname, mostly to allow for the necessary historical distance between these two Adalberts. All the other names I used have a basis in historical individuals and even physical descriptions are often taken from photographs.

The "portrait" by Balling is entitled "Mit dem Gründerabt ein Herz und ein Seele", and from it I obtained the bare outlines of Eduard Biegner's place of birth, his youth, his education, his work in the state lottery, his interest in alternative methods of healing – and the popular belief, repeated everywhere, that he was especially close to Franz Pfanner.

Biegner's appearances throughout this story of Mariannhill are strictly governed by his place in the records, although all the thoughts and many of the actions attributed to him (especially as regards the deaths of the children and attempts at harming Franz's career) are imaginative constructs. The source of his religious name is correct, although this took some research to establish, and I believe that it is a solid clue to his being the monk Pfanner refers to as an epileptic in the original southern African party.

Locating Biegner's home village in the Czech Republic and reading the beginnings of his life history from the still eloquent landscape was one of the rewards of writing this book, as was the extraordinary generosity of Don Sparling of Masaryk University in Brno (Brünn, in its Germanic form). I contacted this Canadian Czechophile prior to my visit to the city, and was welcomed into his office to find every item of furniture covered with books on Brno illustrating exactly the period when Biegner was a student there. The guided walkabout that saturates the relevant sections of the novel (and much more that found its way to the cutting room floor) followed, accompanied by free accommodation in the University Hotel.

This begins a list of thanks that can barely touch upon the debts of gratitude I ran up in writing this book. I shall weave the most important into an account of some of what went into the writing of a work that hovers so close to the historical record.

Joseph Biegner ranks surprisingly high in this regard. The one substantial piece of writing known to be by him is the serialised "Life of Abbot Franz Pfanner" running over several issues of the *South African Catholic Magazine*. (All references to Mariannhill in this publication have usefully been collated as "The Mission Work of the Trappists and Mariannhill as Recorded in The *South African Catholic Magazine* 1891–1924: A Documentation

(Facsimile Edition)" by AAW, printed privately by Mariannhill.) Very much the orthodox view of which *For the Sake of Silence* is meant to be the alternative, often counter, history, Biegner's account is clearly one of the chief sources from which I have drawn. Translated from the German by Rev. W J Leeson, it is written entirely in the third person – "Herr Biegner (the writer of these memories) who later became and is now Fr Joseph Cupertino" rarely shows his hand, other than in a scattering of little homilies throughout the text.

This account is supplemented, at least for the years between Franz Pfanner's studies in Italy and the purchase of Zeekoegat Farm, by "Abbot Francis' Reminiscences", reproduced as a series in English and German in *FN*, the periodical currently published by the Congregation of the Missionaries of Mariannhill. Although it covers only a short period of Franz's life, his voice leaps off the page to give a sure sense of the way in which he took on the world to the last. In all probability dictated to Fr Joseph, the negative of this powerful portrait is the remarkably strong obverse image of the silent scribe writing away in the shadows of Franz's overwhelming presence. A similar effect is created in *Our Spiritual Father Abbot Franz Speaks to Us*, a collection of sermons and articles from the Dunbrody period edited by Fr George Lautenschlager, and also in the torrent of newspaper and magazine letters and articles that poured out of Franz, often through Fr Joseph's silent amens.

Much of the action of the novel is recreated from the many reports concerning Mariannhill scattered throughout the major newspapers of the region, the *Natal Mercury*, the *Natal Witness*, and the *Natal Advertiser*, as well as the already mentioned *South African Catholic Magazine*. These are regularly credited overtly in the text, and the monastery's – well, Pfanner's – energetic relations with the world outside the enclosure often burst forth from them, especially on "public" matters like commercial competition and education.

The most telling account of the struggles internal to Mariannhill and the Order of which it was a part emerges from Fr Anton Roos's study, *Mariannhill: Between Two Ideals*. Subtitled "The inner development of Mariannhill from a Trappist Monastery into a modern Mission Congregation", it was completed in Innsbruck in 1961. It was translated into English by the remarkable archivist of Mariannhill, Sr M Adelgisa Herrman, in 1983. Its dating is significant to the device central to the later sections of my plot, for as late as 1983 Fr Anton, who is by far the best researcher on Mariannhill, felt obliged to retain the original footnote to the case Pfanner brought against Mariawald whilst in Rome: "So far Abbot Franz had only simple vows; before the end of the court case he could not possibly make solemn vows. In the acts so far accessible we cannot find actual proof again that he retrieved this later. This is no proof again that he did not do it, but makes one suspect it."

Biegner's blundering attempts to destroy Franz at the end do, then, have a solid basis in contemporary suspicions. It was only sometime later in the 1980s that Fr Anton was able to confirm in print that Franz Pfanner had indeed made his solemn profession – delayed by three years – at Port du Salute, "a monastery unknown to him" (*Mariannhill: Charisma and Tradition*). When I contacted him in this regard in 2004, Fr Anton wrote in reply that "the information of the solemn vows did come some years after *Between Two Ideals*. I don't know the year. My memory is too old!"

Fr Anton joins the many members of the Congregation of the Missionaries of Mariannhill who were unstinting in their responses to the queries made by this lapsed, at best, Methodist, so ignorant of all that means so much to them. First must come Fr Bernard Pagitsch, the Superior of Mariannhill during the time of my research and writing, who took the trouble to reply to emails from as far afield as London and Austin, Texas, as I kept working on this obsessive project wherever I happened to be. Sr Adelgisa passed away just as I began writing the story, leaving Fr Bernard without an archivist as such, but he always responded helpfully from material he came across in the midst of many pressing duties. Fr Lukas Mettler, too, was extraordinarily helpful, even during a period of recovery from a severe injury.

I owe an enormous debt of gratitude to the School of Oriental and African Studies in London, where, during my year-long tenure as a Commonwealth Fellow, I wrote the first sections of this book. The fellowship was given to me on the unprecedented basis, I think, of a combined scholarly and creative research project, as I announced it from the first. The generosity of the then Dean of my Faculty at the University of Natal, Professor Michael Chapman, who cleared the leave that enabled me to take up this Fellowship, and my colleagues at soas (most especially Professor Nana Wilson Tagoe) has been stretched to the full by the eight-year wait for the outcome of the work begun in that period, and I can only hope that they find this book worth their investment in me.

My thanks must also go to archivists at the Killie Campbell Africana Library, the National Archives in Pietermaritzburg and Cape Town, and the Diocesan Archives in Durban. Special thanks to Dr Joy Brain of the Diocesan Archives: not only were her books *Catholic Beginnings in Natal and Beyond* and *Catholics in Natal II: 1886 1925* indispensable as reference works but it was she who led me to Fr Erasmus Hörner's 152-page document "Positive Facts of Mysterious Occurrences, Demoniacal Possession", handwritten in Port Shepstone, Natal, in 1932. This forms the basis of the account given of the Exorcisms, although I did have to change the dating of the document so that my narrator could have access to it. The text is sometimes used verbatim, but is not to be trusted for reference purposes as I have interpolated, elided, compressed and altered passages for the required effects. In essence, however, nothing has been exaggerated or invented, and full credit must go to Fr Erasmus Hörner for those sections left entirely unaltered.

For the unravelling of church politics behind the demonic possessions, at least as reported by Fr Erasmus, I must thank the Staats und Stadtbibliothek Augsburg, where an unnamed archivist mailed me three microfiche pages containing the thoroughly suppressed – in South Africa – "Litany of Terrible Sayings" referred to, but not revealed, in the Exorcisms, and finally published in the *Augsberger Postzeitung* of 17 August 1907. My thanks to Catherine Dubbeld, of the Malherbe Library at the University of KwaZulu-Natal for finding a machine old enough to read the microfiches, which thankfully it did without breaking down, as spares for it are no longer available. Elke Steinmeyer of the Classics Department of the University of KwaZulu-Natal completed the unravelling of this mystery by translating both the dated typeface and the German.

I have consulted most of the texts on Mariannhill published by its Press and related houses; unfortunately I have had cause to dispute the facts as related in some of them, but I believe this always to have been on well-supported grounds. In this sense, *For the Sake of Silence* does present one of the more accurate accounts of the history of Mariannhill and her missions, especially when it comes to the reluctance the modern missionary congregation displays in referring to its traumatic break with the Trappists.

Chief amongst Mariannhill's publications, for me, is Berchmans Hoffmann's illustrated *The Founder of Mariannhill: A Short Biography of Abbot Franz Pfanner*, given to me as a Pinetown High School pupil studying Mariannhill's architecture for a Matric art project, which is pretty much where my fascination with the monastery began. (I won't count having my appendix removed in an emergency operation in the monastery's hospital when I was eight or nine years old.) I hitchhiked from Pinetown to what seemed like another world on a daily basis for some weeks, and settled myself in various places outside the enclosure to sketch the monastery's buildings. After a few days a Brother noticed me and asked me to join the community for lunch – bean soup and bread. I remember sitting in his room for a while after the meal listening to the just-released *Jesus Christ Superstar*. The monastery was still a comparatively remote place then, with much of the mystery of its enclosure still intact. I only knew of it through Saturday morning drives with my family to its repository to buy fresh bread and honey as a weekend treat. This was one of the last signs of the Trappist ideal of self-sufficiency; another was the leather I would buy from Mariannhill's tannery to make my first guitar strap.

I still have the original copy of Hofmann's book given to me by that Brother – complete with some light paint stains. Many other publications by the monastery have joined it, amongst them Helen Gamble's sometimes suspect *Mariannhill: A Century of Prayer and Work*; Sr M Adelgisa's thorough *100 Years Mariannhill Province*; Fr Lukas Mettler and Sr M Adelgisa's heavily illustrated *Mariannhill 1882–1982*, which contains much wonderful archival photography; and Roos, Balling and Sigrist's work of the same name, even more lavishly illustrated with contemporary and archival photography. I should note at this point that I was allowed to consult one private holding of the collection of early photographs of Mariannhill, which feature heavily in the section of the novel covering the founding of the monastery.

Other works on Mariannhill that underlie my reconstruction of its world are Francis Schimlek's *Mariannhill: A Study in Bantu Life and Missionary Effort* and *Medicine Versus Witchcraft*, works that are at times almost too colourful in their anecdotal take on characters and events and, therefore, the basis for some of the more satirical moments in *For the Sake of Silence*; Sr M Annette Buschgerd's massive tome *For a Great Price: The Story of the Missionary Sisters of the Precious Blood*, which often gives revealing flashes of detail that texts more intimately associated with the male line of Mariannhill would never have allowed through; and Fr Marcel Dischl's *Transkei for Christ: A History of the Catholic Church in the Transkeian Territories*, which was useful far beyond the limits of its title and contains more on Biegner than most works concentrated on Mariannhill itself. *The Catholic Zulu Terminology Dispute* by Rev. J B Sauter CMM was also useful.

The celebrated linguist and ethnographer A T Bryant is rarely associated with the Trappists or Mariannhill, for reasons I trust the novel makes plain. Again, my account of this is true to the records, especially those not commonly made public. Schimlek gives something of the more idealised version, but Roos makes it clear just how destructive a presence Bryant became at the monastery. The oral testimonies collected by George Sombe Mukuka in his remarkable doctoral dissertation, "The Establishment of the Black Catholic Clergy in South Africa from 1887 to 1957", were invaluable in tracing how this destructiveness continued beyond the period Bryant spent at Mariannhill. I make no apologies for presenting this side of such an illustrious figure, even as I remain grateful as a researcher for his works, *The Zulu People As They Were Before the White Man Came* and *History of the Zulus and Neighbouring Tribes*. I should note here that I decided to keep to the often extremely offensive historical ethnographic terminology, seeing no point in sanitising the brutality of the past.

The importance of Bishop James Ricards' *The Catholic Church and the Kaffir: A Brief Sketch of the Progress of Catholicity in South Africa* speaks for itself in the text, I am sure, and whilst admitting to probably overplaying the conceit, I enjoyed working in his history with that of the wonderful "Notre Mère", drawn largely from *The Reminiscences of Amelia de Henningsen*, edited by Margaret Young (Sr Anne Mary, MSA). Like the letters exchanged between Ricards and Sr Gertrude, the enormously revealing correspondence between Ricards and Herr Fraundorfer is collected in *The Dunbrody Episode: The Futile Attempt to Establish the Trappists in the Sundays' River Valley of the Cape Province, South Africa – A Documentation in Three Parts*, collated by Alcuin A Weiswurm.

No work on Catholics in South Africa can even begin without William Eric Brown's *The Catholic Church in South Africa: From its Origins to the Present Day*, and debts are owed to a number of more recent studies of religion in South Africa, including David Chidester's *Religions of South Africa* and Richard Elphick and Rodney Davenport's *Christianity in South Africa: A Political, Social & Cultural History*.

More historical works on South Africa have been consulted than can be listed here, but given the centrality of East Griqualand in *For the Sake of Silence* (I think of it more as an East Griqualand novel than a South

African one), I should mention William Beinart and Colin Bundy's *Hidden Struggles in Rural South Africa*, Robert Ross's *Adam Kok's Griquas: A Study in the Development of Stratification in South Africa*, and A O Jackson's *The Ethnic Composition of the Ciskei and Transkei*. As always, for anything to do with the history of Zululand, I am indebted to Jeff Guy.

The ever-present danger of anachronism aside, it is impossible to approach the Trappist Order today without passing through the extensive writings of that most eloquent (on paper) of Trappists, Thomas Merton. His account of Mariannhill in *The Waters of Siloe* is close to comically inaccurate, but the spiritual world he evokes in his autobiographical account of becoming a Trappist, *The Seven-Storey Mountain*, and a host of other texts, was, of course, invaluable. Several images, much information, and a few echoes of quotations taken from these works of prose and poetry are scattered throughout *For the Sake of Silence* in variously altered forms, difficult to cite specifically. I relied most heavily, perhaps, on the section entitled "Silence" in *No Man is an Island*, the Editor's Foreword by L'abbaye de la Pierre-Qui-Vire to *Silence in Heaven: A Book of the Monastic Life*, as well as Merton's text to this photographic essay, and on Monica Furlong's *Merton: A Biography*. The last, in particular, supplied many of the more telling day-to-day details of Trappist life, and I have used these fairly liberally (suitably adjusted for the periods in question), especially in the early part of the novel.

With regard to the formal structures of the strict observance of Cistercian life, I must thank the Trappist community of Guadalupe Abbey in Lafayette, Oregon, for passing on to me their translation and publication of *The Regulations of the Abbey of Our Lady of La Trappe in the Form of Constitutions* and *The Ancient Usages of the Cistercian Order*. I also used the current *Constitutions and Statutes of the Monks of the Cistercian Order of the Strict Observance*, and various editions of *The Rule of St Benedict*.

In trying to end this account of my debts, I realise I have barely scratched the surface. Twain's *More Tramps Abroad* and Gandhi's "A Band of Vegetarian Missionaries", upon which the accounts of their visits to Mariannhill are based, come to mind, and I was especially grateful for the pungent detail of Terry Eagleton's novel *Saints and Scholars* in re-creating Biegner's time in Vienna. I should note that M is entirely of my own invention.

As for the travel involved, this ranged from some of the more obscure corners of southern Africa to equally obscure corners of Germany, Austria, Italy, the Czech Republic, Ireland and Britain. Much of this travel was undertaken whilst on other or related academic business, for which I must thank the South African National Research Foundation, the then University of Natal and now University of KwaZulu-Natal, and various scholarly hosts who were kind enough to invite me to a variety of conferences and colloquia – sometimes in complete ignorance of the ulterior motives that lay to a greater or lesser degree behind my accepting their invitations.

Travel in southern Africa cost me two cars which, for all their many virtues, were never designed to track down each of the missions and most of the day stations established by the Trappists of Mariannhill. For directions to these often extremely obscure sites, I am indebted to Robert Brusse, architect and colourful speaker extraordinaire. Discussions with him and his public lectures on the architecture of Mariannhill and its missions inform many crucial passages in the novel, as do several of his anecdotes, suitably amended for the textual occasion.

It is more difficult to know how to credit or thank the unnamed porter at Mariawald who understood not a word of my English and broken German other than, I assume, the name Franz Pfanner. When he heard these two words, he surreptitiously let me into what is still an entirely enclosed community, scuttling ahead of me from passageway to passageway, room to room, to check that they were empty. After nothing less than a full tour, I was shown a small portrait of Franz hanging in a hallway and the place setting in the dining hall with his name, now assumed several times over by generations of younger brethren. I celebrated this extraordinary stroke of research fortune with pea soup served at the refectory just outside the enclosure, into which a large frankfurter was dropped for those not of a suitably vegetarian Trappist persuasion. This I washed down with my first Trappist beer, the merits of which I can best illustrate by reporting that I sang loudly all the way along the footpath through the Mariannehöhe back to Heimbach.

It is easier to acknowledge than to thank adequately my wife, travelling companion, and navigator in every sense, to whom this book is dedicated. I will ask you only to imagine a frozen afternoon in Austria, well up an icy mountain road that would, after one necessary research stop, take us over into Italy where good friends awaited us in Vicenza. I climbed out of the car into the crackling, dripping silence of the forbidding hotel and railway station that make up Langen, the town I had asked Cas to direct me towards because it is the birthplace of Franz Pfanner. In my very poor German I asked the station master, the only living being in sight, if this was Langen, and he assured me it was. Franz Pfanner came from a farming community, but I could not imagine anything being farmed on the precipitous black rocks hanging precariously over station, hotel and road alike.

I had given my navigator only one clear instruction on our dash from southern Germany through Austria, and that was to get us past Lake Constance, where I had been briefly and unhappily stranded some years before. This she had done with admirable efficiency, shooting us through Bregenz at the eastern end of the lake and clear across the Vorarlberg, by-passing – time being what it was – Feldkirch, where Franz went to school, and Haselstauden, where he had his first parish. Now we were exactly at the point I had identified on the map, some way up the Arlberg at Langen, after which we were due to turn east on our way to the Otztaler Alps and Italy.

Langen. I could see the thought forming as it occurred to the station master: Ah, Langen, he said; yes, this is Langen, Langen bei Arlberg. Perhaps, he said – and I followed his gaze out into the falling snow and on to the road and back down the Arlberg – perhaps you want Langen bei Bregenz? That, he said, quite unnecessarily, is by Bregenz, at the very tip of Lake Constance. You should have turned left at the tip of Lake Constance.

I walked back out into the silence hardening as the dark came on, and leaned in the car window and said to Cas, Italy and friends that way, Langen all the way back across Austria. How badly do we need to see Franz's birthplace?

We had no idea how strange the trip back to Bregenz and up into the mountains to Langen bei Bregenz would become, but I have a feeling that, even if she had known, Cas would still, as she did, turn the map around and say, At least we could stop in at Feldkirch and Haselstauden.

As I have said, this book is for you, Cas, my first and best reader, editor, partner. May I navigate as well for you.

And Donnée, Maeve and Phoebe – without you there would have been no point. *For the Sake of Silence* is already older than two of you, and each one of you is a part of every page.

Finally: to Jeanne Hromník, for her patience with the text and the author. And, above all, to Annari van der Merwe for her faith in the book – may your epiphany on that bicycle ride prove itself in every way.

MICHAEL CAWOOD GREEN
Durban, November 2007